The Encyclopedia of Operations Management

2010 Edition

A field manual and encyclopedic glossary
of operations management terms and concepts

Arthur V. Hill

The John and Nancy Lindahl Professor
Curtis L. Carlson School of Management
University of Minnesota

Clamshell Beach Press
www.ClamshellBeachPress.com

Clamshell Beach Press

THE ENCYCLOPEDIA OF OPERATIONS MANAGEMENT

Published by Clamshell Beach Press, 10316 Meade Lane, Eden Prairie, MN 55347. Copyright © 2010 by Clamshell Beach Press. All rights reserved. No part of this publication may be reproduced or distributed in any form, or stored in a database or retrieval system without the prior written permission of Clamshell Beach Press.

ISBN-13: 978-0-9793105-2-2
ISBN-10: 0-9793105-2-0

Library of Congress Cataloging-in-Publication Data

Hill, Arthur Van Cleve
   The Encyclopedia of Operations Management / Arthur V. Hill – 2010 Edition

   Library of Congress Control Number: 2007900783

   ISBN-13: 978-0-9793105-2-2
   ISBN-10: 0-9793105-2-0

   1. Production management.

www.ClamshellBeachPress.com

PREFACE

Purpose – The ***Encyclopedia of Operations Management*** is an ideal "field manual" for students, instructors, and practicing managers. For students, the encyclopedia is a useful guide for developing an integrated mental map for the entire field of operations management. It has also proven useful as a reference for students preparing for case discussions, exams, and job interviews. It is particularly helpful for international students who need to quickly learn the language of operations management. For instructors, the encyclopedia is an invaluable desk reference and teaching aid that goes far beyond the typical dictionary of terms. Many instructors will find the numerous figures, graphs, equations, Excel formulas, VBA code, and references helpful information for their lectures and research. For practicing managers, the encyclopedia is a powerful tool for helping their organizations build a standard and precise language. It has also proven to be a valuable tool for Six Sigma, Lean, and Lean Sigma Black Belt training.

This encyclopedia has proven to be a useful required reference for a number of undergraduate and graduate business and engineering core operations management courses. It is also useful for second-level courses in supply chain management, quality management, lean manufacturing, project management, service management, operations strategy, manufacturing management, industrial engineering, and manufacturing engineering.

Coverage – This encyclopedia covers a wide range of disciplines related to operations management including:

- Accounting
- Distribution
- e-business
- Economics
- Finance
- Forecasting
- Human resources
- Industrial engineering
- Industrial relations
- Inventory management
- Lean manufacturing
- Logistics
- Maintenance/reliability engineering
- Management Information Systems
- Marketing/sales
- New product development (NPD)
- Operations research
- Organizational behavior/management
- Personal time management
- Production planning and control
- Purchasing/supply management
- Quality management
- Service management
- Simulation
- Six Sigma/Lean Sigma
- Statistics
- Strategic management
- Supply chain management
- Theory of Constraints
- Transportation

Format – Each entry begins with a short definition, followed by a longer description, and ends with references to additional resources and cross-references (links) to related terms. Essential terms for students are marked with a star (✪) at the end of the short definition. The whitepapers and Excel workbooks referenced in this encyclopedia are marked with the CD icon (◉) in the text and can be found on the ***Operations Management Whitepapers & Workbooks (OMWW) CD*** available from www.ClamshellBeachPress.com. The format is designed to be very compact so that it can be easily carried and used as a "field manual." The web-based Operations Management Basics Exam, which draws heavily on the concepts in this encyclopedia, has a planned release date in mid-2010.

History – When I was on the faculty at IMD International in Switzerland, I gave my MBA students a one-page list of about 50 essential operations management terms that they were required to master. Several students requested help in defining those terms. This encyclopedia grew out my response to that request. Compared to the 2005 edition, the 2007 edition was much more precise, three times longer, and was completely reformatted with extensive cross references to help readers build an integrated mental map of the field. This 2010 edition is more than 25% longer than the 2007 edition with 1250 entries, over 3500 links between entries, and over 204,000 words. More than 350 entries are new or revised and many new links and references were added. The companion ***Operations Management Whitepapers and Workbooks (OMWW) 2009*** includes many new and revised whitepapers and Excel workbooks.

Comments, additions, and edits are welcomed and should be sent to info@ClamshellBeachPress.com. Substantive contributions will be credited in the next edition.

Arthur V. Hill, The John & Nancy Lindahl Professor for Excellence in Business Education
Operations & Management Science Department
Carlson School of Management, University of Minnesota

HOW READERS CAN USE THIS BOOK

If you are like many people, you struggle to build a simple mental framework for the field of operations management. Compared to other business disciplines such as marketing and accounting, operations management sometimes feels like a disjointed set of concepts and tools thrown together with no clear unifying structure. Many frameworks are available in standard textbooks and an award-winning framework was recently published by Hays, Bouzdine-Chameeva, Meyer Goldstein, Hill, and Scavarda (2007). However, none of these frameworks are particularly simple.

Recently I have found a new framework for the operations management discipline that is far simpler and more appealing. I now spend very little time convincing my students to want to study the operations function. Instead, I simply share these three fundamental premises of operations management:

- **All work is a process** – This includes the disciplines of marketing, finance, accounting, HR, MIS, and operations. Process is everything in every discipline and organization, and even in our personal lives.

- **All processes can be improved** – This includes both process design and process improvement to add more value for customers, organizations, shareholders, employees, and society.

- **All processes can be improved by making them better, faster, cheaper, and stronger** – *Better* processes provide improved quality and value. *Faster* processes have shorter cycle times and are more flexible and customizable. *Cheaper* processes apply lean concepts to deliver products and services with less waste and are also achieved by better matching capacity, demand, and inventory. *Stronger* processes have an explicit operations strategy that leverages competitive strengths (core competences) across a global supply chain and mitigates risks by making processes more robust. Of course, it is important to have the right set of metrics to support efforts to make your processes better, faster, cheaper, and stronger.

Students enthusiastically embrace these three premises and are passionate about learning how to make their processes (and their lives) better, faster, cheaper, and stronger. This better, faster, cheaper, and stronger framework for operations management is simple, compelling, easy to remember, and easy to apply to any process in any context.

You can master the concepts and tools for making your processes better, faster, cheaper, and stronger by studying this *Encyclopedia of Operations Management*. Start by studying the bulleted terms in the framework below. Then follow the links at the end of each entry to the related entry that you still need to learn. Pay particular attention to the terms marked with a star (✪) at the end of the short definition. This approach will help you quickly develop a complete mental map of the entire field of operations management -- and help you make your processes better, faster, cheaper, and stronger.

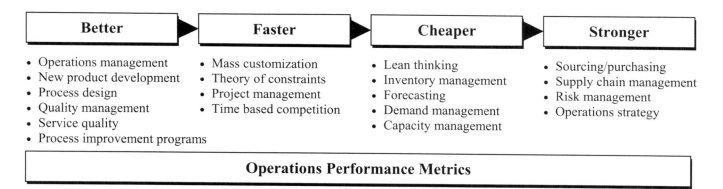

HOW INSTRUCTORS CAN USE THIS BOOK

Instructors have found the ***Encyclopedia of Operations Management*** to be a valuable "field manual" for a variety of courses and training programs. These include:

- **Case courses without textbooks** – The ***Encyclopedia of Operations Management*** is an authoritative supplement for a case course. The ***EOM*** provides a precise "language" for operations management that is not provided in most case courses. The ***EOM*** can help students learn the terms in the context of the cases.

- **Case and/or lecture courses with textbooks** – Even if your course uses a textbook, the ***Encyclopedia of Operations Management*** is a valuable supplement to provide precise definitions for important terms that are not always defined in standard textbooks. Few textbooks provide the extensive linked lists that are provided in the ***EOM*** to help the reader develop a complete mental map of the field.

- **Lean Sigma training courses** – The ***Encyclopedia of Operations Management*** defines nearly all terms that are used in Six Sigma, Lean Sigma, and Lean training programs. Many ***EOM*** entries include examples and references that go well beyond what is offered in any other book available on the market today. The EOM is an indispensable reference for Lean Sigma training programs and is the only reference that pulls together all of the major tools and concepts in a precise easy-to-use "field manual."

Instructors have found practical ways to use the ***Encyclopedia of Operations Management*** including:

- Use the terms in the context of class discussions and refer students to the ***EOM*** for precise definitions.

- Assign key terms to be studied as a part of the syllabus, case studies, and homework assignments.

- Hold students accountable for mastering the key terms used in classroom discussions, exams, and homework assignments. Use homework assignments and exams to test students' understanding of the terms and concepts and their ability to apply concepts and tools to solve practical problems.

ABOUT THE AUTHOR

Arthur V. Hill is the John and Nancy Lindahl Professor in the Operations and Management Science Department of the Carlson School of Management at the University of Minnesota. He holds a B.A. in Mathematics from Indiana University, an M.S. in Industrial Administration, and a Ph.D. in Management from the Krannert School of Management at Purdue University. Professor Hill was the Co-Editor-in-Chief of the ***Journal of Operations Management*** (1993-1995), a leading academic research journal in the field. He is a Fellow of the American Production Inventory Control Society and wrote the APICS CPIM and CIRM certification exams for five years. He is currently the VP-Finance for POMS, the world's leading society for operations management professors.

Dr. Hill has been a professor at the Carlson School of Management for over 30 years and currently teaches supply chain management for both MBA and doctoral students. He also teaches the Carlson Executive MBA core operations management course. He has held faculty positions as a Visiting Associate Professor at Indiana University, Professor of Manufacturing Management at IMD International Lausanne, Switzerland, Guest Professor at Wits Business School in Johannesburg, South Africa, and a Distinguished Visiting Professor at the National University of Singapore. He also helped found a management institute in Moscow. He has won numerous teaching awards, authored over 70 research articles, and consulted for a number of major firms including 3M, Best Buy, Boston Scientific, Cargill, Cummins, General Mills, Home Depot, Honeywell, Honeywell Bull (Switzerland), Buhrmann NV (Netherlands), Medtronic, Methodist Hospital, Nestlé, Northwest Airlines, Park Nicollet Health Services, Radisson, Target, Toro, US Bank, and Wells Fargo. His current research is on process improvement programs and supp¹ chain management. Professor Hill's university website is http://webpages.csom.umn.edu/OMS/ahill/.

QUOTES FROM EXECUTIVES

"Art Hill's new encyclopedia is an excellent source of information for all who are involved in operations management – from business professionals to students. Having both worked and studied under Professor Hill, I know the quality of his work and teaching."

– Michael Hoffman, Chairman and CEO, The Toro Company

"We have experienced Art Hill's effective training first-hand in our Lean Sigma program at Kemps where his program has had an immediate and sustainable impact. Art's new book will be a great resource for all participants in our Lean Sigma program going forward."

– James Green, President and CEO, Kemps, LLC

"The Encyclopedia will take a place on my office bookshelf next to the quality handbook by Dr. Juran as one of my go-to references. This book has packed so much into one reference. I could see it being a great reference when you encounter a need to revisit the fundamentals. Nicely done!"

– Joe Dehler, Vice President, Business Process Improvement, Carlson Companies

"An excellent, quick but thorough reference for anyone involved in managing or improving operations in any organization. The only book of its kind!"

– Dr. Richard Chua, Executive Vice President, Juran Institute, Inc.

"With the pace of change in the business world today, crystal clear communication has become an important management tool. Lack of clarity leads to more waste and errors than any other single factor. This definitive encyclopedia of terms and frameworks should become THE industry standard."

– Connie Fuhrman, Senior Vice President, Operations Transformation, Best Buy (retired)

"An invaluable tool for effectively navigating and understanding the rapidly developing technologies in today's modern age of operations."

– Rick Heupel, Former Vice-President, Asia Operations, Seagate

"A valuable resource for supply chain professionals, executives and managers from all functions in the company."

– Paul Husby, Vice President, 3M Supply Chain and Logistic Operations (retired)

"We've all heard the terms and like to think we can keep them straight, but in this increasingly complex world, having this ready reference is absolutely essential for practitioners and managers alike."

– Tom Platner, Vice President, Engineering & Manufacturing, Fargo Electronics

"It's a great resource to quickly reference specific operations management terms and acronyms for anyone in business or academics. I will use it!"

– Mike St. Martin, Managing Director, FedEx Express

"Finally, a comprehensive tool that will aid both the new and experienced operations practitioner in understanding the evolving technological landscape of manufacturing."

– Sandy Meurlot, Vice President of Operations, The Toro Company

"An excellent, comprehensive, and complete reference that students, consultants, supply chain practitioners, and professionals can use to quickly and easily obtain value to support their educational and professional endeavors."

– Charlie Honke, Partner, Product Lifecycle Management, IBM Global Business Services

"Finally, a definitive and comprehensive source of supply chain terminology defined and explained. This reference work will institutionalize a common understanding of the increasingly complex supply chain world, and will enable advancements in the discipline via that understanding. This book should be within arms reach of everyone involved with leading, managing, or learning about supply chain management."

– Tim Larson, Vice President Purchasing, Michael Foods, Inc.

"In today's fast-paced and complex environment, Art's compilation is a must-have reference for any operations manager, new or experienced."
— Adam Hjerpe, Senior Director of Program Management and Quality, SCS – a UnitedHealth Group company

"The Encyclopedia of Operations Management is very well done and I am enjoying reading it."
— Lee Cockerell, Executive Vice President, Walt Disney World Resort (Retired)

QUOTES FROM PROFESSORS

"I'm thoroughly impressed with everything about it, the scope, the attention to detail, the clarity of explanations, and the references for further reading. I can certainly understand why students have reacted so positively to it."
— Rodney A. Erickson, Executive Vice President and Provost, The Pennsylvania State University

"It is an excellent resource for students and operations managers."
— Professor Kalyan Singhal, McCurdy Professor of Operations Management,
Editor-in-chief, Production and Operations Management, Merrick School of Business, University of Baltimore

"Art has done us a great service with this comprehensive, completely cross-referenced, and clearly communicated collection. It is required reading for all operations professionals."
— Professor D. Clay Whybark, Macon G. Patton Distinguished Professor of Operations
Technology and Innovation Management (OTIM), University of North Carolina – Chapel Hill

"What an amazing reference! I'm preparing a new reading for my MBA students and the Encyclopedia provided the perfect place for me to check definitions. This was really, really helpful."
— Professor Nancy Hyer, Owen Graduate School of Management, Vanderbilt University

"An essential, authoritative resource for students, professors, and practitioners. This is a timely effort and Art has done an excellent job in putting together a much-needed reference. Given the pervasiveness of operations, this reference will be extremely useful to managers and executives from all functional areas."
— Professor Sum Chee Chuong, Associate Professor, National University of Singapore Business School

"This is a GREAT book – fascinating, rich in contents, covering a wide range of disciplines. It will become one of the most precious books in my professional library and will become THE REFERENCE for my students."
— Professor Tatiana Bouzdine-Chameeva, Head of the Department of Information, Decision and Management,
Bordeaux Business School, FRANCE

"A fantastic effort … the first major effort in our field to systematize the knowledge domains in a concise and lucid style."
— Professor Amitabh Raturi, Professor and Director of Industrial Management, University of Cincinnati

ACKNOWLEDGMENTS

First, I thank my wonderful wife Julie and our children (Christopher & Katie, Jonathan & Lindsay, Stephen, and Michael) for their love and support. Second, I thank the countless students and professors who have contributed entries and edits. Third, I thank many friends, family members, and students who have helped me refine this encyclopedia, especially Paul Haverstock, Jonathan Hill, Stephen Hill, Sheryl Holt, Paul Husby, Brian Jacobson, Matthew Larson, Richard Lemons, Vicki Lund, and Brent Moritz. Fourth, I thank my mentor and friend Professor D. Clay Whybark (University of North Carolina) for getting me started on this journey. Last, but certainly not least, I thank John and Nancy Lindahl for their enthusiastic and generous support of the Carlson School of Management, the University of Minnesota, and the John & Nancy Lindahl Professorship.

NEW AND EDITED ENTRIES

The table below lists most (but not all) of the new and revised entries in this edition. New entries are in bold type.

5S	division of labor	**Key Process Output**	planned leadtime	sampling
A3 Report	**double exponential**	**Variable (KPOV)**	**planned order**	scatter diagram
Activity Based Costing	**smoothing**	**KJ Method**	**pooling**	scope creep
(ABC)	**downstream**	knowledge worker	**price elasticity of**	**sentinel event**
addition principle	**Durbin-Watson statistic**	**labor management**	**demand**	service guarantee
Advanced Shipping	**Dutch Auction**	**systems**	**price of non-**	**service profit chain**
Notification (ASN)	**EAN (European Article**	**labor standards**	**conformance**	service quality
adverse event	**Number)**	**leading indicator**	**pro bono**	**shadow board**
affinity diagram	**economics**	leadtime	process map	**Shingo Prize**
agile software	**effectivity date**	**leadtime syndrome**	**Process performance**	simulated annealing
development	**elasticity**	Lean manufacturing	**qualification**	**single source**
alignment	**EPC (Electronic Product**	Lean thinking	process validation	Six Sigma
all-time demand	**Code)**	Less than Truck Load	product lifecycle	SMART
alpha test	**error proofing**	(LTL)	management	sniping
assembly line	**ethnographic research**	**leverage the spend**	**product mix problem**	Society of Manufacturing
autocorrelation	**experience economy**	line extension	**product performance**	Engineers (SME)
backorder	experience engineering	linear programming	**qualification**	socio-technical design
bait and switch	exponential smoothing	linear regression	**product simplification**	sole source
barriers-to-entry	Failure Mode and Effects	**logistic curve**	productivity	**square root law for**
Bass Model	Analysis (FMEA)	**loss leader**	Project Management	**safety stocks**
batch flow	**force-field diagram**	**major setup cost**	Institute (PMI)	square root law for
batch picking	force majeure	Make to Order	**prospective validation**	warehouses
bathtub curve	**first mover advantage**	**makespan**	**prototype**	**stacked leadtime**
best practice	**first pass yield**	**manufacturing leadtime**	**public-private**	stage-gate process
beta test	flowchart	**master schedule**	**partnership**	**Straight Through**
blending problem	**Fourth Party Logistics**	**materials plan**	pull systems	**Processing (STP)**
blue ocean strategy	**(4PL) provider**	**MCE (Manufacturing**	**purchasing leadtime**	supplier scorecard
booking curve	**fuel surcharge**	**Cycle Effectiveness)**	push-pull boundary	**sustainability**
Box-Jenkins forecasting	**functional silo**	Materials Requirements	quality assurance	**swim lanes**
Brooke's Law	**gamma function**	Planning (MRP)	**quality trilogy**	**Third Party Logistics**
bullwhip effect	**geometric mean**	Mean Absolute Percent	queuing theory	**(3PL) provider**
Business Continuity	gemba	Error (MAPE)	RACI Matrix	**Throughput Dollar Days**
Management (BCM)	**Getting Things Done**	**Mean Absolute Scaled**	**Rapid Process**	**(TDD)**
Business Process	**(GTD)**	**Error (MASE)**	**Improvement**	**throughput ratio**
Management (BPM)	goal tree	**Methods Time**	**Workshop (RPIW)**	**time burglar**
buyer/planner	**Gompertz Curve**	**Measurement (MTM)**	red tag	Total Productive
C&E Diagram	green manufacturing	**mindmap**	**resource based view**	Maintenance (TPM)
C&E Matrix	**grey market reseller**	**minor setup cost**	Respond to Order (RTO)	**Total Productive**
causal map	**handoff**	**mistake proofing**	**Results-Only Work**	**Manufacturing (TPM)**
censored data	heijunka	**near miss**	**Environment**	**Transactional Process**
check sheet	Herbie	**Net Promoter Score**	**(ROWE)**	**Improvement**
commercialization	**hub-and-spoke system**	**(NPS)**	**retrospective validation**	transfer batch
commodity	**in-sourcing**	**network effect**	**Return on Assets (ROA)**	**Transportation**
Compounded Annual	**Installation qualification**	**never event**	**Return on Capital**	**Management System**
Growth Rate (CAGR)	**interpolated median**	one-piece flow	**Employed (ROCE)**	**(TMS)**
consortium	**interval notation**	operations strategy	reverse logistics	**triple bottom line**
co-opetition	**Inventory Dollar Days**	opportunity cost	**Richards Curve**	**triple exponential**
core competence	**(IDD)**	**order penetration point**	risk management	**smoothing**
cost driver	**inventory/order**	**order qualifier**	Root Cause Analysis	two-bin system
counting tolerance	**interface**	**Over/Short/Damaged**	(RCA)	**two minute rule**
critical chain	Ishikawa Diagram	**Report (OSD)**	**Root Cause Tree (RCT)**	**tyranny of the urgent**
cross functional team	**Joint Commission**	Overall Equipment	**SaaS (Software as a**	upstream
cumulative leadtime	**(JCAHO)**	Effectiveness (OEE)	**Service)**	**value added ratio**
customer leadtime	**kaikaku**	Pareto Chart	safety leadtime	**value analysis**
cycle counting	kaizen event	**performance**	safety stock	value engineering
cycle stock	Kepner-Tregoe Model	**management system**	Sales & Operations	**voice picking**
cycle time	**Key Process Input**	phase-in/phase out	Planning (S&OP)	**waterfall scheduling**
cycle time efficiency	**Variable (KPIV)**	planning	**Sales, Inventory &**	wave picking
decoupling point	**knapsack problem**	pitch	**Operations Planning**	Weibull Distribution
demand during leadtime		**pro bono**	**(SI&OP)**	

3Ds – The idea that an evaluation of a potential automation project should consider automating tasks that are dirty, dangerous, or dull.

The picture at the right is the PackBot EOD robot from the iRobot Corporation designed to assist bomb squads with explosive ordinance disposal. This is a good example of the second "D."

See *automation*.

3PL – See *Third Party Logistics (3PL) provider*.

5 Whys – A Japanese concept of asking "why" many times in order to get beyond the symptoms and uncover the root cause (or causes) of a problem.

Here is a simple example:
- Why did the ink jet label system stop printing? *The head clogged with ink.*
- Why did the head clog with ink? *The compressed air supply had moisture in it.*
- Why did the compressed air supply have moisture in it? *The desiccant media was saturated.*
- Why was the desiccant media saturated? *The desiccant was not changed prior to expiration.*
- Why was the desiccant not changed prior to expiration? *A change procedure does not exist for the compressed air desiccant.*

Galley (2008) and Gano (2007) argue persuasively that problems rarely have only one cause and that assuming a problem has only one "root" cause can prevent investigators from finding the best solution.

Acknowledgments: CEMBA 06 students Donald Smithmier, Luis Acosta, Aderonke Mordi, Douglas Neimann, Joseph Novotny, Paul Seel, and Pam Aylward contributed to this entry.

The paper "Causal Mapping" is available from www.ClamshellBeachPress.com. ◉

See *Business Process Re-engineering (BPR)*, *causal map*, *impact wheel*, *kaizen event*, *Root Cause Analysis (RCA)*.

5S – A simple, but effective, lean manufacturing methodology that helps organizations simplify, clean, and sustain a productive work environment. ✪

Overview of the 5S program

The 5S methodology originated in Japan and is based on the simple idea that the foundation of a good production system is a clean and safe work environment. Translated from Japanese words that begin with the letter "S," the closest English equivalents normally used are Sort, Set in order, Shine, Standardize, and Sustain. The following list is a combination of many variants of the 5S list found in various publications:

- **Sort** (separate, scrap, sift) – Separate the necessary from the unnecessary and get rid of unnecessary.
- **Set in order** (straighten, store, simplify) – Organize the work area (red/yellow tag campaign, shadow boards, etc.) and put everything in its place.
- **Shine** (scrub, sweep) – Sweep, wash, clean, and shine everything around the work area.
- **Standardize** – Use standard methods to maintain the work area at a high level so that it is easy to keep everything clean for a constant state of readiness.
- **Sustain** (systematize, self-discipline) – Ensure that all 5S policies are followed through the entire organization by means of empowerment, commitment, and accountability.

Detailed description of the 5S program

- **Sort** (*Seiri*) focuses on eliminating unnecessary items from the workplace. An effective visual method to identify these unnecessary items is called "red tagging." A red tag is placed on all items not required to complete the job. These items are then moved to a central holding "quarantine" area. This process is for evaluation of the red tag items. Occasionally-used items are moved to a more organized storage location outside of the work area while unnecessary items are discarded. Sorting is an excellent way to free up valuable floor space and eliminate such things as broken tools, obsolete jigs and fixtures, scrap and excess raw material. Sort "clears the deck" for the 5S process.

- **Set in order** (*Seiton*) focuses on efficient and effective storage and workplace organization methods and can be summarized with the old adage "A place for everything and everything in its place."[1] Questions to ask include: What is needed to do this job? Where should this item be located? How many of each item is needed? Strategies for effective "set in order" include labeling shelves, creating tool holders, painting floors, outlining work areas and locations, making shadow boards, and setting up modular shelving and cabinets for needed items such as trash cans, brooms, mops, and buckets.
- **Shine** (*Seiso*) focuses on cleaning the work area. After the first two steps eliminate clutter and locate the necessary items, the shine step thoroughly cleans the work area. One of the main benefits of the shine step is that workers develop a sense of pride and ownership in a clean and organized work area. Another benefit is that workers can more quickly see issues such as leaks, contamination, vibration, fatigue, breakage, and misalignment.
- **Standardize** (*Seiketsu*) concentrates on standardizing best practice in each work area. Employees are often a valuable source of information for the development of these standards. McDonalds, Pizza Hut, UPS, Blockbuster, and the United States Military are good examples of the value of good work standards. See *standardized work*.
- **Sustain** (*Shitsuke*) is the most difficult "S" to implement and achieve. Many organizations find themselves with a dirty, cluttered shop only a few months after a 5S project. The tendency is to return to the old way of doing things. Sustain focuses on defining a new status quo and new standard for workplace organization. The key is to make sure that the standard work for supervisors is to check daily to ensure that the 5S discipline is being followed. Note that Toyota does not include this last step because it is redundant with Toyota's system of frequent audits of standardized work.

Some lean practitioners add a sixth "S" for safety. They use this "S" to establish safety procedures in and around the process. Most organizations include safety in the 5S process.

Benefits of a 5S program

The benefits of a 5S program include improved visibility of problem conditions, improved safety, reduced waste, improved morale, an increased sense of ownership of the workspace, improved productivity, improved quality, improved maintenance, shorter leadtimes, and a better impression on customers. More fundamentally, a 5S program can help the firm develop a new sense of discipline and order that carries over to all activities.

Understanding of a 5S program for tends to go through four stages as depicted the figure below. First, people often assume that 5S is just cleaning up the work area. Second, people start to understand that 5S is about developing an improved process for how work is done. Third, people understand that 5S is about making this improved work process a standard work process. Fourth, people finally understand that 5S is about developing and practicing a highly disciplined mindset for how work is done.

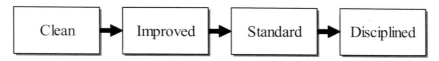

Indications that an organization needs a 5S program

- Space is crowded with parts and tools.
- Unnecessary items are stacked between workers.
- Excess inventory.
- Excess items and machines make it difficult to improve process flow.
- Equipment is dirty and a collection point for miscellaneous materials.
- Tools and equipment are difficult to find.

---

[1] *According to the website www.phrases.org.uk/meanings/14400.html, this phrase goes back well before the year 1827.*

Implementation guidelines for a 5S program

- Take pictures before and after to document and encourage improvement.
- Practice the old slogan, "a place for everything and everything in its place."
- Place tools and instruction manuals close to the point of use.
- Design storage areas with a wide entrance and a shallow depth.
- Lay out the storage area along the wall to save space.
- Place items so that they are easy to access.
- Store similar items together and different items in separate rows.
- Do not stack items together. Use racks or shelves when possible.
- Use small bins to organize small items.
- Use color for quickly identifying items.
- Clearly label items and storage areas to improve visibility.
- Use see-through/transparent covers and doors for visibility.
- Remove unnecessary doors, walls, and other barriers to visibility, movement, and travel.
- Use carts to organize, move, and store tools, jigs, measuring devices.
These guidelines were adapted from http://net1.ist.psu.edu/chu/wcm/5s/guide.htm.
The Japanese characters for 5S are:

整理・整頓・清掃・清潔・躾

The source for the Japanese characters is net1.ist.psu.edu/chu/wcm/5s/5s.htm, November 7, 2004.
See *7 Wastes, facility layout, kaizen event, lean thinking, red tag, shadow board, standardized work, Total Productive Maintenance (TPM), visual control.*

7 Wastes – The seven forms of waste identified by Taiichi Ohno at Toyota. ✪

Taiichi Ohno, the father of the Toyota Production System, defined seven categories of waste (Ohno, 1978). Waste includes any activity that does not add value to the customer. The goal is to eliminate all "muda," the Japanese word for any non-value adding activity. The seven wastes include:

1. **Overproduction** – Producing more than what is needed and/or before it is needed.
2. **Waiting** – Any non-work time waiting for tools, parts, raw material, packaging, inspection, repair, etc.
3. **Transportation** – Wasted effort to transport parts, finished goods, packaging in/out of storage or between processes. This includes long transport distances, double handling, etc.
4. **Extra processing** – Doing more work than necessary. This includes providing higher quality than needed, performing extra operations, watching a machine run, etc.
5. **Inventory** – Maintaining excess inventory of raw materials, in-process parts or finished goods.
6. **Excessive motion** – Any wasted motion or poor ergonomics, especially when picking up or stacking parts, and walking to look for items or people.
7. **Defects (correction)** – Repair, rework, paperwork, recounts, re-packing, etc.
More recently, Jim Womack of LEI added an eighth waste that he calls the waste of human potential.

One of the best approaches for eliminating the Seven (or Eight) Wastes is to implement a 5S program. The *lean thinking* entry suggests many specific approaches for eliminating each of these eight wastes.

Macomber and Howell (2004) identify several additional wastes including too much information, complexity, the design of goods and services that do not meet the users' needs, providing something the customer does not value, not listening, not speaking, assigning people to roles that they are not suited for, not supporting people in their roles, and high turnover.

See *5S, efficiency, Lean Enterprise Institute (LEI), lean thinking, muda, overproduction.*

A

A3 Report – A form for creating a project charter used at Toyota and other firms that practice lean manufacturing.

The A3 Report is essentially a combined project charter and project progress report on a single sheet that defines the problem, root causes, and corrective actions. It often also includes sketches, graphics, process m~

and other visual means of summarizing the current condition and future state. Some lean consultants insist that an A3 Report should be done by hand.

The A3 report is named after the size of the paper that is used. A3 paper is two side-by-side A4 pages, where an A4 page is 210 x 297 mm and an A3 page is 297 x 420 (about 11 x 17 inches). An A3 template (form) can be found at www.gemba.com/uploadedFiles/A3%20Report%20Form.pdf.

See the *project charter* entry for an outline for an A3 Report.

The paper "A3 Problem Solving" is available on the **OMWW CD** available from www.ClamshellBeachPress.com. ●

See *lean thinking*, *process map*, *project charter*.

ABAP (Advanced Business Application Programming) – SAP's proprietary object-oriented programming language.
See *SAP*.

ABC – See *Activity-Based Costing (ABC)*.

ABC classification – A method for prioritizing items in an inventory system where A-items are considered to be the most important. ✪

The ABC classification is usually implemented based on the annual dollar volume, which is the product of the annual unit sales and unit cost (the annual cost of goods sold). High annual volume items are classified as A-items and low annual dollar volume items are classified as C-items. Based on Pareto's Law, the ABC classification system demands more careful management of A-items where these items are ordered more often, counted more often, located closer to the door, and forecasted more carefully. Conversely, C-items are not as important from an investment point of view and therefore should be ordered and counted infrequently.

One justification for this approach is based on the economic order quantity model. Higher dollar volume items are ordered more often and therefore have a higher transaction volume, which means that they are more likely to have data accuracy problems.

The first step in the ABC analysis is to create a ranked list of items by cost of goods sold (annual dollar volume). The top 20% of the items are labeled A-items. The next 30% of the items in the list are labeled B-items, and the remaining 50% are labeled C-items. Of course, these percentages can vary depending upon the needs of the firm. The A-items will likely make up roughly 80% of the total annual dollar volume, B-items will likely make up about 15%, and C-items about 5%.

The graph below shows a typical ABC distribution, where the x-axis is the percent of items and the y-axis is the percent of total annual dollar usage. The graph shows that the first 20% of the items represent about 80% of the annual dollar usage. Items must be first sorted by annual dollar volume to create this graph.

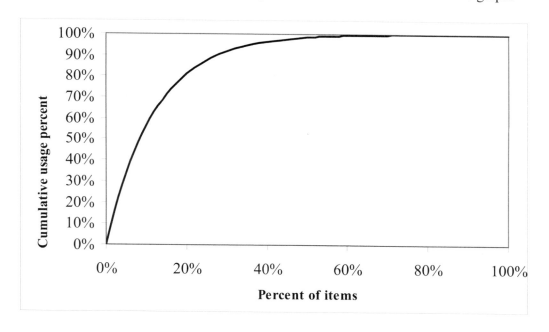

Some firms use other variables for prioritizing items in the ABC classification. Other variables might include the stockout cost (such as medical criticality), shelf life, sales volume, and profit margin.

Note that the ABC inventory classification has nothing to do with Activity Based Costing.

The paper "ABC Classification Analysis" and an Excel workbook "ABC classification analysis.xls" are on the **OMWW CD** available from www.ClamshellBeachPress.com. ⊙

See *cost of goods sold, cycle counting, Economic Order Quantity (EOQ), Pareto Chart, Pareto's Law, Warehouse Management System (WMS)*.

absorption costing – An accounting practice for measuring product costs.

Under absorption costing, product costs are calculated as the sum of the direct cost such as labor and materials and indirect (fixed) costs such as administrative overhead. Overhead costs from each workcenter are assigned to products as they pass through the workcenter. Traditionally, the overhead (indirect) cost is normally assigned to the product based on the number of direct labor hours. With Activity Based Costing systems, overhead may be assigned to products based on other "cost-drivers" such as product complexity.

Absorption costing is often criticized because it tends to drive operations managers to produce more inventory in order to absorb more overhead. This is clearly contrary to the lean manufacturing philosophy. Throughput accounting attempts to address some of these issues.

See *Activity Based Costing (ABC), standard cost, throughput accounting, variable costing*.

absorptive capacity – A limit on a firm's ability to take in scientific or technological information.

Absorptive capacity can be examined on multiple levels (individual, group, firm, and national level), but is usually studied in the context of a firm. Conducting internal R&D projects can build absorptive capacity, which often leads firms to conduct R&D internally rather than to outsource. The theory involves organizational learning, industrial economics, the resource-based view of the firm, and dynamic capabilities. The term was first introduced in the article Cohen and Levinthal (1990). According to the ISI Web of Science, this article has been cited over 1500 times.

Adapted from en.wikipedia.org/wiki/Absorptive_capacity and economics.about.com/cs/economics glossary/g/absorptive_cap.htm.

See *New Product Development (NPD)*.

Acceptable Quality Level (AQL) – The maximum percent defective that is considered satisfactory as a process average by the producer and consumer.

When deciding whether or not to accept a batch, a sample of *n* parts is taken from the batch and a decision is made to accept the batch if the percent of defects is less than the AQL. The AQL is the highest proportion defective that is considered acceptable as a long-run average for the process. (Thanks to Professor Douglas N. Hales at Clemson University for helpful edits on parts of this entry.)

For example, if 4% nonconforming product is acceptable to both the producer and consumer (e.g., AQL=4.0), the producer agrees to produce an average of no more than 4% nonconforming product.

See *acceptance sampling, consumer's risk, Lot Tolerance Percent Defective (LTPD), producer's risk, Zero Defects*.

acceptance sampling – Sampling methods used to make accept/reject decisions for each lot. ✪

With attribute sampling plans, accept/reject decisions are based on a count of the number of defects and defectives. In contrast, with variable sampling plans, accept/reject decisions are based on measurements. Plans requiring only a single sample set are known as single sampling plans; double, multiple, and sequential sampling plans may require additional samples.

For example, an attribute single sampling plan with a sample size $n = 50$ and an accept number $a = 1$ requires that a sample of 50 units be inspected. If the number of defectives in that sample is one or zero, the lot is accepted. Otherwise it is rejected. Ideally, when a sampling plan is used, all bad lots will be rejected and all good lots will be accepted. However, because accept/reject decisions are based on a sample of the lot, there is always a chance of making an incorrect decision. So what protection does a sampling plan offer? The behavior of a sampling plan can be described by its operating characteristic curve, which plots the percent defective against the corresponding probabilities of acceptance. Adapted from Dr. Wayne Taylor, www.variation.com/techlib/as-9.html.

See *Acceptable Quality Level (AQL), attribute, consumer's risk, inspection, Lot Tolerance Percent Defective (LTPD), operating characteristic curve, producer's risk, sampling, Statistical Process Control (SPC), Statistical Quality Control (SQC).*

Accounts Payable (A/P) – The money owed to suppliers for goods and services purchased on credit. Analysts look at a company's relationship of accounts payable to purchases for indications of sound financial management.

See *Accounts Receivable (A/R), terms.*

Accounts Receivable (A/R) – The money that is owed to an organization by customers for products and services provided on credit.

The accounts receivable is treated as a current asset on the balance sheet. A specific sale is generally treated as an account receivable after the customer is sent an invoice. Accounts receivable usually includes an allowance for bad debts. The term accounts receivable is also used to refer to the department that applies cash received from customers against open invoices and manages invoice adjustments and credit memos.

See *Accounts Payable (A/P).*

active item – Any inventory item that has been used or sold in the recent past (e.g., the last year).

It is common for some retailers to have 200,000 items in their item master, but only 20,000 "active" items.

See *Stock Keeping Unit (SKU).*

Activity Based Costing (ABC) – An accounting practice that identifies the cost drivers (variables) that have the most influence on the product (or service) cost and then allocates overhead cost to products and services based on these cost drivers. ✪

Allocating overhead (particularly manufacturing overhead) is an important activity for many firms. This allocation is needed so that the management can have a reasonably accurate product cost that can be used to conduct product profitability analysis. This can often help management make important decisions about pricing, product rationalization, marketing and sales efforts, etc.

Traditional standard costing systems usually allocate overhead cost based on direct labor. For example, consider a product that requires one hour of labor and $30 of materials. If the direct labor wage rate (without overhead) is $20 and the overhead burden rate is $200 per direct labor hour, the standard cost for the product is then direct materials ($20), direct labor ($30), and allocated overhead ($200), for a total cost of $250.

One common criticism of traditional standard costing systems is that it does not make sense to allocate the largest cost (the overhead) based on the smallest cost (the direct labor cost). (Overhead is often the largest component of the standard cost and direct labor cost is often the smallest component.) Traditional standard costing systems assume that the only resource that has any relation to overhead is direct labor -- and that all other resources and activities required to create the product or service cannot be related to overhead.

In contrast, Activity Based Costing begins by identifying the major activities and resources required in the process of creating a product or service. ABC then identifies the "cost pools" (overhead cost) for each activity or resource. Finally, ABC defines an equitable way of allocating (assigning) the overhead cost from the cost pools to the products and services based on a variable called a "cost driver."

A cost driver should reflect the amount of the cost pool resource consumed in the creation of the product or service. Cost drivers might include the number of setups (for a shared setup team), direct materials cost (for allocating purchasing overhead), direct labor time (for allocating labor-related overhead), total throughput time (for allocating manufacturing overhead), inspection time (for allocating quality control overhead), space used (for allocating building related overhead).

Activity Based Management (ABM) is the use of the Activity Based Costing tools by process owners to control and improve their operations. Building an Activity Based Cost model requires a process analysis, which requires management to become more knowledgeable about the business and evaluate value-added and non-value-added activities. The cost analysis and the process understanding that is derived from a ABC system can provide strong support for important managerial decisions such as outsourcing, insourcing, capacity expansion, and other important "what if" issues.

Some argue that all manufacturing overhead cost should be allocated and should be allocated based on direct labor (or some other arbitrary cost driver) even if the cost is not traceable to any production activity. However, most experts agree that the sole purpose of an ABC system is to provide management with information that is helpful for decision making. Arbitrary allocation of overhead cost does not support this purpose in any way.

Even with Activity Based Costing, certain costs related to the sustenance of the business may still be lumped into an overhead cost bucket without being allocated to the product.

Acknowledgments: CEMBA 09 students Brian Clark, Brent Niccum, Tushar Patel, Rebecca Savoie, and Kate Walker contributed to this entry. Matthew Larson (CSOM BA Business '08) also contributed to this entry.

See *absorption costing, burden rate, hidden factory, outsourcing, overhead, standard cost, throughput accounting, variable costing.*

Activity Based Management (ABM) – See *Activity Based Costing (ABC).*

addition principle – Combining two tasks or jobs and assigning them to one resource (person, machine, contractor, etc.). ✪

A common strategy for improving a process is to combine two or more process steps so that one resource (person, machine, contractor, etc.) does all of them. This strategy has many potential advantages, including reducing cost, reducing cycle time, reducing the number of queues, reducing the number of handoffs, reducing lost customer information, reducing customer waiting time, improving customer satisfaction, improving quality, improving job design, accelerating learning, developing people, and improving accountability.

The addition principle is an application of job enlargement where a worker takes on some of a co-worker's job and/or job enrichment where a worker takes on part the boss' job. This is closely related to the queuing theory concept of pooling.

The application of the addition principle is particularly effective in the service context where it can impact customer waiting time and put more of a "face" on the service process. For example, many years ago Citibank reduced the number of handoffs in its international letter of credit operation from about 14 to 1. Instead of having 14 different people each handle one small step, one person handled all 14 steps required by the letter of credit. This change dramatically reduced customer leadtime, improved quality, and improved process visibility. They required new workers to be bilingual, which also improved service quality. The visibility of the new process allowed them to further improve the process and prepared the way for automating the process. However, implementing this new process was not without problems. The clerical people in the old process had to be replaced by better trained people, and the new process increased risk because it eliminated some of the financial system "checks and balances" in the old process.

See *job enlargement, pooling.*

adoption curve – The major phases in the product lifecycle that reflect the market's acceptance of a new product or technology.

According to the Product Development & Management Association (www.pdma.org), consumers move from (a) a cognitive state (becoming aware of and knowledgeable about a product) to (b) an emotional state (liking and then preferring the product) and finally into (c) a behavioral state (deciding and then purchasing the product).

At the market level, the new product is first purchased by the market innovators (roughly 2.5% of the market), followed by early adopters (roughly 13.5% of the market), followed by the early majority (34%), late majority (34%), and finally, the laggards (16%).

Adapted from www.pdma.org/library/glossary.html, December 9, 2006.

See *Bass Model, New Product Development (NPD), product lifecycle management.*

Advanced Planning and Scheduling (APS) – An information system used by manufacturers, distributors, and retailers to assist in supply chain planning and scheduling by applying statistical and mathematical optimization tools.

Most APS systems augment ERP system functionality by providing forecasting, inventory planning, scheduling, and optimization tools not historically found in ERP systems. For example, APS systems can calculate optimal safety stocks, create detailed schedules that do not exceed available capacity (finite scheduling), and find the near-optimal assignments of products to plants. In contrast, traditional ERP systems were fundamentally transaction processing system that implemented (but did not calculate) user-defined safety stocks, created plans that regularly exceeded available capacity (infinite loading), and did not optimize anything.

At the time of this writing, the best-known dedicated APS software vendors are i2 Technologies and Manugistics. SAP now has an APS module called APO, which stands for Advanced Planning and Optimization. According to SAP's website, "SAP APO is a software solution that enables dynamic supply chain management. It includes applications for detailed planning, optimization and scheduling, allowing the supply chain to be accurately and globally monitored even beyond enterprise boundaries. SAP APO is a component of mySAP Supply Chain Management." Oracle now has APS capabilities as well.

The sales script for these APS systems in the past (exaggerated here for sake of emphasis) has been that the big ERP systems (SAP, Oracle, etc.) were "brain dead" and had little intelligence built into them. These big ERP systems were only transaction processing systems and did little in the way of creating detailed schedules, forecasting, or optimization. The promise of the APS systems was that they were "smart" and could make the ERP systems a lot smarter. However, recently the lines have blurred and nearly all ERP systems such as SAP and Oracle now offer add-on products that do much of what only the APS systems offered to do in the past.

Many APS users have found that many APS features were hard to implement and maintain. These difficulties have resulted in some negative assessments of APS systems in general. The three main complaints are:

Massive data requirements – Capacity information on almost every workcenter for every hour in the day.

Complexity – Few managers understand mathematical algorithms used in an APS.

Integration – The APS must work alongside the ERP system and must share a common database.

The entry on *finite scheduling* discusses some of the needs that motivated the development of APS systems.

See *backward scheduling, closed-loop MRP, Enterprise Resources Planning (ERP), finite scheduling, I2, infinite loading, job shop scheduling, Manugistics, Materials Requirements Planning (MRP), SAP.*

Advanced Shipping Notification (ASN) – An electronic file sent from a distribution center (DC) to a receiving facility (often a cross-dock) to advise the receiving facility of the expected arrival of incoming goods.

In the typical usage, an ASN file is sent immediately when a trailer (destined for a given receiving facility) leaves the DC. The ASN file should be received by the receiving facility well in advance of the trailer actually arriving at the facility. The ASN is typically received and processed by the Transportation Management System (TMS) or Warehouse Management System (WMS) in use at the receiving facility.

The ASN file serves three important purposes:

1. The receiving facility uses the ASN to plan inventory or load movement (interline hauls or ground-route distribution) based on the expected inbound mix of goods. Such planning may include scheduling of other resources (drivers, warehouse personnel) or even advance calls to customers to inform them of their expected delivery time windows.

2. The TMS or WMS systems at the receiving facility may use the expected inbound mix of goods to prepare warehouse employees to receive the goods (downloading the information to wireless bar-code scanners, or alerting warehouse planning staff to the total incoming volume of goods they should expect).

3. The TMS or WMS system may ultimately use the expected inbound goods to form the basis of an Over/Short/Damaged Report (OSD) report upon actual scanning of the inbound goods.

The ASN file typically contains the following information for the trailer and for each item in the shipment:

- For the trailer itself:
  - Trailer ID (usually corresponding to numbers stenciled on the side of the trailer)
  - Originating facility (Distribution Center ID)
  - Date the trailer left the originating facility
  - Destination facility (Cross Dock or receiving warehouse ID)
  - Date the trailer is expected to arrive at the destination facility
  - Total number of items contained
  - Total cube (volume) of items contained
- For each item in the trailer:
  - Part number (SKU)
  - Bar-code identifier
  - Destination (perhaps by ID such as store number or by full consignee name, address, etc.)
  - Quantities
  - Cubic volume
  - Description
  - Hazardous status

When the trailer (or other shipping container) arrives, the contents of the trailer can be electronically compared to the contents of the ASN file as the trailer is unloaded. Any missing items or unexpected items would be highlighted on the Over/Short/Damaged Report (OSD) report.

Although commonly used in over-the-road trucking, an ASN can be sent in relation to any shipment, including air, rail, road, and sea. An ASN file is often sent in the agreed-upon EDI 210 ("Advanced Shipping Notification") format. However, technically, an ASN could be any file format agreed-upon by the originating and receiving facilities. A low-tech solution would be to simply fax the manifest of goods on the trailer to the receiving facility as soon as the trailer leaves the originating facility.

Acknowledgments: CEMBA 09 students David Collins, Judy Djugash, Kaaren Howe, Kristi Olson, Michael Pynch, Lynn Sellman, and Travis Swenson contributed to this entry.

See *cross-docking, Electronic Data Interchange (EDI), Over/Short/Damaged Report (OSD Report), Transportation Management System (TMS), Warehouse Management System (WMS).*

adverse event – A healthcare term used to describe any unintended and undesirable medical occurrence experienced by a patient as a result of medical therapy or other intervention, regardless of the cause or degree of severity.

The term adverse event is often used in the context of drug therapy and/or clinical trials. In the drug therapy context, it is also called an adverse reaction or an adverse drug reaction.

Very serious adverse events are usually called sentinel events or "never events"; however, a few sources treat the terms "adverse event" and "sentinel event" as synonyms. The term "near miss" is used to describe an event that could have harmed the patient, but was avoided through planned or unplanned actions.

Barach and Small (2000) report lessons for healthcare organizations from non-medical "near miss" reporting systems. This interesting report begins by emphasizing that most near misses and preventable adverse events are not reported and that healthcare systems could be improved significantly if more of these events were reported. The report further argues that healthcare could benefit from what has been learned in other industries. The authors studied reporting systems in aviation, nuclear power technology, petrochemical processing, steel production, military operations, and air transportation as well as in healthcare. They argue that reporting near misses is better than reporting only adverse events because the greater frequency enables better quantitative analysis and provides more information to process improvement programs. Many of the non-medical industries have developed incident reporting systems that focus on near misses, provide incentives for voluntary reporting (e.g., limited liability, anonymous reporting, and confidentiality), bolster accountability, and implement systems for data collection, analysis, and improvement.

The key to encouraging reporting of near misses and adverse events is to lower the "cost" of reporting to the medical professions. Many organizations allow for anonymous reporting, which makes it possible for the person reporting the error or event to keep their identity confidential. It is also important to make the process easy to use. One organization has a website that allows nurses and doctors to anonymously enter information about adverse events.

See *Joint Commission (JCAHO), sentinel event.*

advertising allowance (ad allowance) – The money provided by a manufacturer to a distributor or retailer for advertising a specific product or brand.

affinity diagram – A "bottoms-up" group brainstorming methodology designed to help groups generate and organize a large number of ideas into related groups to make sense of a complex problem; also known as the KJ Method and KJ Analysis. ✪

Affinity diagrams are a simple yet powerful way to extract qualitative data from a group, help the group cluster similar ideas, and finally develop a consensus view on a subject. For example, an affinity diagram might be used to clarify the question, "What are the root causes of our quality problems?"

Despite the name, affinity diagrams are not really diagrams. Occasionally, circles are drawn around clusters of similar concepts and lines or trees are drawn to connect similar clusters, but these drawings are not central to the affinity diagramming methodology.

For example, affinity diagrams are often used with Quality Function Development (QFD) to sort and organize the large amount of customer needs data. To do this, the facilitator instructs each individual in a group to identify all known customer needs and write them down on Post-it™ notes, with each need on an individual piece of paper. The group then organizes these notes into clusters and develops a heading for each cluster.

Affinity diagrams can be used for several purposes such as:

- Adding structure to a large or complicated issue. For example, "What are the issues relative to implementing a thematic approach to teaching?" or "How do we attract the Summer Olympics to the Twin Cities in 2020?"
- Breaking down a complicated issue into broad categories. For example, "Which departments are more likely to implement TQM in this school?" or "What are the major steps needed for this complex project?"
- Gaining agreement on an issue or situation. For example, "Which direction should the school take to restructure its curriculum?" or "How should a new product be marketed?"

The steps for creating an affinity diagram include:

1. State the issue or problem to be explored. Start with a clear statement of the problem or goal and provide a time limit for the session. Usually 45-60 minutes is sufficient.
2. Brainstorm ideas for the issue or problem. Each participant should think of ideas and write them on individual notes. This usually does not require more than 10 minutes.
3. Have each person share one note at a time and place their Post-it™ note on the wall without discussion.
4. Have the group then arrange the notes into related groups. If some notes do not fit in any group, it is best to keep these separate and not try to force them into a group. The KJ Method requires that people not communicate during this phase. People are allowed to add new notes and also to replicate a note if they believe that a note belongs in two groups.
5. Create a title for each group that best describes the theme of each group of notes and write the title on a note and stick it on the wall above the group. Discussion is allowed during this phase.
6. It is a good idea to then arrange the groups in a logical order, which might require additional headers.

A good example of an affinity diagram can be found at http://syque.com/quality_tools/tools/TOOLS04.htm, December 27, 2007.

See *brainstorming, causal map, cluster analysis, Kepner-Tregoe Model, KJ Method, Nominal Group Technique (NGT), Quality Function Deployment (QFD), Root Cause Analysis (RCA).*

aggregate inventory management – The analysis of a large set of items in an inventory system with a focus on lotsizing and safety stock policies to study the tradeoffs between carrying cost and service levels.

Inventories with thousands of items are difficult to manage because of the amount of data involved. Aggregate inventory management tools allow managers to group items and explore opportunities to reduce inventory and improve service levels by controlling target service level, carrying charge, and setup costs parameters for each group of items. Aggregate inventory analysis typically applies economic order quantity logic and safety stock equations in light of warehouse space limitations, market requirements, and company strategies. Aggregate inventory analysis often results in a simultaneous reduction in overall inventory and improvement in overall service levels. This is accomplished by reducing the safety stock inventory for those items that have unnecessarily high safety stocks and increasing the safety stock inventory for those items that have poor service levels.

The Excel workbooks "Aggregate inventory analysis.xls" and "safety stock.xls" are on the **OMWW CD** available from www.ClamshellBeachPress.com. ●

See *inventory management, inventory turnover, lotsizing methods, safety stock, unit of measure.*

aggregate production planning – The process of creating a high-level production plan, usually in monthly time buckets for families of items, and often measured in a high-level common unit of measure such as units, gallons, or pounds. ✪

In academic circles, the result of the aggregate production planning process is called the "aggregate plan," whereas in many practitioner circles (including APICS) it is known simply as the "production plan." Aggregate planning is particularly difficult for firms with seasonal products. Firms such as Polaris (snowmobiles and ATVs) and Toro (snow blowers and lawnmowers) have to build inventory in the off-season in anticipation of the peak demand season.

Aggregate planning (production planning) is just one step in the Sales & Operations Planning (S&OP) process. S&OP is a broader and higher-level business process that includes sales, marketing, finance, and operations and oversees the creation of the business plan, the sales plan, and the production plan. (See the *Sales & Operations Planning (S&OP)* entry for more information on this topic.)

Whereas the business plan is usually defined in dollars (profit, revenue, and cost), the aggregate production plan is usually defined by units or some other aggregate output (or input) measure, such as shop hours worked, gallons produced, crude oil started, etc. An aggregate measure is particularly useful when the production plan includes many dissimilar products.

The goal is to meet customer demand at the lowest cost. Relevant costs for aggregate planning decisions include inventory carrying costs, capacity change costs (hiring, training, firing, facility expansion or contraction, equipment expansion or reduction), and possibly the opportunity costs of lost sales.

The linear programming formulation for the aggregate production planning problem has been in the operations management and operations research literature since the 1960s. It assumes that the demand is known over the planning horizon of T periods with certainty. The problem is to find the optimal production plan, workforce plan, and inventory plan to meet the demand at the lowest cost.

$$\text{Minimize: } z = \sum_{t=1}^{T} (c_H H_t + c_F F_t + c_{OT} OT_t + c_W W_t + c_C I_t)$$

$$\text{Subject to: } I_t = I_{t-1} + P_t - D_t, \text{ for } t = 1, 2, \ldots, T$$

$$P_t = r(W_t + OT_t), \text{ for } t = 1, 2, \ldots, T$$

$$OT_t \leq 1.5 W_t, \text{ for } t = 1, 2, \ldots, T$$

$$W_t = W_{t-1} + H_t - F_t, \text{ for } t = 1, 2, \ldots, T$$

where,

T	Number of periods in the planning horizon.
t	Period index, $t = 1, 2, \ldots, T$.
c_H	Cost of hiring one worker.
H_t	Number of workers hired in period t.
c_F	Cost of firing one worker.
F_t	Number of workers fired in period t.
c_{OT}	Cost of using one full-time equivalent worker to work overtime for one period.
OT_t	Number of workers working over time period t, expressed in full time equivalents. (The constraint above assumes that overtime is limited to 1.5 times regular time work.)
c_W	Cost of employing one worker for one period.
W_t	Number of workers employed in period t.
c_C	Cost of carrying one unit for one period.
I_t	Inventory (in units) at the end of period t.
P_t	The production rate in period t. This is just the number of units produced in period t.
D_t	Number of units demanded in period t.
r	Number of units produced by one worker per period.

The objective function is to minimize the sum of the hiring, firing, overtime, regular time, and carrying costs. The first constraint is the inventory balancing equation, which requires that the new inventory at the end of period t is the old inventory plus what is produced minus what is sold. The second constraint defines the number of units produced in period t as a function of the number of workers working in that period. The third constraint limits overtime to 1.5 times the regular time. Finally, the fourth constraint defines the number of regular time workers as the old number plus the number hired less the number fired.

The model can be extended in many ways such as adding additional capacity constraints on equipment or the workforce, allowing for lost sales (with deviation variables), allowing for uncertain demand (stochastic programming), uncertain constraints (chance constrained programming), quadratic cost functions (LDR and SDR), learning, etc.

While the model has been around for a long time, few firms have found it useful. The basic model requires the assumption that demand is known with certainty, which is usually far from reality. The model also requires the estimation of a number of cost parameters such as the firing cost, hiring cost, and the carrying cost, which are often hard to estimate. Finally, the linear programming modeling approach does not seem to fit well with the organizational dynamics that surround such difficult decisions as firing employees or building inventory.

See *anticipation stock, Business Requirements Planning (BRP), carrying charge, carrying cost, chase strategy, flexibility, hockey stick effect, Linear Programming (LP), Master Production Schedule (MPS), Materials Requirements Planning (MRP), Sales & Operations Planning (S&OP), unit of measure.*

agile manufacturing – A set of business strategies for competitiveness in a turbulent business environment.

Companies that successfully embrace agile manufacturing principles can sometimes achieve the following:

- New markets for niche, customized products and services
- Long-term relationships with customers
- Faster concept-to-cash time
- Turning change into market opportunity
- Multiple win/win partnerships

The following are attributes of agile organizations:

- Strategize to fragment mass markets into niche markets.
- Compete on the basis of customer-perceived value.
- Produce multiple products and services in market-determined quantities.
- Design solutions interactively with customers.
- Organize for proficiency in change and rapid response.
- Manage through leadership, motivation, support and trust.
- Exploit information and communication technologies to the fullest.
- Leverage all its capabilities, resources, and assets regardless of location.
- Work in entrepreneurial and empowered teams.
- Partner with other companies as a strategy of choice, not a last resort.

The main texts on this subject include Goldman, Nagel, and Preiss (1995) and Metes, Gundry, and Bradish (1997). Much of the content above was adapted from http://www.agility.co.uk/ai.html.

See *operations strategy, Quick Response Manufacturing, Time-based Competition.*

agile software development – A software development methodology that promotes quick development of small parts of a project to ensure that the developers meet user requirements; also known as agile modeling.

Agile software development promotes iterative software development with high stakeholder involvement and open collaboration throughout the life of a software development project. It uses small increments with minimal planning. Agile attempts to find the smallest workable piece of functionality and then deliver it quickly -- and then continually improve it throughout the life of the project as directed by the user community. This helps to reduce the risk that the project will fail to meet user requirements.

In contrast, the "waterfall" requires "gates" (approvals) for each step of the development process: requirements, analysis, design, coding, and testing. Progress is measured by the adherence to the pre-planned schedule and the delivery of the outputs for each phase. The waterfall approach, therefore, is not nearly as iterative as the agile process.

The Agile Modeling website (http://www.agilemodeling.com) has extensive content of this subject.

See *cross functional team, lean thinking.*

AGV – See *Automated Guided Vehicle.*

AHP – See *Analytical Hierarchy Process.*

AI – See *artificial intelligence.*

alpha test – See *prototype.*

alignment – The degree to which people and/or organizational units share the same goals.

Two or more people or organizational units are said to be "aligned" when they are both working together towards the same goals. They are said to be "misaligned" when they are working towards conflicting goals. Alignment is usually driven by reward systems.

For example, sales organizations often forecast demand higher than the actual demand because sales people tend to be much more concerned about running out of stock (and losing sales) than they are about having too much inventory. In other words, they are prone to "add safety stock to the forecast." Given that sales organizations are typically rewarded only on the basis of sales, this bias is completely logical. However, this behavior is generally not aligned with the overall objectives of the firm.

See *balanced scorecard, forecast bias.*

algorithm – A formal procedure for solving a problem.

An algorithm is usually expressed as a series of steps and implemented in a computer program. For example, some algorithms for solving the Traveling Salesperson Problem can require thousands of lines of computer code. Some algorithms are designed to guarantee an optimal (mathematically best) solution and are said to be "exact" or "optimal" algorithms. Other algorithms seek to find the optimal solution, but do not guarantee that the optimal solution will be found and are known as heuristics or heuristic algorithms.

See *heuristic, Traveling Salesperson Problem (TSP)*.

alliance – A formal cooperative arrangement with another firm, which could be for almost any purpose such as new product development, sharing information, entering a new market, etc. Alliances usually involve sharing both risks and rewards.

allocated stock – A term used by manufacturing and distribution firms for the quantity of an item that has been reserved, but not yet withdrawn or issued from stock. This is sometimes called "committed inventory."

See *inventory position*.

all-time demand – The total of all future requirements (demand) for an item. ✪

The all-time demand is sometimes called the "all-time" or the "lifetime" requirement. The all-time demand is the sum of the demand until the product termination date or until the end of time.

Forecasting the all-time (lifetime) demand

In many situations, organizations need to forecast the remaining lifetime demand for a product or component. Examples of when this all-time demand forecast is important include:

- The final purchase (the "final buy") of the item – If an item is near the end of its useful life and the organization needs to make one last purchase, it will need to forecast the lifetime demand. Future purchases will be extremely expensive due to the problems the supplier will have in finding or building the tooling needed to make the item, finding or developing the workers' skills, and finding or developing suppliers for the components and raw materials needed.
- The final manufacturing lot for an item – If an item is near the end of its useful life and the manufacturer needs to make one last run of the item, it will need to forecast the lifetime demand. Future manufacturing will likely be very expensive.
- Identifying scrap inventory of an item – It is often wise to scrap unnecessary inventory long before an item is completely discontinued. It is necessary to have a reasonably accurate estimate of the lifetime demand for the item to determine how many units should be scrapped.
- Identifying when it is time to discontinue an item – A forecast of the lifetime demand can be useful input to an evaluation of the timing for discontinuing an item.

The geometric decay model

Several empirical studies such as Hill, Giard, and Mabert (1989) have found that the demand during the end-of-life phase of the product life cycle often follows a geometric decay pattern. The geometric series suggests that the demand in any period is a constant times the demand in the previous period (i.e., $d_t = \beta d_{t-1}$), where $0 < \beta < 1$. The beta parameter is called the common ratio because $\beta = d_1 / d_0 = ... = d_{t+1} / d_t$. Given that period 0 had demand of d_0 units, the forecasted demand for period 1 is $f_1 = \beta d_0$ and for period 2 is $f_2 = \beta f_1 = \beta^2 d_0$. In general, given that period 0 demand is d_0 units, the forecasted demand t periods into the future is $f_t = \beta^t d_0$.

The cumulative forecasted demand through the next T periods after period 0 is the sum of the finite geometric series $F_T = f_1 + f_2 + ... + f_T = \beta d_0 + \beta^2 d_0 + ... + \beta^T d_0$. Multiplying both sides of this equation by β yields $\beta F_T = \beta^2 d_0 + \beta^3 d_0 + ... + \beta^{T+1} d_0$ and then subtracting this new equation from the first one yields $F_T - \beta F_T = \beta d_0 - \beta^{T+1} d_0$, which simplifies to $F_T(1-\beta) = d_0 \beta (1 - \beta^T)$. Given that $\beta < 1$, it is clear that

$1 - \beta \neq 0$, which means that it is possible to divide both sides by $1 - \beta$, which yields $F_T = d_0 \beta (1 - \beta^T) / (1 - \beta)$. At the limit as $T \to \infty$, $\beta^T \to 0$ and the sum of the all-time demand after period 0 is $F_\infty = d_0 \beta / (1 - \beta)$.

In summary, given that the actual demand for the most recent period (period 0) was d_0, the forecast of the cumulative demand over the next T time periods is $F_T = d_0 \beta (1 - \beta^T) / (1 - \beta)$. The cumulative demand from now until the end of time is then $F_\infty = d_0 \beta / (1 - \beta)$.

Example with a graph

The following graph shows the geometric decay for four historical data points (100, 80, 64, and 32). With $\beta = 0.737$, the all-time demand forecast is $F_\infty = d_0 \beta / (1 - \beta) = (100)(0.737)/(1 - 0.737) = 116$ units, and a forecast over a $T = 16$ period horizon is 113 units.

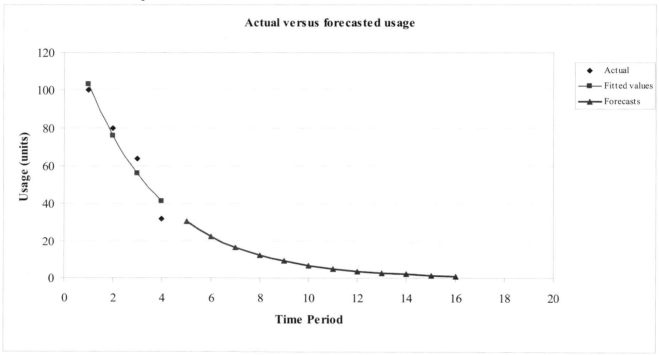

Estimating the beta (β) parameter

The geometric decay forecasting model requires an estimate of the beta (β) parameter from historical data. Several approaches are available for this estimation problem.

The first and last demand approach – The simplest approach for estimating the beta (β) parameter is to take two non-zero historical values of sales (d_a, d_b). The d_b value should be the most current actual demand value available and d_a (with $a < b$ and $d_b < d_a$) should be from a time period after the time series began to decline. Beta can be estimated with $\beta = (d_b / d_a)^{1/(b-a)}$. In the above example, $d_a = d_0 = 100$ is the first value and $d_b = d_3 = 32$ is the last value. The beta parameter is then $\beta = (32/100)^{1/(3-0)} = 0.32^{1/3} \approx 0.684$. Unfortunately, this approach is only sensitive to the first and last values, which may not be representative of the time series. Therefore, it is not the best approach for important problems.

The graphical approach – Another approach is to graph the time series $\ln(d_t)$ against t on semi-log paper and draw a line that appears to have a good fit with the points. The parameter b, the slope of the fitted line, is then $b = \ln(\beta)$ and $\beta = \exp(b)$. However, this approach relies on human intuition and is susceptible to error.

The linear regression approach – A more statistical approach is to perform the log-transformation on the sales data and use linear regression to estimate beta. The model is as follows:

$$d_t = \beta^t d_0 e_t$$

$$\ln(d_t) = t\ln(\beta) + \ln(d_0) + \ln(e_t)$$

$$y_t = a + bt + e_t$$

$$\hat{y}_t = \hat{a} + \hat{b}t$$

where e_t is the multiplicative error in period t. The forecasted value for period t is $\hat{y}_t = \ln(d_t)$ with parameters $\hat{b} = \ln(\beta)$ and $\hat{a} = \ln(d_0)$ estimated using linear regression. Unfortunately, this approach has several problems.

- If the actual demand, d_t, is zero in any period, the procedure fails because it is impossible to take the natural log of zero. This problem is sometimes "fixed" by adding one to all demands and then subtracting one from all forecasts, but this is "cheating" and results in questionable forecasts.
- The procedure gives more weight to the early data because the natural log of a large number is much higher than that of a small number. This added influence of the early data on the curve fitting procedure may not be desirable.
- The R^2 value for this linear regression is not very meaningful after the natural log transformation. The R^2 here is the percent of the variance explained for the *transformed* demand graph rather than for the original demand graph.
- The standard deviation of the error from the regression is not the standard deviation of the forecast error.
- The errors are likely serially correlated (correlated over time) which violates an important assumption of linear regression.

The non-linear optimization approach – The approach implemented in the lida.xls Excel workbook uses the forecasting model $\hat{y}_t = \alpha\beta^{t-1} + e_t$ where e_t is the additive error term in period t, $\hat{y}_t$ is the forecasted value for period t, and the parameters alpha (α) and beta (β) are estimated using non-linear optimization (such as the Excel Solver) to minimize the sum of the squared errors over the historical demand time series. The alpha parameter is an estimate of the initial demand value (i.e., d_0), and the beta parameter is the common ratio for the geometric series. This approach avoids all of the problems listed above for linear regression, except for the serial correlation problem. However, this approach ignores the fact that the average error is likely to be declining over time. For the previous example, the optimal (least squares) estimates for alpha and beta are (103.3, 0.737) and are shown in the above graph.

The book by Hill (1992) develops these concepts further.

The paper "Forecasting Lifetime Demand" and the Excel workbook "LIDA.xls" are on the **OMWW CD** available from www.ClamshellBeachPress.com. ●

See *all-time order, Bass Model, demand, forecast horizon, forecasting, obsolescence, product lifecycle management, slow moving demand, termination date.*

all-time order – The last order for a particular product in the last phase of its life cycle.

The all-time order is sometimes called the "lifetime buy" or "last buy." The all-time order should be large enough so the inventory provided will satisfy nearly all expected future demand and balance the cost of a stockout with the cost of carrying inventory.

See *all-time demand, product lifecycle management.*

alternate routing – A sequence of steps that can be used to assemble or manufacture a component or product.

The alternate routing is a backup used when the primary routing is not viable due to downtime or congestion.

See *routing, Theory of Constraints (TOC).*

American Society for Quality (ASQ) – A professional association that advances learning, quality improvement, and knowledge exchange to improve business results and create better workplaces and communities worldwide.

ASQ has more than 100,000 individual and organizational members. Founded in 1946, and headquartered in Milwaukee, Wisconsin, the ASQ was formerly known as the ASQC, the American Society for Quality Control. Since 1991, ASQ has administered the Malcolm Baldrige National Quality Award, which annually recognizes companies and organizations that have achieved performance excellence. ASQ publishes many practitioner and academic journals including *Quality Progress*, *Journal for Quality and Participation*, *Journal of Quality Technology*, *Quality Engineering*, *Quality Management Journal*, *Six Sigma Forum Magazine*, *Software Quality Professional*, and *Technometrics*. The ASQ website is www.asq.org.

See *Operations Management (OM)*.

Analysis of Variance – See *ANOVA (Analysis of Variance)*.

Analytical Hierarchy Process (AHP) – A decision-making tool developed by T.L. Saaty for complex, multi-criteria problems where both qualitative and quantitative aspects of a problem need to be incorporated; also known as Analytic Hierarchy Process.

A methodology for decision-making that consists of (1) breaking down a complex, unstructured situation into its component parts and then arranging those into a hierarchy order, (2) assigning numerical values to subjective judgments on the relative importance of each component, and (3) synthesizing the judgments to determine which component has the highest priority.

Without the AHP methodology, decision-makers are prone to fall into traps. The most obvious case of this problem is when assigning direct numbers to represent a judgmental scale in order to choose the best alternative. For example, consider the 3-valued scale (1, 3, 5) with 1=low, 3=medium, and 5=high. At first glance, this scale is acceptable because each step represents a two-unit increase. However, in relative terms, it is absolutely wrong and biased. Notice that moving from 1 to 3 is an increase of (3−1)/1=200% and from 3 to 5 yields a change of only (5−3)/3=67%. The error is in thinking in absolute terms rather than in relative terms.

Adapted from meritdecision.com/ahp.htm, January 16, 2004.

See *causal map, conjoint analysis, force-field diagram, Kano Analysis, Kepner-Tregoe Model, New Product Development (NPD), Pugh Matrix, Triz, Voice of the Customer (VOC)*.

anchoring – Allowing estimates or thinking to be influenced by some starting information or current conditions; also used to describe the difficulty of changing behavior that is heavily influenced by old habits.

According to the *Forecasting Dictionary* (Armstrong, 2001), the initial value (or anchor) can be based on tradition, previous history, or available data. Anchoring is a significant problem in many operations contexts including forecasting and subjective estimation of probabilities. For example, when making a subjective forecast, people often anchor on the previous period demand.

In one interesting study, Tversky and Kahneman (1974) asked subjects to predict the percentage of nations that were African in the United Nations. They selected an initial value by spinning a wheel in the subject's presence. The subjects were then asked to revise this number upward or downward to obtain an answer. This information-free initial value had a strong influence on the estimate. Those starting with 10% made predictions averaging 25%. In contrast, those starting with 65% made predictions averaging 45%.

See *forecasting, newsvendor model*.

andon light – A Japanese term (pronounced "Ann-Don") that refers to a warning light or board on (or near) a machine or assembly line that calls attention to defects or equipment problems; also called an andon board.

The number of lights and their possible colors can vary, even by workcenter within a plant. Most implementations have three colors – green, yellow, and red – and are often combined with an audible signal such as music or an alarm. Like a stoplight, the green means normal, the yellow means trouble, and the red means stop.

Another source (kbe.cov.ac.uk/EMDATA/5Bjapmfg.html, November 8, 2004) recommends the following colors:

- Red = Machine breakdown.
- Blue = Defective component.
- White = End of production batch.
- Yellow = Waiting for set-up.
- Green = Material shortage.
- No light = System operating normally

The Japanese word for andon (行灯) means lamp.

When a worker pulls an andon cord (or pushes a button), the red light goes on, the line is stopped, and a supervisor or technician responds immediately to help diagnose and correct the problem. It is important for management to define exactly who is responsible as the support person. The big idea here is to have a simple visual system that immediately calls for the right kind of help from the right people when needed.

See *assembly line, error proofing, jidoka, lean thinking, visual control.*

ANOVA (Analysis of Variance) – A statistical procedure used to test if samples from two or more groups come from populations with equal means.

ANOVA is closely related to multiple regression in that both are linear models and both use the *F* test to test for significance. In fact, regression can be used to conduct an ANOVA, including exploring multiple-way interaction terms.

Multivariate Analysis of Variance (MANOVA) is an extension of ANOVA and is defined as "an extension of analysis of variance (or ANOVA) used to accommodate more than one dependent variable. MANOVA measures the group differences between two or more metric dependent variables simultaneously, using a set of categorical non-metric independent variables." Source: Sarah Babcock, University of Richmond, http://www.richmond.edu/~pli/psy538/manova02/definition.html

See *confidence interval, Design of Experiments (DOE), linear regression, sampling, Taguchi methods, t-test.*

anticipation stock – Inventory held in order to (1) satisfy seasonal demand, (2) cope with expected reduced capacity due to maintenance or anticipated strike, or (3) store seasonal supply for a level demand throughout the year (for example, a crop that is harvested only once per year).

See *aggregate production planning.*

APICS (The Association for Operations Management) – A professional society for operations managers, including production, inventory, supply chain, materials management, purchasing, and logistics.

The acronym APICS stands for the American Production and Inventory Control Society. However, in recent years APICS is using the broader name "The Association for Operations Management" despite the fact that the name no longer matches the acronym.

The APICS website (www.APICS.org) states "The Association for Operations Management is the global leader and premier source of the body of knowledge in operations management, including production, inventory, supply chain, materials management, purchasing, and logistics." Since 1957, individuals and companies have relied on APICS for training, certifications, comprehensive resources, and a worldwide network of accomplished industry professionals. APICS confers the CIRM, CPIM, and CSCP certifications.

APICS produces a number of trade publications and a practitioner/research journal entitled the ***Production & Inventory Management Journal***.

The APICS website is www.apics.org.

See *Operations Management (OM).*

A-plant – See *VAT analysis.*

appraisal cost – An expense associated with measuring quality through inspection and testing. ✪

Many popular quality consultants argue that appraisal costs should be eliminated and that firms should not try to "inspect quality into the product," but should instead "design quality into the product and process."

See *cost of quality.*

APS – See *Advanced Planning and Scheduling (APS).*

AQL – See *Acceptable Quality Level.*

arbitrage – Buying something in one market and reselling it at a higher price in another market.

Arbitrage involves a combination of matching deals to exploit the imbalance in prices between two or more markets and profiting from the difference between the market prices. A person who engages in arbitrage is called an arbitrageur.

Arbitrage is a combination of transactions designed to profit from an existing discrepancy among prices, exchange rates, and/or interest rates in different markets, often without risk of these changing. The simplest form of arbitrage is the simultaneous purchase and sale of something in different markets. More complex forms include triangular arbitrage. To arbitrage is to make a combination of bets such that if one bet loses, another one wins, with the implication of having an edge, at no risk (or at least low risk). A hedge has a similar meaning, but it does not carry the implication of having an edge.

See *hedging.*

ARIMA – Autoregressive Integrated Moving Average. See *Box-Jenkins forecasting.*

ARMA – Autoregressive Moving Average. See *Box-Jenkins forecasting*.

artificial intelligence (AI) – Software that uses algorithms to give the appearance of "intelligence" to a computer. Many applications of AI have been made in operations, including decision support systems, scheduling, forecasting, computer-aided design, character recognition, pattern recognition, and speech/voice recognition.
See *neural net, robotics*.

ASN – See *Advanced Shipping Notification (ASN)*.

AS/RS – See *Automated Storage & Retrieval System (AS/RS)*.

ASQ – See *American Society for Quality*.

Assemble to Order (ATO) – A customer interface strategy that stocks standard components and modules in order to quickly assemble products that meet a wide variety of customer requirements. ✪
This approach allows for a large variety of final products with a relatively short customer leadtime. Examples of ATO processes include Burger King, which assembles hamburgers with many options while the customer waits, and Dell Computer, which assembles and ships a wide variety of computers on short notice. ATO systems have no finished goods inventory, but usually stock major components. Pack to Order and Configure to Order systems are special cases of ATO.
See *Build to Order (BTO), Make to Stock (MTS), mass customization, Respond to Order (RTO)*.

assembly line – The organization of a series of workers and/or machines in a straight line (or a U-shaped line) so that discrete products can be moved easily from one station to the next in order to repetitively build a product; also called a production line.
On an assembly line, each worker (or machine) performs one relatively simple task and then moves the product to the next worker (or machine).
Assembly lines are best suited for assembling large batches of standard products and therefore require a highly standardized process. Unlike continuous processes for liquids or powders which can move through pipes, assembly lines are for discrete products and often use conveyer belts to move products between workers. Assembly lines use a product layout, which means the sequence is determined by the product requirements. Some automated assembly lines require substantial capital investment, which makes them hard to change.
See *andon light, cycle time, discrete manufacturing, facility layout, line balancing, mixed model assembly, product layout*.

assignable cause – See *special cause variation*.

assignment problem – A mathematical programming problem of matching one group of items (jobs, trucks, etc.) with another group of locations (machines, cities, etc.) in order to minimize the sum of the costs.
The assignment problem is usually shown as a table or a matrix and requires that exactly one match is found in each row and each column. For example, the problem of matching students to jobs in which there are N students and N jobs results in an N x N table of possible assignments. Each student must be assigned to exactly one job and each job must be assigned to exactly one student. The "cost" of assigning student i to job j is c_{ij}, which may be some measure of the student's disutility (dislike) for that job. This problem can be solved efficiently on a computer with special-purpose assignment algorithms, network optimization algorithms, and general-purpose linear programming algorithms. Even though it is an integer programming problem, it can be solved with any general linear programming package and be guaranteed to produce integer solutions because the problem is unimodular. The mathematical programming is formulated as follows:

$$\text{Minimize} \sum_{i=1}^{N} \sum_{j=1}^{N} c_{ij} x_{ij}$$

$$\text{Subject to} \sum_{i=1}^{N} x_{ij} = 1 \text{ for all } j$$

$$\sum_{j=1}^{N} x_{ij} = 1 \text{ for all } i$$

where $x_{ij} \in \{0,1\}$ for all (i, j) and where c_{ij} is the cost for item i to location j.

The Excel workbook "spat.xls" on the **OMWW CD** available from www.ClamshellBeachPress.com uses a network optimization routine to assign students to teams in order to maximize student satisfaction. ⬤

See *Integer Programming (IP), Linear Programming (LP), network optimization, transportation problem, Traveling Salesperson Problem (TSP)*.

Association for Manufacturing Excellence (AME) – A practitioner-based professional society dedicated to cultivating understanding, analysis and exchange of productivity methods and their successful application in the pursuit of excellence.

Founded in 1985, AME was the first major professional society in North America to promote lean manufacturing principles. AME events and workshops focus on hands-on learning. AME publishes the award-winning Target magazine and puts on several regional and national events each year.

The AME website is www.ame.org.

See *Operations Management (OM)*.

assortment – A retailer's selection of merchandise to display. This includes both the depth and breadth of products carried. Also known as "merchandise assortment" and "product assortment."

See *planogram*.

ATO – See *Assemble to Order*.

ATP – See *Available-to-Promise (ATP)*.

attribute – A quality management term used to describe a zero-one (binary) property of a product by which its quality will be judged by some stakeholder.

Inspection can be performed by variables or by attributes. Inspection by variables is usually done for process control and is performed with an x-bar chart (to control the mean) or an r-chart (to control the range or variance). Inspection by attributes is usually for lot control (acceptance sampling) and is performed with a p-chart (to control the percent defective) or a c-chart (to control the number of defects).

See *acceptance sampling, Statistical Process Control (SPC)*.

autocorrelation – A measure of the strength of the relationship between a time-series variable in periods t and $t-k$; also called serial correlation.

Autocorrelation measures the correlation between a variable in period t and period $t-k$, e.g., x_t and the x_{t-k}.

The autocorrelation at lag k is defined mathematically as $\rho_k = \dfrac{Cov(x_t, x_{t-k})}{\sqrt{Var(x_t)Var(x_{t-k})}} = \dfrac{Cov(x_t, x_{t-k})}{Var(x_t)}$, where $Var(x_t)$

$= Var(x_{t-k})$ for a weakly stationary process.

Autocorrelation is one way to check for randomness in time series data. The Box-Jenkins forecasting method takes advantage of the autocorrelation structure in the time series to forecast into the future. The Durbin-Watson test can be used to test for first-order (e.g., $k=1$) autocorrelation.

See *Box-Jenkins forecasting, Durbin-Watson statistic*.

Automated Guided Vehicle (AGV) – An unmanned, computer-controlled vehicle equipped with a guidance and collision-avoidance system; sometimes known as an Automated Guided Vehicle System (AGVS).

An AGV is used to transport materials and/or tools between workstations. An AGV typically follows a path defined by wires embedded in the floor. Some firms have found AGVs to be unreliable and do not have a good return on investment. See http://www.inventoryops.com/pics_auto.htm for a nice photo.

See *automation, robotics*.

Automated Storage & Retrieval System (AS/RS) – A computer controlled automated robotic device used for storing and retrieving items from storage locations; also called ASRS.

Automated Storage and Retrieval Systems are a combination of equipment, controls, and information systems which automatically handle, store, and retrieve materials, components, tools, raw material, subassemblies, or products with great speed and accuracy. Consequently, they are used in many manufacturing and warehousing applications. An AS/RS includes one or more of the following technologies: Horizontal Carousels, Vertical Carousels, Vertical Lift Modules (VLM), and the traditional Crane-in-Aisle Storage & Retrieval systems that utilize a storage retrieval (SR) crane.

See *automation, batch picking, zone picking*.

automation – The practice of developing machines to do work that was formerly done manually. ✪

Automation is best used in situations where the work is dangerous, dirty, or dull ("the 3D's"). For example, welding is dangerous, cleaning a long underground sewer line is dirty, and inserting transistors on a printed circuit board is dull. All three of these tasks can and should be automated when possible. Repetitive (dull) work often results in poor quality work, so automated equipment is more likely to produce defect-free results.

See *3Ds, Automated Guided Vehicle (AGV), Automated Storage & Retrieval System (AS/RS), cellular manufacturing, Flexible Manufacturing System (FMS), jidoka, robotics.*

autonomation – See *error proofing, jidoka, Toyota Production System (TPS).*

autonomous maintenance – A Total Productive Maintenance (TPM) principle of making each worker responsible for both maintaining and operating a machine.

Maintenance activities include cleaning, lubricating, adjusting, inspecting, and repair.

See *maintenance, Total Productive Maintenance (TPM).*

autonomous team – See *new product development team.*

availability – A measure used in the reliability and maintenance literature for the percentage of time that a product can be operated.

According to Schroeder (2007), availability is $MTBF/(MTBF + MTTR)$, where $MTBF$ is the mean time between failure and $MTTR$ is the mean time to repair.

See *maintenance, Mean Time Between Failure (MTBF), Mean Time To Repair (MTTR).*

Available-to-Promise (ATP) – The uncommitted inventory and planned production balance in the first period.

The ATP is normally calculated for each period in which an MPS receipt is scheduled. In the first period, the ATP quantity includes on-hand inventory less customer orders that are due and overdue. ATP information is used to support the customer order promising process.

See *Master Production Schedule (MPS).*

B

B2B – Business-to-business transactions between manufacturers, distributors, wholesalers, jobbers, retailers, and governmental organizations and other industrial organizations.

See *B2C, dot-com, e-commerce.*

B2C – Business-to-consumer transactions between a business and consumers.

See *B2B, dot-com, e-commerce.*

back loading – See *backward loading.*

backflushing – A means of reducing the number of inventory transactions (and the related transaction cost) by relieving (reducing) the inventory count for an item only when the order is completed or shipped; also called explode-to-deduct.

For example, a computer keyboard manufacturer has two alternatives for keeping track of the number of letter A's stored in inventory. With the traditional approach, the firm counts the number of keys that are issued (moved) to the assembly area in the plant. This can be quite costly. In fact, it is possible the cost of counting the inventory could even exceed the value of the inventory. With backflushing, the firm reduces the letter A inventory count when an order is shipped to a customer. The bill of material for a keyboard calls for one letter A to be attached to each keyboard; if the firm ships 100 keyboards, it will also ship exactly 100 letter A's.

Backflushing gives an imprecise inventory count because of the delay between the time that the product is issued to the shop floor and the time that the balance is updated. However, it can reduce the shop-floor data transaction cost significantly.

See http://www.inventoryops.com/backflushing.htm, September 7, 2006.

See *cycle counting, job order costing.*

backhaul – The return trip for a vehicle.

The backhaul can be with a full, partial, or empty load. An empty backhaul is called deadheading.

See *deadhead, logistics.*

backlog – The total amount of unfilled sales orders, usually expressed in terms of sales revenue or hours of work.

The backlog is sometimes measured in terms of the number of periods (hours, days, weeks, or months) that would be required to work off the sales orders if no new work were received. The order backlog can disappear when economic conditions change and customers cancel their orders.

See *backorder, stockout.*

backorder – A customer demand for which no stock is available and where the customer is prepared to wait for the item to arrive in stock.

If a firm cannot immediately satisfy a customer's order, the customer is asked to wait. This order is called a "backorder" and is usually filled as soon as stock becomes available. If a product is not available, it is said to be "on backorder." Taken together, the backorders for a firm is called the "order backlog." The order backlog is a waiting line (queue) of orders waiting to be filled. In a sense, the order backlog is an "inventory" of demand.

See *backlog, stockout.*

backward integration – See *vertical integration.*

backward loading – A planning method that plans backwards from the due date to determine the start date; sometimes called back loading.

The word "loading" means that the plan is created in time-buckets and is not a detailed schedule. For example, an executive needs to prepare for a trip in one month and "loads" each of the next four weeks with 10 hours of work. This is not a detailed schedule. Backward loading might fill up a time "bucket" (say a half-day) until the capacity is fully committed.

See *backward scheduling, finite scheduling.*

backward scheduling – A scheduling method that plans backwards from the due date (or time) to determine the start date (or time).

Unlike backward loading, backward scheduling creates a detailed schedule for each operation based on the planned available capacity.

See *Advanced Planning and Scheduling (APS), backward loading, forward scheduling.*

bait and switch – See *loss leader.*

balanced scorecard – A strategy execution and reporting tool that presents managers with a limited number of "balanced" key performance metrics so they can assess how well the firm is achieving the strategy. ✪

Overview of the balanced scorecard

A balanced scorecard is a popular framework that translates a company's vision and strategy into a coherent set of performance measures that was first proposed by Robert Kaplan and David Norton in a famous article in the ***Harvard Business Review*** (Kaplan & Norton, 1992). Kaplan & Norton proceeded to write a number of other articles and books expanding the idea to strategy maps (Kaplan & Norton, 2000, 2004), strategic measurement (Kaplan & Norton, 2004), and strategic alignment (Kaplan & Norton, 2006). A balanced business scorecard helps businesses evaluate how well they are meeting their strategic objectives. It typically has four perspectives, financial, customer, internal, and learning and growth, each with a number of measures. The balanced scorecard includes measures of performance that are lagging indicators (return on capital, profit), current indicators (cycle time), and leading indicators (customer satisfaction[2], new product adoption rates).

The following figure illustrates the balanced scorecard.

---

[2] *Some authors argue that customer satisfaction is a "medium-term" indicator. This author's view is that customer satisfaction today is a leading indicator of future sales.*

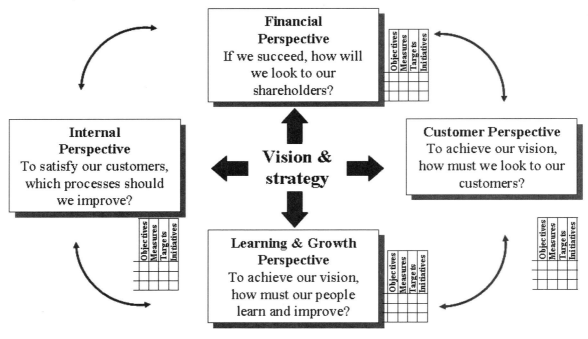

Adapted very slighted from: Kaplan, Robert S., and David P. Norton, *The Strategy-Focused Organization: How Balanced Scorecard Companies Thrive in the New Business Environment*, Harvard Business School Press, 2000, page 73.

Balanced metrics

It is critical to understand that the strategy is reflected in the balance between the perspectives and the measures. All firms measure both cost and service, but it becomes a strategy when the leadership of the firm decides that it will compete on high quality service with the understanding that its cost (and price) will be higher. A balanced scorecard should be "balanced" in at least five different ways:

- Financial and non-financial measures
- Short term and long term
- Lagging indicators and leading indicators
- Internal metrics and external metrics
- Customer value and cost

Suggestions for implementation

The following suggestions can improve how the balanced scorecard is implemented:
- **Make it a strategic planning tool rather than just a strategy execution tool.** While the strategy map is a powerful way to gain alignment for a strategy, it is more than that. The strategy mapping process can be used to help create and communicate the strategy – not just implement it. A good strategy analysis should include industry and competitive analysis and consider causal linkages between competitive and industry trends and the organization's strategy.
- **Include other perspectives.** As mentioned above, Kaplan and Norton allow for only four perspectives -- financial, customer, internal, and learning and growth. They treat suppliers are treated as "internal" and give suppliers very little visibility in their framework. Given that because purchased materials, components, and services comprise a large percentage of the cost of goods sold for most firms, suppliers deserve much more visibility – and should have their own "box." Employees are very important stakeholders but are never mentioned explicitly in the Kaplan and Norton framework. The framework implies that employees are included in learning and growth, but use learning and growth also includes information systems. Therefore,

this author contends that employees should also be given their own "box." In some cases it makes sense to include additional stakeholders such as partners, distributors, regulatory/legal, and society.

- **Include the learning rate for all key metrics.** "Learning and growth" focuses on people and information systems but rarely includes learning metrics. Learning rate (rate of change) can, and should, be measured for key metrics with the half-life curve, the learning curve, or just the first derivative (slope) of metrics (e.g., improve by 10% this year).

- **Make the names for the perspectives more parallel and more meaningful.** "Financial" is an adjective, "customers" is a noun, and "learning and growth" is also a noun. The parallel names shareholders, customers, suppliers, processes, and employees are all nouns.

- **Make sure that the metrics are balanced.** Schneiderman (1999) recommends that the ratio of non-financial to financial metrics be 6:1. It is often a good idea to define a strategy in terms of tradeoffs. For example, service level and inventory investment are a key tradeoff for many manufacturing, retail, and distribution firms. Both long and short term metrics should be included. From an operations management point of view, it is important to have one at least one metric for each process from each of these three dimensions: quality (better), time (faster), and cost (cheaper).

- **Avoid having too many metrics.** Kaplan and Norton (2006) argue that focus and alignment are the goals. However, Schneiderman (1999) argues that too many metrics make focus and alignment impossible. Many organizations find that as metrics cascade down their organization, the number of metrics explodes. This is not a problem with the balanced scorecard *per se*, but rather with the way that many firms implement it.

- **Limit the scorecard to one page.** Schneiderman (1999) recommends that the scorecard be limited to one sheet of paper with large font (more specifically to 8½ x 11 paper in 18 point font).

- **Carefully define both the "as is" performance and the "entitlement."** Entitlement is the best possible performance (usually without significant capital investment), but is often hard to estimate due to lack of data and lack of process understanding.

- **The process should end with projects not just metrics and targets** – Many strategy mapping exercises end with the selection of metrics and setting targets for these metrics. However, this is not enough. Very often "moving the needle" on these metrics will take a project that spans organizational boundaries and create a new "normal" for the organization. Therefore, the process is not done until a few (not too many) strategic initiatives have been defined, project charters for these initiatives have been created, and the projects are appropriated resourced and staffed.

The following figure is Professor Hill's modified version of the balanced scorecard, which includes suppliers and employees as separate perspectives and learning as a rate of change for a few key metrics:

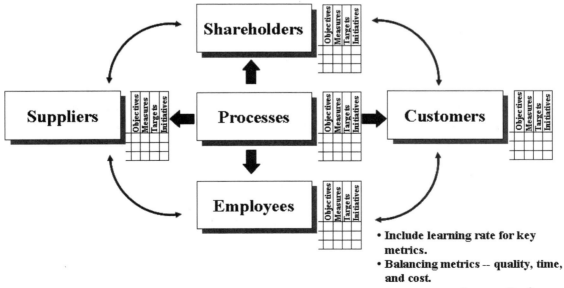

- Include learning rate for key metrics.
- Balancing metrics -- quality, time, and cost.

Source: Professor Arthur V. Hill

Balanced scorecard and learning and growth

Kaplan and Norton's "learning and growth" perspective does a nice job of focusing on developing people and systems (Kaplan & Norton, 1992). However, the operations management literature has a long history of measuring and improving learning for all metrics important to the firm. Calculus teaches that in order to understand a variable such as the height above ground at time t, it is helpful to also know the velocity at time t. Defining height above ground as $s(t)$, the velocity at time t is first derivative of $s(t)$ (e.g., $v(t) = ds(t)/dt$). To take this concept one step further, it is also interesting to know the second derivative, which is the acceleration. The teaching point here is all keys metrics should be measured by both the current position and the rate of change. This concept suggests that "learning and growth" should be a metric in every box of the balanced scorecard.

The papers "Strategy Mapping," "Causal Mapping," and "Learning Models" are on the *OMWW CD* available from www.ClamshellBeachPress.com. ⊙

See *alignment, benchmarking, causal map, corporate portal, cycle time, dashboard, DuPont Analysis, financial performance metrics, gainsharing, hoshin, inventory turnover, Key Performance Indicator (KPI), leading indicator, learning curve, learning organization, mission statement, operations performance metrics, operations strategy, strategy map, supplier scorecard, Y-tree.*

balking – Refusal to join a queue.

When customers arrive to a system and find a long line, they will often exit the system. This is called "balking." Customers are said to "balk" when they leave the system.

See *queuing theory.*

barcode – Information encoded into a pattern of parallel bars and spaces that can be read (optically) by a scanner and then translated into an alphanumeric identification code.

The information encoded in a barcode is a unique serialization that can be correlated with other information from a database. Barcodes are particularly well suited for tracking products through a process. A popular example is the UPC code used on retail packaging. Radio Frequency Identification (RFID) is a newer technology that is replacing barcodes in many retail applications.

See *EPC (Electronic Product Code), Radio Frequency Identification (RFID), Stock Keeping Unit (SKU), Universal Product Code (UPC).*

barriers-to-entry – See *core competence, switching cost.*

base stock system – See *periodic review system.*

Bass Model – A well-known approach for modeling the sales pattern for the lifecycle of a new product introduction developed by Professor Frank Bass.

Overview of the Bass Model

The demand for a new music title or any other type of new product follows a similar demand pattern through its product lifecycle, with early growth, maturity, and finally decline. The Bass Model (and its many extensions) has been used in thousands of applications and has motivated literally hundreds of academic research papers. The basic idea is that some products take off immediately due to the early adopters (the "innovators") who immediately make purchases. The "imitators" do not buy right away, but buy soon after they see others with the product. The model requires three parameters:

m Total market potential, which is the total number of unit sales that we expect to sell over the life of the product. This is the sum of the demand during the product life and is also the area under the curve.

p Innovation coefficient, which primarily affects the shape of the curve during the beginning of the lifecycle. (This parameter is also called the external influence or the advertising effect.)

q Imitation coefficient, which primarily affects the shape of the curve after the peak of the product lifecycle. This parameter is also called the internal influence or word-of-mouth effect.

In summary, m is the scale parameter and p and q are the shape parameters. With these three parameters, the Bass Model can predict almost any realistic new product introduction demand pattern. The challenge is to estimate m, p, and q for a new product introduction. The best approach for handling this problem is to predict m based on marketing research and to select the p and q parameters based on past experience with similar products.

The Bass Model

The basic idea of the Bass Model (Bass, 1969) is that the probability of an initial purchase of a product will be made at time t (given no purchase has yet been made) is a linear function of the proportion of the population that has already purchased the product. Define $F(t)$ as the fraction of the installed base through time t and $f(t) = dF(t)/dt$ as the rate of change in the installed base fraction at time t. The fundamental model is given by $f(t)/(1-F(t)) = p+qF(t)$. Assuming that $F(0) = 0$, this gives:

$$F(t) = \frac{1-e^{-(p+qt)}}{1+\dfrac{q}{p}e^{-(p+q)t}} \quad \text{and} \quad f(t) = \frac{((p+q)^2/p)e^{-p(p+q)t}}{\left(1+\dfrac{q}{p}e^{-(p+q)t}\right)^2}$$

From this, the cumulative sales through period t can be estimated as $S(t) = mF(t)$ and the rate of change in the install base at time t is $dS(t)/dt = mf(t)$. The time of peak sales is $t^* = \ln(q/p)/(p+q)$. The Bass Model has been extended in many ways, but those extensions are outside the scope of this encyclopedia. Mahajan, Muller, Eitan and Bass (1995) provide a summary of many of the extensions of the Bass Model.

Bass Model parameter estimation

Historical data can be used to estimate the parameters p and q. Define $N(t)$ as the cumulative historical sales through time t. Simple linear regression can now be run using the model $y(t) = a+bN(t)-cN(t)^2$ and then m, p, and q can be estimated with these equations solved in this order: $m = b+\sqrt{b^2+4ac}/(-2a)$, $p = a/m$, and $q = cm$. The average value of p is around 0.03, but it is often less than 0.01. The value of q is typically in the range (0.3, 0.5) with an average around 0.38.

Bass Model example

Parameters	
Total sales (m)	87
Innovation (p)	0.1000
Imitation (q)	0.3800

Time period	Predicted sales	Predicted cumulative sales
1	9	9
2	11	20
3	12	32
4	13	45
5	12	58
6	10	68
7	8	76
8	5	80
9	3	83
10	2	85
11	1	86
12	0	86

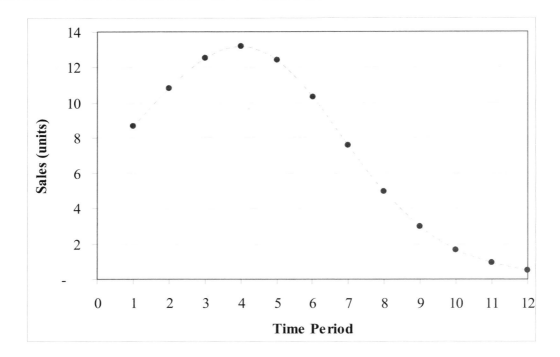

The entry on the logistic curve presents other similar but simpler models such as the logistic curve, the Richards Curve, and the Gompertz Curve.

The Excel workbook "Bass Model.xls" is on the **OMWW CD** available from www.ClamshellBeachPress.com. This Excel workbook finds the best fit parameters for historical data. The above example is from this Excel workbook. ●

See *adoption curve, all-time demand, forecasting, logistic curve, network effect, product lifecycle management.*

batch flow – See *batch process*.

batch picking – An order picking method where orders are organized into small groups (batches) and all items needed to fill these orders are collected from storage locations as one task.

Batch picking is usually associated with pickers using multi-tiered picking carts moving up and down aisles picking batches of usually 4 to 12 orders; however, batch picking is also common when working with automated material handling equipment such as carousels.

See *Automated Storage & Retrieval System (AS/RS), picking, wave picking, zone picking.*

batch process – A system that discrete produces in relatively small lotsizes.

A batch process is usually associated with a job-shop that has general purpose equipment. This is also called a process layout, where the location of the equipment is not dictated by the product but rather by groups of similar equipment. Batch processes nearly always require significant setups.

If a system produces only lotsizes of one, it is not producing batches. If it is producing in very large lotsizes over long periods of time, it is said to be a dedicated process and does not have any setups.

See *batch-and-queue, continuous process, discrete manufacturing, job shop, setup cost, setup time.*

batch-and-queue – A negative term often used by promoters of lean manufacturing to criticize manufacturing operations that have large lotsizes, large queues, long queue times, and long cycle times.

One-piece flow is a better method because it eliminates batches, which reduces the average time in queue and the average number in queue (assuming that no additional setup time is required).

See *batch process, continuous flow, lean thinking, one-piece flow, overproduction, value added ratio.*

batchsize – See *lotsize*.

bathtub curve – A U-shaped curve used in reliability theory and reliability engineering that shows a typical hazard function with products more likely to fail either early or late in their useful life. ✪

Over many years reliability engineers have observed population failure rates as units age over time and have developed what is known as the "bathtub curve." The bathtub curve has three phases:

Infant mortality period – The initial region begins at time zero when a customer first begins to use the product. This region is characterized by a high but rapidly decreasing failure rate and is known as the early failure period or infant mortality period. Immediate failures are known as dead on arrival or DOA.

Normal failure period – After the infant mortality period has passed, the failure rate levels off and remains roughly constant for the majority of the useful life of the product. This long period with a fairly level failure rate is known as the intrinsic failure period, stable failure period, or random failure period. The constant failure rate level is called the intrinsic failure rate. Most systems spend most of their lifetime operating in this flat portion of the bathtub curve.

End of life wear out period – Finally, if units from the population remain in use long enough, the failure rate begins to increase again as materials wear out and degradation failures occur at an increasing rate. This is also known as the "wear out failure period."

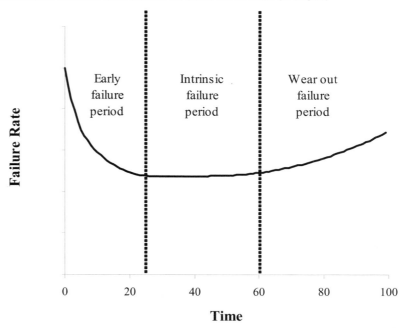

The graph on the right demonstrates a simple bathtub curve, showing the infant mortality period, the normal failure period, and the end of life wear out period.

Examples of the bathtub curve

For example, a newly purchased light bulb will sometimes fail when you first install it (or very shortly thereafter). However, if it survives the first few hours, it is likely to last for many months until it fails. Another example is human life. The death rate of infants is relatively high, but if an infant makes it through the first couple of weeks, the mortality rate does not increase until old age.

The Weibull distribution for the bathtub curve

The Weibull distribution is a flexible life distribution model that can be used to characterize failure distributions in all three phases of the bathtub curve. The basic Weibull distribution has two parameters (a shape parameter and a scale parameter). The scale parameter determines when, in time, a given portion of the population will fail (e.g., 63.2%). The shape parameter is the key feature of the Weibull distribution that enables it to be applied to any phase of the bathtub curve. A beta less than one models a failure rate that decreases with time, as in the infant mortality period. A beta equal to one models a constant failure rate, as in the normal life period. A beta greater than 1 models an increasing failure rate, as during wear-out. There are several ways to view this distribution, including probability plots, survival plots and failure rate versus time plots. The bathtub curve is a failure rate versus time plot.

Service parts and the bathtub curve

The bathtub curve can inform decisions regarding service parts. However, the need for service parts at the end of the product life cycle is affected by retirement (removal) of the equipment in the field. While the bathtub curve suggests that the demand for service parts at the end of life might increase, this affect is mitigated by the retirement of machines from the field, making it difficult to predict the demand for service parts at the end of the product life cycle. If the mean failure rate over the life of the product can be estimated, the newsvendor model can be solved with Poisson distributed demand to set the target inventory for service parts.

See *maintenance, Mean Time Between Failure (MTBF), newsvendor model, Poisson distribution, predictive maintenance, preventive maintenance, product lifecycle management, Total Productive Maintenance (TPM), Weibull distribution.*

beer game – A popular simulation game to help people understand the bullwhip problem in supply chains and learn how to deal with the problem in practical ways.

The beer game was designed by Professor John Sterman (1992) at MIT to demonstrate the bullwhip in supply chains. It emphasizes the importance of information flow along the supply chain and shows how humans tend to overreact and to overcompensate for small changes in demand, which results in magnified fluctuations in demand that are passed down the supply chain.

The class is divided into teams of four players at each table. The four players include a retailer, warehouse, distributor, and a factory. The "products" are pennies, which represent cases of beer. Each player maintains an inventory and keeps track of backorders. Players receive orders from suppliers after a one-week delay. The instructor privately communicates the demand to the retailer, with a demand for four cases per week for the first four weeks and eight cases per week for the remainder of the game.

The results of the game are fairly predictable with nearly all teams falling into the trap of wild oscillations. At the end of the game, the instructor asks the factory players to estimate the actual demand history. They usually guess that demand varied widely throughout the game. Students are often surprised to learn that demand was steady except for the initial jump. The teaching points of the game revolve around how the internal factors drive the demand variations and about how this "bullwhip" can be managed.

See *bullwhip effect.*

benchmarking – Comparing products or processes to a standard in order to evaluate and improve performance. ✪

Benchmarking can be done for either product or process performance. Internal process benchmarking sets the standard by comparing processes in the same firm (e.g., another department, region, machine, worker, etc.). External process benchmarking sets the standard based on a process from another firm. Competitive benchmarking sets the standard based on a competitor's product or process.

Many professional trade organizations provide benchmarking standards. For example, several quality awards such as the Deming Award in Japan, The European Quality Award in Europe, and the Malcolm Baldrige Award in the U.S.A. serve as benchmarks for quality performance. The PRTM consulting firm (and other firms) provides benchmarking consulting using the SCOR framework.

Defining a numerical benchmark is only part of the benchmarking process. Real improvement only comes when a "best in class" process or product is understood in detail and when the technology is transferred. Some firms foolishly benchmark against another firm that is convenient, easy to find, close by, etc. Clearly, it is better to benchmark the best in the world.

Benchmarking can be informal or formal. Formal benchmarking involves mapping processes, sharing process maps, comparing numbers, etc. The goal is to measure not only the current status of the variable, but also the rate of change.

See *balanced scorecard, best practices, entitlement, operations performance metrics, process improvement program, SCOR model, Six Sigma, supplier scorecard, Y-tree.*

best practices – A set of activities that has been demonstrated to produce very good results; the best known performing process, methodology, or technique.

The term "best practices" is often used in the context of a multi-divisional or multi-location firm that has similar processes in many locations. A best practice is developed by some consensus process (such as the nominal group technique) and then shared across the organizational boundaries. For example, Wells Fargo bank has nearly identical processes such as a teller process and a MICR encoding process in many different locations around North America. Wells Fargo is always looking to identify, document, and implement the "best practice" for each process throughout the system.

The challenge, of course, is to identify what is truly the best performing process in light of imperfect information caused by differences in performance measures, process environments, process implementations, and local organizational cultures. To be more accurate, many consulting firms now use the term "leading practice" instead of best practice.

The concept of best practices is closely related to benchmarking and is also closely related to Frederick Taylor's (1911) notion of "one best method" for each process.

See *benchmarking, scientific management*.

beta distribution – A continuous probability distribution used for task times in the absence of data or for a random proportion, such as the proportion of defective items.

Historically, the PERT literature recommended that task times be modeled with the beta distribution with mean $(a + 4m + b)/6$ and variance $(b − a)^2/36$. The *PERT* entry critically reviews this model.

Density and distribution functions: The density function for the beta distribution for $x > 0$ is $f(x) = x^{\alpha-1}(1-x)^{\beta-1} / B(\alpha,\beta)$, where $B(\alpha,\beta) = \Gamma(\alpha)\Gamma(\beta)/\Gamma(\alpha+\beta)$ is the beta function and $\Gamma(\alpha)$ is the gamma function. (Note: In Excel the gamma function is EXP(GAMMALN(α).) The beta distribution function has no closed form.

Statistics: The statistics for the beta include range $[0,1]$, mean $\alpha/(\alpha+\beta)$, variance $\alpha\beta/((\alpha+\beta)^2(\alpha+\beta+1))$, and

$$\text{mode} = \begin{cases} (\alpha-1)/(\alpha+\beta-2) & \text{if } \alpha > 1, \beta > 1 \\ 0 \text{ and } 1 & \text{if } \alpha < 1, \beta < 1 \\ 0 & \text{if } \alpha < 1, \beta \geq 1 \text{ or } \alpha = 1, \beta > 1 \\ 1 & \text{if } \alpha \geq 1, \beta < 1 \text{ or } \alpha > 1, \beta = 1 \\ \text{does not uniquely exist} & \text{if } \alpha = \beta = 1 \end{cases}$$

Estimating parameters: Law and Kelton (2000) remark that finding the Maximum Likelihood Estimates (MLE) for the two parameters requires solving equations involving the digamma function with numeric methods (not a trivial task) or referencing a table (not an ideal approach). However, Wikipedia provides the following simple equations to estimate the parameters based on the sample mean and sample variance: $\alpha = \overline{x}^2(1-\overline{x})/s^2 - \overline{x}$ and $\beta = \overline{x}(1-\overline{x})^2/s^2 + \overline{x} - 1$.

Excel: Excel provides both the distribution function BETADIST(x, α, β) and the inverse function BETAINV(p, α, β), but does not provide a beta density function. The beta density function in Excel is x^(α - 1)*(1- x)^(β -1)/EXP(GAMMALN(α)+GAMMALN(β)-GAMMALN(α + β))

Excel simulation: In an Excel simulation, beta random variates can be generated with the inverse transform method using x = BETAINV(RAND(), α, β).

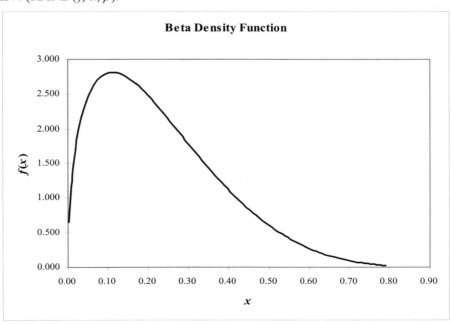

Graph: The following graph is the beta density function with parameters $(\alpha, \beta) = (1.5, 5.0)$.

The Excel workbook "Distributions.xls" is on the **OMWW CD** available from www.ClamshellBeachPress.com.

See *gamma distribution*, *gamma function*, *Project Evaluation and Review Technique (PERT)*, *Weibull distribution*.

beta test – An external test of a pre-production product, typically used in the software development context.

A beta test is an evaluation of new software by a user under actual work conditions and is the final test before release to the public. The purpose of a beta test is to verify that the product functions properly in actual customer use. The term is often used in the context of software released to a limited population of users for evaluation before the final release to customers. In contrast, the alpha test is the first test conducted by the developer in test conditions.

See *prototype*.

bias – In the statistics context, the difference between the expectation and the true value of a parameter; in the forecasting context, an average forecast error different from zero; in the electrical engineering context, a systematic deviation of a value from a reference value; in the behavioral context, a point of view that prevents impartial judgment on an issue.

See *forecast bias*.

Bill of Lading – A contractual document issued by the shipper to the carrier that serves many purposes such as (1) providing a receipt for the goods delivered to the carrier for shipment, (2) describing the goods, including the quantity and weight, (3) providing evidence of title, (4) instructing the carrier on how the goods should be shipped, and (5) providing a receiving document for the customer; sometimes abbreviated B/L.

See *waybill*.

Bill of Material (BOM) – A listing of components, parts, and other items needed to manufacture a product, showing the quantity of each required for each intermediate item.

The BOM is usually drawn as a tree structure with the end items at the top. A BOM is similar to a parts list except that it usually shows how the product is fabricated and assembled, organized in multiple levels where each level is an inventoriable item. It is also called a product structure, formula, recipe, or ingredients list.

A single-level BOM shows only the components required immediately to make one item.

See *commonality*, *effectivity date*, *Engineering Change Order (ECO)*, *Enterprise Resources Planning (ERP)*, *Materials Requirements Planning (MRP)*, *phantom bill of material*, *routing*, *VAT analysis*.

Bill of Resources – A list of the machine and/or labor hours required to make one unit of a product.

The Bill of Resources should only include a few key resources (i.e., those resources that normally have the tightest capacity constraints). Rough cut capacity planning uses the bill of resources to convert the master schedule into a rough cut capacity plan.

See *capacity*, *Rough Cut Capacity Planning (RCCP)*, *Theory of Constraints (TOC)*.

binary logistic regression – See *logistic regression*.

binomial distribution – A discrete probability distribution used for the number of successes (or failures) in t independent trials with probability p for success in each trial.

The binomial is a useful tool for quality control purposes.

Probability mass function: $p(x) = \binom{t}{x} p^x (1-p)^{t-x}$ where $\binom{t}{x}$ is the binomial coefficient, which is the combinations of t things taken x as a time, e.g., $\binom{t}{x} = \dfrac{t!}{x!(t-x)!}$.

Statistics: Range $\{0, 1, \ldots, t\}$, mean tp, variance $tp(1-p)$, and mode $\lfloor p(t+1) \rfloor$.

Excel: In Excel, the probability mass function is BINOMDIST(x, t, p, FALSE) and the probability distribution function is BINOMDIST(x, t, p, TRUE). Excel does not have an inverse function for binomial.

Excel simulation: An Excel simulation might use the inverse transform method to generate binomial random variates using a direct search. See the entry for the Poisson distribution for the VBA code for this.

Graph: The following graph is the binomial probability mass function with $t = 20$ trials of a fair coin ($p = 0.5$).

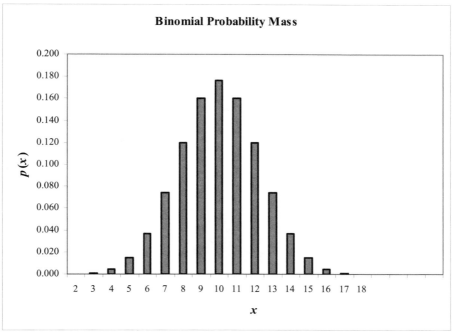

The Excel workbook "Distributions.xls" is on the ***OMWW CD*** available from www.ClamshellBeachPress.com.

See *hypergeometric distribution, Poisson distribution*.

Black Belt – See *Six Sigma*.

blanket order – See *blanket purchase order*.

blanket purchase order – An agreement with a supplier that specifies the price, minimum quantity, and maximum quantity to be purchased over a defined time period (usually a year); sometimes called a "blanket order" or "standing order."

Purchase orders are placed "against" the blanket order to define the quantity and due date for a specific delivery. The advantage of a blanket purchase order for both the customer and the supplier is that it locks in the price so it does not need to be renegotiated very often. The supplier usually gives the customer a quantity discount for the blanket order. Any company representative who knows the purchase order number can purchase items until the value of the blanket order has been exceeded. Providing a blanket order to a supplier may reduce the leadtime and improve on-time delivery.

See *purchasing*.

blending problem – See *linear programming*.

blocking – Not allowing a process to produce when the output storage area (e.g., container, kanban square) is full.

Blocking is good for non-bottleneck processes because it keeps them from overproducing (i.e., producing before the output is needed). Blocking avoids "overproduction" and keeps the total work-in-process inventory down to a reasonable level. Blocking for a bottleneck process is bad because it causes the system to lose valuable capacity – an hour lost on the bottleneck is an hour lost for the entire system. Starving and blocking are often discussed in the same context.

See *CONWIP, kanban, lean thinking, starving, Theory of Constraints (TOC), Work-in-Process (WIP) inventory*.

blue ocean strategy – A business strategy that finds new business opportunities in markets that are not already crowded with competitors.

Kim & Mauborgne (2005), both professors at INSEAD in France, communicate their concept by first describing the traditional "red ocean strategy," where the ocean is blood red with competitors. In contrast, the blue ocean strategy seeks to avoid competing in an existing market space and instead seeks to create an uncontested market space. This approach does not attempt to "beat the competition" but to make the competition irrelevant and create and capture new demand. Those who have been successful with this strategy have found that they can command good margins, high customer loyalty, and highly differentiated products.

Examples of strategic moves that created blue oceans of new, untapped demand:
- Nintendo Wii
- NetJets (fractional Jet ownership)
- Cirque du Soleil (circus reinvented for the entertainment market)
- Starbucks (coffee as low-cost luxury for high-end consumers)
- eBay (online auctioning)
- Sony Walkman (personal portable stereos)
- Japanese fuel-efficient autos
- Chrysler minivan
- Apple personal computer
- Dell's built-to-order computers

See *operations strategy*.

BOL – See *Bill of Lading*.

BOM – See *Bill of Material (BOM)*.

bonded warehouse – Any facility or dedicated portion of a facility where imported goods are stored until custom duties are paid.

In the United States, a bonded warehouse must be approved by the U.S. Treasury Department and under bond/guarantee for observance of revenue laws.

A bonded warehouse can be particularly useful when products are received well in advance of sale because the import fees are not usually paid until the products are shipped from the bonded warehouse.

See *logistics*.

booking curve – A graph used to show the expected cumulative demand for a scheduled (booked) service (such as an airline) over time and compare it to the actual cumulative bookings (demand); sometimes called the sales booking curve.

A booking curve is an important yield management tool that guides decision makers with respect to pricing and capacity allocation as the service date (e.g., date of departure) draws near. The graph to the right shows a typical booking curve for an airline. Note that the *x*-axis counts down the number of days until departure. (Some organizations draw the curve with the *x*-axes

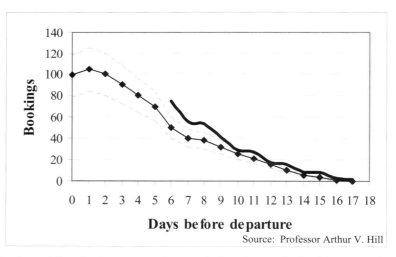

Days before departure

Source: Professor Arthur V. Hill

counting up from a negative value.) The middle dotted line is the expected cumulative demand. In this example, the expected cumulative demand declines slightly on the day of departure. This could be caused by "no-shows" and last-minute cancellations. The heavy line is the actual cumulative demand from 17 days before departure to 6 days before departure.

People involved in yield management track the actual cumulative demand and compare it to the expected cumulative demand on the booking curve. When the actual cumulative demand is outside the upper or lower control policy limits (shown in the example with dashed lines), decision makers might intervene to either change prices or reallocate capacity. For example, in the example above, the actual cumulative demand is above the expected cumulative demand and above the control limits. This suggests that they should raise the price or open up more capacity to try to "capture" more revenue.

Acknowledgments: CSOM MBA students Randall Thorson, Chaouki Khamis, and Mahesh Rege contributed to an early version of this entry.

See *bookings, yield management.*

bookings – The sum of the value of all orders received (but not necessarily shipped) after subtracting all discounts, coupons, allowances, and rebates.

Bookings are recorded in the period in which the order is received, which is often different from the period in which the product is shipped and different from the period in which the sales are recorded.

See *booking curve, demand.*

BOR – See *Bill of Resources.*

bottleneck – Any system constraint that holds the organization back from greater achievement of its goals. ✪

In a system, a bottleneck is any resource that has capacity less than the demand placed on it. Goldratt expands this definition to include any philosophies, assumptions, mindsets, etc. that limit a system from performing better. When the bottleneck is the market demand, the organization can often only achieve higher revenues and profits by making the system more flexible to the market's demands.

See *capacity, Herbie, Theory of Constraints (TOC), utilization.*

bounded rationality – The concept that human and firm behavior is limited by partial information and is unable to thoroughly evaluate all alternatives.

Many models in the social sciences and in economics assume that people and firms are completely rational and will always make choices that they believe will achieve their goals. However, Herbert Simon (1957) pointed out that people are only partly rational and often behave irrationally in many ways. Simon noted that people have limits in formulating and solving complex problems and in processing (receiving, storing, retrieving, transmitting) information. As a result, people and firms often use simple rules (heuristics) to make decisions because of the complexity of evaluating all of the alternatives.

See *satisficing.*

boxcar – An enclosed railcar, typically 40 to 50 feet long used for packaged freight and bulk commodities.

See *logistics.*

Box-Jenkins forecasting – A sophisticated statistical time-series forecasting technique.

Box-Jenkins methods develop forecasts as a function of the actual demands and the forecast errors at lagged time intervals using both moving average (MA) and autoregressive (AR) terms. The autoregressive model is a weighted sum of the past actual data. The AR model of order p is:

$$x_t = \delta + \sum_{k=1}^{p} \phi_k x_{t-k} + \varepsilon_t$$

where x_t is the actual value in period t, $\delta = \left(1 - \sum_{k=1}^{p} \phi_k\right)\mu$ (with process mean μ), constants ϕ_k estimated using a least squares direct search, and ε_t is the error in period t. The AR model can be written as a regression model using past values of a variable to predict future values.

The moving average is a weighted sum of the past forecast errors. The MA model of order q is:

$$x_t = \mu + \sum_{k=1}^{q} \theta_k \varepsilon_{t-k}$$

where μ is the process mean, parameters θ_k estimated using a least squares direct search, and the ε_{t-k} are the errors in period $t-k$. The MA model can be written as a regression model using past errors to predict future values.

The Autoregressive-moving average model ARMA(p, q) combines these:

$$x_t = \sum_{k=1}^{p} \phi_k x_{t-k} + \sum_{k=1}^{q} \theta_k \varepsilon_{t-k}$$

The trend is handled with regular differencing $x'_t = x_t - x_{t-1}$ and seasonality is handled with seasonal differencing $x'_t = x_t - x_{t-L}$, where the time series has an L period season.

The Box-Jenkins methodology has three main steps:

1. **Specification** – Select which lagged terms should be included in the model.
2. **Estimation** – Estimate the least squares parameters ϕ_k and θ_k for the model specified in the first step. A direct search method such as the Marquardt search is applied to accomplish this.
3. **Diagnostic checking** – Check the sample autocorrelations and sample partial autocorrelations[3] for opportunities to improve the model by adding (or deleting) terms. A chi-squared test is performed to determine if the partial correlations are significant. A correlogram graph is an important part of this process. The table below shows typical rules for interpreting the correlogram and adding new terms to a model.

Shape	Model
Decaying to zero	AR
Alternating, decaying to zero	AR
One or more "spikes" – otherwise zero	MA
Decay starting after a few lags	ARMA
All close to zero	Random
High values at fixed intervals	Seasonality
Not decaying to zero	Take first differences

The Box-Jenkins model has been extended in several ways. Automatic fitting software is available that requires less human intervention. Multivariate models are also available that create forecasts based on more than one time series.

Contrary to early expectations, some empirical studies have shown that Box-Jenkins forecasting models do not consistently perform better than much simpler exponential smoothing methods.

Recommended references include Box, Jenkins, Reinsel, and Jenkins (1994) and Armstrong (2000).

See the Institute of Business Forecasting website for more information www.ibf.org.

See *Durbin-Watson statistic, econometric forecasting, exponential smoothing, forecast error metrics, forecasting, moving average, time-series forecasting.*

Box-Muller method for generating normal random deviates – See *normal distribution.*

BPR – See *Business Process Re-engineering (BPR).*

brainstorming – Using a group of people to generate creative ideas to solve a problem.

Nearly all brainstorming approaches have one rule in common – no one is allowed to debate any idea. This is because it is important to allow for a free flow of many ideas before evaluating any of them. The Nominal Group Technique (NGT) is one of the more popular structured approaches to brainstorming.

See *affinity diagram, causal map, Delphi forecasting, Ideation, impact wheel, Nominal Group Technique (NGT), quality circles.*

brand – A set of associations linked to a name, mark, or symbol associated with a product or service.

A brand is much like a reputation. It is a surrogate measure of quality built over many years and many contacts with the products, services, and people associated with the brand. However, a brand can be damaged quickly. For example, when Firestone tires were implicated in many SUV rollovers and deaths in the 1990s, the Firestone brand was damaged significantly.

Interestingly, brands can be purchased and used for competitive advantage. For example, the Schwinn bike brand, founded in Chicago in 1985, was bought by a Korean firm when the firm ran into financial difficulty. Similarly, when Nordic Track faced financial problems, the brand was purchased by another firm. The Schwinn and Nordic Track brands continue to live on after the companies that developed them went out of business.

See *brand equity, category management, service guarantee.*

---

[3] *The partial autocorrelation at lag k is the autocorrelation between x_t and x_{t-k} that is not accounted for by lags 1 through $k-1$.*

brand equity – The value assigned to an organization's product or service.
> See *brand*.

breadboard – A proof-of-concept modeling technique that represents how a product will work, but not how a product will look.
> See *New Product Development (NPD)*, *prototype*.

break-even analysis – A financial calculation for determining the unit sales required to cover costs. ✪
> If the demand is below the break-even point, the costs will exceed the revenues. Break-even analysis focuses on the relationships between fixed cost, variable cost, and profit.
>
> Break-even analysis is a rather crude approach to financial analysis. Most finance professors recommend using a better approach such as net present value or Economic Value Added (EVA).
> See *financial performance metrics*, *payback period*.

break-even point – See *break-even analysis*.

Brooke's Law – See *project management*.

brownfield – See *greenfield*.

BRP – See *Business Requirements Planning*.

buffer management – A Theory of Constraints (TOC) concept of strategically placing "extra" inventory or time in front of constrained resources to protect the system from disruption.
> See *Theory of Constraints (TOC)*.

buffer stock – See *safety stock*.

Build to Order (BTO) – A process that produces products in response to a customer order.
> Some authors equate this to assemble to order (ATO), while others equate it to Make to Order (MTO). Gunasekaran and Ngai (2005, page 424) note "some confusion in these writings between make to order (MTO) and BTO. The leadtimes are longer in MTO than in BTO. In MTO, components and parts are made and then assembled. In the case of BTO, the components and parts are ready for assembly." This quote implies that BTO is the same as ATO.
> See *Assemble to Order (ATO)*, *Make to Order (MTO)*, *Respond to Order (RTO)*.

bullwhip effect – A pattern of increasing variability in the demand from the customer back to the retailer, back to the distributor, back to the manufacturer, back to the supplier, etc. ✪
> The four causes of the bullwhip effect include (1) forecast updating, (2) periodic ordering/order batching, (3) price fluctuations, and (4) shortage gaming. Even if customer demand is constant, the raw materials supplier will often see high variability in demand as fluctuations are amplified along the supply chain.
>
> The primary solution to this problem is for the retailer to regularly share actual and projected demand information. Other solutions include vendor-managed inventories, reducing order sizes by reducing ordering costs, using everyday low prices (instead of promotional prices), avoiding allocation based on orders placed, and reducing cycle time.
>
> The following is a more complete explanation of the subject excerpted from "The Bullwhip Effect in Supply Chains," by Lee, Padmanabhan, and Whang (1997) with some extensions.
>
> **Demand forecast updating** – Ordinarily, every company in a supply chain forecasts its demand myopically, that is by looking at the past demands they have faced from their own direct customers. Since each upstream chain member sees fluctuations in demand caused by the bullwhip effect from downstream, that member orders accordingly, creating further swings for the upstream suppliers. This occurs even when the ultimate demand is relatively stable. **Solution:** Encourage all members of a supply chain to use the same demand data coming from the furthest downstream points (e.g., point of sale data). Technologies such as point-of-sale (POS) data collection, Electronic Data Interchange (EDI), vendor-managed inventories (VMI), as well as leadtime reduction can all help to mitigate the problem. Reducing leadtime is often the best way to improving forecast accuracy.
>
> **Order batching** – Companies sending orders to upstream suppliers usually do so periodically, ordering batches that last several days or weeks, which reduces transportation costs, transaction costs, or both. These tactics contribute to larger demand fluctuations further up the chain. **Solution:** Reduce transaction costs through various forms of electronic ordering, reduce setup costs by applying SMED, offer discounts for mixed-load ordering (to reduce the demand for solid loads of one product), use third party logistics providers (3PLs) to

economically combine many small replenishments for/to many suppliers/customers, and do not offer quantity discounts to encourage customers to place large orders.

Price fluctuation – Frequent price changes (both up and down) can lead buyers to purchase large quantities when prices are low to try to avoid buying when prices are high. This "forward buying" practice is common in the grocery industry and creates havoc upstream in the supply chain. **Solution:** Encourage sellers to stabilize their prices (e.g., use everyday low prices). Activity-based costing systems can highlight excessive costs in the supply chain caused by price fluctuations and forward buying. This helps provide the incentives for the entire chain to operate with relatively stable prices.

Rationing and shortage gaming – Cyclical industries face alternating periods of oversupply and undersupply. When buyers know that a shortage is imminent and rationing will occur, they will often increase the size of their orders to ensure that they get the amounts they need. **Solution:** Allocate inventory among customers based on past usage, not on present orders and share information on sales, capacity, and inventory so buyers are not surprised by shortages.

The underweighting open orders problem – Buyers sometimes seem to forget what orders have already been placed and therefore tend to focus on the on-hand physical inventory rather than the inventory position (on-hand plus on-order). To teach this point, I tell the short story: "I have a headache and take two aspirin. Five minutes later, I still have a headache, should I take two more?" **Solution:** Use a system that gives good visibility to open orders and the inventory position. Train suppliers to avoid foolishly applying "lean systems" that place orders based only on the on-hand inventory without regard for the on-order quantities.

See *beer game, buyer/planner, forward buy, leadtime syndrome, Parkinson's Laws, SCOR model, supply chain management, Third Party Logistics (3PL) provider, upstream, value chain.*

burden rate – A percentage or fixed-dollar amount of the departmental or product overhead expense that is allocated to production on the basis of labor hours, machine hours, labor dollars, material dollars, units, or some other basis; also known as overhead rate.

See *Activity Based Costing (ABC), outsourcing, overhead, setup cost, standard cost.*

business capability – A business function that an organization performs or can perform.

A description of a business capability should separate the function from the process. In other words, the description of a capability should describe what can be done without describing the details of how it is done, what technology is used, who performs it, etc. The details of the people, process, and technology are prone to change fairly often, but the capability will not.

A business capability framework is a collection of an organization's business capabilities organized in a hierarchy. For example, at the highest level, a firm might have six business capabilities: plan, buy, move, sell, enable, and analyze. Each of these can then be broken down at the next level into many more capabilities.

Acknowledgments: CEMBA 09 students Aaron Anderson, Cullen Glass, Helen McIntyre, Marcellus Spears, and Geir Tonnesen contributed to this entry.

See *process capability and performance.*

business case – The economic justification for a proposed project or product that often includes estimates of both the economic and non-economic benefits; also called a business case analysis.

A business case is intended to answer two fundamental business questions: Why this project? and Why now? Answering these two questions helps the decision maker(s) prioritize the project vis-à-vis other projects. The best way to collect the data to answer these two questions is to follow these four steps:

1. **Gather baseline data** – For example, cycle time for order entry for the time period X to Y has increased from A to B.
2. **Quantify the problem or opportunity** – For example, what is the cost of excessive order entry cycle time?
3. **Analyze stakeholders needs (especially customers)** – For example, analyze raw comments from surveys and focus groups.
4. **Define "best-in-class" performance** – For example, our benchmark partner has a cycle time for this process that is one-half of ours.

In some cases, a business case analysis will analyze two or more competing business alternatives.

See *project charter.*

Business Continuity Management (BCM) – A management process for identifying potential events that might threaten an organization and building safeguards that protect the interests of the stakeholders; also known as Business Continuity Planning (BCP).

BCM integrates the disciplines of emergency management, crisis management, business continuity, and IT disaster recovery with the goal of creating organizational resilience, which is the ability to withstand and reduce the impact of a crisis event. BCM provides the contingency planning process for sustaining operations during a disaster such as labor unrest, natural disaster, war, etc.

The BCM process entails (1) proactively identifying and managing risks to critical operations, (2) developing continuity strategies and contingency plans that ensure an effective recovery of critical operations within a pre-defined time period after a crisis event, (3) periodically exercising and reviewing BCM arrangements, and (4) creating a risk management culture by embedding BCM into day-to-day operations and business decisions.

The Council of Supply Chain Management Professionals provides suggestions for helping companies do continuity planning in their document *Securing the Supply Chain Research*. A copy of this research is available on the CSCMP website, www.cscmp.org.

Some of the above ideas were adapted from www.thebci.org, May 5, 2008.

Acknowledgments: CSOM MBA students Jeremy Green, Tanya Raso, and Amy Schmidt contributed to this entry.

See *Failure Mode and Effects Analysis (FMEA)*.

Business Continuity Planning (BCP) – See *Business Continuity Management (BCM)*.

business intelligence – A broad category of applications and technologies for gathering, storing, retrieving, and analyzing data to help managers make better business decisions and to gain competitive advantage. A good business intelligence capability should provide decision makers with good quality and timely information on:

- Customers (e.g., demographics of current customers)
- Markets (e.g., market position)
- Industry (e.g., changes in the economy, expected regulatory changes)
- Operations (historical performance, capabilities)
- Competitors
- Business partners

See *knowledge management, learning organization*.

Business Process Management (BPM) – An information systems approach for improving business processes through the application of software tools, ideally resulting in a robust, efficient, and adaptable information system to support the business.

BPM generally includes tools for process design, process execution, and process monitoring. Information system tools for process design include tools for documenting processes (process maps and data models) and computer simulation. These tools often have a graphical and visual interface. Information system tools for process execution often start with a graphical model of the process, and use business rules to quickly develop an information system that supports the process. Information system tools for process monitoring capture real-time information so that the process can be controlled. For example, a factory manager might want to track an order as it passes through the plant.

See *Business Process Re-engineering (BPR), process improvement program, process map*.

Business Process Outsourcing – The practice of outsourcing non-core internal functions to third parties; sometimes abbreviated BPO.

Typical outsourced functions include logistics, accounts payable, accounts receivable, payroll, and human resources. Other areas can include IT development or complete management of the IT functions of the enterprise. For example, Best Buy outsourced all of its Information Systems to Accenture. Accenture and IBM are two of many service providers of business process outsourcing services.

See *contract manufacturer, make versus buy decision, MRO (Maintenance-Repair-Operations), outsourcing, purchasing, Service Level Agreement (SLA), sourcing, supply chain management*.

Business Process Re-engineering (BPR) – A radical change in the way that an organization operates. ✪

Business Process Re-engineering involves a fundamental rethinking of the business systems. BPR typically includes eliminating non-value-added steps, automating some steps, changing organization charts, and restructuring reward systems. It often includes job enlargement, which reduces the number of queues and gives the customer a single point of contact. In many firms, BPR has a bad reputation because it is associated with downsizing (firing people).

Hammer and Champy (1993) are credited with popularizing business process re-engineering. Their website www.hammerandco.com offers more recent books and a process and enterprise maturity model.

The paper "The Process Improvement Checklist" is on the *OMWW CD* available from www.ClamshellBeachPress.com. This checklist includes a comprehensive list of the best process improvement ideas used in most process improvement projects. ◉

See *5 Whys, Business Process Management (BPM), error proofing, job enlargement, process improvement program, stakeholder analysis, standardized work, work simplification*.

Business Requirements Planning (BRP) – BRP is a conceptual model showing how business planning, master planning, materials planning, and capacity planning processes should work together.

The BRP model starts the business plan (profits), sales plan (revenues), and production plan (costs and aggregate units). Once the production plan has been checked to make sure that the resources are available and that the top level plans are consistent, it is used as input to the master production schedule, which is a plan (in units) for the firm's end products (or major subassemblies).

The Materials Requirements Planning (MRP) module translates the MPS into a materials plan (orders defined by quantities and due dates). CRP translates the materials plan into a capacity plan (defined in terms of shop hours). Note that few firms use CRP.

Ultimately, the system creates both purchase orders for suppliers and shop orders for the firm's own factories. Orders in the action bucket (the first period) are released and become scheduled receipts. This planning process is supported by the ERP database, which provides information on items (the item master), the bill of material (the linked list of items required for each item), and the routings (the sequence of steps required to make an item).

The following diagram shows the BRP model developed by Schultz (1989).

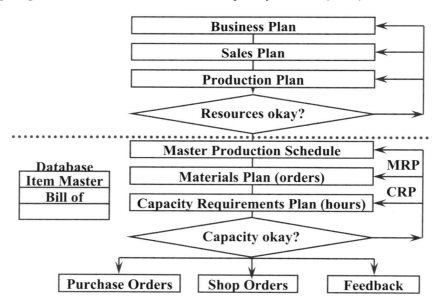

The term "Business Requirements Planning" is not widely used. The concept is closely related to Sales and Operations Planning, which has become a standard term in North America.

Source: Adapted from *Business Requirements Planning* by Terry Schultz (1989). Thanks to Professor Douglas N. Hales at Clemson University for helpful edits on this entry.

See *aggregate production planning, Capacity Requirements Planning (CRP), closed-loop MRP, Enterprise Resources Planning (ERP), Master Production Schedule (MPS), Resource Requirements Planning (RRP), Rough Cut Capacity Planning (RCCP), Sales & Operations Planning (S&OP)*.

buyer/planner – A person who has the dual responsibility of selecting suppliers, negotiating agreements, and placing purchase orders with suppliers and also performs material planning for the factory.

In many firms the buying responsibility is separated from the planning responsibility. The buyer is responsible only for placing purchase orders with suppliers and the planner handles releasing (starting) factory orders and also expediting and de-expediting factory orders.

The advantages of combining the two roles into a single buyer/planner role are:

- Both roles require essentially the same types of skills – Ability to plan ahead, use systems, know part numbers and product structures, know suppliers, understand the capacity constraints of the factory, understand how to expedite (and de-expedite) orders, and understand true customer requirements and priorities.
- Firms can find synergy between the two roles because the planning function in the factory is often heavily affected by the availability of materials and the buying function is heavily affected by the priorities of the factory.

See *bullwhip effect*, *supplier scorecard*.

C

C&E diagram – See *causal map*.

C&E Matrix – An analysis tool used to collect subjective data to make quantitative estimates of the impact of the Key Process Input Variables (KPIVs) on Key Process Output Variables (KPOVs) in order to identify the most important KPIVs for a process improvement program.

In any process improvement program, it is important to determine which Key Process Input Variables (KPIVs) have the most impact on the Key Process Output Variables (KPOVs). The C&E Matrix is a practical way to collect subjective estimates of the importance of the KPIVs on the KPOVs.

Building the C&E Matrix begins by defining the KPOVs along the columns on the top of the matrix (table) and the KPIVs along the rows on the left side. (See the example below.) Experts then estimate the importance of each KPOV to the customer. This is typically done on a 1-10 scale, where 1 is unimportant and 10 is critically important. Each pair of input and output variables is then scored on a 0-10 scale, where the score is the degree to which the input variable impacts (causes) the output variable. The sum of the weighted scores is then used to rank the input variables to determine which input variables deserve the most attention and analysis.

The example below illustrates the matrix for three KPOVs and seven KPIVs. KPOV 1 to KPOV 3 are the names of the output variables with customer importance weights (w_1, w_2, w_3). The $s_{i,j}$ values are the impact scores for input variable i on output variable j. The weighted score for each KPIV is then calculated as the sum of the weights and the impact scores. Stated mathematically, the weighted score for the i-th KPIV is defined as

$$ws_i = \sum_{j=1}^{J} w_j s_{i,j}$$, where J is the number of KPOVs. These scores are then ranked in the far right column.

C&E Matrix example

			Key Process Output Variables			Weighted score	Rank
		KPOV importance to customers	w_1	w_2	w_3		
		KPOV name	KPOV 1	KPOV 2	KPOV 3		
Key Process Input Variables	Process step 1	KPIV 1	$s_{1,1}$	$s_{1,2}$	$s_{1,3}$	ws_1	r_1
		KPIV 2	$s_{2,1}$	$s_{2,2}$	$s_{2,3}$	ws_2	r_2
	Process step 2	KPIV 3	$s_{3,1}$	$s_{3,2}$	$s_{3,3}$	ws_3	r_3
		KPIV 4	$s_{4,1}$	$s_{4,2}$	$s_{4,3}$	ws_4	r_4
	Process step 3	KPIV 5	$s_{5,1}$	$s_{5,2}$	$s_{5,3}$	ws_5	r_5
		KPIV 6	$s_{6,1}$	$s_{6,2}$	$s_{6,3}$	ws_6	r_6
		KPIV 7	$s_{7,1}$	$s_{7,2}$	$s_{7,3}$	ws_7	r_7

The website www.kevinotto.com/RSS/Software/DMAIC%20C&E%20Matrix%20Template.xls provides a free C&E Matrix template.

The C&E Matrix is closely related to the C&E Diagram and the causal map. The C&E Matrix is special type of causal map represented in matrix form that has only one set of input variables (the KPIVs) and one set of output variables (the KPOVs). This can be generalized by including all variables on both the rows and columns. This generalized matrix, called the adjacency matrix in the academic literature, allows for input variables to cause other input variables. This matrix can also be represented as a causal map. The "reachability" matrix is an extension of the adjacency matrix and represents how many steps it takes to get from one node to another in the network. Scavarda, Bouzdine-Chameeva, Goldstein, Hays, and Hill (2006) discuss many of these issues.

Some firms and consultants confuse a C&E Matrix with the Kepner-Tregoe Model (KT). KT is a simple scoring system for alternative courses of action, where each alternative is scored on a number of different dimensions, and each dimension has an assigned weight. The idea is that the alternative with the highest weighted sum is likely to be the best one. The C&E Matrix is about scoring input variables that *cause* output variables. In the KT framework, the dimensions do not *cause* the alternatives; they simply help us evaluate them.

See *causal map, Kepner-Tregoe Model, Key Process Output Variable (KPOV), Six Sigma*.

CAD – See *Computer Aided Design*.

CAD/CAM – See *Computer Aided Design/Computer Aided Manufacturing*.

CAGR – See *Compounded Annual Growth Rate (CAGR)*.

CAI – See *Computer Aided Inspection*.

call center – An organization that provides remote customer contact via telephone.

A call center can provide customer service in forms such as (1) a help desk operation that provides technical support for software or hardware, (2) a reservations center for a hotel, airline, or other service, (3) a dispatch operation that sends technicians or other servers on service calls, and (4) order entry/sales center that accepts orders for products from customers.

A well-managed call center can have a major impact on customer relationships and on firm profitability. Call center management software monitors system status (number in queue, average talk time, etc.) and measures customer representative productivity. Advanced systems also provide forecasting and scheduling assistance. Well-managed call centers receive customer requests for help through phone calls, faxes, emails, regular mail, and information coming in through the web. Representatives respond via interpersonal conversations on the phone, phone messages sent automatically, fax-on-demand, interactive voice responses, and e-mail. Web-based information can provide help by dealing with a large percentage of common problems that customers might have and providing downloadable files for customer use. By taking advantage of integrated voice, video, and data, information can be delivered in a variety of compelling ways that enhance the user experience, encourage customer self-service, and dramatically reduce the cost of providing customer support.

The Excel workbook "staffit.xls" is available from www.ClamshellBeachPress.com. This is an M/G/s queuing model with costing features to help firms determine appropriate staffing levels ("staffing fit") for each period of the day. However, any closed form queueing model is limited by the fact that call centers have a non-stationary arrival process (e.g., the mean arrival rate changes over time).

See *queuing theory*.

CAM – See *Computer Aided Manufacturing*.

cannibalization – The sales of a new product that will be taken from the firm's other products.

For example, a new computer model might take sales from an existing model and therefore add nothing to the firm's overall market share or bottom line.

capability – See *Design for Six Sigma (DFSS), process capability and performance*.

Capability Maturity Model (CMM) – A five-level methodology for measuring and improving processes.

CMM began as an approach for evaluating the "maturity" of software development organizations, but has since been extended to other organizations as well. Many CMM models have been developed for software acquisition, people issues, project management, new product development, supply chain management, etc. This discussion focuses on the Capability Maturity Model for Software (SW-CMM). The CMM for Software is one of the best-known products of the Carnegie Mellon University Software Engineering Institute (SEI). CMM is based heavily on the book *Managing the Software Process* (Humphries, 1989). The actual development of the CMM was done by the SEI at Carnegie Mellon University and the Mitre Corporation in response to a request to provide the federal government with a method for assessing the capability of its software contractors.

In a nutshell, the SW-CMM model documents and organizes software engineering practices that exist in organizations. It provides a framework for organizing evolutionary steps into five maturity levels that lay successive foundations for continuous process improvement. Each maturity level comprises a set of process goals that, when satisfied, stabilize an important component of the software process.

The five CMM levels

Level 1 - Initial – The software process is characterized as ad hoc, and occasionally even chaotic. Few processes are defined, and success depends on individual effort and heroics. Level 1 software project success depends on having quality people.

In spite of this ad hoc, chaotic environment, maturity level 1 organizations often produce products and services that work; however, they frequently exceed the budget and schedule of their projects. Maturity level 1 organizations are characterized by a tendency to over commit, abandon processes in the time of crisis, and being unable to repeat past successes.

Level 2 - Repeatable – Basic project management processes are established to track cost and schedule activities. The minimum process discipline is in place to repeat earlier successes on projects with similar applications and scope. There is still a significant risk of exceeding cost and time estimates. Process discipline helps ensure that existing practices are retained during times of stress. When these practices are in place, projects are performed and managed according to their documented plans. Project status and the delivery of services are visible to management at defined points (for example, at major milestones and at the completion of major tasks).

Level 3 - Defined – The software process for both management and engineering activities is documented, standardized, and integrated into a standard software process for the organization. All projects use an approved, tailored version of the organization's standard software process for developing and maintaining software.

A critical distinction between level 2 and level 3 is the scope of standards, process descriptions, and procedures. At level 2, the standards, process descriptions, and procedures may be quite different in each specific instance of the process (for example, on a particular project). At level 3, the standards, process descriptions, and procedures for a project are tailored from the organization's set of standard processes to suit a particular project or organizational unit.

Level 4 - Managed – Detailed measures of the software process and product quality are collected. Both the software process and products are quantitatively understood and controlled. Using precise measurements, management can effectively control the software development effort. In particular, management can identify ways to adjust and adapt the process to particular projects without measurable losses of quality or deviations from specifications. At this level, the organization sets a quantitative quality goal for both the software process and software maintenance.

A critical distinction between maturity level 3 and maturity level 4 is the predictability of process performance. At maturity level 4, the performance of processes is controlled using statistical and other quantitative techniques, and is quantitatively predictable unlike maturity level 3 where processes are only qualitatively predictable.

Level 5 - Optimizing – Maturity level 5 focuses on continually improving process performance through both incremental and innovative technological improvements. Quantitative process-improvement objectives for the organization are established, continually revised to reflect changing business objectives, and used as criteria in managing process improvement. The effects of deployed process improvements are measured and evaluated against the quantitative process-improvement objectives. Both the defined processes and the organization's set of standard processes are targets of measurable improvement activities. Process improvements to address common causes of process variation and measurably improve the organization's processes are identified, evaluated, and deployed. Optimizing processes that are nimble, adaptable, and innovative depends on the participation of an empowered workforce aligned with the business values and objectives of the organization. The organization's ability to rapidly respond to changes and opportunities is enhanced by finding ways to accelerate and share learning.

A critical distinction between maturity level 4 and maturity level 5 is the type of process variation addressed. At maturity level 4, processes are concerned with addressing special causes of process variation and providing statistical predictability of the results. Though processes may produce predictable results, the results may be insufficient to achieve the established objectives. At maturity level 5, processes are concerned with addressing common causes of process variation and changing the process (i.e., shifting the mean of the process performance) to improve process performance (while maintaining statistical probability) and achieve the established quantitative process-improvement objectives.

CMMI – Capability Maturity Model Integrated

Although these models have proved useful to many organizations, the use of multiple models has been problematic. Further, applying multiple models that are not integrated within and across an organization is costly in terms of training, appraisals, and improvement activities. The CMM Integration project was formed to sort out the problem of using multiple CMMs. The CMMI Product Team's mission was to combine the following:
- The Capability Maturity Model for Software (SW-CMM) v2.0 draft C
- The Systems Engineering Capability Model (SECM)
- The Integrated Product Development Capability Maturity Model (IPD-CMM) v0.98
- Supplier sourcing

CMMI is the designated successor of the three source models. The SEI has released a policy to sunset the Software CMM and previous versions of the CMMI. [3] The same can be said for the SECM and the IPD-CMM; these models were superseded by CMMI.

Many of the above concepts are from http://en.wikipedia.org/wiki/Capability_Maturity_Model #Level_1_-_Initial, November 4, 2006.)

Interestingly, level 5 is very similar to the ideal defined in the Six Sigma and lean thinking philosophies.

See *lean thinking*, *operations performance metrics*, *Six Sigma*.

capacity – The maximum rate of output for a process, measured in units of output per unit of time. ✪

The unit of time may be of any length (a day, a shift, a minute, etc.). Note that it is redundant (and ignorant) to use the phrase "maximum capacity" because a capacity is a maximum. It is more correct to just say "capacity."

Some people make a distinction between nominal capacity, demonstrated capacity, and theoretical capacity. These distinctions are of little value. Demonstrated capacity is the capacity that the process has actually been able to sustain over a long period. However, in the long run, the demonstrated capacity will never exceed the market demand. The theoretical capacity is the maximum production rate based on mathematical or engineering calculations, which sometimes do not consider all relevant variables; therefore, it is quite possible that the capacity can be greater than or less than the theoretical value. (It is fairly common for factories to work at 110% of their theoretical capacity.)

Capacity should not be confused with load. If an elevator has three people on it, what is its capacity? This is a trick question. The capacity might be 2, 3, 20, etc. If it has three people on it, the elevator has a current load of three and probably has a capacity of at least three. For many years, this was a favorite question on the APICS certification exams. It was amazing how many people answered this question incorrectly.

The best capacity will minimize the total relevant cost, which is the sum of the capacity and waiting costs. All systems have a tradeoff between capacity utilization and waiting time. These two variables have a non-linear relationship. As utilization goes to 100%, the waiting time tends to go to infinity. Maximizing utilization is not the goal of the organization. The goal in this case is to minimize the sum of two relevant costs – the cost of the capacity and the cost of waiting. For example, the optimal utilization for a fire engine is not 100% – it is closer to 1%. The copy machine in an office is sitting idle right now, so should the employees go make some copies to keep it utilized? Of course not! The goal is to find the optimal balance between the cost of the machine and the cost of professors and staff members waiting. In this case, the office manager has decided to have utilization less than 5% for the machine. In contrast, some expensive machines such as a bottling system will run three shifts per day 365 days per year. The cost of downtime is the lost profit from the system and is quite expensive.

The newsvendor model can be used to find the optimal capacity. However, the model requires that the analyst define a time horizon, estimate the distribution of demand, and estimate the cost of having one unit of capacity too much, and the cost of having one unit of capacity too little.

In many markets, customers buy capacity rather than products. For example, a customer might buy the capacity of a foundry for one day per week. This can often help the customer reduce the procurement leadtime. If the customer does not need the capacity, the supplier will still get paid.

See *Bill of Resources, bottleneck, Capacity Requirements Planning (CRP), closed-loop MRP, Little's Law, newsvendor model, Overall Equipment Effectiveness (OEE), process design, queuing theory, Resource Requirements Planning (RRP), Rough Cut Capacity Planning (RCCP), safety capacity, utilization, yield management.*

Capacity Requirements Planning (CRP) – The planning process used in conjunction with MRP to convert open and planned shop orders into a load report in planned shop hours for each workcenter.

The CRP process is executed after the MRP planning process. CRP uses order start date, order quantity, routing, standard setup times, and standard run times to estimate the number of shop hours that will be required for each workcenter. It is possible for CRP to indicate that a capacity problem exists during specific time periods even when Resource Requirements Planning (RRP) and Rough Cut Capacity Planning (RCCP) have indicated that sufficient capacity is available. This is due to the fact that RRP and RCCP are not as accurate as CRP with respect to the timing of the shop load.

See *Business Requirements Planning (BRP), capacity, closed-loop MRP, Master Production Schedule (MPS), Resource Requirements Planning (RRP), Rough Cut Capacity Planning (RCCP), Sales & Operations Planning (S&OP).*

capacity utilization – See *utilization.*

CAPEX – An abbreviation for the CAPital EXpenditure used as the initial investment in new machines, equipment, and facilities.

See *capital.*

capital – Money available for investing in assets that produce output.

See *CAPEX, capital intensive.*

capital intensive – Requiring a large expenditure of capital in comparison to labor.

A capital intensive industry requires large investments to produce a particular good. Good examples include power generation and oil refining.

See *capital, labor intensive.*

carrying charge – The cost of holding one dollar of inventory for one year expressed as a percentage of the unit cost. ✪

This parameter is used to help inventory managers make economic tradeoffs between inventory levels, order sizes, and other inventory control variables. The carrying charge is usually expressed as the cost of carrying one dollar of inventory for one year and therefore has a unit of measure of $/$/year. Reasonable values are in the range of 15-40%.

The carrying charge is the sum of four factors: (1) the marginal cost of capital or the weighted average cost of capital (WACC), (2) a risk premium for obsolete inventory, (3) storage and administration cost, and (4) a policy adjustment factor. This rate should only reflect costs that vary with the size of the inventory and should not include costs that vary with the number of inventory transactions (orders, receipts, etc). A good approach for determining if a particular cost driver should be included in the carrying charge is to ask the question, "How will this cost be affected if the inventory is doubled (or halved)?" If the answer is "not at all," then that cost driver is probably not relevant (at least not in the short term). It is difficult to make a precise estimate for the carrying charge. Many firms erroneously set this to the WACC and therefore underestimate the cost of carrying inventory.

The paper "Estimating Carrying Cost" is on the **OMWW CD** available from www.ClamshellBeachPress.com.

See *aggregate production planning, carrying cost, Economic Order Quantity (EOQ), hockey stick effect, inventory turnover, obsolescence, setup cost, shrinkage.*

carrying cost – The marginal cost to the firm for holding one unit of inventory for a period of time (typically one year). ✪

Overview

The carrying cost is usually calculated as the average inventory investment times the carrying charge. For example, if the annual carrying charge is 25% and the average inventory is $100,000, the carrying cost is $25,000 per year.

Many firms incorrectly use the end-of-year inventory in this calculation, which is fine if the end-of-year inventory is close to the average inventory during the year. However, it is quite common for firms to have a "hockey stick" sales and shipment pattern where the end of year inventory is significantly less than the average inventory during the year. Technically, this type of average is called a "time-integrated average" and can be estimated fairly accurately by averaging the inventory at a number of points during the year.

Manufacturing and inventory managers must carefully apply managerial accounting principles in decision making. A critical element in many decisions is the estimation of the inventory carrying cost, sometimes called the "holding cost." Typical decisions include the following:

- **Service level tradeoff decisions** – Many make to stock manufacturers, distributors, and retailers sell standard products from inventory to customers who arrive randomly. In these situations, the firm's service level improves with a larger finished goods inventory. Therefore, tradeoffs have to be made between inventory and service. Firms that assemble to order, make to order, or engineer to order generally carry no finished inventory and therefore have no finished goods inventory carrying cost. However, these firms often have to make inventory/service tradeoff decisions for their components and raw material inventory.

- **Capacity/process design decisions** – An investment in capacity is sometimes justified by a reduction in the inventory carrying cost. Increased capacity can help the firm be more responsive to customers without the need for large inventories. This is particularly true for manufacturers that have seasonal demand and/or style products. Similarly, investing in process improvement and vertical integration can also significantly reduce cycle times and inventory levels.

- **Lot size decisions** – A small order size requires a firm to place many orders which results in a small "cycle" inventory. Assuming instantaneous delivery with order quantity Q, the average cycle inventory is approximately Q/2. Even though small manufacturing order sizes provide low average cycle inventory, they require more setups which, in turn, may require significant capacity leading to a large queue inventory and a large overall carrying cost.

- **Hedging and quantity discount decisions** – The inventory carrying cost is also an important issue when considering opportunities to buy early or to buy in large quantities to get a lower price. In each of these decisions, the decision maker must make tradeoffs between a larger carrying cost and a lower purchase price.

- **In-sourcing versus outsourcing decisions** – When trying to decide if a component or a product should be manufactured in-house or purchased from a supplier, the inventory carrying cost is often a significant factor. Due to longer leadtimes, firms generally increase inventory levels to support an outsourcing decision. It is important that the proper carrying cost be used to support this analysis. (Note that in some cases, outsourcing can decrease inventory and carrying cost.)

The above decisions require a "managerial economics" approach to decision making, which means that the only costs that should be considered are those costs that vary directly with the amount of inventory. All other costs are irrelevant to the decision.

Estimating the inventory carrying charge

As mentioned above, the carrying cost is usually calculated as the product of the carrying charge (sometimes called the "holding charge") and the unit cost. The carrying charge is an annual rate, usually expressed as the cost per dollar of inventory investment per year. Volume and weight should also be a factor in estimating storage cost, but most managers find that the benefit of considering these issues is rarely worth the additional work to capture and store the additional information.

The carrying charge is a function of four variables: (1) the cost of capital, (2) storage cost, (3) obsolescence risk, and (4) policy adjustment. Each of these is discussed below.

- **Cost of capital** – Firms have alternative uses for money. The cost of capital reflects the opportunity cost of the money tied up in the inventory. The finance organization in most firms has already done a careful analysis of this subject and can provide this parameter for the carrying charge analysis. Many firms use the weighted average cost of capital here. However, some argue that the marginal cost of capital should be used instead; they ask the rhetorical question, "If you found a dollar on the floor today, how would you invest that dollar and what is your rate of return on that investment?" Note that the marginal cost of capital might be quite different from the weighted average cost of capital.

- **Storage cost** – The firm should consider only those storage costs that vary with the inventory level. These costs include warehousing, handling, insurance and taxes, depreciation, and shrinkage:
  - Warehousing – Only the variable portion of warehousing related costs should be included. Many firms already have sufficient warehouse space available. If this is the case, they should not increase the carrying charge for warehousing until the inventory levels demand that additional warehousing cost will soon be incurred. Some authors advocate using the full cost of the warehouse space, including the cost for heating and cooling the space.
  - Handling – This cost is the variable cost of handling additional inventory and should not include costs that are a function of the number of transactions or the number of units purchased. The relevant question to ask here is, "What would the handling cost be with 10% more inventory?" The answer to this question is typically that the firm will have to spend more on counting inventory (e.g., cycle counting cost will increase). The inventory level might affect the cost of counting, the cost of stock picking, and other related costs.
  - Insurance and taxes – The insurance and tax portion of the carrying charge is a function of the amount of inventory invested and can be added to the carrying charge. Insurance is generally a function of the maximum inventory investment anticipated. Taxes are usually a function of the end-of-year inventory investment and vary from state to state in the United States.
  - Depreciation – Some authors include warehouse and equipment depreciation here. However, if the firm has depreciation regardless of the level of inventory, it clearly should not be included. Again, the managerial economics approach to this problem leads us to focus on only those costs that clearly vary with the inventory level.
  - Shrinkage – Shrinkage can be caused by theft, spoilage, deterioration, or loss. Some authors combine shrinkage with obsolescence.

- **Obsolescence risk** – The risk of obsolescence tends to increase with inventory, particularly for firms that deal with high technology products such as computers or perishable products such as food. The obsolescence component here is analogous to the "risk premium" that is added to the cost of capital in many financial models. This category could be further broken down into (1) loss of quantity (spoilage, pilferage, breakage, and obsolescence) and (2) loss of value (end of product life, partial spoilage, and reduced market value). Note that in some unusual situations, inventory can increase in value over time (e.g., antiques). If obsolescence is included in the overhead component of the unit cost, the carrying charge parameter should not include an obsolescence risk component. In other words, be careful not to double-count obsolescence risk in both the unit cost and the carrying charge parameter. One approach to estimating obsolescence risk is to determine the total obsolescence cost for the previous year and divide by the average inventory investment. However, obsolescence is typically a function of many variables such as new product introductions and competitive actions that have more to do with the planning process than the inventory level itself. Again, the essential point here is that the carrying cost should only include costs that increase (or decrease) with changes in the average inventory level.

- **Policy adjustment** – Many manufacturing firms have found that "lean manufacturing" and "just-in-time" manufacturing principles have provided very positive benefits. Reducing inventory forces the firm to shorten cycle times, improve coordination and communication, improve quality, decrease new product development leadtimes, and improve responsiveness to customers. This component of the carrying cost reflects management's desire to pursue this policy. For example, at one time Hewlett-Packard used a 45% inventory carrying charge, with only about one-half of this charge based on measurable costs. Another firm reported using a 75% carrying charge (Harding, 1999). However, most texts and articles report a carrying charge in the 15% to 35% range. This component of the carrying cost reflects management's desire to drive inventory from its system. The policy adjustment factor is, by necessity, found only through trial and error. If management believes that its inventory is too high, the carrying charge parameter should be increased. Conversely, if management believes that more inventory is needed to improve service or buffer production, the carrying charge is lowered.

Issues to consider when using carrying cost

- **Double-counting overhead** – As mentioned above, the carrying cost calculation requires both the carrying charge and the unit cost. Selecting the right unit cost for the carrying cost calculation is not trivial. For purchased components and raw materials, the accounting system will generally have a reasonable cost estimate. However, for manufactured components, the unit cost in the accounting system usually includes allocated overhead. Recall that the carrying charge should be applied only to variable costs (direct material and direct labor). Goldratt takes this concept a step further and argues that for managerial accounting purposes, the unit cost should only include the materials cost and a few other out-of-pocket costs. It should not include either overhead or direct labor. This concept is called "throughput accounting" and is gaining popularity in some firms such as 3M. Nearly all overhead costs are irrelevant to the inventory level decisions listed above. For example, the warehouse manager's salary will not change if inventory is increased by 10%. Similarly, the maintenance has little to do with inventory levels. However, most accountants argue that "all costs are variable in the long term." Clearly, overhead costs such as inventory storage and handling should be included in either the unit cost (as overhead) or in the carrying charge, but not in both.
- **Irrelevant costs** – It is tempting when computing the carrying cost to include costs in the calculation that have nothing whatsoever to do with inventory level. For example, the following expenses are listed in one or more sources (Harding 1999):
  - Moving material from the receiving dock to the proper bin location
  - Receiving/issuing parts
  - Receiving inspection
  - Buyers
  - Purchasing
  - Invoice processing
  - Rework
  - Inbound logistics and delivery
  - Rent
  - Warehouse supplies and equipment
  - Payroll for all warehouse personnel

  Most of these expenses vary with the number of units purchased, not the inventory held. The inventory carrying cost is not an inventory transaction cost; it is the cost of holding inventory, not receiving or shipping inventory. Do not confuse the rate of flow of units through a warehouse for the average inventory level stored in the warehouse.
- **Discounted cash flow analysis versus carrying cost** – Many of the decisions listed above should be analyzed with a discounted cash flow analysis to compare two or more alternatives. These analyses discount projected cash flows to compute net present values. The discount rate handles the capital cost and obsolescence risk portions of the carrying cost. Storage cost, taxes, and insurance are accounted for in the projected cash flows. The policy adjustment is handled by a qualitative comparison of the alternatives. This is the correct approach for handling important financial decisions. This approach also handles the cash flows for taxes and capital investments much better than a static (single period) analysis, particularly when the single period analysis attempts to allocate overhead on a "unit cost" basis. The carrying cost approach is only appropriate for a relatively "quick and dirty" analysis or the analysis of a situation that is not very complicated.
- **Double counting capital cost** – It is important to not double count the financial costs. For example, evaluating an alternative project by discounting the cash flows over time should not use a carrying cost that includes the cost of capital.
- **The average inventory** – The carrying cost over a year should be based on the time-weighted average inventory (sometimes called the "time-integrated average inventory"). A good estimate of this cost is the

yearly average of the end-of-month inventory investment. This average is a good approximation unless the firm has a practice of reducing inventories at the end of the month.

Summary ideas for carrying cost

Carrying cost is an important element of many analyses involving inventory levels, service levels, capacity, hedging, and outsourcing. A managerial economics approach should be used to support the analysis of decisions involving carrying costs. A discounted cash flow analysis is more appropriate than using a carrying cost in situations that involve longer planning horizons and/or significant capital investments. Carrying cost is the product of the carrying charge parameter and the unit cost. The carrying charge parameter is a function of four variables: (1) the cost of capital, (2) storage cost, (3) obsolescence risk, and (4) policy adjustment. When estimating the carrying charge, be careful to only consider variables that vary with the inventory level.

When estimating the unit cost for the carrying cost calculation, most authors argues for ignoring allocated overhead. However, given that it is difficult for most organizations to know their unit cost without overhead, it is reasonable for them to use the fully burdened cost and use the appropriate carrying charge that does not double count handling, storage, or other overhead costs.

Many authors argue that a large component of the carrying charge parameter is a policy adjustment parameter that is used to drive inventory and cycle times to appropriate levels. As a result, the carrying charge is often much higher than the identifiable costs would suggest.

The paper "Estimating Carrying Cost" is on the *OMWW CD* available from www.ClamshellBeachPress.com.

See *aggregate production planning, carrying charge, Economic Order Quantity (EOQ), hockey stick effect, inventory turnover, opportunity cost, setup cost.*

cash cow – The firm or business unit that holds a strong position in a weak industry and is being "milked" to provide cash for other business units; the cash cow is often in a mature industry and therefore not a good place for significant capital investments.
See *operations strategy.*

Cash on Delivery (COD) – Indicates payment that must be made for goods and transportation charges at the time of delivery.
See *FOB, terms, waybill.*

category killer – A term used in marketing and strategic management to describe a dominant product or service that tends to have a natural monopoly in a market.
One of the best examples is eBay, an on-line auction website that attracts large numbers of buyers and sellers simply because it is the largest on-line auction.

category management – The retail practice of segmenting items (SKUs) into groups called categories in order to make it easier to manage assortments, inventories, shelf-space allocation, promotions, and purchases.
Benefits claimed for a good category management system include increased sales due to better space allocation and better stocking levels, lower cost due to lower inventories, and increased customer retention due to better matching of supply and demand. (Adapted from www.oracle.com/applications/retail/library/data-sheets/category-mgt.pdf, January 4, 2007).
The category management in retailing is analogous to the commodity management function in purchasing.
See *brand.*

causal forecasting – See *econometric forecasting, forecasting.*

causal map – A graphical tool often used for identifying the root causes of a problem; also known as a cause and effect diagram (C&E Diagram), Ishikawa Diagram, fishbone diagram, cause map, impact wheel, root cause tree, fault tree analysis, and current reality trees. ✪
A causal map is a diagram that shows the cause and effect relationships in a system. Causal maps can add value to organizations in many ways:
- **Process improvement and problem solving** – Causal maps are a powerful tool for gaining a deep understanding of any process improvement problem. As the old adage goes, "A problem well-defined is a problem half-solved." The causal map is a great way to help organizations understand the system of causes

result in blocked goals and then to find solutions to the problem rather than just the symptoms of the problem.

- **Risk mitigation** – Causal maps are a powerful tool for helping firms identify possible causes of a problem and develop risk mitigation strategies for these possible causes.
- **Gaining consensus** – The brainstorming process of creating a causal map is also a powerful tool for "gaining a shared understanding" of how a system works. The discussion, debate, and deliberation process in building a causal map is often more important than the map itself.
- **Training and teaching** – A good causal map can dramatically reduce the time required to communicate complex relationships for training, teaching, and documentation purposes.
- **Identifying the critical metrics** – Many organizations have too many metrics, which causes managers to lose sight of the critical variables in the system. A good causal map can help managers identify the critical variables that drive performance and require high-level attention. Focusing on these few critical metrics leads to strategic alignment, which in turn leads to organizational success.

Ishikawa Diagram

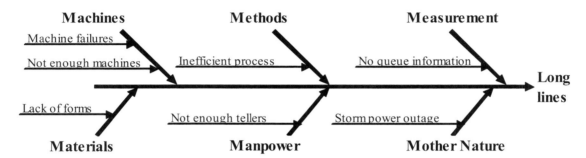

Source: Arthur V. Hill

The Ishikawa Diagram (also known as a fishbone diagram, cause and effect diagram, and C&E Diagram) was developed by Dr. Kaoru Ishikawa (1943-1969) and is the most popular form of a causal map. The Ishikawa Diagram is a special type of a causal map that shows the relationships between the problem (at the "head" of the fishbone) and six potential causes of a problem: machines, methods, measurements, materials, manpower, and Mother Nature. The following figure is a simple example of an Ishikawa Diagram for analyzing long waiting lines for tellers in a bank.

The Ishikawa Diagram is usually developed in a brainstorming context. The process begins by placing the name of a basic problem of interest at the far right of the diagram at the "head" of the main "backbone" of the fish. The main causes of the problem are drawn as bones off the main backbone. The categories often used as a starting point include machines (equipment), methods, measurement, materials, manpower (people), and Mother Nature (environment). Other causes can be chosen as needed. Brainstorming is typically done to add possible causes to the main bones and more specific causes to the bones on the main bones. This subdivision into ever increasing specificity continues as long as the problem areas can be further subdivided. The practical maximum depth of this tree is usually about four or five levels.

Causal maps

Causal maps can be more general than the Ishikawa Diagram and can overcome all of the following criticisms of the Ishikawa Diagram:
- The Ishikawa Diagram can only analyze one output variable at a time.
- Many people have trouble working backwards from the problem on the far right side of the page.
- The Ishikawa Diagram is hard to read and even harder to draw, especially when the problem requires more than two levels of causation.
- The Diagram is also hard to create on a computer.
- The alliteration of "M"s is sexist with the terms manpower and Mother Nature.

- The six M's do not include all possible causes of a problem.

Causal mapping does not require the fishbone structure or the six M's and is therefore more general than an Ishikawa Diagram. Other special cases of causal maps include impact wheels (from one cause to many effects), Root Cause Trees (from one effect to many causes), and strategy maps.

Drawing conventions

The Ishikawa Diagram starts with the result on the far right. With Root Cause Trees (RCT), current reality trees (Goldratt 1994), and strategy maps (Kaplan & Norton, 2004), the result is usually written at the top of the page. With an FMEA analysis and issues trees, the result is written on the left and then broken into its root causes on the right.

The diagram below presents a causal map example based on book ***Time Based Competition*** strategy (Stalk & Hout, 1988, 1990) with the result on the far left. This is a strategy map using a causal mapping format rather than the standard Kaplan and Norton (1992) four-perspective format. This strategy reduces cycle times to drive out costs and offer shorter customer leadtimes. Reducing customer leadtimes segments the market, leaving the price-sensitive customers to the competition. This strategy map could be taken a step further to show how the firm could achieve lower cycle time through setup time reduction, vendor relationships, 5S, plant re-layout, etc.

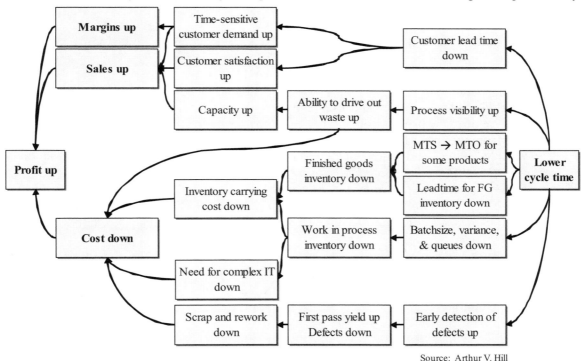

Source: Arthur V. Hill

Brainstorming

Regardless of the format used, these diagrams are usually created through a brainstorming process, often with the help of Post-it™ notes. The team brainstorms to identify the root causes of each node. The process continues until all causes (nodes) and relationships (arcs) have been identified. It is possible that some "loops" will occur in the diagram. A loop can occur for a vicious cycle or virtuous cycle. For example, a vicious cycle occurs when an alcoholic person drinks and is criticized by family members, which may, in turn, cause them to drink even more, be criticized further, etc. A virtuous cycle is similar except that the result is positive instead of negative.

Scavarda, Bouzdine-Chameeva, Goldstein, Hays, and Hill (2006) developed a method for building collective causal maps from a group of experts. This method assigns weights to each causal relationship and results in a meaningful graphical representation of the causal map with the more important causal relationships shown with darker arrows.

Software for causal mapping

Software tools are available to help brainstorm and document the cause and effect diagrams (cf., www.skymark.com/pathmaker/tour/cause.asp and decision explorer). However, Galley (2008) insists that Excel is the best tool. The paper "An Overview of Mapping Tools for Process Improvement" builds the argument for using Excel.

Process improvement

The C&E Matrix provides a means for experts to assign weights to certain causal input variables. The same can be done with a causal map. All that needs to be done is to score each input variable on several dimensions that are important to customers and then create a weighted score for each input variable. Priority is then given to those variables that are believed to have the most impact on customers. Alternatively, experts can "vote" (using multi-voting) for the causes that they believe should be the focus for further analysis.

Conclusions

Causal maps should not be confused with concept maps, knowledge maps, and mindmaps that nearly always show similarities (but not causality) between objects. For example, monkeys and apes are very similar, but monkeys do not cause apes. Therefore, a knowledge map would show a strong connection between monkeys and apes, but a causal map would not.

People think in "visual" ways. A good causal map is worth 1000 words and can significantly reduce meeting time and the time to achieve the benefit from a process improvement project.

The papers "Mapping Tools for Process Improvement," "Mindmapping," "Strategy Mapping," "Causal Mapping," "Process Mapping," and "Value Stream Mapping" are available from Clamshell Beach Press. ☉

See *5 Whys, affinity diagram, Analytical Hierarchy Process (AHP), balanced scorecard, brainstorming, C&E Matrix, decision tree, Failure Mode and Effects Analysis (FMEA), fault tree analysis, ideation, impact wheel, issue tree, MECE, mindmap, Nominal Group Technique (NGT), Pareto Chart, Pareto's Law, Root Cause Analysis (RCA), Root Cause Tree (RCT), seven tools of quality, Six Sigma, strategy map, Total Quality Management (TQM), Y-tree.*

cause and effect diagram – See *causal map.*

cause map – A trademarked term for a causal map coined by Mark Galley of ThinkReliability.

Cause mapping is a registered trademark of Novem, Inc. doing business as ThinkReliability (www.thinkreliability.com).

See *causal map.*

c-chart – A quality control chart used to display and monitor the number of defects per sample in a production process.

Whereas a p-chart controls the percentage of units that are defective, a c-chart controls the number of defects per unit. Note that one unit can have multiple defects.

See *control chart, Statistical Process Control (SPC).*

cell – See *cellular manufacturing.*

cellular manufacturing – The use of groups of machines usually organized in a U-shaped layout that is dedicated to processing parts or products that require similar sequences of operations. ✪

While a cell does not necessarily make the same parts repeatedly, it does make the same family of parts or products. The machines and fixtures within the cell are typically arranged so close to each other that there is no need to allow for storage between the operations or handling with hand trucks or pallet jacks. Cells offer a way to simplify production control and scheduling and shorten the manufacturing cycle time required to complete the product. They also reduce inventories and therefore manufacturing space required to satisfy production requirements.

As Professor Rajan Suri states, "[The] ideal cell really should complete a sequence of operations that were traditionally completed in separate functional units. It is really important also that the people – the human resources – in the cell have training on more than one of the operations in the cell. Ideally, of course, they would be able to do all of them, but that might be too much. They should at least have the ability to do two or three of the operations in the cell. Finally, it is really important that the team in the cell be a team-based organization and that it has ownership of everything that goes on in the cell. This includes deciding how to achieve performance goals." (Source: wiscinfo.doit.wisc.edu/erdman/pdf/News%20 Summer2001.pdf, November 29, 2003).

The advantages of a cell over a process layout include reduced travel time, reduced setup time, reduced queue time, reduced work-in-process inventory, reduced materials handling cost, quicker detection of defects, simpler scheduling, better morale, and easier training. When firms create cells, they often also implement self-managed work team and cross-training concepts to run the cell. While this practice is not necessary to have a cell, it is often a good approach.

The main disadvantage of a cell is that the machines dedicated to a cell may not have sufficient utilization to justify the capital expense. Consequently, cellular manufacturing is often difficult to implement in a facility that uses expensive, large machines. It is hard to justify the purchase of an "extra" $5 million machine so that each cell can have a dedicated machine.

Professors Hyer and Wemmerlov have written a good book on the subject (Hyer & Wemmerlov, 2002) and an interesting article on the application of cellular thinking to administrative work (Hyer & Wemmerlov, 2002).

See *automation, Chaku-Chaku, cross-training, facility layout, Flexible Manufacturing System (FMS), focused factory, group technology, handoff, lean thinking, utilization, workcenter, Work-in-Process (WIP) inventory.*

censored data – Data that is incomplete because it does not include a subpopulation of the data.

A good example of censored data is demand data that does not include data for lost sales. A retailer reports that the sales were 100 for a particular date. However, the firm ran out of stock during the day and does not have information on how many units were demanded but not sold due to lack of inventory. The demand data for this firm is said to be "censored."

See *forecasting*.

centered moving average – See *exponential smoothing, moving average*.

center-of-gravity model for facility location – A method for locating a single facility on an x-y coordinate system in order to attempt to minimize the weighted travel distances.

This is called the "infinite set" facility location problem because the "depot" can be located at any point on the x-y coordinate axis. The model treats the x and y dimensions independently and finds the first moment in each dimension. The one depot must serve N markets with locations (x_i, y_i) and demands D_i units. The center-of-gravity location for the depot is then $x_0 = \sum_{i=1}^{N} D_i x_i / \sum_{i=1}^{N} x_i$ and $y_0 = \sum_{i=1}^{N} D_i y_i / \sum_{i=1}^{N} y_i$. This model is sometimes called the "center of mass" or the "centroid" model.

This model does not guarantee optimality and can only locate a single depot. Center-of-gravity locations can be far from optimal.

In contrast, the numeric-analytic location model guarantees optimality for a single depot location, can be extended (heuristically) to multiple depots, and can also be extended (heuristically) to multiple depots with latitude and longitude data.

More information on this subject is available in the paper "Location Theory" on the **OMWW CD** available from www.ClamshellBeachPress.com. ⬤

See *facility location, gravity model for competitive retail store location, numeric-analytic location model*.

central limit theorem – An important probability theory concept that can be stated informally as: "The sum or average of many independent random variables will be approximately normally distributed."

For example, the first figure below shows a probability distribution that is clearly non-normal. The second figure shows the distribution of a random variable that is the average of two independent random variates drawn from the first distribution. The third and fourth figures show the probability distributions when the number of random variates in the average increases to four and eight. In each successive figure, the distribution for the average of the random variates is closer to normal. This example shows that as the number of random variates in the average increases, the distribution of the average converges to the normal distribution.

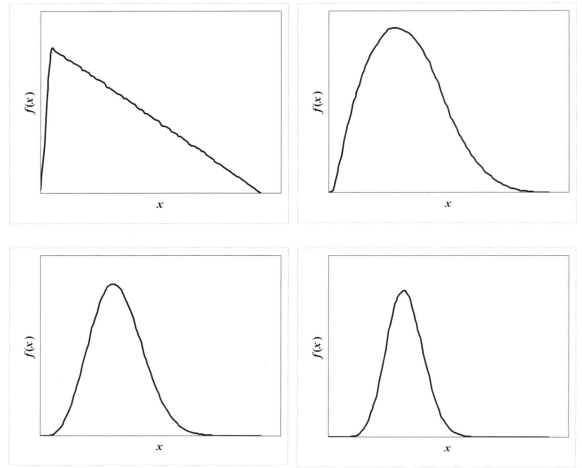

Source: Professor Arthur V. Hill

See *confidence interval*, *Law of Large Numbers*, *normal distribution*, *sample size calculation*, *sampling*.

certification – See *supplier qualification and certification*.

Chaku-Chaku – The Japanese phrase "Load, Load" used to describe the practice of facilitating one-piece flow in a manufacturing cell, where equipment automatically unloads parts so the operator can move parts between machines with minimal wasted motion.

  With Chaku-Chaku, the operator is responsible for moving parts from machine to machine around an oval or circular-shaped cell and also for monitoring machine performance. When arriving at a machine in the cell, the operator will find a completed part already removed from the machine and the machine ready for a new part. The operator then starts a new part (from the previous machine), picks up the completed part from the machine, and then carries the part to the next machine in the cell to repeat the process.

  Acknowledgments: CEMBA 06 students Donald Smithmier, Luis Acosta, Aderonke Mordi, Douglas Neimann, Joseph Novotny, Paul Seel, and Pam Aylward contributed to this entry.

  See *cellular manufacturing*, *multiple-machine handling*.

champion – A senior manager who sponsors a program or project.

  The champion's role is to define the strategic direction with some passion, ensure that resources are available, provide accountability through regular reviews, and deal with political resistance. This term is often used in the context of Six Sigma, Lean Sigma, and lean programs. This role can be either formal or informal.

  See *deployment leader*, *lean thinking*, *program management office*, *project charter*, *Six Sigma*.

changeover cost – See *setup cost*.

changeover time – See *setup time*.

channel conflict – Competition between players (often within the same firm) who are trying to sell to the same customers.

For example, a personal computer company might try to compete with its own distributors (such as Sears) for customers by selling directly to customers. This is often an issue when a retail channel is in competition with a web based channel set up by the company. Channel conflict is not a new phenomenon with the Internet, but has become more obvious with the disruptions caused by the Internet.

See *disintermediation, distribution channel*.

channel integration – The practice of extending strategic alliances to the suppliers (and their suppliers) and to customers (and to their customers).

See *supply chain management*.

channel partner – A firm that works with another firm to provide products and services to customers.

Channel partners for a manufacturing firm generally include distributors, sales representatives, logistics firms, transportation firms, and retailers. Note that the term "partner" is imprecise because relationships with distributors and other "channel partners" are rarely legal partnerships.

See *supply chain management*.

chase strategy – An approach to production planning that changes the production rate to match a seasonal demand rate and therefore is able to keep finished goods inventory quite low.

In contrast, the level strategy maintains a constant production rate and builds inventory in the off-season to meet the demand in the peak season. Many firms are able to economically implement a chase strategy for one product and a level employment strategy overall by offering counter-seasonal products. For example, a company that makes snow skis might also make water skis to maintain a constant workforce without building large inventories in the off-season.

See *aggregate production planning, Sales & Operations Planning (S&OP)*.

check digit – A single number (digit) usually between 0 and 9 that is usually placed at the end an identifying number (such as a part number, bank account, credit card number, or employee ID) and is used to perform a quick test to see if the identifying number is clearly invalid.

The check digit is usually the last digit in the identifying number and is computed from the base number, which is the identifying number without the check digit. By comparing the check digit computed from the base number with the check digit that is part of the identifying number, it is possible to quickly check if an identifying number is clearly invalid without accessing a database of valid identifying numbers. This is particularly powerful for remote data entry of credit card numbers and part numbers. These applications typically have enormous databases that make number validation relatively expensive. However, it is important to understand that identifying numbers with valid check digits are not necessarily valid identifying numbers; the check digit only determines if the identifying number is clearly invalid.

A simple approach for checking the validity of a number is to multiply the last digit (the check digit) by one, the second to last digit by two, the third to last digit by one, etc. Then sum all of the *digits* in these products (including the check digit), divide by 10, and find the remainder. The number is proven invalid if the remainder is not zero.

For example, the account number 5249 has the check digit 9. The products are 1x9=9, 2x4=8, 1x2=2, and 2x5=10. The sum of the digits is 9+8+2+1+0=20, which is divisible by 10 and therefore is a valid check digit. We add the digits, which means that 10 is treated as 1+0=1 rather than a 10. The above procedure works with most credit card and bank account numbers. See the website www.beachnet.com/~hstiles/cardtype.html.

The check digit for all books registered with an International Standard Book Number is the last digit of the ISBN. The check digit approach for this is slightly different than the account number approach above. The ISBN method weights the digits from 10 down to 1, sums the products, and then returns the check digit as modulus 11 of this sum. An upper case X is used in lieu of 10.

For example, the book ***Operations Management for Competitive Advantage*** 11-th edition text by Chase, Jacobs, and Aquilano (2006) has ISBN 0-07-312151-7, which is 0073121517 without the dashes. The ending "7" is the check digit so the base number is 007312151. Multiplying 10x0=0, 9x0=0, 8x7=56, 7x3=21, 6x1=6,

5x2=10, 4x1=4, 3x5=15, and 2x1=2 and adding the products 0+0+56+21+6+10+4+15+2=114. Dividing 114 by 11 leaves a remainder of 7, which is the correct check digit for this ISBN. The new 13-digit ISBN uses a slightly different approach.

The Excel workbook "Check digit.xls" is on the **OMWW CD** available from www.ClamshellBeachPress.com.

See *item number, Stock Keeping Unit (SKU)*.

check sheet – A simple approach for collecting defect data; sometimes also called a tally sheet.

A check sheet is a form that can be used to collect and count defects. Check sheets are considered one of the seven tools of quality. The user makes a check mark every time a defect of that type occurs in that time period. The table below provides a simple example of a check sheet that records the causes for machine downtime.

	Mon	Tue	Wed	Thu	Fri	Totals
Machine jam	✓✓✓✓✓✓	✓✓✓✓✓	✓✓✓✓✓	✓✓✓✓✓	✓✓✓✓	25
Machine failure	✓✓	✓			✓	4
Materials shortage	✓✓	✓✓✓✓	✓	✓	✓✓	10
Power outage				✓		1
Totals	10	10	6	7	7	40

A different format for a check sheet shows a drawing (schematic) of a product (such as a shirt) and count the problems by location on the drawing. A check sheet is a useful tool for collecting the raw data for a Pareto analysis. Check sheets should be used in the gemba, the place where work is done, so that workers and supervisors can see them and update them on a regular basis.

See *error proofing, Pareto Chart, seven tools of quality*.

chi-square goodness of fit test – A statistical test used to determine if a set of data fits a hypothesized discrete probability distribution.

The chi-square test statistic is $\chi^2 = \sum_{i=1}^{k} \frac{(O_i - E_i)^2}{E_i}$, where O_i is the observed frequency in the i-th bin and E_i is

the expected frequency. E_i is $n(F(x_{it}) - F(x_{ib}))$, where $n = \sum_{i=1}^{k} O_i$ is the total number of observations, $F(x)$ is the

distribution function for the hypothesized distribution, and (x_{ib}, x_{it}) are the limits for bin i. It is important that each bin has at least five observations.

The hypothesis that the data follows the hypothesized distribution is rejected if the calculated χ^2 test statistic is greater than $\chi^2_{1-\alpha, k-1}$, the chi-square distribution value with $k - 1$ degrees of freedom and significance level of α. The formula for this in Excel is CHIINV($1 - \alpha$, $k-1$).

Failure to reject the null hypothesis of no difference should not be interpreted as "accepting the null hypothesis." For smaller sample sizes, good-of-fit tests are not very powerful and will only detect major differences. On the other hand, for a larger sample size, these tests will almost always reject the null hypothesis because it is almost never exactly true. As Law and Kelton (2002) state, "This is an unfortunate property of these tests, since it is usually sufficient to have a distribution that is 'nearly' correct."

The Kolmogorov-Smirnov (K-S) test is generally believed to be a better test for continuous distributions.

See *Kolmogorov-Smirnov test (K-S test)*.

CIM – See *Computer Integrated Manufacturing*.

clean room – A work area where air quality, flow, flow direction, temperature, and humidity are carefully regulated in order to protect sensitive equipment and materials.

Clean rooms are frequently found in electronics, pharmaceutical, biopharmaceutical, medical device, and other manufacturing environments. Clean rooms are important features in the production of integrated circuits, hard drives, medical devices, and other high-tech and sterile products. The air in a clean room is repeatedly filtered to remove dust particles and other impurities.

A typical office building air contains from 500,000 to 1,000,000 particles (0.5 microns or larger) per cubic foot of air. A human hair is about 75-100 microns in diameter, but a particle 200 times smaller (0.5 micron) than the human hair can cause a major disaster in a clean room. Contamination can lead to expensive downtime and increased production cost. The billion dollar NASA Hubble Space Telescope was damaged because of a particle smaller than 0.5 microns.

People are a major source of contamination. A person sitting or standing motionless will produce about 100,000 particles of 0.3 microns and larger per minute. A person walking at 5 miles/hour will produce about 10 million particles per minute.

The measure of the air quality in a clean room is defined in Federal Standard 209E. A Class 10,000 clean room can have no more than 10,000 particles larger than 0.5 microns in any given cubic foot of air. A Class 1000 clean room can have no more than 1000 particles and a Class 100 clean rooms can have no more than 100 particles. Hard disk drive manufacturing, for example, requires a Class 100 clean room.

People who work in clean rooms must wear special protective clothing called "bunny suits" that do not give off lint particles and prevent human skin and hair particles from entering the room's atmosphere.

Adapted from www.webopedia.com/TERM/C/clean_room.html and www.coastwidelabs.com, December 6, 2006.

click-and-mortar – A hybrid between a dot-com and a "brick-and-mortar" operation.

See *dot-com*.

clockspeed – The rate of new product introduction in an industry or firm.

High clockspeed industries, such as consumer electronics, often have product lifecyles of less than a year. Low clockspeed industries, such as industrial chemicals, may have product lifecycles measured in decades. High clockspeed industries can be used to understand the dynamics of change that will, in the long run, affect all industries, much like fruit flies with short life spans can be used to understand the dynamics of genetic change in an accelerated genetic environment. The term was popularized in the book *Clockspeed* by Professor Charles Fine from the Sloan School at MIT (Fine, 1995).

See *New Product Development (NPD)*, *time to market*.

closed-loop MRP – An imprecise concept of a capacity feedback loop in a Materials Requirements Planning system; sometimes called "closed-loop" planning.

Some consultants and MRP/ERP software vendors used to claim that their systems were "closed-loop" planning systems. Although they were never very precise in what this meant, they implied that their systems provided rapid feedback to managers on capacity/load imbalance problems. They implied that their closed-loop systems could somehow automatically fix the problems when the load exceeded the capacity. Unfortunately, the reality is that few planning systems provide quick feedback on capacity problems and automatically reschedule to the fix capacity/load imbalance problems. Advanced Planning and Scheduling (APS) Systems are intended to create schedules that do not violate capacity.

See *Advanced Planning and Scheduling (APS)*, *Business Requirements Planning (BRP)*, *capacity*, *Capacity Requirements Planning (CRP)*, *finite scheduling*, *Materials Requirements Planning (MRP)*, *Sales & Operations Planning (S&OP)*.

cluster analysis – A method for creating groups of similar items.

Overview of cluster analysis

Cluster analysis is an exploratory data analysis tool that sorts items (objects, cases) into groups (sets, clusters) so that the similarity between the objects in a group is high and the similarity between groups is low. Each item is described by a set of measures (also called attributes, variables, or dimensions). The dissimilarity between two items is a function of these measures. Cluster analysis, therefore, can be used to discover structures in data without explaining why they exist.

For example, biologists have organized different species of living beings into clusters. In this taxonomy, man belongs to the primates, the mammals, the amniotes, the vertebrates, and the animals. The higher the level of aggregation, the less similar are the members in the respective class. For example, man has more in common with all other primates than with more "distant" members of the mammals (e.g., dogs).

Unlike most exploratory data analysis tools, cluster analysis is not a statistical technique, but rather a collection of algorithms that put objects into clusters according to well-defined rules. Therefore, statistical testing is not possible with cluster analysis. The final number of clusters can be a user-input to the algorithm or can be based on a stopping rule. The final result is a set of clusters (groups) of relatively homogeneous items.

Applications

Cluster analysis has been applied to a wide variety of research problems and is a powerful tool whenever a large amount of information is available and the researcher has little prior knowledge of how to make sense out of it. Examples of cluster analysis include:
- Marketing research: Cluster consumers into market segments to better understand the relationships between different groups of consumers/potential customers. Also widely used to group like products to define product position.
- Location analysis: Cluster customers based on their locations.
- Quality management: Cluster problem causes based on their attributes.
- Cellular manufacturing: Cluster parts based on their routings.

Dendrogram

A dendrogram is a graphical representation of the step-by-step clustering process. In the dendrogram below, the first step divides the entire group of items (set A) into four sets (B, C, D, and E). In the second step, set B is further divided into sets F and G, set C is further divided into sets H and I, and set E is further divided into sets J and K. In the last step, set G is further divided into sets L and M, and set J is further divided into sets N, O, and P. Therefore, the final clusters are on the bottom row (sets F, L, M, H, I, D, N, O, P, and K). Note that each of these final sets may include only one item or many items.

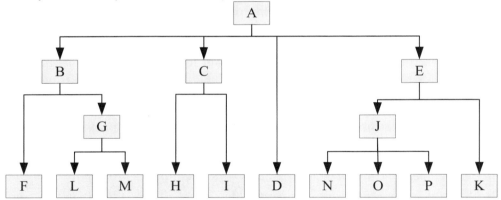

Source: Professor Arthur V. Hill

Distance measures

The distance between any two objects is a measure of the dissimilarity between them. Distance measures can be computed from the variables (attributes, dimensions) that describe each item. The simplest way to measure the distance between two items is with the Pythagorean distance. When we have just two variables (x_i, y_i) to describe each item i, the Pythagorean distance between points i and j is $d_{ij} = \sqrt{(x_i - x_j)^2 + (y_i - y_j)^2}$. With three variables (x_i, y_i, z_i) to describe each item, the Pythagorean distance is $d_{ij} = \sqrt{(x_i - x_j)^2 + (y_i - y_j)^2 + (z_i - z_j)^2}$. With K variables, x_{ik} is defined as the measurement on the k-th variable for item i and the Pythagorean distance between items i and j is:

$$d_{ij} = \sqrt{(x_{i1} - x_{j1})^2 + (x_{i2} - x_{j2})^2 + ... + (x_{iK} - x_{jK})^2} = \sqrt{\sum_{k=1}^{K}(x_{ik} - x_{jk})^2}$$

The Minkowski metric is a more generalized distance metric. If item i has K attributes $(x_{i1}, x_{i2}, \ldots, x_{iK})$, the distance between item i and item j is given by $d_{ij} = (\sum_{k=1}^{K} | x_{ki} - x_{kj} |^r)^{1/r}$. The Minkowski metric is equal to the Euclidean distance when $r = 2$ and the Manhattan square distance when $r = 1$.

When two or more variables are used to define distance, the one with the larger magnitude will tend to dominate. Therefore, it is common to first standardize all variables (e.g., $x'_{ki} = (x_{ki} - \overline{x}_k)/s_k$, where $\overline{x}_k$ is the sample mean for the k-th variable and s_k is the sample standard deviation. However, even with standardization, not all variables should have the same weight in the summation. Unfortunately, it is usually not clear how to determine how much weight should be given to each variable.

Cluster analysis algorithms

A variety of clustering algorithms are available. The objective function for the clustering algorithms include the complete-linkage (or farthest-neighbor), single-linkage (or nearest-neighbor), group-average, and Ward's method. Ward's method is one of the more commonly used methods and measures the distance (dissimilarity) between any two sets (S_I, S_J) as the sum of the squared distances between all pairs of items in the two sets:

$$D(S_I, S_J) = \sum_{i \in S_I} \sum_{j \in S_J} d_{ij}^2$$

Divisive methods start with all items in one cluster and then proceed to split (partition) the cases into smaller and smaller clusters. Agglomerative methods begin with each item treated as a separate cluster and then proceed to combine them into larger and larger clusters until all observations belong to one final cluster.

SPSS offers three general approaches to cluster analysis. These include:
- *Hierarchical clustering* – Users select the distance measure, select the linking method for forming clusters, and then determine how many clusters best suit the data.
- *K-means clustering* – Users specify the number of clusters in advance and the algorithm assigns items to the K clusters. K-means clustering is much less computer-intensive than hierarchical clustering and is therefore preferred when datasets are very large (e.g., $N > 1000$).
- *Two-step clustering* – The algorithm creates pre-clusters, and then clusters the pre-clusters.

(Some of the above content was adapted from chass.ncsu.edu/garson/PA765/cluster.htm, January 21, 2007.)

Cluster analysis versus factor analysis

We often have a data matrix where each row in an item (case, object) and each column is a variable that describes that item. Cluster analysis is a means of grouping the rows (items) that are similar. In contrast, factor analysis and principal component analysis are statistical techniques for grouping similar (highly correlated) variables to reduce the number of variables. In other words, cluster analysis groups items whereas factor analysis groups variables.

See *affinity diagram, data mining, data warehouse, factor analysis, logistic regression, Manhattan square distance, Minkowski distance metric, Principal Components Analysis (PCA)*.

CMM – See *Capability Maturity Model*

CNC – See *Computer Numerical Control*.

co-competition – See *co-opetition*.

COD – See *Cash on Delivery (COD)*.

coefficient of variation – A measure of the variability relative to the mean, measured as the standard deviation divided by the mean.

The coefficient of variation is used as a measure of the variability relative to the mean. For a sample of data, with a sample standard deviation s and sample mean $\overline{x}$, the coefficient of variation is $CV = s/\overline{x}$. The CV has no unit of measure (i.e., it is a "unit-less" quantity).

The coefficient of variation is often a good indicator of the distribution of the random variable. For example, a *CV* of 1 suggests an exponential distribution. More generally, the *k* parameter of a *k*-Erlang (or gamma) distribution is $k = \overline{x}^2 / s^2 = 1 / CV^2$.

In forecasting, a good rule of thumb is that any item with a demand that has a coefficient of variation less than 1 has a "lumpy" demand and therefore should not be forecasted with exponential smoothing methods.

See *Erlang distribution*, *exponential distribution*, *exponential smoothing*, *forecasting*, *lumpy demand*, *standard deviation*.

Collaborative Planning Forecasting and Replenishment (CPFR) – A business practice that combines the intelligence of multiple trading partners in the planning and fulfillment of customer demand. (Source www.vics.org/committees/cpfr)

CPFR is designed to improve the flow of goods from the raw material suppliers to the manufacturer and ultimately to the retailers' shelves. It is also designed to quickly identify any discrepancies in the forecasts, inventory, and ordering data so that the problems can be corrected before they impact sales or profits.

With CPRF, customers share their sales history, sales projections, and other important information with their business partners who, in turn, share their raw material availability, leadtimes, and other important information with the customers. The information is then integrated, synchronized, and used to eliminate excess inventory and improve in-stock positions, making the supply chain more profitable.

CPFR has data and process model standards developed for collaboration between suppliers and an enterprise with methods for planning (agreement between the trading partners to conduct business in a certain way), forecasting (agreed-to methods, technology and timing for sales, promotions, and order forecasting), and replenishment (order generation and order fulfillment). The Voluntary Inter-Industry Commerce Standards (VICS) committee, a group dedicated to the adoption of bar-coding and EDI in the department store/mass merchandise industries, has established CPFR standards for the consumer goods industry that are published by the Uniform Code Council (UCC).

See www.cpfr.org for information on the VICS committee.

See *continuous replenishment planning*, *Efficient Consumer Response*, *forecasting*.

Collaborative Product Development – See *Early Supplier Development*, *New Product Development*.

co-location – The practice of locating people from different functions or different organizations next to each other in order to improve communications.

Co-location has proven to be very helpful for both customers and suppliers when suppliers have representatives working at their customers' sites. For example, many manufacturers have representatives working in Bentonville, Arkansas at the world headquarters for Wal-Mart.

Co-location also makes sense for many large and complex organizations to co-locate workers from different functions to improve communications. For example, the business unit manager for the 3M Post-it™ products business reported that one of his keys to success was the co-location of his office next to his marketing and manufacturing directors. (Source: Personal communication with Tom Ensign.)

See *JIT II*, *learning organization*.

commercialization – The process of managing a new product through pilot production, production ramp-up, and product launch into the channels of distribution.

See *New Product Development (NPD)*.

commodity – A basic product that is homogenous and cannot be easily differentiated by suppliers.

With commodities, all suppliers offer essentially the same good or product, which means that the commodity products from two or more suppliers are essentially interchangeable and uniform. As a result, the main differentiator for commodities is the supplier's price. Commodities are often inputs in the production of other goods or services.

Common examples of commodities include basic resources and agricultural products such as metals, oil, coal, food products such as wheat, and metals. However, many industries have found that over time once highly differentiated products will quickly become "commoditized" and less differentiated over time. For example, simple handheld calculators were once a highly differentiated luxury item costing hundreds of dollars. Today, they are fairly undifferentiated and becoming a "commoditized" product that sells for under $20.

Many commodities are traded on an exchange. Well-established physical commodities have actively traded spot and derivative markets. In some cases, minimum commodity quality standards (known as a basis grade) are set by the exchange.

Suppliers often try to differentiate commodity products with packaging, quality, information, and/or service and delivery. However, in many cases, customers only care about the price. It is often important for sellers to make sure that their products continue to be differentiated so that their products are not treated like a commodity and purchased only on the basis of price.

The word "commodity" is also used in the purchasing world to mean any group of purchased materials or components, also known as a commodity class. In this context, a commodity can be any group of purchased items including highly engineered items. For example, Boston Scientific might have a manager for a commodity group that includes all machined products.

See *purchasing*.

common carrier – An organization that transports people or goods and offers its services to the public, typically on regular routes and regular schedules.

In contrast, private carriers do not provide service to the public and provide transport on an irregular or ad hoc basis. Examples of common carriers include airlines, railroads, bus lines, cruise ships, and many trucking companies. Although common carriers generally transport people or goods, the term may also refer to telecommunications providers and public utilities in the United States.

A common carrier must obtain a certificate of public convenience and necessity from the Federal Trade Commission for interstate traffic. By the common law, a common carrier is generally liable for all losses which may occur to property entrusted to its charge in the course of business, with four exceptions: (1) an act of God, (2) an act of public enemies, (3) fault or fraud by the shipper, or (4) an inherent defect in the goods. Carriers typically incorporate further exceptions into a contract of carriage, often specifically claiming not to be a common carrier.

See *logistics*, *private carrier*.

common cause variation – The normal random variation in output for a process when it is under control.

See *control chart*, *special cause variation*, *Statistical Process Control (SPC)*, *tampering*.

commonality – The degree to which parts are used in many different products. ✪

For example, in the drawing to the right, the "universal" box in the middle front replaces all of the other boxes in the back. This change to this common box dramatically reduced inventory and manufacturing cost. (This photo is used with permission from Honeywell.) Honeywell calls this a "universal" box.

Increasing commonality can lead to economies of scope though the following mechanism:

- **Reduced setup (ordering) cost** – Because the robust component has a higher demand rate, its economic order quantity is larger and it does not have to be ordered as many times as the current components. This saves on ordering cost.
- **Potential quantity discounts** – In general, robust components will cost more because they have a wider range of uses. However, robust components will have higher demand and therefore might qualify for a quantity discount on the price.
- **Reduced cycle (lotsize) inventory** – The economic order quantity logic suggests that the robust component will have a larger order size than either one of the current components. However, the total cycle stock for the robust component will be less than the sum of the cycle stock for the two current components. This will result in lower carrying cost.
- **Reduced safety stock inventory and/or improved service levels** – The variance of the demand during leadtime for the robust component will likely be about equal to the sum of the variance of the demand for the two current components. When this is true, the safety stock inventory for the robust component will be better. Conversely, the firm can keep the same safety stock level and improve the service level – or make improvements in both. This can result in lower carrying cost, lower stockout cost, or both.

- **Reduced forecasting error** – Based on the same logic as above, the robust component will have a lower forecast error variance than the sum of the variances of the two current components. Again, this can reduce safety stock inventory, improve service levels, or both.
- **Reduce product design cost** – If the firm is using truly robust components, it can use these components in many different products and not have to "re-invent the wheel" with each new product design.
- **Reduced purchasing and manufacturing overhead** – As the number of components are reduced, overhead needed to maintain the engineering drawings, tooling, etc. can also be reduced.
- **Increased reliability** – In some cases, a more robust part is also more reliable and easier to maintain.

The paper "Commonality" and the Excel workbook "commonality.xls" are on the *OMWW CD* available from www.ClamshellBeachPress.com. ⊙

See *Bill of Material (BOM), cycle stock, economy of scale, economy of scope, Engineer to Order (ETO), mass customization, modular design (modularity), robust, value engineering.*

Compounded Annual Growth Rate (CAGR) – The annual rate of growth for an investment that assumes that the compounded growth rate per year is constant between the first and last values; also called the internal rate of return (IRR).

The CAGR is also called a "smoothed rate of return" because it measures the growth of an investment as if it had grown at a steady rate on an annually compounded basis. Mathematically, the CAGR is the geometric mean growth rate.

The equation for the Compounded Annual Growth Rate over n years is $CAGR = \left(\dfrac{\text{ending value}}{\text{beginning value}} \right)^{1/n} - 1$.

For example, if someone made an initial investment worth \$10,000 at the end of 2007, \$11,000 at the end of 2008, \$12,000 at the end of 2009, and \$19,500 at the end of 2010, the Compounded Annual Growth Rate (CAGR) over this $n = 3$ year period is $(19,500 / 10,000)^{1/3} - 1 = 24.9\%$. In other words, if the growth rate over the three years was constant each year, it would be an annual growth rate of 24.9%. To prove this, we can see that \$10,000 x 1.249 x 1.249 x 1.249 = \$19,500. Note that this example has balances for four years (2007, 2008, 2009, and 2010), but only three years for computing growth. In summary, the CAGR is not the average (arithmetic mean) annual return but rather the geometric mean return.

The Excel functions IRR(*values_range*) and XIRR(*values_range, dates_range*) can be used to calculate the CAGR. IRR is for periodic returns and XIRR allows the user to define a schedule of cash flows. Both functions require at least one positive and one negative value. If this function is not available in Excel and returns the #NAME? error, install and load the Analysis ToolPak add-in.

See *financial performance metrics, geometric mean, Internal Rate of Return (IRR).*

Computer Aided Design (CAD) – A combination of hardware and software that enables engineers and architects to design everything from furniture to airplanes.

In addition to the software, CAD systems usually require a high-quality graphics monitor, a mouse, light pen, or digitizing tablet for drawing, and a special printer or plotter for printing design specifications. CAD systems allow an engineer to view a design from any angle and to zoom in or out for close-ups and long-distance views. In addition, the computer keeps track of design dependencies so that when the engineer changes one value, all other values that depend on it are automatically changed. Until the mid 1980s, CAD systems were specially constructed computers. Today, CAD software runs on general-purpose workstations and personal computers.

See *Computer Aided Design/Computer Aided Manufacturing (CAD/CAM), Computer Numerical Control (CNC), New Product Development (NPD).*

Computer Aided Design/Computer Aided Manufacturing (CAD/CAM) – Computer systems used to design and manufacture products.

An engineer can use the system to both design a product and to generate the instructions that can be used to control a manufacturing process.

See *Computer Aided Design (CAD).*

Computer Aided Inspection (CAI) – A system for performing inspection through the use of computer hardware and software technologies.

CAI tools are categorized as either contact methods or non-contact methods. Since contact methods involve touching the surface of a product, these methods are undesirable where contamination is a concern. Contact methods are slower and cost less than non-contact methods. Non-contact methods were used for about 40% of CAI in 2003.

Contact methods – Coordinate Measuring Machines (CMMs) use a Computer Numerically Controlled (CNC) mechanical probe to inspect parts to an accuracy of as little as 0.0002 inches. However, the CMM probe may damage or deform a product's surface. With many sample points or complex product contours, CMMs may be too slow to support the desired product inspection rate.

Non-contact methods/Vision systems – A camera is used to take a video image of a part. The image is processed by software and electronic hardware to compare it against a reference template. The vision system determines the placement, size, and shape of holes and the presence of part features. The snapshot of the image usually requires a strobe or high intensity light to produce an adequate part to background contrast.

Non-contact methods/Laser-scan micrometers – These systems use reflected laser light to measure part dimensions and are used to inspect single dimensions on highly repetitive work such as intervals, diameters, widths, heights, and linearity.

Acknowledgments: This entry was adapted from material provided by MOT 04 student, Mr. Brian Dye.

See *inspection*.

Computer Aided Manufacturing (CAM) – See *Computer Aided Design (CAD), Computer Aided Design/Computer Aided Manufacturing (CAD/CAM), Computer Numerical Control (CNC)*.

Computer Integrated Manufacturing (CIM) – See *Computer Aided Design (CAD), Computer Aided Design/Computer Aided Manufacturing (CAD/CAM), Computer Numerical Control (CNC)*.

Computer Numerical Control (CNC) – A type of controller that is typically found on machining centers and other machine tools.

CNC machines typically cut and form metal. A CNC is comprised of a machine tool used to turn, drill or grind different types of parts, and a computer that controls the sequence of processes performed by the machine. Robots that are not machine tools are not considered CNC. Note that not all computer-controlled machines are CNC.

Acknowledgments: MOT 04 students Steven Gort, Keith McLaughlin, David Mitchell, Steven Siegel, Steven Smith, and Myra Urness contributed to this entry.

See *Computer Aided Design (CAD)*.

computer simulation – See *simulation*.

concurrent engineering – A systematic approach to the integrated, simultaneous design of products and their related processes, including manufacture and support.

This approach is intended to cause the developer, from the outset, to consider all elements of the product lifecycle from concept through disposal, including quality control, cost, scheduling, and user requirements. CE is synonymous with simultaneous engineering and integrated product development. Typically, concurrent engineering involves the formation of cross functional teams. This allows engineers and managers of different disciplines to work together simultaneously in developing product and process designs.

See *cross functional team, Integrated Product Development (IPD), New Product Development (NPD), Quality Function Deployment (QFD), simultaneous engineering, waterfall scheduling*.

conference room pilot – An approach for testing and implementing a new information system in which a group of people test the system with a test database.

The conference room pilot uses realistic test data, but the system is not "live," which means that production data is not changed during the pilot test and no decisions are made that affect actual operations.

confidence interval – A range of values that will contain the true mean for a random variable with a user-specified level of confidence based on a given sample of data.

Given a set of $n > 30$ random observations on a random variable, the confidence interval on the true mean is given by $\overline{x} \pm z_{\alpha/2} s / \sqrt{n}$, where $\overline{x}$ is the sample mean, s is the sample standard deviation, and $z_{\alpha/2} = F^{-1}(1 - \alpha/2)$ is the z value associated with probability $\alpha/2$. If n random samples are taken many times, this interval will capture the true mean about $100 \cdot \alpha / 2$ percent of the time. A detailed description of the procedure follows:

Step 0. **Define the parameters.** Specify the number of observations (n) that have been collected, the estimated size of the population (N), and the confidence level parameter (α). If the size of N is large but unknown, use an extremely large number (e.g., $N = 10^{10}$).

Step 1. **Compute the sample mean and standard deviation.** Compute the sample mean $\bar{x}$ and sample standard deviation s from the n observations.

Step 2. **Find the z or t value.**

When $n < 30$, use the $t_{\alpha/2, n-1}$ value from a student-t table or the Excel statement TINV(α, $n -1$). (Note: The arguments in this Excel function are correct. The Excel functions TINV and NORMSINV are inconsistent in how they handle the probability parameter (α). TINV returns the probability associated with the two-tailed Student's t-distribution.) When $n \geq 30$, use the $z_{\alpha/2}$ value from a normal table or the Excel statement NORMSINV($1 - \alpha / 2$).

Step 3. **Compute the half-width.** Compute the half-width of the confidence interval using $h = z_{\alpha/2} s / \sqrt{n}$ (replace $z_{\alpha/2}$ with $t_{\alpha/2, n-1}$ when $n < 30$). If the sample size n is large relative to the total population N (e.g., $n / N > 0.05$), use $h = z_{\alpha/2} s \sqrt{1/n - 1/N}$ instead. The term $\sqrt{1/n - 1/N}$ is called the finite population correction factor. For $n \geq 30$, the half-width can also be found using the Excel function CONFIDENCE(α, s, n). This Excel function should not be used when $n < 30$.

Step 4. **Write the confidence interval.** Write the $100(1 - \alpha)\%$ confidence interval as ($\bar{x} \pm h$).

Confidence intervals are a useful concept based on the central limit theorem and do not require any assumptions about the distribution of x. The entry on sample size calculations has more detail on this subject.

The paper "Estimating Confidence Intervals and Required Sample Sizes" and the Excel workbook "confidence intervals.xls" are on the ***OMWW CD*** available from www.ClamshellBeachPress.com. ◉

See *ANOVA (Analysis of Variance)*, *central limit theorem*, *dollar unit sampling*, *normal distribution*, *sample size calculation*, *sampling*, *simulation*, *standard deviation*, *t-test*.

configuration control – See *configuration management*.

configuration management – The process of defining and controlling the information that defines a system.

Configuration control includes all of the activities needed to control the changes to a configuration after it has been formally documented. Configuration control includes the evaluation, coordination, approval, or rejection of changes.

The best configuration management (CM) process is one that can (1) accommodate change, (2) accommodate reuse of proven standards and best practices, (3) assure that all requirements remain clear, concise, and valid, (4) communicate promptly and precisely, and (5) assure that the results conform in each case. CM includes several elements: requirements management, change management, release management, data management, records management, document control, and library management. CM provides the infrastructure that enables an organization to "change faster and document better." CM also accommodates change and keeps requirements clear, concise, valid, and synchronized. A strong CM process is the foundation of a sound business process infrastructure. Adapted from the home page of The Institute of Configuration Management Institute (www.icmhq.com).

See *New Product Development (NPD)*.

configurator – A software tool (usually with a web interface) that allows customers, order entry people, or sales people to create a customized order or model number by selecting various product features from menus.

Ideally, a configurator will (1) encourage customers to select standard, high-margin combinations of features, (2) prevent customers from selecting prohibitive combinations of features, (3) discourage customers from selecting low margin (or negative margin) combinations, and (4) create a manufacturing order that can be sent electronically to manufacturing. In some cases, the configurator creates instructions for automated equipment. Configurators might contain many expert rules and might draw heavily on science, engineering, and manufacturing expertise. In conclusion, the ideal configurator is easy for the customer to use, creates product configurations that customers want, and guides customers to product configurations that the firm can make and sell profitably.

For example, mycereal.com, General Mills' custom blended breakfast cereal, had a configurator that included tremendous amounts of food science so that customers would get healthy food and tasty portions. Lifetouch provides software to high schools so that they can configure their own student ID cards, populate a database with student photos, and then send a file to the firm's ID card manufacturing facility.

See *Configure to Order (CTO), Engineer to Order (ETO), mass customization.*

Configure to Order (CTO) – A customer interface strategy that adjusts parameters or adds modules to a product in response to a customer's order.

In a Configure to Order system, a firm sells standard products that require parameter adjustments or modules to be added in response to a customer order. Examples include setting the height of a seat for a riding mower, selecting the language option for a software package, or setting some customer-specific parameters for a medical device. Some people call this re-configure to order. The entry on "Respond to Order" discusses a number of similar customer-interface strategies.

See *configurator, Respond to Order (RTO).*

conformance quality – The degree to which the product or service meets the design specifications or standards.

Conformance quality is generally measured by the yield rate (the percentage of units started that are not defective) or the scrap rate (the percentage of units started that have to be discarded because they are defective).

For example, marketing and new product development have set a performance standard (a specification limit) that a new wristwatch should be able to survive in 100 meters of water. However, the manufacturing process is sometimes fails to properly apply the glue around the back of the watch, which results in 10% of all watches failing to meet the standard. In this example, the yield rate is 90% and the percent defective is 10%.

See *performance quality, product design quality, quality, yield.*

congestion pricing – The practice of charging a higher price for a service during the peak demand periods in order to discourage arrivals to the system.

For example, the city of Singapore assesses a very high charge to drivers who enter the downtown areas during the workday. This practice is now being used in many large metropolitan areas in the world. Similar examples can be found in telephone rates, electricity (power) usage, computer usage, restaurants, and other service businesses.

See *yield management.*

conjoint analysis – An analytical marketing research technique that measures the tradeoffs made by respondents among product attributes.

Conjoint analysis is a useful tool for both product concept generation and evaluation by rating product attributes in terms of their importance in the market. The method involves the measurement of the collective effects of two or more independent variables (e.g., color, size, ease of use, cost, etc.) on the classification of a dependent variable ("overall liking," purchase intention, "best buy," or any other evaluative measurement). The stimulus is a combination of product-attribute. Various mixed and matched product attributes are put together and rated by the respondent. For example, does the respondent prefer a large, powerful, spacious car that is relatively expensive in its operation, or one that is smaller, less powerful, but more economic to operate.

Once the unique product combinations are established, conjoint studies typically collect data via the use of one of the following:

1. A paired-comparison methodology, where each of the hypothetical products is directly compared to another product and one of the products is selected over the other. For example, with 16 unique products, a total of 120 binary choices are required.
2. A ranking methodology, where product configurations are rank-ordered relative to preferences of the respondent. This is probably the most common method for collecting conjoint data.

For the paired-comparisons model, a telephone survey is often difficult because of the amount of time required to go through each of the possible comparisons. Since there are a significant number of repeats in the presentation of the description for each option, the amount of time required to go through the entire process on the telephone is prohibitive.

Adapted from mrainc.com/trad_conj.html, March 18, 2005

See *Analytical Hierarchy Process (AHP).*

---

consignment inventory – Stock held by a customer that is owned by the supplier.

Payment on consignment inventory is usually made when stock is sold or used by the customer. Here are some examples: (1) Many retailers for Christmas craft items will only pay their suppliers when the craft items are sold. (2) Medtronic has many pacemakers in hospital inventories which are still owned by Medtronic until sold to a patient. (3) Some manufacturers of fasteners will make their products available to assemblers and not require that their customers pay until the fasteners are used.

See *Vendor Managed Inventory (VMI)*.

consortium – An association or coalition of two or more individuals, companies, firms, or not-for-profit organizations (or any combination thereof) that pool resources such as buying power, research capability, manufacturing capability, libraries, or information to achieve a common goal.

Acknowledgments: CSOM MBA students Dwight Porter, James Sonterre, and John Tiedeman contributed to this entry. This content was adapted from Wikipedia, May 3, 2008.

Constant WIP – See *CONWIP*.

consumable goods – An item or product that is used up (consumed) in a relatively short period of time.

In the economics literature, consumable goods are defined as products that are used up fairly quickly and therefore have to be replaced frequently. This is in contrast to durable or capital goods such as cars, furniture, and houses that people keep for a long time and have a useful life of more than five years.

In the Maintenance, Repair, and Operations (MRO) context, consumables are items purchased by a firm, but do not become part of the product sold to customers. For example, 3M sandpaper might be used for final surface conditioning of a product. Other examples include paper, oil, and grease.

In a marketing context, many firms make more money selling consumable products than they do selling capital goods or other products. The most famous example of this is Gillette, which almost gives away razors in order to sell razor blades.

consumer packaged goods – Consumable goods such as food and beverages, footwear and apparel, tobacco, and cleaning products.

Some examples of consumer packaged goods include breakfast cereal (such as General Mill's Cheerios) and soap (such as Proctor and Gamble's Ivory soap).

consumer's risk – The risk of accepting a lot of defective products.

More formally, consumer's risk is the probability of accepting a lot with a defect level equal to the LTPD for a given sampling plan. The consumer suffers when this occurs because a lot with unacceptable quality was accepted. This is called a Type II error. The symbol β is commonly used for the Type II risk.

See *Acceptable Quality Level (AQL)*, *acceptance sampling*, *Lot Tolerance Percent Defective (LTPD)*, *operating characteristic curve*, *producer's risk*, *Type I and II errors*.

container – See *shipping container*.

continuous flow – Producing and moving small batches (ideally with a lotsize of one unit) through a series of processing steps with almost no inventory and almost no waiting between steps.

See *batch-and-queue*, *discrete manufacturing*, *lean thinking*, *one-piece flow*, *product layout*.

continuous improvement – See *kaizen*, *lean thinking*, *Six Sigma*, *Total Quality Management (TQM)*.

continuous process – A process that makes only one product with dedicated equipment and never needs to handle changeovers (setups).

Examples of a continuous process include oil refining, paper making, and chemical processing.

See *batch process*, *discrete manufacturing*, *setup cost*, *setup time*.

continuous replenishment planning – The practice of working with distribution channel members to change from distributor-generated purchase orders to replenishment based on actual sales and forecast data.

The principal goal of continuous replenishment planning is to reduce the cost of producing and moving product through the vendor-retailer supply chain. The object is for all stages of the supply chain to operate with greater knowledge of downstream inventory conditions, thereby allowing for a synchronized flow of product from the manufacturer through point-of-sale. Source: Vergin and Barr (1999).

See *Collaborative Planning Forecasting and Replenishment (CPFR)*, *Efficient Consumer Response*.

continuous review system – A system for managing an inventory that compares the inventory position (on-hand plus on-order less allocated) with the reorder point for every transaction and places a replenishment order when the position is less than the reorder point.

See *inventory position, periodic review system, reorder point.*

contract manufacturer – An outsourced supplier providing manufacturing under an agreement with the customer.

Porter (2000) noted that some of the most prevalent sources of this friction in a contract manufacturing relationship include:
- Traditional financial metrics.
- Difficulty defining core competencies.
- Fear of losing intellectual capital and expertise.
- Difficulty finding qualified manufacturing-services companies.
- Difficulty attracting good contract manufacturers for less desirable programs.
- Difficulty understanding and documenting capabilities of contract manufacturers.
- Difficulty earning most-favored-customer status.
- Necessity of managing risk exposure.
- Trouble with technology and/or knowledge transfer.
- Unforeseeable problems (such as parts shortages).

See *Business Process Outsourcing, Original Equipment Manufacturer (OEM), outsourcing, supply chain management.*

control chart – A graphical tool used to plot the statistics from samples of a process over time and to keep the system in control. ✪

If all points are within the upper and lower statistical control limits, variation may be ascribed to "common causes" and the process is said to be "in control." If points fall outside the limits, it is an indication that "special causes" of variation are occurring and the process is said to be "out of control." Eliminating the special causes first and then reducing common causes can improve quality. Control charts are based on the work of Shewhart (1939).

See *c-chart, common cause variation, p-chart, process capability and performance, r-chart, seven tools of quality, Six Sigma, special cause variation, specification limits, Statistical Process Control (SPC), tampering, x-bar chart.*

control plan – A formal document that defines how an organization will continue to benefit from an organizational intervention, such as a Six Sigma project.

When a process improvement project has been completed, it is extremely important that the organization "sustain the gains." This is often difficult given the normal organizational "entropy," where the system tends to fall back into the old state of disorder. A good control plan includes the following elements:
- **Procedure** – What solutions were implemented to attain the project goals? What control device is in place?
- **Nature of control** – How does the control measure sustain the gain? What is the control measure for early detection?
- **What to check** – What does the responsible party inspect/observe? What are the failure modes?
- **Action/Reaction** – What does the responsible party do if the situation is out of control?
- **Responsible party** – Name and function. See the *RACI Matrix* entry for a methodology for doing this.

If statistical process control is appropriate, the following data items should be specified for each Key Process Output Variable (KPOV): Target value, lower specification limit, upper specification limit, C_{pk}, and the measurement system used to collect the data.

See *RACI Matrix, Six Sigma.*

CONWIP – An approach for manufacturing planning and control that maintains a constant work-in-process inventory in the system.

With CONWIP (Spearman, Hopp, and Woodruff, 1989), every time the last step in the process completes one unit, the first step in the process is given permission to start one unit. As a result, CONWIP maintains a constant WIP inventory. This is similar to the Theory of Constraints "drum buffer rope" (DBR) concept, except that CONWIP does not send a signal from the bottleneck, but rather sends the signal from the final step in the process. This concept is similar to a JIT pull system, except that CONWIP does not need to have buffers (kanbans) between each pair of workcenters. Given that CONWIP does not require the firm to identify the bottleneck and does not need to implement any type of kanban system between workcenters, it is clearly easier to operate than many other systems. CONWIP can be implemented with a simple visual control system that has the final operation signal the first operation every time a unit is completed. CONWIP can be applied at almost any level – at a machine, a workcenter, a plant, or even an entire supply chain. Some research suggests that CONWIP is superior to both DBR and JIT in terms of system performance (inventory, capacity, etc.).

See *blocking, Drum-Buffer-Rope (DBR), pacemaker, POLCA (Paired-cell Overlapping Loops of Cards with Authorization), pull systems, Theory of Constraints (TOC), Work-in-Process (WIP) inventory.*

co-opetition (co-competition) – A blending of the words cooperation and competition to suggest that competing firms can sometimes work together for mutual benefit; sometimes called co-opetition, co-competition, or coopetition.

Cooperation with suppliers, customers and firms producing complementary or related products can lead to expansion of the market and the formation of new business relationships, perhaps even the creation of new forms of business. An example can be found in group buying where multiple, normally competitive, buying group members leverage the buying power of the group to gain reduced prices.

This concept was developed in the book *Co-opetition* (Brandenburger & Nalebuff, 1996) by Adam Brandenburger (Harvard Business School) and Barry Nalebuff (Yale School of Management). Apparently, Ray Noorda, the founder of Novell, coined the term. The concept and term have been taken up enthusiastically in the computer industry where strategic alliances are common in order to develop new products and markets, particularly between software and hardware firms. For example, some industry observers have suggested that Apple and Microsoft need each other and, in fact, are involved in co-opetition.

See *game theory.*

co-opt – See *stakeholder analysis.*

co-packer – A supplier (outsource partner) that produces goods under the customer's brand.

The term "co-packer" is most frequently used in a consumer packaged goods context, but is also used in other industries. For example, Ecolab, a manufacturer of a variety of industrial cleaning products, uses co-packers to manufacture many of its cleaning agents that require very specialized chemical processes.

See *outsourcing.*

core capabilities – See *core competence.*

core competence – Skills that enable an organization to differentiate its products and services from its competitors; nearly synonymous with distinctive competence. ✪

Coyne, Hall, and Clifford (1997) defined a core competence in the *McKinsey Quarterly* as "a combination of complementary skills and knowledge bases embedded in a group or team that results in the ability to execute one or more critical processes to a world-class standard." This definition is similar but not identical to the above definition. Nearly all definitions of core competence include the point that a core competence is an attribute of the organization and not just an attribute of a single individual in that organization.

A core competence is unique, hard to copy, and can lead the firm into new products and markets. Some authors make a distinction between core competencies and distinctive competence. They define core competence as the basic product and process technologies and skills that all firms need to compete in an industry, and distinctive competence as the set of technologies and skills that a firm uses to differentiate itself in the market. However, it appears that many authors now use the terms almost synonymously. Knowledge of a firm's core competence can lead its management team to find new products and guide its thinking about outsourcing.

Many marketing experts and students tend to define a core competence as a differentiated product. However, a core competence is not a product or service, but rather the processes, abilities, and unique attributes (differentiated processes) that allow the organization to develop and deliver differentiated "core products."

Three requirements for a valid distinctive competence are:
1. It must be unique and present a barrier to entry for new competitors.
2. The unique competence must offer real value to the marketplace. Something being merely unique without offering value is not a distinctive competence.
3. The unique competence must be credible in the marketplace. Its existence and value have to be accepted and believed.

A popular phrase in many MBA classrooms is "An organization should never outsource its core competence." With that said, it is interesting to see how many firms find that they are outsourcing today what they defined as their core competence less than five years ago. It may just be that core competences, like strategies, tend to change and adapt over time as the markets, products, and technologies change. Clearly, an organization's set of core competences cannot remain stagnant in a rapidly changing environment.

In this author's experience, most executives cannot identify their core competence when asked. However, one insightful way to help an organization identify its core competence is to ask the question, "What would keep a competitor from capturing 100% of your market share tomorrow?" This "barriers to entry" question usually identifies the organization's core competence. Barriers to entry can include:

- Proprietary product or process technology
- Product differentiation (often based on process differentiation)
- Economies of scale (that lead to a lower cost structure)
- Brand equity
- Switching cost
- Government protection, subsidies, and/or patent
- Access to raw materials (special relationship or location)
- Access to customers (good location)

Another good question to ask to identify a core competence is, "Why do customers buy your product instead of another product?" This is the customer's view of core competence.

The book **Beyond the Core: Expand Your Market without Abandoning Your Roots** by Zook (2004) emphasizes the need for firms to stay close to their core products and core competence. His book offers a systematic approach for choosing among a range of possible "adjacency moves," while always staying close to the core products and core competency.

See *focused factory, operations strategy, outsourcing, resource based view.*

corporate portal – A web-based system that allows businesses to make internal (IS/IT) systems or information available in a single location and format.

Portals are often used on the Internet to allow access to internal information by providing a secure connection (dashboard) for employees, vendors, or customers.

See *balanced scorecard, dashboard, extranet, intranet.*

correlation – A measure of the strength of linear association between two variables.

If two variables are correlated, they tend to vary together. In other words, when one is higher than its mean, the other one is too; when one is lower than its mean, the other is too. Correlation is always in the range $(-1, 1)$, where a negative sign shows an inverse relationship. The coefficient of determination (also known as r-squared), is the square of the correlation coefficient. For example, if the correlation is $r = -0.7$, the coefficient of determination is $r^2 = 0.49$. The r-squared value is often described as the percent of the variation "explained."

Correlation is necessary for causation. While correlation may sometimes infer causation, correlation does not mean causation. For example, shoe size and reading skill are correlated. This does not mean that large feet causes better reading. It simply means that young children do not read as well as adults. For another example, roosters might make noise at sunrise, but the rooster's noise does not cause the sun to rise.

See *linear regression.*

cost driver – See *Activity Based Costing.*

cost of goods sold – All direct costs incurred in producing the product or service.

Cost of goods sold usually includes direct materials, incoming transportation, direct labor cost, production facilities, and other overhead labor and expenses that are part of the manufacturing process. It does not include indirect costs such as administration, marketing, and selling costs that cannot be directly attributed to producing the product. This is sometimes called "cost of goods," "cost of sales," or "cost of products sold."

See *ABC classification, gross profit margin.*

cost of quality – A framework coined by quality leader Mr. Phillip Crosby and used to measure all quality-related costs; now called the "price of non-conformance." ✪

The cost of quality concept was popularized by Phillip Crosby, a well-known author and consultant, who wrote a book by the same name. Crosby focuses on four absolutes:

- Quality is defined as conformance to requirements.
- The system for causing quality is prevention, not appraisal.
- The performance standard is zero defects.
- The measurement of quality is the cost of quality (now called the price of nonconformance).

More recently, Crosby has replaced "the cost of quality" with the "price of nonconformance" in response to quality professionals who did not like the older term. This author prefers the term "the cost of bad quality."

The price of nonconformance assigns an economic value to all waste caused by poor quality. Examples of the price of nonconformance include wasted materials, wasted capacity, wasted labor time, expediting, inventory, customer complaints, service recovery, downtime, reconciliation, and warranty.

According to Feigenbaum (1983), the cost of quality framework includes these four elements:

Prevention costs – Cost of designing quality into the product and process. This includes product design, process design, work selection, and worker training. Some authors also add the cost of assessing and improving process capability. Many firms find that this cost is hardest to measure.

Appraisal costs – Cost of inspection, testing, auditing, and design reviews for both products and procedures.

Internal failure costs – Cost of rework, scrap, wasted labor cost, wasted lost machine capacity, and poor morale. Lost capacity for a bottleneck process can result in lost gross margin as well.

External failure costs – Warranty, repair, lost gross margin/refunds, customer support, lost customer good will, damage to the brand, damage to channel partnerships, law suits.

An important teaching point with this framework is that most organizations need to move the costs up the list. In other words, it is usually better to have internal failure costs than external, better to have appraisal than internal failure, and better to have prevention than appraisal. A couple of metaphors are helpful here. It is better to avoid smoking (prevention) than to try to heal cancer. It is better to avoid toxic waste than to try to clean it up.

See *appraisal cost, inspection, process capability and performance, quality*.

Council of Logistics Management (CLM) – See *Council of Supply Chain Management Professionals (CSCMP)*.

Council of Supply Chain Management Professionals (CSCMP) – A professional society with the mission "to lead the evolving Supply Chain Management profession by developing, advancing, and disseminating Supply Chain knowledge and research."

Founded in 1963, the Council of Supply Chain Management Professionals (CSCMP) is an association for individuals involved in supply chain management. CSCMP provides educational, career development, and networking opportunities to its members. CSCMP was originally founded as the National Council of Physical Distribution Management (NCPDM) in January 1963. NCPDM was formed by a visionary group of educators, consultants, and managers who envisioned the integration of transportation, warehousing, and inventory as the future of the discipline. At that time, physical distribution was just beginning to edge its way into the corporate lexicon and make its considerable presence felt in the business community. In 1985, recognizing the growing field of logistics, the association's focus broadened as it changed its name to the Council of Logistics Management (CLM). It stayed that way until 2004 when CLM's Executive Committee voted to become CSCMP, effective in 2005.

CSCMP publishes a number of trade journals and the academic journal *The Journal of Business Logistics*. The website for CSCMP is www.cscmp.org.

See *Operations Management (OM)*.

counting tolerance – The margin for error used when counting items in an inventory.

An item count is considered wrong only when the count is off by more than the "counting tolerance," which is usually a percentage defined for each category of items. High value items will usually have a counting tolerance of zero; very low value items might have a counting tolerance of 10% or more.

See *cycle counting*.

C_p – See *process capability and performance*.

CPFR – See *Collaborative Planning Forecasting and Replenishment*.

C_{pk} – See *process capability and performance*.

CPM – See *Critical Path Method (CPM)*.

CRAFT – See *facility layout*.

critical chain – The set of tasks that determines the overall duration of a project, taking into account both precedence and resource dependencies.

The critical chain is similar to the critical path except that it goes one major step further and factors in resource constraints. The steps in the critical chain approach are as follows:

1. Compute the early start, early finish, late start, late finish, and slack times just as is normally done with the critical path method. The path through the network with the longest total time is called the critical path. The critical path is the path (or paths) with the shortest slack.

2. Create a detailed schedule, starting from the current date and moving forward in time. When a task is complete, begin the next task in the precedence network if the required resources are available. When a resource becomes available assign it to the task that has the least amount of slack time as computed in step 1. Continue this process until the schedule is complete for all activities. This new schedule is called the critical chain and will be longer than the critical path, which only considers the precedence constraints. The critical chain will still follow the precedence constraints, but will never have any resource used more than its capacity.

3. Strategically add time buffers to protect activities on the critical chain from starting late. Non-critical chain activities that precede the critical chain should be planned to be done early so that the critical chain is protected from disruption.

The consulting/software firm Realization (www.Realization.com) markets software called Concerto that implements critical chain concepts in Microsoft Project.

See *critical path, Critical Path Method (CPM), Earned Value Management (EVM), Project Evaluation and Review Technique (PERT), project management, slack time, Theory of Constraints (TOC)*.

critical incidents method – An approach for identifying the underlying dimensions of customer satisfaction.

The critical incidents method involves collecting a large number of customer (or worker) complaints and compliments and then analyzing them to identify the underlying quality dimension (timeliness, friendliness, etc.). It is important to note that in analyzing a complaint or a complement, it does not matter if it is a negative (complaint) or a positive (compliment); the goal is to simply identify the underlying dimensions of quality, regardless if they are satisfiers or dissatisfiers.

This technique is a very useful approach for identifying the key dimensions of service quality for use on a customer satisfaction survey. This technique can also be used in other contexts such as job analysis to identify the critical dimensions of worker satisfaction.

See *service quality, Voice of the Customer (VOC)*.

critical path – The longest path through a project-planning network. ✪

Management should focus its attention only on critical path activities and not allow non-critical activities to become critical.

The only way to speed up a project is to reduce the task time for activities along the critical path. This is sometimes called "crashing." Crashing non-critical activities will not improve the project completion date. A method for finding the critical path is presented in the discussion of CPM.

Activities not on the critical path can become critical if they are delayed. This suggests that project managers need to (1) constantly monitor project schedules and (2) practice good risk management to prepare for contingencies.

It is possible for a network to have two or more critical paths.

See *critical chain, Critical Path Method (CPM), Failure Mode and Effects Analysis (FMEA), project management*.

Critical Path Method (CPM) – An approach for project planning and scheduling that focuses on the longest path through the project planning network. ✪

Project scheduling begins with the work breakdown structure that defines the "tree" of activities that make up the project. Each task at the bottom of the tree is then defined in terms of a name, task time, resources (people, machines, money, etc.), and a set of precedence relationships. The set of precedence relationships for a task is the set of tasks that need to be completed before the task can be started.

The simple example below illustrates the scheduling process. This project network has five tasks (A-F) with the times (in days) noted by each task. The scheduling process has two passes: a forward pass to create the early start and early finish times and a backward pass to create the last finish and last start times for each task.

The forward pass begins with task A, which has an early start at the beginning of day 1 (ES = 1) and an early finish at the end of day 1 (EF = 1). Task B cannot start until task A is completed and therefore has an early start at the beginning of day 2 (ES = 2). Task B requires 2 days and has an early finish at the end of day 3 (EF = 3). The forward pass continues until every node is assigned both an early start (ES) and early finish (EF).

The backward pass begins with the desired completion date for the project, which is the late finish for the last task (task E). The required completion date for this project is the end of day 11 (i.e., LF = 11). Planning backwards from this completion date, task E has a late start date at the beginning of day 10 (LS = 10). Continuing this backward pass creates the late finish and late start for all nodes. The notation in parentheses beside each task node is (Early Start, Late Start, Early Finish, Late Finish) = (ES, LS, EF, LF).

The slack for any task is the difference between the early start and the late start, which is always the same as the difference between the early finish and late finish. The critical path is the path through the network that has the smallest slack. In this example, the critical path is A→D→E.

CPM project network example

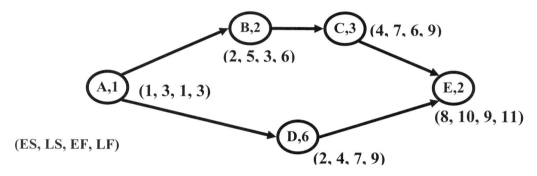

Management should prioritize tasks along the critical path for both resource allocation and crashing. When a resource (e.g., person, tool, or machine) becomes free, a good rule for re-allocating this resource is to use the minimum slack rule, which simply assigns the resource to the open task that has the least slack. This is essentially the same process used to identify the critical chain.

If it is necessary to reduce the total project time, the project manager should find the task on the critical path that can be reduced (crashed) at the lowest cost per unit time, make the change, and then repeat the crashing process until the desired project completion time is achieved or until the cost exceeds the benefit. Crashing non-critical activities will not improve the project completion date.

Activities not on the critical path can become critical if they are delayed. This suggests that project managers need to (1) constantly monitor project schedules, and (2) practice good risk management to prepare for contingencies. Note that it is possible for a project network to have two or more critical paths.

The above figure uses the "activity-on-node" approach. The alternative "activity-on-arc" approach is presented in many textbooks, but is more difficult to understand and is only rarely used in practice.

At the time of this writing, the two best known project scheduling packages are Microsoft Project and Primavera (www.primeavera.com). Project is best for smaller projects and Primavera is best for larger projects. Many other commercial packages are available.

See *CPM, critical chain, critical path, Gantt Chart, Project Evaluation and Review Technique (PERT), project management, slack time, work breakdown structure (WBS)*.

critical ratio – See *newsvendor model*.

Critical To Quality (CTQ) – Key measurable characteristics of a product or process that require performance standards or specification limits to satisfy the customer (internal or external) requirements; also called Key Process Output Variable (KPOV).

CTQ may include the upper and lower specification limits or any other factors related to the product or service. A CTQ usually must be interpreted from a qualitative customer statement to an actionable, quantitative business specification. CTQs are what the customer expects of a product. The customer's requirements must be expressed in measurable terms using tools such as DFMEA.

Here is a simple example of customer CTQ:

Area: Book Publishing
Customer Quote: "I can't tolerate any typographical errors in books I purchase."
CTQ Name: Typographic Quality
CTQ Measure: Number of typographical errors
CTQ Specification: Zero typographical errors
Defect: Any typographical errors
Unit: A word
Opportunity: Words per book
Defects: 2 typographical errors
Units: 125,000 (500 words/page x 250 pages/book)
Opportunities: 1 per word
Process Sigma: 5.659 (Using Sigma calculator at http://www.isixsigma.com)
   See *Key Process Output Variable (KPOV)*, *Six Sigma*, *Voice of the Customer (VOC)*.

CRM – See *Customer Relationship Management (CRM)*.

cross functional team – A group of employees from different parts of an organization who come together and use their different viewpoints and skills to address a problem.

Many organizational problems cannot be solved by a single business function. For example, a new product development project might require expertise from marketing, sales, manufacturing, engineering, etc. Cross functional teams are often the best approach for addressing these problems. A cross functional team may be self-directed or directed by a sponsor (or sponsors) within the organization. Cross functional teams are a common component of concurrent engineering, agile software development, and lean sigma projects.

Acknowledgments: CEMBA 10 students Chas Anderson, Grant Bistram, Robert Doty, Oscar Hernandez, Yevette Jaszczak, Vasanti Mudkanna, and Jeff Thaler contributed to this entry.

See *agile software development*, *concurrent engineering*, *lean sigma*, *Quality Function Deployment (QFD)*.

cross-docking – A distribution strategy that moves products directly from incoming trucks to outgoing trucks without placing inventory on shelves in the warehouse or distribution center.

Products that are good candidates for cross-docking have high demand, standardized packaging, and no special handling needs (e.g., security or refrigeration). This is a common strategy for retail distribution where trucks carry large shipments from factories to the cross-dock facility, which loads other trucks with mixed assortments to send to retail stores.

Cross-docking has many advantages over traditional warehouse facilities, including:

- Reduced inventory and carrying cost. The firm replaces inventory with information and coordination.
- Reduced transportation cost. For Less than Truck Load (LTL) and small package carriers, cross-docking is a way to reduce transportation costs by consolidating shipments to achieve truck-load quantities.
- Reduced labor cost. Cross-docking avoids costly moves to and from shelves in the warehouse.
- Improves customer service. Cross-docked shipments typically spend less than 24 hours in a cross-dock.

The figure below shows a cross-docking process with a top-down view of eight trucks.

Napolitano (2000) proposed the following classification scheme:

Manufacturing cross-docking for receiving and consolidating inbound supplies to support Just-in-Time manufacturing. For example, a manufacturer might lease a warehouse close to its plant, and use it to prep subassemblies or consolidate kits of parts. Because demand for the parts is known, say from the output of an MRP system, there is no need to maintain stock.

Distributor cross-docking for consolidating inbound products from different vendors into a multi-SKU pallet, which is delivered as soon as the last product is received. For example, computer distributors often source components from different manufacturers and consolidate them into one shipment in merge-in-transit centers, before delivering them to the customer.

Transportation cross-docking for consolidating shipments from different shippers in the LTL and small package industries to gain economies of scale. For small package carriers, material movement in the cross-dock is by a network of conveyors and sorters; for LTL carriers it is mostly by manual handling and forklifts.

Retail cross-docking for receiving product from multiple vendors and sorting onto outbound trucks for different stores. Cross-docking has been cited as a major reason Wal-Mart surpassed Kmart in retail sales in the 1980s.

Opportunistic cross-docking which is transferring an item directly from the receiving dock to the shipping dock to meet a known demand in any type of warehouse.

The common elements to all of these operations are consolidation and extremely short cycle times, usually less than a day. The short cycle time is possible because the destination for an item is known before or determined upon receipt.

Adapted from web.nps.navy.mil/~krgue/Teaching/teaching.html.

See *Advanced Shipping Notification (ASN), logistics, Over/Short/Damaged Report (OSD Report), Transportation Management System (TMS), Warehouse Management System (WMS)*.

cross-training – Training workers in several different areas or functions outside of their normal job responsibilities.

Having workers learn a wide variety of tasks has many advantages including:

Increased flexibility – Workers can provide backup when the primary worker is unavailable or when the demand exceeds the capacity. This makes it easy to improve flow and reduce inventory. This increased flexibility allows the line workers to dynamically balance the line without any help from an industrial engineer.

Process improvement – When workers have a broader understanding of the organization, they can be more knowledgeable about how to improve it.

Develops human capital – Cross-trained workers are more valuable to the company and often find more satisfaction in their job. Crosstraining is often an investment in the future for a firm.

See *cellular manufacturing, facility layout, job enlargement, job rotation, lean thinking, learning organization, line balancing, socio-technical design, workforce agility*.

CTO – See *Configure to Order (CTO)*.

CTQ – See *Critical To Quality (CTQ)*.

cumulative leadtime – The critical path leadtime (longest) required to purchase material and create a product to offer to the market; also known as the stacked leadtime.

The cumulative leadtime usually includes the longest time required to purchase (procure), fabricate (cut, mold, weld, finish, etc.), assemble, test, package, and ship a product. The customer leadtime might be much less than the cumulative leadtime if intermediate products (e.g., subassemblies) are inventoried.

See *customer leadtime, leadtime, push-pull boundary*.

customer leadtime – The customer wait time for an order; the difference between the time a customer places and receives an order. ✪

If the supplier holds a finished goods inventory, the customer leadtime can be very close to zero. For example, the customer leadtime in a retail store is usually only the time between the customer selecting and paying for an item.

The customer leadtime begins after the push-pull boundary.

See *cumulative leadtime, leadtime, push-pull boundary*.

customer profitability – The revenue a customer generates minus the costs needed to acquire and retain that customer.

This is closely related to the concepts of customer equity or lifetime value. Without a method for estimating customer profitability, a firm may spend scarce marketing dollars to retain its unprofitable (or low profit) customers and may mistreat its most profitable customers.

See *Customer Relationship Management (CRM)*.

Customer Relationship Management (CRM) – An information system that leverages a number of customer-facing activities to help an organization better understand its customers so that it can better match its products and services to customer needs and thereby increase sales.

While CRM involves information technology, it is fundamentally a strategic process (not an IT project) for helping organizations better understand their customers' needs, better meet those needs, and increase sales and profits. A good CRM system provides many benefits such as:

- Provide exactly the services and products that customers want.
- Offer better customer service

- Allow for more effective cross selling (selling complementary products).
- Help sales staff close deals faster.
- Help the firm retain current customers and discover new ones.
- Collect timely complete information on customers through multiple customer interfaces, including call centers, e-mail, point-of-sale operations, and direct contact with the sales force.
- Reduce the transaction cost for buying products and services.
- Provide immediate access to order status.
- Provide support that will reduce the costs of using products and services.
- Help management develop a deeper understanding of customer buying behavior "sliced and diced" in a number of ways such as geography, demographics, channel, etc.

See *customer profitability*, *target price*, *Voice of the Customer (VOC)*.

customer satisfaction – See *service quality*.

customization point – See *push-pull boundary*.

cycle counting – A methodology for counting items in a storage location on regular schedule that prioritizes the more important items and systematically improves the record keeping process. ✪

Instead of counting all items with a year-end physical inventory count, cycle counting counts items throughout the year with the "important" items counted much more often than other items. Cycle counting is an application of Pareto's Law where the "important few" items are counted often and the "trivial many" items are counted infrequently. Both cycle counting and the annual physical inventory count will result in accurate inventory balances (at least once per year). However, cycle counting does a much better job of identifying the root problems that cause inaccurate inventory balances; therefore, cycle counting does a much better job of improving inventory accuracy over time. A good cycle counting program should completely eliminate the need for an annual physical inventory count.

	Year end physical inventory	Cycle counting
Frequency	Once per year	Daily for a sample of items
Correct balance?	Yes, once per year	Yes, almost always
Fix root problems?	No, symptoms only	Yes
Accountability for accuracy?	No	Yes
Prioritizes counting effort?	No	Yes

Some factors to consider when determining how often to count an item include:
- Criteria set by accounting and external auditors for the elimination of the annual physical inventory count.
- External regulations that require specific count frequencies.
- Annual dollar volume of an item.
- Annual unit volume of an item.
- Pilferage risk associated with the item.
- Unit cost of an item.
- Current inventory accuracy level for that particular item.

Some rules for determining how often to count an item include: (1) count items with higher annual usage more often (the ABC system), (2) count just before an order is placed, (3) count just before a new order is placed on the shelf, (4) count when the physical inventory balance is zero, (5) count when the physical inventory balance is negative, and (6) count after a specified number of transactions. Rules 2 and 3 are ways of implementing rule 1 because "A" items will be ordered more often. Rule 3 minimizes the number of units that need to be counted because the shelf is nearly empty when an order arrives. Rules 2 and 3 can be implemented so that every n-th order is counted.

An item count is considered wrong only when the count is off by more than the "counting tolerance," which is usually a percentage defined for each category of items. High value items will usually have a counting tolerance of zero; very low value items might have a counting tolerance of 10% or more.

Tompkins Associates provides more information on this topic at tompkinsinc.com/publications/monograph/ monographList/WP-19_Cycle_Counting.pdf?monographID=WP-19.

See *ABC classification, backflushing, Pareto's Law, shrinkage.*

cycle service level – See *safety stock.*

cycle stock – The inventory that exists because lotsize quantities are greater than one; also called the lotsize inventory. ✪

Cycle stock generally follows a "saw tooth" pattern. For instantaneous replenishment and constant average demand, the average cycle stock is $Q/2$, where Q is the fixed order quantity. Therefore, an organization can reduce cycle stock only by reducing lotsizes. Lotsizes can be reduced economically only by reducing the ordering (setup) cost.

See *Economic Order Quantity (EOQ), instantaneous replenishment, lotsize, safety stock.*

cycle time – (1) The time between completions (or starts) of a unit of work (also known as takt time) or (2) the time from beginning to end for a unit of work (also known as throughput time and flow time). (Note: These two definitions are quite different, but both are used in practice.) ✪

Historically, cycle time was defined in industrial engineering as the time between completions (or starts) of a process step. For example, this could be measured as the time between units "falling off" of the end of a manufacturing process or the maximum work time allowed for each worker on an assembly line. In lean terminology, the target cycle time (time between completions) aligned to the market demand rate is called the takt time (see the entry for *takt time*). This is the definition for cycle time used in LEI's **Lean Lexicon** (Marchwinski & Shook 2006).

In contrast, cycle time can also be defined as the cumulative time (also called total throughput time, total flow time, and production leadtime) required for a unit from start to end, and can be measured as the completion time minus the start time for the same unit. In other words, the first definition is the time between units and the second definition is the time to complete one unit.

The second definition (throughput) has become the more widely used term in practice in North America and it is now common to use the terms throughput time (or flow time) and cycle time synonymously.

For example, an assembly line in an appliance factory has one dishwasher coming off of the end of the line every minute and a target time of one minute for each of the 40 steps in the assembly process. Using definition (1), this is a cycle time of one minute. However, using definition (2), a dishwasher that started at 8:00 am will be not complete until 8:40 am, which means that the assembly line has a cycle time (throughput or flow time) of 40 minutes. Definition (1) focuses on the time between units being completed, whereas definition (2) focuses on the time to complete one unit from beginning to end.

It is often difficult to estimate the average cycle time (throughput time) for a complex product because it is not clear when the product is started. Given that each required component might have a different starting time, it is hard to determine the total cycle time for the completed product. A simple approach for estimating the cycle time (and also the periods supply) is to use the inverse of the inventory turnover ratio for the work-in-process (WIP) inventory. Therefore, if the WIP inventory turnover for a product is four turns per year, the "dollar weighted cycle time" is three months.

In queuing theory terms, the average time between completions is usually assumed to be the same as the average time between arrivals and is labeled as $1/\lambda$, where λ (lambda) is the mean arrival rate. The average time is system is labeled W_s. See the entry on *queueing theory* for more details.

This author prefers to use the term "leadtime" to indicate a planning factor rather than the actual time. The entry on *leadtime* discusses the differences between cycle time and leadtime.

See *assembly line, balanced scorecard, inventory turnover, leadtime, operations performance metrics, order-to-cash, periods supply, pitch, purchasing leadtime, station time, takt time, touch time, value added ratio.*

cycle time efficiency – See *value added ratio.*

D

dashboard – A performance measurement and reporting tool that provides a quick summary for the business unit or project status.

Ideally, a dashboard has a limited number of metrics (key performance indicators) to make it easy to comprehend and to manage. The term "dashboard" is a metaphor for an automobile's instrument panel with a speedometer, tachometer, fuel gauge, and oil warning light.

Many firms use simple "red, yellow, green" indicators to signal when the organization is not meeting its targets. Ideally, a dashboard should include both financial and non-financial measures and should be reviewed regularly. The dashboard/scorecards philosophy can also be applied to external supply chain partners.

See *Balanced Scorecard, corporate portal, Key Performance Indicator (KPI), operations performance metrics, supplier scorecard.*

Data Envelopment Analysis (DEA) – A performance measurement technique that can be used to measure the efficiency of an organization relative to other organizations with multiple inputs and outputs.

DEA has been used to measure and improve efficiency in many industry contexts such as banks, police stations, hospitals, tax offices, prisons, defense bases, schools and university departments. For example, consider a bank that operates many branch banks, each having different numbers of transactions and different teller staffing levels. The table below displays the data for this example. (This example is adapted from http://people.brunel.ac.uk/~mastjjb/jeb/or/dea.html, January 6, 2007.)

Branch bank	Number of tellers	Personal transactions per day	Personal transactions per teller	Relative efficiency
St. Paul	18	125	6.94	100%
Edina	16	44	2.75	40%
Bloomington	17	80	4.71	68%
Minneapolis	11	23	2.09	30%

The simplest approach for measuring efficiency for a branch is to calculate the ratio of an output measure (transactions) to an input measure (tellers). In DEA terminology, the branches are viewed as taking inputs (tellers) and converting them with varying degrees of efficiency into outputs (transactions). The St. Paul branch has the highest efficiency ratio in terms of the number of transactions per teller. The efficiency ratio for the St. Paul branch could be used as a target for the other branches and the relative efficiency of the other branches can be measured in comparison to that target.

This simple example has only one input (tellers) and one output (transactions). To take the example one step further, consider how the bank might measure efficiency when it has both personal and business transactions. The bank will likely find that one branch is more efficient at personal transactions and another is more efficient at business transactions. See the data in the table below.

Branch bank	Number of tellers	Personal transactions per day	Business transactions per day	Personal transactions per teller	Business transactions per teller
St. Paul	18	125	50	6.94	2.78
Edina	16	44	20	2.75	1.25
Bloomington	17	80	55	4.71	3.24
Minneapolis	11	23	10	2.09	0.91

With this data, the St. Paul branch is still the most efficient for personal transactions per teller, but the Bloomington branch is the most efficient for business transactions. One simple way to handle this problem for two ratios is to graph the data. The figure below shows that the "efficient frontier" is the convex hull (region) defined by the Bloomington and St. Paul branches and that the Edina and Minneapolis branches are relatively inefficient. From this graph, it is easy to see why it is called Data Envelopment Analysis.

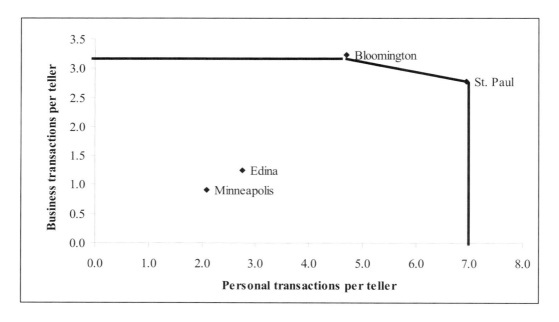

The measurement becomes much more difficult when multiple inputs and/or outputs are involved. DEA uses linear programming to measure the efficiency of multiple Decision Maker Units (DMUs) when the production process presents a structure of multiple inputs and outputs.

The benefits of DEA over other approaches are that (1) it does not require an explicit mathematical form for the production function, (2) it is useful in uncovering relationships that remain hidden for other methodologies, (3) it is capable of handling multiple inputs and outputs, (4) it can be used with any input-output measurement, and (5) it allows sources of inefficiency to be analyzed and quantified for every evaluated unit.

In the DEA methodology, developed by Charnes, Cooper, and Rhodes (1978), efficiency is defined as a weighted sum of outputs to a weighted sum of inputs, where the weights structure is calculated by means of mathematical programming and constant returns to scale are assumed. In 1984, Banker, Charnes, and Cooper developed a model with variable returns to scale. Adapted from en.wikipedia.org/wiki/ Data_Envelopment_Analysis, September 8, 2006.

See *operations performance metrics, production function, productivity.*

data mining – The process of analyzing a database (often in a data warehouse) to identify previously unknown patterns and relationships in the data and predict behavior of customers, prospective customers, etc.

Data mining tools make use of both statistical and software engineering tools and are often used in conjunction with very large databases. Ideally, data mining allows the user to visualize the data by providing graphical outputs. Standard data mining tools include cluster analysis, tree analysis, binary logistic regression, and neural nets.

For example, data mining software can help retail companies find customers with common interests, can screen potential donors for a college, and identify the key characteristics that should be considered in granting credit to a new customer.

Data mining is also known as knowledge-discovery in databases (KDD).

The major software vendors in the market are SAS Enterprise Miner (www.sas.com /technologies/analytics/datamining/miner), SPSS Clemintine (www.spss.com/data_mining), and XLMiner (www.resample.com/xlminer).

See *cluster analysis, data warehouse, logistic regression, neural network.*

data warehouse – A data warehouse is a database designed to support business analysis and decision making.

The data warehouse loads data from various systems at regular intervals. Data warehouse software usually includes sophisticated compression and hashing techniques for fast searches, advanced filtering, *ad hoc* inquiries, and user-designed reports.

See *cluster analysis*, *data mining*, *logistic regression*.

days of inventory – See *periods supply*.

days supply – See *periods supply*.

DBR – See *Drum-Buffer-Rope (DBR)*.

DC – See *Distribution Center (DC)*.

DEA – See *Data Envelopment Analysis*.

deadhead – The return of an empty transportation container to its point of origin.

See *backhaul*, *logistics*.

death spiral – See *make versus buy decision*.

Decision Sciences Institute (DSI) – A multidisciplinary international professional society that is dedicated to advancing knowledge and improving instruction in all business and related disciplines.

DSI facilitates the development and dissemination of knowledge in the diverse disciplines of the decision sciences through publications, conferences, and other services.

DSI publishes the **Decision Sciences Journal** (**DSJ**) and the **Decision Sciences Journal of Innovative Education**.

The DSI website is www.decisionsciences.org.

See *Operations Management (OM)*.

decision theory – See *decision tree*.

decision tree – A graphical decision tool for drawing and analyzing possible decisions and/or chance outcomes. ✪

A decision tree is a basic tool in the fields of decision analysis (decision theory) and risk management. A decision tree is usually drawn in time order from left to right. Decision nodes are usually drawn with squares and chance nodes are drawn with circles. When probabilities are assigned to each chance node, the decision nodes can be evaluated in terms of the expected monetary value.

The figure below is a simple decision tree with one decision node (build or not) and one chance node (win Chery contract). (Author's note: Chery is a rapidly growing Chinese automobile manufacturer.) This example could be taken another step by assigning probabilities to each arc coming out of the chance node and then computing the expected monetary value for each decision alternative.

See *causal map*, *force-field diagram*, *issue tree*, *Kepner-Tregoe Model*, *MECE*, *Operations Research (OR)*, *Pugh Matrix*, *risk assessment*.

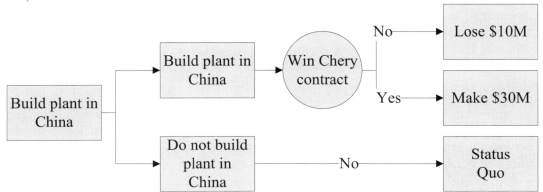

decreasing returns to scale – See *diseconomy of scale*.

decoupling point – See *push-pull boundary*.

deductive reasoning – See *inductive reasoning*.

de-expediting – See *expediting*.

Defects Per Million Opportunities (DPMO) – See *sigma level*.

delegation – The transfer of the responsibility for a job or task from one person or organization to another.

Tasks should be assigned to the most productive resource, which may be outside of an organization. Delegation, therefore, can be a powerful tool for managers to increase their productivity. Outsourcing is a form of delegation.

Delegation is similar to, but not identical to, the division of labor principle. Whereas division of labor splits a task into two or more pieces and then delegates, delegation does not require that the task be split.

Good questions to ask to help a manager decide if a task should be delegated: (1) Do you have time to complete the task? (2) Does this task require your personal supervision and attention? (3) Is your personal skill or expertise required for this task? (4) If you do not do the task yourself, will your reputation (or the reputation of your organization) be damaged? (5) Is there anyone on your team with the skill or expertise to complete the task? (6) Is there someone on your team who would benefit from the experience of performing the task?

In contract law, the term delegation is used to describe the act of giving another person the responsibility of carrying out the duty agreed to in a contract. Three parties are concerned with this process: the delegator (the party with the obligation to perform the duty), the delegatee (the party that assumes the responsibility of performing the duty) and the obligee (the party to whom this duty is owed).

See *division of labor, outsourcing, Vendor Managed Inventory (VMI)*.

delivery time – The time required to move, ship, or mail a product from a supplier to a customer.

See *service level*.

Delphi forecasting – A qualitative method that collects and refines opinions from a panel of anonymous experts in order to make forecasts. ✪

Named after the Greek oracle at Delphi to whom the Greeks visited for information about their future, the Delphi Method is an iterative procedure for collecting and refining the opinions of a panel of experts. The collective judgment of experts is considered more reliable than individual statements and is thus more objective in its outcomes. Delphi forecasting is usually applied to estimate unknown parameters, typically forecasting dates for long-term change in the fields of science and technology.

A survey instrument is used over several iterations. Both statistical and commentary feedback is provided with each iteration. After two or three iterations, opinions converge and a final report is made. The typical steps in a Delphi study are as follows:

Step 1. Define the questions that need to be asked.

Step 2. Identify the experts, who ideally have differing points of view on the questions defined in Step 1.

Step 3. Create the survey instrument. For technological forecasting, the questions are often phrased in the form, "In what year do you believe that event X will occur."

Step 4. Recruit the experts to respond to this round. Ask them to individually and independently respond to the survey questions with both quantitative responses (e.g., the year that the event will happen) and commentary feedback (assumptions, justifications, explanations). Note that the experts' identities should remain anonymous so feedback from famous or powerful people is not given undue weight.

Step 5. Summarize the results from this round and give statistical and commentary feedback to the expert panel. The statistical feedback is usually presented in the form of a histogram and some basic descriptive statistics.

Step 6. Conduct the next round of the survey if needed.

Delphi overcomes many problems with face-to-face meetings such as (1) domination by a few strong personalities, (2) anchoring on the first ideas that are presented, (3) pressure on participants to conform, and (4) regularly becoming overburdened with non-essential information.

See *brainstorming, forecasting, technological forecasting*.

demand – The quantity the market will buy per period at a particular price.

In inventory theory, it is often important to differentiate between demand and sales. Demand is how many units would have been sold if inventory was available; sales is how many units were actually sold. In other words demand = sales + lost sales. See the *forecasting* entry for more discussion on this issue.

See *all-time demand, bookings, dependent demand, elasticity, exponential smoothing, forecasting, independent demand*.

demand chain management – Supply chain management that focuses the customer end of the supply chain and uses signals (such as point-of-sale data) from the customer to trigger production.

See *supply chain management*.

demand during leadtime – An inventory/purchasing concept of the demand during the replenishment leadtime.

In inventory management, it is important to set the reorder point large enough to be able to cover the demand (sales) while the firm waits for a replenishment order to arrive. The demand during leadtime is a random variable with a mean, standard deviation, etc.

See *leadtime, reorder point, safety stock.*

demand filter – An exception reporting and control tool for time series forecasting.

When the absolute value of the forecast error is very large, the demand filter triggers an exception report to warn the user. The simplest rule is to test if the forecast error is larger than plus or minus three times the standard deviation of the forecast error.

The demand filter at the end of period t is the absolute value of the forecast error divided by an estimate of the standard deviation of the error. One approach for handing this is to define the demand filter at the end of period t as $DF_t = |E_t| / \sqrt{SMSE_{t-1}}$, where $|E_t|$ is the absolute value of the forecast error and $\sqrt{SMSE_{t-1}}$ is the square root of the smoothed mean squared error (an estimate of the recent standard deviation of the forecast error). This uses the smoothed *MSE* because the demand filter is typically implemented in a time-series forecasting context. The demand filter exception report is created whenever DF_t exceeds some critical value, DF^*. Assuming that the errors (E_t) are normally distributed, DF_t is a standard normal random variable. Therefore, it can be compared to a z value used in basic statistics textbooks. Therefore, a reasonable control limit is $DF^* = 3$. In other words, the system should create an exception report whenever the demand filter exceeds a value of 3. It is important to use the smoothed Mean Squared Error from the *previous* period in the demand filter so an outlier is not included in the estimation of the standard deviation of the forecast error. Alternative forms for the demand filter include $DF_t = |E_t| / \sqrt{SVAR_t}$ and $DF_t = |E_t| / (1.25 SMAD_t)$.

See *exponential smoothing, forecast bias, forecast error metrics, forecasting, Mean Absolute Percent Error (MAPE), tracking signal.*

demand flow – Another word for Just-in-Time (JIT) manufacturing.

See *lean thinking.*

demand management – This term has two related but not identical meanings – (1) the name of an organizational function (e.g., the demand management organization); and (2) the name of a set of practices that are designed to influence demand. ✪

The **demand management organization** is a relatively new organizational form in North America. This organization can report to either the manufacturing or sales organization and is charged with creating forecasts, managing the S&OP process, and influencing both supply (manufacturing, purchasing, inventory, logistics) policies and demand (sales, marketing, pricing) polices.

Demand management practices include those activities that both collect demand information and affect the demand to better meet the capacity. Demand can be influenced through pricing, advertising, promotions, other customer communications, and other mechanisms.

See *forecasting, Sales & Operations Planning (S&OP).*

Deming's 14 points – A summary of the quality improvement philosophy developed and taught by W. Edwards Deming (1900-1993).

William Edwards Deming was an American statistician, college professor, author, lecturer, and consultant. Deming is widely credited with improving production in the United States during World War II, although he is perhaps best known for his work in Japan. From 1950 onward he taught top management how to improve design, product quality, testing, and sales. Deming made a significant contribution to Japan's ability to produce innovative high-quality products. Deming is regarded as having had more impact upon Japanese manufacturing and business than any other individual not of Japanese heritage. (Adapted from http://en.wikipedia.org/wiki/ W._Edwards_Deming, January 17, 2007.)

Deming's work is outlined in two books, *Out of the Crisis* (1986) and *The New Economics for Industry* (2000), in which he spells out his System of Profound Knowledge. The fourteen points are summarized below. (Author's note: The titles below were not in the original 14 points. Many variations for some of Deming's points can be found on the web. The list below is from Wikipedia with the exception of point 6.)

1. **Create constancy of purpose** – Create constancy of purpose toward improvement of product and service, with the aim to become competitive and to stay in business, and to provide jobs.

2. **Adopt the new philosophy** – Adopt a new philosophy of cooperation (win-win) in which everybody wins and put it into practice by teaching it to employees, customers and suppliers.

3. **Cease dependence on inspection to achieve quality** – Cease dependence on mass inspection to achieve quality. Instead, improve the process and build quality into the product in the first place.

4. **End the practice of awarding business on the basis of price alone** – End the practice of awarding business on the basis of price tag alone. Instead, minimize total cost in the long run. Move toward a single supplier for any one item, based on a long-term relationship of loyalty and trust.

5. **Continuously improve every process** – Improve constantly, and forever, the system of production, service, planning, of any activity. This will improve quality and productivity and thus constantly decrease costs.

6. **Institute training on the job** – Institute modern methods of training on the job for all, including management, to make better use of every employee. New skills are required to keep up with changes in materials, methods, product and service design, machinery, techniques, and service.

7. **Improve leadership** – Adopt and institute leadership for the management of people, recognizing their different abilities, capabilities, and aspiration. The aim of leadership should be to help people, machines, and gadgets do a better job. Leadership of management is in need of overhaul, as well as leadership of production workers.

8. **Drive out fear** – Drive out fear and build trust so that everyone can work more effectively.

9. **Break down functional silos** – Break down barriers between departments. Abolish competition and build a win-win system of cooperation within the organization. People in research, design, sales, and production must work as a team to foresee problems of production and use that might be encountered with the product or service.

10. **Eliminate slogans** – Eliminate slogans, exhortations, and targets asking for zero defects or new levels of productivity. Such exhortations only create adversarial relationships, as the bulk of the causes of low quality and low productivity belong to the system and thus lie beyond the power of the workforce.

11. **Eliminate quotas** – Eliminate numerical goals, numerical quotas and management by objectives. Substitute leadership.

12. **Encourage pride in work** – Remove barriers that rob people of joy in their work. This will mean abolishing the annual rating or merit system that ranks people and creates competition and conflict.

13. **Institute educational programs** – Institute a vigorous program of education and self-improvement.

14. **Take action** – Put everybody in the company to work to accomplish the transformation. The transformation is everybody's job.

　　See *functional silo, inspection, Six Sigma, Total Quality Management (TQM)*.

demurrage – The carrier charges and fees applied when rail freight cars and ships are retained beyond a specified loading or unloading time.

　　See *terms*.

dendrogram – See *cluster analysis*.

dependent demand – Demand that is derived from higher level plans and therefore should be planned rather than forecasted.

　　In a manufacturing firm, dependent demand is calculated (not forecasted) from the production plan of higher-level items. End-item demand is usually forecasted. A production plan (aggregate production plan) and a Master Production Schedule (MPS) are created in light of this forecast. These plans will not be identical to the forecast because of the need to build inventory, draw down inventory, or level the production rate. Demand for components that go into end-items is considered dependent demand, because this demand is planned based on the production plan for the end-item. This dependent demand should not be forecasted.

　　See *demand, independent demand*.

deployment leader – A person who leads the Six Sigma program in one part of a business, often a division, strategic business unit, or functional area (operations, new product development, sales, etc.).

　　In some firms, the deployment leader is not assigned full time to the Six Sigma program. Deployment leaders usually report to the overall program champion, at least with a dotted line reporting relationship.

　　See *champion, Six Sigma*.

Design Failure Mode and Effects Analysis (DFMEA) – The application of FMEA principles to design.

The Failure Mode and Affects Analysis (FMEA) tool can be used to anticipate and mitigate risks in both a process improvement context (where a process is already in place) and a design context (where the design does not yet exist). However, a process FMEA and a design FMEA have some significant differences. The term FMEA normally refers to a process FMEA.

The major distinction between the process FMEA (sometimes called PFMEA) and DFMEA is in scoring detectability. A process FMEA scores detection on whether it can be prevented or detected within the existing process, whereas a DFMEA looks at both the prevention of the cause and a level of understanding or amount of experimentation as part of the detection grade. It is extremely difficult to find a consistent detection grading criteria that covers both process FMEA and DFMEA, so they are rarely interchangeable.

For example, a process FMEA for an extruder might include the following information:

Cause: Thermocouple broken
Mode: Extruder runs too cold and there is poor flow polymer
Effect: Uneven web caliper
Detection score = 2 (occasional preventive maintenance plus machine readouts ensure a high likelihood that a problem will be detected before it becomes an issue.)

A DFMEA run on the design of the extruder might look at the extruder design from this angle:

Cause: Hanger design of the die is incorrect
Mode: Extruder flows unevenly for good polymer flow
Effect: Uneven web caliper
Detection score: 8 (unless modeling was done on polymer flow through the die, it is unlikely that the design would catch this before building)

The source for this comparison of DFMEA and FMEA is adapted from an email from Rodney Hehenberger, Technical Manager, Materials and Optics Laboratory, Occupational Health and Environmental Safety Division, 3M, January 10, 2007.

See *Failure Mode and Effects Analysis (FMEA)*.

Design for Assembly (DFA) – Design for manufacturing concepts applied to assembly.

See *Design for Manufacturing (DFM)*.

Design for Disassembly – A set of principles used to guide designers in designing products that are easy to disassemble for re-manufacturing and/or repair operations.

Design for Disassembly enables a product and its parts to be easily reused, re-manufactured, refurbished, or recycled at end of life. In the long run, Design for Disassembly could make it possible to eliminate the need for landfills and incineration of mixed waste. Products would be designed so they never become waste, but instead become inputs to new products at the end of their useful lives. Design for Disassembly is a key strategy within the larger area of sustainable product design, which is concerned with a more proactive approach to environmentally responsible design. As environmental concerns grow in the world, re-manufacturing will continue to grow in importance. In Europe, this is already a major issue with manufacturers such as VW being required to design products that can be easily disassembled.

See *Design for Manufacturing (DFM), remanufacturing*.

Design for Environment – See *Design for Disassembly (DFD) and remanufacturing*.

Design for Manufacturing (DFM) – A set of methodologies and principles that can be used to guide the design process so that product fabrication and assembly will have low cost, low assembly time, high labor productivity, low manufacturing cycle time, low work-in-process inventory, high conformance quality, low manufacturing ramp-up time, and short time to market. ✪

This is the best-known of dozens of DFx ("design-for") acronyms.

See *Design for Assembly (DFA)*, *Design for Disassembly*, *Design for Reliability (DFR)*.

Design for Manufacturing and Assembly (DFMA) – See *Design for Manufacturing (DFM)*.

Design for Quality – See *Design for Manufacturing (DFM)*.

Design for Reliability (DFR) – A concurrent engineering program where the reliability engineer is part of the product development team working with the design engineers to design reliable products with low overall life-cycle costs. Source: https://www.reliabilityanalysislab.com/DFR0802.asp. Much more detail can be found on this site.

See *Design for Manufacturing (DFM)*.

Design for Six Sigma (DFSS) – An extension of the Six Sigma program that is a methodology for developing new products and driving quality measurement into the new product development process.

The rationale for DFSS is that it is much easier to design quality into a product than it is to fix problems after the design is complete. Instead of using the Six Sigma DMAIC framework, DFSS uses IDOV (Identify, Design, Optimize, and Validate) or DMADV (Define, Measure, Analyze, Design, and Verify). More detail on DMADV follows:

- Define - Define the project goals and customer (internal and external) deliverables
- Measure - Measure and determine customer needs and specifications
- Analyze - Analyze the process options to meet the customer needs
- Design - Design (detailed) the process to meet the customer needs
- Verify - Verify the design performance and ability to meet customer needs

DMAIC and DFSS have the following in common:

- Six Sigma methodologies used to drive defects to less than 3.4 per million opportunities.
- Data intensive solution approaches. Cold, hard facts are more valued than intuition in Six Sigma.
- Implemented by Green Belts, Black Belts, and Master Black Belts.
- Ways to help meet the business/financial bottom-line numbers.
- Implemented with the support of a champion and process owner.

Generally speaking, the Six Sigma DFSS methodology is used for new product development whereas the Six Sigma DMAIC methodology is used for process improvement. The DMAIC methodology should be used instead of DMADV when a product or process already exists but is not meeting customer specification or is not performing adequately. The DMADV methodology should be used instead of the DMAIC methodology when (1) a product or process does not exist and needs to be developed, or (2) the existing product or process exists and has been optimized and still does not meet customer specifications or Six Sigma level.

Design for Six Sigma does not replace the stage-gate process, but enhances it by providing additional statistical rigor to the gate criteria. Instead of check sheets and gut decisions, teams are required to bring facts and analytic data to the gate reviews to validate that the tools, tasks, and deliverables are met.

C_{pk} is a measure of how well the product performance meets the customer's needs. This is a key DFSS metric throughout the development cycle and is used to ensure that Six Sigma quality is designed into the product from the start.

See *DMAIC, New Product Development (NPD), process capability and performance, Pugh Matrix, Six Sigma, stage-gate process*.

Design of Experiments (DOE) – A family of statistical tools designed to build quality into the product and process designs so the need for inspection is reduced.

DOE achieves this by optimizing product and process designs and by making product and process designs robust against manufacturing variability. Experimental designs are used to identify or screen important factors affecting a process, and to develop empirical models of processes. Design of Experiment techniques enable teams to learn about process behavior by running a series of experiments. The goal is to obtain the maximum amount of useful information in the minimum number of runs. Tradeoffs as to amount of information gained for the number of runs are known before running the experiments.

DOE is a very important and complex subject that is beyond the scope of this encyclopedia. Refer to any good linear models texts such as Kutner, Neter, Nachtsheim, and Wasserman (2004).

See *ANOVA (Analysis of Variance), Gauge R&R, Six Sigma, Taguchi methods*.

Design Structure Matrix (DSM) – A compact matrix representation showing the precedence relationships and information flows in a system/project.

DSM contains a list of all constituent subsystems/activities and the corresponding information exchange and dependency patterns. That is, what information pieces (parameters) are required to start a certain activity and where does the information generated by the activity feed into (i.e., which other tasks within the matrix utilize the output information)? The DSM provides insights about how to manage a complex system/project and highlights issues of information needs and requirements, task sequencing, and iterations.

In the DSM, the tasks for a project are listed on the rows and then repeated for the columns. An X mark indicates the existence and direction of information flow (or a dependency in a general sense) from one activity in the project (i.e. matrix) to another. Reading across a row reveals the input/dependency flows by an X mark placed at the intersection of that row with the column that bears the name of the input task. Reading across a column reveals the output information flows from that activity to other activities by placing an X in a similar manner described above. A green mark below the main diagonal represents a forward flow of information. The red marks above the main diagonal reveal a feedback from a later (i.e. downstream) activity to an earlier (i.e. upstream) one. This means that the earlier activity has to be repeated in light of the late arrival of new information. Some DSM researchers and practitioners use an opposite convention for the feed-forward and feedback marks. Adapted from dsmweb.org/DSM_def.htm, July 9, 2005.

See *project management*.

DFA – See *Design for Assembly (DFA)*.

DFD – See *Design for Disassembly*.

DFM – See *Design for Manufacturing*.

DFMA – See *Design for Manufacturing and Assembly*.

DFMEA – See *Design Failure Mode and Effects Analysis (DFMEA)*.

DFSS – See *Design for Six Sigma (DFSS)*.

digital convergence – The combining of a number of technologies such as entertainment (movies, videos, music, TV), printing (books, newspapers, magazines), news (TV, newspapers, radio), communications (phone, mobile phone, data communications), computing (personal computers, mainframe computers), and many other important technologies that touch most people almost every day.

The term "convergence" implies that these technologies will become more integrated and will tend to radically change each other. For example, cable TV operators are offering high-speed Internet, digital telephone, and other services as well. The lines between the technologies that offer entertainment, data transfer, and communications are blurring more and more every day.

direct labor cost – The labor cost that is clearly assignable to a part or product. ✪

This usually includes the hourly wage and fringe benefits for a worker to produce a part. Direct labor cost does not include materials cost or overhead.

See *overhead*.

direct ship – See *drop ship*.

direct store shipment – See *drop ship*.

discrete lotsize – See *lot-for-lot*.

discrete manufacturing – A process that creates products by fabricating or assembling distinct parts.

Good examples of discrete manufacturing include building a computer or an automobile. In contrast, a continuous process deals with materials such as liquids or powders. Examples of continuous processes include oil refining, chemical processing, or paper manufacturing.

See *assembly line, batch process, continuous flow, continuous process, job shop*.

discrete uniform distribution – See *uniform distribution*.

discriminant analysis – A statistical technique that predicts group membership; also called linear discriminant analysis.

See *linear regression, logistic regression*.

diseconomy of scale – The forces that cause organizations to have higher unit costs as volume increases. ✪

Most business managers are familiar with the concept of economies of scale where the unit cost decreases as the volume increases. The less-familiar concept of diseconomies of scale is where the unit cost increases as the volume increases. In many industries, firms will have economies of scale until they grow to be quite large.

For example, it is said that the optimal hospital size is about 400 beds and that larger hospitals tend to become less efficient due to the complexity of the operation, which is a function of the number of employees and the distance people have to travel. (Source: Private communication with a hospital researcher.) This is also said to be true for high schools, with the optimal school size probably between 400 and 600 students. (Source: Personal communication with the high school principal at SWCHS in Chaska, Minnesota.) A watch factory in Moscow once had 7000 people making watches and a US defense factory was so large that workers had to ride bicycles. (Source: Personal experience of the author.) These factories were not very competitive due to their size. The following is a list of reasons why the unit cost might increase with volume:

- **Coordination and communication problems** – As firm size increases, coordination and communication becomes much more difficult and often leads to the creation of a large bureaucracy.
- **Top-heavy management** – As firm size increases, management expense as a percent of the total budget tends to increase.
- **Duplication of effort** – As firm size increases, it is common for firms to waste money on duplicate efforts and systems. It is reported that General Motors had two in-house CAD/CAM systems and still purchased other CAD/CAM systems from outside firms.
- **Protection from consequences** – In a small firm, most managers immediately see and experience the consequences of their decisions. In many large firms, managers are transferred every few years and rarely have to live with their bad decisions very long and therefore do not learn from their mistakes.
- **Inertia** – It is often very hard for a large organization to change directions. A VP of MIS for a large bank in Seattle reported that it was nearly impossible for his bank to make any significant changes. It was just too hard to understand all of the linkages between the more than 10 million lines of code. (Source: Private communication with the author.)
- **Self-competition** – The managing directors for a large paper products firm in Europe identified their biggest problem as competition with the other operating companies within the same firm. (Source: author's teaching experience at IMD.)
- **Transportation** – If output for a national or international market is concentrated at one large plant in a single location, transport costs of raw materials and finished goods to and from distant markets may offset scale economies of production at the large plant.

A few of the ideas above were adapted from http://en.wikipedia.org/wiki/Diseconomies_of_scale.

See *economy of scale*, *pooling*.

disintermediation – Displacing a distributor in the channel.

A distributor is an intermediary between a manufacturer and its customers, because it "mediates" the relationship between the two. When a firm removes a distributor between it and its customers, it is said to have disintermediated the distributor and has practiced disintermediation. This is a common occurrence when manufacturing firms replaces distributors with an Internet website that sells directly to customers. Re-intermediation occurs when the distributor finds a way to assert itself back into the channel, possibly by offering its own website and better service.

See *channel conflict*, *Supply Chain Management*.

dispatching rules – Policies used to determine which job (work order) is selected to start next on a process.

These are sometimes called "job shop dispatching" or priority rules. For example, a manger arrives at work on a Monday morning and has twenty tasks waiting on her desk. Which task should she handle first? She might take the one that is the most urgent (e.g., has the earliest due date), or the longest one, or the one that has the most economic value, etc. In a very similar way, a shop supervisor might have to select the next job for a machine using the same types of dispatching rules.

The best-known dispatching rules include First-In-First-Out (FIFO), shortest processing time, earliest due date, minimum slack time, and critical ratio. The FIFO rule may be the "fairest" rule, but does not perform well with respect to average flow time or due date performance in a typical job shop. It can be proven that the shortest processing time rule will minimize the mean (average) flow time, but does poorly with respect to on-time delivery. MRP systems back-schedule from the due date, and therefore are essentially using a minimum slack rule, which has been shown to perform fairly well in a wide variety of contexts.

See *expediting*, *First-In-First-Out (FIFO)*, *heijunka*, *job shop*, *job shop scheduling*, *service level*, *tardiness*.

disruptive technology – A term coined by Professor Clayton M. Christensen (Christensen, 1997; Christensen and Raynor, 2003) at Harvard Business School to describe a new technological innovation, product, or service that eventually overturns the existing dominant technology in the market, despite the fact that the disruptive technology is both radically different than the leading technology and often has poorer performance (at least initially) than the leading technology.

The disruptive technology often starts by gaining market share in the lower price (and less demanding) segment of the market and then moves up-market through performance improvements and finally displaces the incumbent's product.   By contrast, Christensen states that a sustaining technology provides improved performance and will almost always be incorporated into the incumbent's product.

In some markets, the rate at which products improve is faster than the rate at which customers can learn and adopt the new performance. Therefore, at some point the performance of the product overshoots the needs of certain customer segments. At this point, a disruptive technology may enter the market and provide a product that has lower performance than the incumbent, but exceeds the requirements of certain segments thereby gaining a foothold in the market.

Christensen distinguishes between "low-end disruption" (that targets customers who do not need the full performance valued by customers at the high-end of the market) and "new-market disruption" (that targets customers who could previously not be served profitably by the incumbent). The disruptive company will naturally aim to improve its margin and therefore innovate to capture the next level of customers. The incumbent will not want to engage in a price war with a simpler product with lower production costs and will move up-market and focus on its more attractive customers. After a number of iterations, the incumbent has been squeezed into successively smaller markets. When the disruptive technology finally meets the demands of its last segment, the incumbent technology disappears. The table below lists examples of disruptive technologies.

Disruptive Technology	Displaced Technology
• Railways	• Canals
• Automobile	• Railways
• Digital cameras	• Photographic film
• Voice over IP	• Analog and fixed digital telephone systems
• Internet protocol suite	• Proprietary or fixed-configuration networks
• Mini steel mills	• Vertically integrated steel mills
• Personal computers	• Minicomputers
• Desktop publishing	• Phototypesetting and manual pasteup
• Linux and BSD	• Unix
• Flash drives	• Floppy disk drives
• Container ships and containerization	• Break cargo ships and Stevedores

Adapted from http://en.wikipedia.org/wiki/Disruptive_technology, November 16, 2006.
See *New Product Development (NPD)*, *technology road map*.

distinctive competence – See *core competence*.

distribution – Management of the outbound logistics to the customer, often involving transportation, warehousing, inventory control, material handling, order administration, site and location analysis, industrial packaging, data processing, and the communications. ✪

Distribution includes all activities related to physical distribution, as well as the return of goods to the manufacturer. The term "Physical Distribution" is a synonym.
See *distribution center (DC)*, *distribution channel*, *DRP*, *inventory management*, *logistics*, *reverse logistics*.

Distribution Center (DC) – A location used to warehouse and ship products.
See *distribution*, *logistics*.

distribution channel – One or more companies or individuals who participate in the flow of goods and services from the manufacturer to the final user or consumer.
These firms are sometimes called "channel partners."
See *channel conflict*, *distribution*, *logistics*.

Distribution Requirements Planning (DRP) – A planning system for managing inventory at branch warehouses.

Distribution Resource Planning is an extension of MRP into the planning of the key resources in a distribution system. According to Vollmann, Berry, Whybark, and Jacobs (2004, Chapter 8), "DRP provides the basis for integrating supply chain inventory information and physical distribution activities with the Manufacturing Planning and Control system." DRP performs many functions such as:
• Managing the flow of materials between firms, warehouses, distribution centers.
• Helping manage the material flows like MRP does in manufacturing.

- Linking firms in the supply chain by providing planning records that carry demand information from receiving points to supply points and vice versa.

DRP can use a time-phased order point approach to plan orders at the branch warehouse level. These orders are exploded via MRP logic to become gross requirements on the supplying source enabling the translation of inventory plans into material flows. In the case of multi-level distribution networks, this explosion process can continue down through the various levels of regional warehouses, master warehouse, factory warehouse etc. and become input to the master production schedule.

See *Enterprise Resources Planning (ERP)*, *logistics*, *Materials Requirements Planning (MRP)*.

division of labor – Dividing a job into small, simple, standard steps and assigning one worker to each step.

Frederick Taylor (1911) promoted the concept of dividing work into small pieces so workers could quickly learn a job without much training. Division of labor and standardization of parts led to rifles made by several people in the 1800s and led to the model T Ford in the 1900s. Division of labor is the opposite of job enlargement, a practice that has workers take on more tasks rather than fewer.

In the last thirty years or more, many managers have found that taking division of labor too far can lead to boredom, does not develop the whole person, and does not build a learning organization. Division of labor creates many queues and waits and also requires more coordination and supervision. Many process improvement projects enlarge jobs to remove queues and reduce cycle time.

On the other hand, some organizations report situations where processes can be improved by dedicating individuals or teams to certain process steps. For example, Mercy Hospital in Minnesota found that having a team of two people dedicated to the receiving process improved both quality cost. This was because their focus drove improvements in both standardization and efficiency.

Good managers divide their own labor into those activities that only they can do and delegate much of the rest of it to assistants and other suppliers. In a strategic sense, both vendor managed inventories and outsourcing can be viewed as examples of division of labor, where the work is divided into some pieces that are done internally and other pieces of work that are done by other organizations.

See *delegation*, *job enlargement*, *scientific management*, *standardized work*.

DMADV – See *Design for Six Sigma (DFSS)*, *Six Sigma*.

DMAIC – A Six Sigma problem-solving approach with the following five steps: Define, Measure, Analyze, Improve, and Control.

Six Sigma projects are almost always managed with a five-step process called problem-solving approach called DMAIC. These steps are described in the table below.

Define	Requirements, Goals, Problems, Scope
	• What is the problem?
	• What are the objectives?
	• What is our scope?
	• What are the metrics?
	• What is a defect?
Measure	Validate problem, inputs, key steps, efficiency data
	• What data do we have?
	• What data do we need?
	• What is our baseline performance?
Analyze	Develop/validate hypothesis, identify root causes, assess process design
	• What are our hypotheses?
	• What are the Critical To Quality (CTQ) drivers?
	• What is the transfer function between causes and results?
	• What are the root causes?
	• What variability can we not explain?
Improve	Remove root causes, standardize solutions, implement new process
	Implement new process design to remove root causes.
	Change reward systems.

Control	Establish standard measures and reviews to maintain performance
	Establish standard measures and reviews to maintain performance.
	Hold institutional gains. "Sustain the gain."

Source: Professor Arthur V. Hill

In some firms, the process is "gated," which means that the project team is not allowed to progress to the next step until the Master Black Belt or someone else in leadership has signed off on the step.

See *Design for Six Sigma (DFSS), Lean Sigma, PDCA (Plan-Do-Check-Act), Six Sigma, stage-gate process*.

dock-to-stock – The practice of moving receipts from the receiving dock directly to inventory without performing any inspection.

Dock-to-stock eliminates the cost of incoming inspection for the customer and reduces handling cost. Obviously, it requires that the supplier assure good quality products.

See *logistics, supplier qualification and certification, Warehouse Management System (WMS)*.

DOE – See *design of experiments (DOE)*.

dollar unit sampling – An auditing technique for stratified sampling transactions that allows the auditor to make statistically reliable statements about the misspecification error.

The auditing profession has considered the problem of how to make statistically reliable statements about an audit when some transactions are more important than others and when the probability of a defect is very small. The best approach is an extension of stratified random sampling called "dollar unit sampling." In the auditing literature, dollar unit sampling is also known as probability proportionate to size sampling and monetary unit sampling. Roberts (1978, p. 125) states that "When the proportion of population units with monetary differences is expected to be small and the audit objective is to test for the possibility of a material overstatement, dollar unit sampling is the best statistical technique."

A dollar unit sampling audit enables the auditor to make statistical statements about the results of an audit such as "Based on this audit, we are 95% confident that the total overstatement amount for this population is no more than $500."

The paper "Dollar Unit Sampling" and the Excel workbook "DUS.xls" are on the *OMWW CD* available from www.ClamshellBeachPress.com. ◉

See *confidence interval, Poisson distribution, sample size calculation, sampling*.

dot-com – Companies that sell products or services over the Intranet.

Dot-com companies do not sell their products or services through brick and mortar channels. Products are typically ordered over the Internet and shipped from warehouses directly to the customer. Services are typically information services provided through the Internet. Amazon.com and ebay.com are probably the two most famous of these firms. Many companies have become hybrids of the "brick" and "dot-com" models and are referred to as "bricks and clicks." Many startup firms in the late 1990s selling had "two managers, two computers, and a dream that was too big." Dot-coms often struggle with order fulfillment operations such as warehousing, forecasting, inventory control, and shipping.

See *B2B, B2C, click-and-mortar*.

double exponential smoothing – See *exponential smoothing*.

double marginalization – An economics term that describes a situation in which two firms in a supply chain both have monopoly power and each producer adds its own monopoly mark-up to the price.

The price of the finished product is higher than it would be if the two producers were vertically integrated.

See *economics*.

double sampling plan – See *acceptance sampling*.

downstream – See *upstream*.

DPMO – Defects Per Million Opportunities; sometimes called DPPM, which means defective parts per million.

See *Six Sigma*.

DPPM – See *DPMO*.

drop ship – A shipment that goes directly from the manufacturer to a retail store (or customer), bypassing distribution centers.

When a distributor (or retailer) has a supplier send an order directly to a customer, it is said to be "drop-shipped" to the customer. Drop shipments reduce the customer's leadtime, but usually increase the distribution cost. Drop ship can be used as either a noun or a verb. This is also called direct store shipment (DSD) or direct ship.

See *logistics*.

DRP – See *Distribution Requirement Planning (DRP)*.

Drum-Buffer-Rope (DBR) – A Theory of Constraints concept that sends a signal every time the bottleneck completes one unit, giving upstream operations the authority to produce. ✪

DBR is a production control system based on the Theory of Constraints (TOC) philosophy. Like other TOC concepts, DBR focuses on maximizing the utilization of the bottleneck (the constrained resource) and subordinates all non-bottleneck resources so they meet the needs of the bottleneck.

Drum – The completion of one unit at the bottleneck is the drum that signals (authorizes) all upstream workcenters to produce one unit. The un-constrained resources must serve the constrained resource.

Buffer – The buffer is a time cushion used to protect the bottleneck from running out of work (starving).

Rope – The rope pulls production from the non-bottleneck resources to the bottleneck. The rope is a schedule that dictates the timing of the release of raw materials or jobs into the system. This schedule is designed to make all the workstations perform at the pace of the drum.

The DRB concept is essentially identical to the concept of a "pacemaker workcenter" used in lean manufacturing.

The paper "Drum-Buffer-Rope" is available on the *OMWW CD* available from www.ClamshellBeachPress.com.◉

See *CONWIP, lean thinking, pacemaker, POLCA (Paired-cell Overlapping Loops of Cards with Authorization), Theory of Constraints (TOC), upstream*.

DSI – See *The Decision Sciences Institute*.

DSM – See *Design Structure Matrix*.

DuPont Analysis – An economic analysis that can be used to show the return on investment as a function of inventory and other economic variables.

Operations managers can use the DuPont Analysis to analyze the impact of changes in inventory investment on Return on Investment (ROI). The DuPont Analysis can be used to show how much (1) the carrying cost goes down when inventory goes down, (2) profit (return) goes up when the cost goes down, (3) investment goes down when inventory investment goes down, and finally, (4) ROI, the ratio of the return to investment, will go up dramatically as the numerator (return) goes up while the denominator (investment) goes down at the same time. This assumes that revenue is not affected by inventory, which may not be true for a make to stock firm unless the inventory reduction is managed very carefully. From an inventory management point of view, the DuPont Analysis is less important when interest rates and carrying charges are low.

The DuPont Analysis is an early and simplified version of a strategy map (and a Y-tree) that shows the sensitivity of the firm's ROI to changes in input variables (drivers) such as inventory. (Note: Many organizations change the ROI calculation to an EVA or economic profit calculation.)

The following is an example of a DuPont Analysis for a hypothetical firm.

The Excel workbook "Dupont.xls" is on the *OMWW CD* available from www.ClamshellBeachPress.com. The above example is from this Excel workbook. ◉

See *balanced scorecard, financial performance metrics, inventory turnover, Return on Net Assets (RONA), strategy map, Y-tree*.

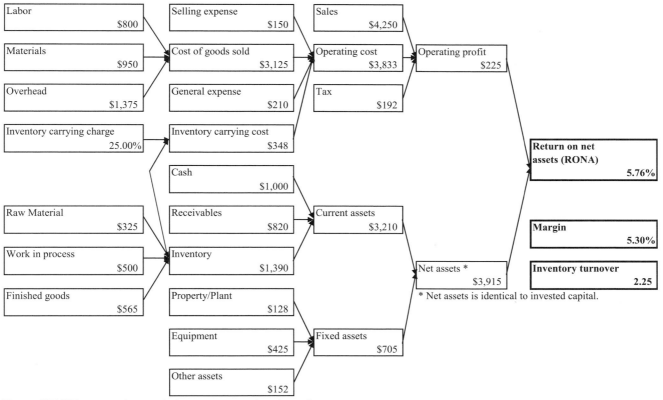

DuPont STOP – A safety training program developed at DuPont.

The Safety Training Observation Program (STOP) is a widely-used safety program that teaches workplace safety auditing skills, with steps to reinforce safe work practices and correct unsafe practices. See the website http://www2.dupont.com/Safety_Products/en_US/products for more information.

durable goods – See *consumable goods*.

Durbin-Watson Statistic – A statistical test for first-order autocorrelation (serial correlation) in time series data.

Autocorrelation is the correlation between a variable in one period and the previous period. For example, the weather temperature is highly autocorrelated, which means that the correlation between the weather in one day tends to vary with the weather on the previous day. If today is hot, then so is tomorrow.

The Durbin-Watson Statistic is used to test for first-order autocorrelation in time series data. It is most commonly used to test for autocorrelation in the residuals for regression models that deal with time series data. It is often also used to test for autocorrelation in the forecast error for a time series forecasting model. The following discussion will use the term "error" (e_t) to mean either the residuals from a regression or the forecast error for a forecasting model.

The Durbin-Watson test compares the error in period t with the error in period $t-1$. The following equation is the Durbin-Watson test statistic (d):

$$d = \frac{\sum_{t=2}^{n}(e_t - e_{t-1})^2}{\sum_{t=1}^{n}e_t^{\,2}}$$

where, t is the time period, e_t is the residual in period t, and n is the total number of observations available.

The table below can be used to help interpret the Durbin-Watson test statistic (d):

Value of d	Interpretation
$d < 2$	Residuals are positively autocorrelated
$d \approx 2$	Residuals are uncorrelated
$d > 2$	Residuals are negatively autocorrelated
$d \approx 4$	Residuals are strongly negatively autocorrelated

The test statistic (d) is constrained to the range (0, 4) with a midpoint of 2. A value of d close to 2 suggests that the time series has no autocorrelation. A low value of d (e.g., close to zero) suggests positive autocorrelation because the differences between e_t and e_{t-1} are relatively small. A high value of d (e.g., close to four) suggests negative autocorrelation because the differences between e_t and e_{t-1} are relatively large.

The Durbin-Watson test can be used to test for both position and negative autocorrelation. However, typically, the null hypothesis is no significant autocorrelation and the alterative hypothesis positive autocorrelation.

The tables below define the acceptance and rejection ranges for the null hypothesis and the critical values for the lower and upper critical points for the Durbin-Watson test.

Durbin-Watson regions for acceptance and rejection of the null hypothesis

$(0, d_L)$	(d_L, d_U)	$(d_U, 4- d_U)$	$(4- d_U, 4- d_L)$	$(4- d_L, 4)$
Reject null hypothesis of positive autocorrelation	Neither accept nor reject	Accept null hypothesis of no autocorrelation	Neither accept nor reject	Reject null hypothesis of negative autocorrelation

Upper and lower critical values (d_L and d_U) for an α significance level

Sample size	α	$k = 1$		$k = 2$		$k = 3$		$k = 4$		$k = 5$	
		d_L	d_U	d_L	d_U	d_L	d_U	d_L	d_U	d_L	d_U
15	0.010	0.81	1.07	0.70	1.25	0.59	1.46	0.49	1.70	0.39	1.96
	0.050	1.08	1.36	0.95	1.54	0.82	1.75	0.69	1.97	0.56	2.21
20	0.010	0.95	1.15	0.86	1.27	0.77	1.41	0.63	1.57	0.60	1.74
	0.050	1.20	1.41	1.10	1.54	1.00	1.68	0.90	1.83	0.79	1.99
25	0.010	1.05	1.21	0.98	1.30	0.90	1.41	0.83	1.52	0.75	1.65
	0.050	1.29	1.45	1.21	1.55	1.12	1.66	1.04	1.77	0.95	1.89
30	0.010	1.13	1.26	1.07	1.34	1.01	1.42	0.94	1.51	0.88	1.61
	0.050	1.35	1.49	1.28	1.57	1.21	1.65	1.14	1.74	1.07	1.83
40	0.010	1.25	1.34	1.20	1.40	1.15	1.46	1.10	1.52	1.05	1.58
	0.050	1.44	1.54	1.39	1.60	1.34	1.66	1.29	1.72	1.23	1.79
50	0.010	1.32	1.40	1.28	1.45	1.24	1.49	1.20	1.54	1.16	1.59
	0.050	1.50	1.59	1.46	1.63	1.42	1.67	1.38	1.72	1.34	1.77
60	0.010	1.38	1.45	1.35	1.48	1.32	1.52	1.28	1.56	1.25	1.60
	0.050	1.55	1.62	1.51	1.65	1.48	1.69	1.44	1.73	1.41	1.77
80	0.010	1.47	1.52	1.44	1.54	1.42	1.57	1.39	1.60	1.36	1.62
	0.050	1.61	1.66	1.59	1.69	1.56	1.72	1.53	1.74	1.51	1.77
100+	0.010	1.52	1.56	1.50	1.58	1.48	1.60	1.45	1.63	1.44	1.65
	0.050	1.65	1.69	1.63	1.72	1.61	1.74	1.59	1.76	1.57	1.78

k = Number of independent variables

See *Box-Jenkins forecasting, time series forecasting*.

Dutch auction – An auction method where the price is lowered until a bidder is prepared to pay; also known as a descending bid auction.

In a Dutch auction, the auctioneer begins with the seller's asking price and then lowers the price until a bidder is willing to accept the price or until a predetermined reserve price (the seller's minimum acceptable price) is reached. The winning bidder pays the last announced price. The Dutch auction is named for the Dutch tulip auctions in the Netherlands.

See *e-auction, e-business, e-commerce, e-procurement, reverse auction, sniping.*

E

EAN (European Article Number) – See *Universal Product Code (UPC).*

Early Supplier Involvement (ESI) – The collaborative product development practice of getting suppliers involved early in the product design process.

Good suppliers have core competences around their product technology. Therefore, firms that involve their suppliers in product development at an early stage can take advantage of these core competencies and potentially reap financial and competitive rewards.

Companies that involve suppliers early report the following benefits: (a) reduced product development time, (b) improved quality and features, (c) reduced product or service costs, and (d) reduced design changes. Companies do best when they give suppliers the leeway to come up with their own designs rather than simply manufacturing parts to the customer's detailed specifications. Suppliers often have more expertise than their customers in their product technologies.

See *JIT II, New Product Development (NPD).*

Earned Value Management (EVM) – A methodology used to measure and communicate the progress of a project by taking into account the work completed, the time taken, and the costs incurred to date.

EVM helps evaluate and control task/project risk by measuring progress in monetary terms. EVM is sometimes required to be used in commercial and government contracts. Under EVM, work is planned, budgeted, and scheduled in time-phased "planned value" increments, constituting a cost and a schedule measurement baseline.

The description below applies EVM to a task; however, the same concept can easily be extended to an entire project. Time and material is spent in completing a task. If managed well, the task will be completed with time to spare and with no wasted materials or cost. If managed poorly, the task will take longer and waste materials. By taking a snap-shot of the task and calculating the Earned value metrics, it is possible to compare the planned cost and schedule with the actual cost and schedule and assess the progress of the task. When considering an entire project, it is possible to extrapolate to estimate the probable completion date and cost.

The basics of EVM can best be shown on an S-curve. In its simplest form, the S-curve is a graph showing how the task budget is planned to be spent over time. The three curves on the graph represent:

- Budgeted cost for work scheduled – The budgets for all activities planned.
- Actual cost of work performed – The actual costs of the work charged so far.
- Budgeted cost of work performed – The planned costs of the work allocated to the completed activities.

Earned value is defined as the percentage project complete times the project budget. The schedule variance is the difference between the earned value and the planned budget. Cost variance is the difference between the Earned value and the actual costs of the works.

The benefits for project managers of the earned value approach come from:

- Disciplined planning conducted via established methods.
- Availability of metrics that show variances from plan in order to generate necessary corrective actions.
  Sources: nnh.com/ev/papers.html, www.acq.osd.mil/pm, and projectmagazine.com/nov00/ evm1.html.

See *critical chain, project management, work breakdown structure (WBS).*

e-auction – A web-based tool for making a market more efficient.

The best example of an electronic auction is the popular ebay.com. A **reverse auction** is where the buyer calls for bids for something from potential suppliers. For example, General Electric will notify a group of qualified suppliers that they are invited to participate in an electronic auction. The date and product specifications are defined by the buyer. At the time of the auction, the participating bidders assemble at a common Internet site and bid for the contract.

See *Dutch auction, e-business, e-commerce, e-procurement, reverse auction, sniping.*

EBITDA – Earnings Before Interest, Taxes, Depreciation, and Amortization, an indicator of a company's financial performance calculated as revenue minus expenses (excluding tax, interest, depreciation, and amortization).

EBITDA is sometimes called EBIDTA, Earnings Before Interest, Taxes, Depreciation and Amortization. EBITDA is an approximate measure of a company's operating cash flow based on data from the company's income statement. EBITDA is calculated by looking at earnings before the deduction of interest expenses, taxes, depreciation, and amortization. This measure of earnings is of particular interest in cases where companies have large amounts of fixed assets that are subject to heavy depreciation charges (such as manufacturing companies). Since the accounting and financing effects on company earnings do not factor into EBITDA, it is a good way to compare companies within and across industries. This measure is also of interest to a company's creditors, since EBITDA is essentially the income that a company has free for interest payments. In general, EBITDA is a useful measure only for large companies with significant assets and/or a significant amount of debt financing. It is rarely a useful measure for evaluating a small company with no significant loans. Source: www.investorwords.com/5883/EBIDTA.html, May 13, 2005.

EBITDA is a good metric to evaluate profitability but not cash flow. Unfortunately, however, EBITDA is often used as a measure of cash flow, which is a very dangerous and misleading thing to do because there is a significant difference between the two. Operating cash flow is a better measure of how much cash a company is generating because it adds non-cash charges (depreciation and amortization) back to net income and includes the changes in working capital that also use/provide cash (such as changes in receivables, payables and inventories). These working capital factors are the key to determining how much cash a company is generating. If investors do not include changes in working capital in their analysis and rely solely on EBITDA, they may miss clues that indicate whether or not a company is losing money because it cannot sell its products. Adapted from www.investopedia.com/articles/analyst/020602.asp, May 16, 2005.

See *financial performance metrics*.

e-business – Electronic networking strategies that include e-commerce and also internal processes such as production, inventory management, human resources, and finance.

See *Dutch auction, e-auction, e-commerce, e-procurement, extranet, intranet, reverse auction, sniping*.

ECO – See *Engineering Change Order*.

e-commerce – Electronic networking strategies dealing with processes that touch customers, suppliers, and other outward facing functions such as sales, marketing, order entry, delivery, customer service, and purchasing.

E-commerce involves three types of integration: (1) vertical integration of front-end website applications to existing transaction systems, (2) cross-business integration of a company with websites of customers, suppliers, or intermediaries such as web-based marketplaces, and (3) integration of technology with redesigned processes for order handling, purchasing, or customer service (Bartels 2000).

See *B2B, B2C, Dutch auction, e-auction, e-business, e-procurement, sniping*.

econometric forecasting – A forecasting method that considers a number of different leading economic indicators such as disposable income, meals eaten away from home, etc. to make forecasts.

Econometric models use leading indicators to make forecasts. For example, a sharp rise in the cost of gasoline may well be a good indicator (predictor) of an increased demand rate for fuel efficient cars.

Most econometric studies use multiple regression models. For example, the Onan Division of Cummings Engine developed a regression model and found that fast food sales and disposable income could be used to forecast the sales of recreational vehicles one quarter ahead.

See *Box-Jenkins forecasting, forecasting, leading indicator, linear regression*.

Economic Lot Scheduling Problem (ELSP) – A class of lotsizing problems that involves finding the optimal (or near optimal) order size (or cycle length) in order to minimize the sum of the carrying and ordering (setup) costs for multiple items that share the same capacity (the "bottleneck").

Even though the problem has the word "scheduling" in its name, it is really a lotsizing problem rather than a scheduling problem. This document presents both the problem formulation and a solution methodology for solving the problem. More details can be found in the Silver *et al.* (1998) text.

Define the following terms:

A Time available for the bottleneck.

c_i Cost per unit for item i.

D_i Annual demand for item i in units $\{i = 1, 2, ..., N\}$.

n_i Number of order cycles per year for item i.

N Number of items.

Q_i Lotsize item i in units, where $Q_i = D_i / n_i$. The average lotsize is $Q_i / 2 = \frac{1}{2} D_i / n_i$.

r Carrying charge. Average carrying cost per period is $rc_i Q_i / 2$.

S_i Setup cost per order for item i.

s_i Setup time per order for item i in hours.

t_i Run time per unit for item i in hours.

U Target utilization for the bottleneck, where UA is the target time available for production.

The goal is to minimize the sum of the relevant costs, which include the setup and carrying cost:

$$\text{Minimize } z = \sum_{i=1}^{N} n_i S_i + \sum_{i=1}^{N} rc_i Q_i / 2 = \sum_{i=1}^{N} (n_i S_i + \tfrac{1}{2} rc_i D_i / n_i)$$

Note that the problem can be solved with zero setup costs and/or with zero run times. The bottleneck capacity cannot be violated. Therefore, the total of the run time and the setup time on this capacity cannot violate the product of the time available and the target utilization, e.g., $\sum_{i=1}^{N} (D_i t_i + n_i s_i) \le UA$.

If we solve the unconstrained problem and find that the capacity constraint is satisfied, the algorithm is done. (Note: If the total run time exceeds the available capacity, the problem is a capacity problem and is not an ELSP.) If the capacity constraint is not satisfied, we must introduce an additional "setup cost" associated with the setup time in the form of a Lagrange multiplier. To do this, we move the equality constraint into the objective function with a Lagrange multiplier (λ):

$$L(n_i, \lambda) = \sum_{i=1}^{N} (n_i S_i + \tfrac{1}{2} rc_i D_i / n_i) + \lambda [\sum_{i=1}^{N} (D_i t_i + n_i s_i) - UA]$$

We then take the partial derivative of the Lagrange function and set it equal to zero and find that the optimal number of order cycles per year for a given Lagrange multiplier is given by $n_i^* = \sqrt{rc_i D_i / 2 / (S_i + \lambda s_i)}$. In order to find the optimal Lagrange multiplier (λ^*) that will exactly satisfy the equality constraint, we conduct a direct search. We start with $\lambda = 0$ and check if the capacity inequality constraint is satisfied, e.g., $\sum_{i=1}^{N} (D_i t_i + s_i n_i^*) \le UA$. If this inequality is not satisfied, the optimal solution will be at full capacity utilization and the constraint becomes an equality constraint. Newton's method can be used to find the optimal Lagrange multiplier (λ^*) to solve this problem. Newton's Method for this problem requires that we define an equation for the difference between the current and target utilization, e.g., $y(\lambda) = \sum_{i=1}^{N} (D_i t_i + s_i n_i^*) - UA$. The goal is to find the "root" for this equation. This is the point where the equation equals zero. In order to do this, we take the first derivative and find that step $k+1$ for Newton's Method is defined as $\lambda_{k+1} = \lambda_k - y(\lambda_k) / y'(\lambda_k)$. We initialize at $\lambda = 0$ and terminate the procedure when $y(\lambda)$ is close enough to zero. The final Lagrange multiplier (λ) is the shadow price for the constraint. In other words, the Lagrange multiplier is the economic value of increasing the capacity constraint by one hour.

This methodology can be implemented fairly easily for any manufacturing process that builds to stock and has a fairly level demand throughout the year. The procedure finds the optimal order intervals n_i^* for all items. When the demand varies over time, it is better to use the periods supply (n_i^*) parameter than the optimal order quantities $Q_i^* = D_i / n_i^*$ control parameter. It may also be important to find the optimal safety stock for these order quantities, where the leadtime for each item is based on the order interval. The time-phase order point system can then be used to determine which product to start next.

The paper "Economic Lot Scheduling Problem (ELSP)" and the Excel workbook "elsp.xls" are on the **OMWW CD** available from www.ClamshellBeachPress.com. ●

See *Economic Order Quantity (EOQ), lotsizing methods, run time, setup time.*

Economic Order Quantity (EOQ) – The optimal order quantity (batch size or lotsize) that minimizes the sum of the carrying and ordering costs. ✪

If the lotsize is too large, the inventory carrying cost will too high. If the lotsize is too small, the ordering (or setup) cost will be too high. The equation for the total incremental cost is $TIC = (D/Q)S + (Q/2)ic$, where D is the annual demand in units, Q is the order quantity in units, S is the order cost per order, i is the carrying charge per dollar per year, and c is the unit cost. The first term in the TIC equation is the annual ordering cost. The firm will have D/Q orders per year and each one costs S. The second term is the carrying cost. The firm will have an average cycle inventory investment of $cQ/2$ and a carrying charge of i dollars per dollar per year.

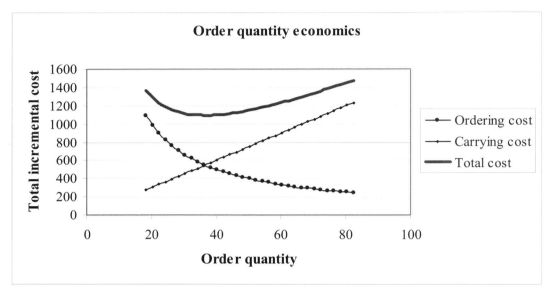

The optimal order quantity is found by taking the first derivative of the TIC function with respect to Q and setting it to zero. The optimal order quantity (the EOQ) is then $\sqrt{2DS/(ic)}$.

The EOQ model is considered to be of limited practical value for three reasons. First, it is very difficult to estimate all four parameters in the model. As a joke, the EOQ can be rewritten as $EOQ = \sqrt{2\,??/(??)}$. Second, even with perfect estimates of the parameters, the total incremental cost function is very flat near the optimal solution, which means that the total incremental cost is not sensitive to errors in the EOQ. Third, managerial intuition is usually good at finding the EOQ without the equation. It is obvious to most managers that high-volume, expensive items should be ordered more often.

On the positive side, the EOQ model has several advantages. First, the EOQ model helps people get a better understanding of lotsizing issues and can help both students and managers refine their thinking about the managerial economics of the lotsizing problem. Second, in some cases the tradeoffs do have a significant economic impact, especially when accumulated over many items. Third, the EOQ model is the foundation for several other models such as the quantity discount model.

The Excel workbook "EOQ.xls" is on the **OMWW CD** available from www.ClamshellBeachPress.com. This workbook can be used to estimate the inferred setup cost over carrying charge ratio from historical data. ◉

See *ABC classification, carrying charge, carrying cost, cycle stock, Economic Lot Scheduling Problem (ELSP), fixed order quantity, lotsize, lotsizing methods, Period Order Quantity (POQ), quantity discount, safety stock, time-varying demand lotsizing problem.*

Economic Value Added (EVA) – A financial performance metric that measures the true economic profit of an enterprise from the shareholders' point of view.

EVA is the net operating profit minus an appropriate charge for the opportunity cost of all capital invested in an enterprise. As such, EVA is an estimate of true "economic" profit, or the amount by which earnings exceed or fall short of the required minimum rate of return that shareholders and lenders could get by investing in other securities of comparable risk. The capital charge is the most distinctive and important aspect of EVA. Under conventional accounting, most companies appear profitable but many in fact are not. As Peter Drucker argued in a Harvard Business Review article, "Until a business returns a profit that is greater than its cost of capital, it operates at a loss. Never mind that it pays taxes as if it had a genuine profit. The enterprise still returns less to the economy than it devours in resources … until then it does not create wealth; it destroys it." EVA corrects this error by explicitly recognizing that when managers employ capital, they must pay for it, just as if it were a wage. By taking all capital costs into account, including the cost of equity, EVA shows the dollar amount of wealth a business has created or destroyed in each reporting period. In other words, EVA is profit the way shareholders define it. If the shareholders expect, say, a 10% return on their investment, they "make money" only to the extent that their share of after-tax operating profits exceeds 10% of equity capital. Everything before that is just building up to the minimum acceptable compensation for investing in a risky enterprise. Adapted from http://www.sternstewart.com/ evaabout/whatis.php, May 31, 2005.

Economic profit is a similar concept but is not adjusted in the same way as EVA.

Stern Stewart & Company owns a registered trademark for the name EVA for a brand of software and financial consulting/training services. The proprietary component of what Stern Stewart & Co. does is the adjustments. The amortization of goodwill or capitalization of brand advertising and other similar adjustments are the translations that occur to Economic Profit to make it EVA.

See *financial performance metrics*.

economics – The social science that studies how people and groups (families, businesses, organizations, governments, and societies) choose to produce, distribute, consume, and allocate limited goods and services.

Economics deals primarily with supply and demand of scarce goods and services and how people and societies assign prices to these goods and services in order to allocate them in some rational way.

The word economics is from the Greek for house (οίκος = oikos) and custom or law (νόμος = nomos); in other words, economics is about the "rules of the house(hold)." (This definition from the Greek is adapted from en.wikipedia.org/wiki/Economics, February 26, 2008).

See *demand, double marginalization, economy of scale, economy of scope, elasticity, production function*.

economy of scale – A concept from economics the cost per unit goes down as the production volume increases. ✪

Stated in more precise terms from the field of economics, economies of scale is the decrease in the marginal cost of production as a firm's scale of operations increases. Economies of scale can be accomplished because as production increases, the cost of producing each additional unit falls. The increase in efficiency often comes by means of allocating the fixed costs over a larger number of units.

See *commonality, diseconomy of scale, economics, economy of scope, network effect*.

economy of scope – A concept from economics that states that the cost per unit will decline as the variety of products increases. ✪

In other words, economies of scope arise from synergies in the production of similar goods. A firm with economics of scope can reduce its cost per unit by having a wide variety of products that share resources. Scope economies exist whenever the same investment can support multiple profitable activities less expensively in combination than separately.

According to www.csuchico.edu/mgmt/strategy/module7/tsld031.htm, the following is true about economies of scope:

- Economies of scope arise from the ability to eliminate costs by operating two or more businesses under the same corporate umbrella.
- These economies exist whenever it is less costly for two or more businesses to operate under centralized management than to function independently.
- Cost savings opportunities can stem from interrelationships anywhere along a business' value chain.

See *commonality, economics, economy of scale, mass customization*.

ECR – See *Efficient Consumer Response*.

EDI – See *Electronic Data Interchange (EDI)*.

effectiveness – Capability to produce a desired result, without respect to efficiency. ✪

For example, the maintenance engineers in a milk plant found that a particular disinfectant was very effective in killing all of the bacteria in a vat that was used to produce cottage cheese. However, if the disinfectant was very expensive and required significant time to use, the firm might be able to find another more efficient approach that was equally effective. In summary, effectiveness is about getting the right job done and efficiency is about getting the job done using the minimum resources.

See *efficiency*, *Overall Equipment Effectiveness (OEE)*.

effectivity date – The calendar date that an engineering change order for the Bill of Material (BOM) will come into effect; sometimes called the effective date.

Most ERP systems include software for managing the Bill of Material (BOM). In addition to storing the current product structure (bill of material), these systems are usually also able to store future product structures that will be implemented at some future date (the effectivity date). When the effectivity date is reached, the second structure comes into effect.

The effectivity date may be determined by the effectivity quantity. With an effectivity quantity, the engineering change comes into effect when the current inventory has fallen to zero or to a specified quantity. However, one problem with this approach is that the inventory position usually does not fall to zero instantaneously. When this is the case, the replenishment system may generate a new purchase order for the old item. A second problem is that the small quantity of remnant stock which remains may be uneconomical to use, leading to its scrap.

Adapted from www.glossaryofmanufacturing.com, April 8, 2007.

See *Bill of Material (BOM)*.

effectivity quantity – See *effectivity date*.

efficiency – (1) Industrial engineering: The ratio of the standard processing time to the average actual processing time; a process that can perform at a very low cost compared to some standard. (2) LEI's ***Lean Lexicon*** (Marchwinski & Shook 2006): Meeting exact customer requirements with the minimum amount of resources. (3) Economics: Market efficiency is the degree and speed to which a market accurately incorporates information into prices. ✪

The industrial engineering definition is probably the most widely accepted definition in the operations field. For example, if a process has a standard time of 100 minutes per unit and an operator can maintain an average of 90 minutes per unit, the operator is said to have an efficiency of 100/90 = 111%.

See *7 Wastes*, *effectiveness*, *Overall Equipment Effectiveness (OEE)*, *productivity*, *utilization*.

Efficient Consumer Response – A consumer goods initiative aimed at reducing inefficient practices and waste in the supply chain.

Efficient Consumer Response is an application of JIT and lean thinking to retail distribution, primarily in the grocery industry. Efficient Consumer Response is defined by the Joint Industry Project for Efficient Consumer Response (1994) as follows:

A strategy in which the grocery retailer, distributor, and supplier trading partners work closely together to eliminate excess costs from the grocery supply chain. Efficient Consumer Response focuses particularly on four major opportunities to improve efficiency:

1. Optimizing store assortments and space allocations to increase category sales per square foot and inventory turnover.
2. Streamlining the distribution of goods from the point of manufacture to the retail shelf.
3. Reducing the cost of trade and consumer promotion.
4. Reducing the cost of developing and introducing new products.

(Adapted from gartner4.gartnerweb.com/public/static/hotc/hc00088697.html, October 27, 2000.)

See *Collaborative Planning Forecasting and Replenishment (CPFR)*, *continuous replenishment planning*, *Quick Response Manufacturing*.

e-kanban – See *faxban*.

elasticity – An economics term used to describe the sensitivity of the demand to a change in price.

For example, Target is a major discount retailer in North America. When the inventory analysts at Target want to clear (dispose) end-of-season inventory, they want to know the elasticity (sensitivity) of the demand to a reduced price. They use a linear model based on percentages that relates the percent increase in demand to a percent decrease in price (e.g., a 5% decrease in price will result in a 10% increase in the average demand).

The three main approaches for modeling the price-elasticity of demand include the linear model, the power model, and the exponential model. The linear model is $D(p) = \alpha - \beta p$, where $D(p)$ is the demand at price p

and α and β are the parameters of the model to be estimated from historical data. The power model is $D(p) = \alpha p^{-\beta}$. The exponential model is $D(p) = \alpha e^{-\beta p}$. The β parameter is the elasticity parameter for all three models. All three models show that the demand decreases as the price increases. The linear model is the easiest to use, but the power and exponential models generally make more sense. For the power model, the demand is infinite when price is zero; for the exponential model, the demand is α when the price is zero. Therefore, the exponential model makes the most sense for most operations/inventory/pricing models.

See *demand, economics, forecasting.*

Electronic Data Interchange (EDI) – A system and related set of standards that firms can use to communicate routine business transactions between computers without human intervention.

EDI transactions can include information for inquiries, planning, purchasing, acknowledgments, pricing, order status, scheduling, test results, shipping and receiving, invoices, payments, and financial reporting. The simplest form of EDI is to send purchase orders to suppliers. More advanced forms of EDI include sending invoices, electronic payments, and planned orders (requirements). The advantages of EDI include:

- Reduced transaction cost – Electronic transactions are cheaper than manual/paper ones.
- Reduced transaction time – Electronic ordering is nearly simultaneous, versus days or weeks for a manual/paper transaction sent via mail.
- Improved forecast accuracy – Forward visibility of the customer's requirements can dramatically improve forecast accuracy. For many firms, this is the most important benefit.
- Improved data quality – Sending information electronically can improve quality because it eliminates almost all the human data entry from the process.

With the rapid growth of e-commerce, many expect that the phrase "EDI" will soon die. E-commerce will, of course, serve the same purposes as EDI and will have to include all of the same functionality.

The web page http://www.etechnologycorp.com/edi_e-commerce.htm has an excellent summary of the subject.

EDI can be used to electronically manage inter-company activity. EDI can be designed as an XML application.

See *Advanced Shipping Notification (ASN), Enterprise Resources Planning (ERP), forward visibility, Over/Short/Damaged Report (OSD Report), Transportation Management System (TMS), XML (eXtensible Markup Language).*

Electronic Product Code – See *EPC (Electronic Product Code).*

emergency maintenance – An unplanned maintenance problem that often results in lost productivity.

See *maintenance, predictive maintenance, preventive maintenance, Total Productive Maintenance (TPM).*

employee turnover – The average percentage of employees who exit a firm per year. ✪

For example, the turnover for hotel staff is very high, often on the order of 100%. This means that the number of employees exiting a firm in a year (voluntarily or involuntarily) equals the number employed. Employee turnover can be greater than 100% (e.g., 200% employee turnover means an average tenure of 6 months). Employee turnover is a surrogate measure of employee satisfaction.

See *inventory turnover, turnover.*

Engineer to Order (ETO) – A customer interface strategy with engineering done in response to a customer order; sometimes called design to order. ✪

An engineer to order system is characterized by:

- Products designed in order to the customer's specifications.
- Quoted leadtimes usually equal to engineering, procurement, fabrication, assembly, pack, and shipping time.
- Components can be stock items or designed specifically to the order.
- Supply orders are typically pegged directly to the customer order.
- Common parts may not be stocked unless their procurement time is less than that of the engineered parts.
- Engineering may be treated as a workcenter with its backlog scheduled as if it were part of the factory.
- Actual costing is favored because many items are purchased or manufactured only one time.

Examples of ETO products include the space shuttle, stamping dies, plastic molds, and specialized capital equipment. In an ETO process, engineering must be integrated into the factory functions in order to serve the customer.

In an Engineer to Order environment, the major opportunities for improvement are usually found in:

- On-line engineering change order control with an electronic approval process.
- Automatic notification of pending ECOs (Engineering Change Orders) during purchase order creation.
- Reducing the number of SKUs without limiting customer selection.

See *commonality, configurator, Make to Order (MTO), Make to Stock (MTS), mass customization, Respond to Order (RTO)*.

Engineering Change Order (ECO) – A document used to communicate a change in a product design.

Improving the engineering change order process can be a major opportunity for improvement for many firms. ECOs tend to be error-prone and the timing is complicated by current inventories, documentation, training, etc. The timing for an ECO can be dependent on the current inventory. In other words, it is possible to phase out an older component when the current inventory position goes to zero.

See *Bill of Material (BOM)*.

Enterprise Resources Planning (ERP) – Integrated applications software that corporations use to run their businesses. ✪

ERP systems typically handle accounts payable, accounts receivable, general ledger, payroll, Materials Requirements Planning (MRP), purchasing, sales, human resources, and many other interrelated systems. One of the key concepts for an ERP system is that the firm stores data in one and only one location. In other words, the organization has only a single database that all departments share. SAP and Oracle are the two main ERP systems vendors currently on the market.

ERP systems grew out of Materials Requirements Planning (MRP) systems that were developed in the 1970s and 1980s. The Materials Requirements Planning module in an ERP system supports manufacturing organizations by the timely release of production and purchase orders using the production plan for finished goods to determine the materials plan for the components and materials required to make the product. The MRP module is driven by the master production schedule (MPS) which defines the requirements for the end-items. The three key inputs to the MRP module are (1) the master production schedule, (2) inventory status records, and (3) product structure records.

See *Advanced Planning and Scheduling (APS), Bill of Material (BOM), Business Requirements Planning (BRP), Distribution Requirements Planning (DRP), Electronic Data Interchange (EDI), Materials Requirements Planning (MRP), SAP*.

entitlement – A Six Sigma term used as a measurement of the best possible performance of a process, usually without significant capital investment.

Entitlement is an important process improvement concept that is particularly useful in project selection. It is usually defined as the best performance possible for a process without significant capital investment. However, some firms define it as the performance of the perfect process. As the term implies, the organization is "entitled" to this level of performance based on the investments already made.

Knowing the entitlement for a process defines the size of opportunity for improvement. If entitlement is 500 units per day and the baseline performance is 250 units per day, the process has significant room for improvement. If higher production rates are needed, a search for a totally new process may be in order (i.e., re-engineering or DFSS).

The concept of par for a golf hole is a good metaphor for the entitlement concept. The par on a hole represents what score is possible and reasonable to expect. On one hole a golfer may score under than par, but it is unrealistic to expect such performance on every hole, or even on average. Of course, all golfers have their own unique capability, so the official par does not represent process entitlement for the average duffer. The appropriate entitlement for professionals is be better than par, but for most golfers much worse than par. Note that standard golfing handicaps are usually based on average performance, which is not the same concept as entitlement. Note also that some industry leaders define entitlement as the absolute best performance possible, which in golf is a hole in one on every hole.

Entitlement should be determined for all key process performance measures (yield, cost of poor quality, capacity, downtime, waste, etc.). Entitlement may be predicted by engineering and scientific models, nameplate capacity provided by the equipment manufacturer, or simply the best prolonged performance observed to date.

Entitlement can also be predicted from empirical relationships. In one instance it was observed that a process operating at a cost of $0.36/unit had at one time operated at $0.16/unit (correcting for inflation). This suggests that the process entitlement (as determined by best prolonged performance) should be $0.16/unit. On further investigation it was observed that there was a linear relationship between defects and cost/unit of the form Cost = $0.12 + 3(defects)/1,000,000. Therefore if defects could be reduced to very low levels, the true process entitlement may be as low as $0.12/unit.

The following steps should be followed when using entitlement for project selection:
1. Look at the gap between baseline performance (current state) and entitlement (desired state).
2. Identify a project scope that will close the gap and can be completed in less than 4-6 months.
3. Assess the bottom line impact of the project and compare it to other potential projects.

The gap between the baseline and entitlement is rarely closed in the course of a single project. It is common for several projects to be required.

Keep in mind that process entitlement can, and often does, change as more is learned about the process. After a few Six Sigma projects, process are sometimes performing beyond the initial entitlement level.

See *benchmarking, Six Sigma*.

EOQ – See *Economic Order Quantity (EOQ)*.

EPC (Electronic Product Code) – An abbreviation for Electronic Product Code; the next generation of the Universal Product Code (UPC) system for RFID tags administered by EPCglobal Inc. (www.epcglobalinc.org).

The EPC number can be from 64 to 256 bits and contains at least the following fields: (1) EPC version, (2) company identification number assigned by EPCglobal, (3) product number (object class), and (4) unique serial number. A 96-bit EPC is capable of differentiating 68 billion items for each of 16 million products within each of 268 million companies. Unlike UPC bar codes, which do not have serial numbers, the EPC enables tracking of individual items because every item can be uniquely identified. Adapted from http://www.techweb.com/encyclopedia/defineterm.jhtml?term=EPC, January 16, 2007.

For example, an EPC can differentiate between the first can of soup in a shipment from the 1,000-th can. Each label can also lead to a wealth of information about that product. For example, it can enumerate 16 million types of Campbell's soup and more than a trillion cans of each type. Adapted from www.baselinemag.com, December 21, 2004.

See *barcode, item number, Radio Frequency Identification (RFID), traceability, Universal Product Code (UPC)*.

e-procurement – A web-based information system that improves corporate purchasing operations by handling the specification, authorization, competitive bidding, and acquisition of products and services through catalogs, auctions, requests for proposals, and requests for quotes.

See *Dutch auction, e-auction, e-business, e-commerce, purchasing, reverse auction*.

ergonomics – The scientific discipline concerned with the understanding of interactions among humans and other elements of a system, and the profession that applies theory, principles, data, and methods to design in order to optimize human well-being and overall system performance; ergonomics is also called human factors. ✪

Source: This is the approved definition of the International Ergonomics Association, www.iea.cc/ergonomics, representing 19,000 ergonomists worldwide and was provided by Professor Jan Dul, Professor of Ergonomics Management, Department of Management of Technology and Innovation, Rotterdam School of Management, Erasmus School of Business, Erasmus University Rotterdam.

See *error proofing, process design, socio-technical design*.

Erlang distribution – A continuous probability distribution useful for modeling task times.

The Erlang distribution was developed by Danish mathematician A. K. Erlang (1878-1929) to examine the waiting times for telephone calls. The distribution has two parameters, the shape parameter (k), which must be an integer, and the scale parameter (β). The Erlang distribution is a special case of the Gamma distribution with parameters k and β, where k is an integer. The Erlang is the distribution of the sum of k independent identically distributed random variables each having an exponential distribution with mean β. The exponential is a special case of the Erlang with $k = 1$.

Density and distribution functions: The Erlang density and distribution functions for $x > 0$ are:

$$f(x) = e^{-x/\beta} \frac{\beta^{-k} x^{k-1}}{(k-1)!} \; ; \; F(x) = 1 - e^{-x/\beta} \sum_{j=0}^{k-1} \frac{(\beta x)^j}{j!}$$

Statistics: Range $[0, \infty)$, mean $k\beta$, variance $k\beta^2$, and mode $(k-1)\beta$. Given the sample mean ($\bar{x}$) and standard deviation (s), the k parameter of an Erlang distribution can be estimated as $k = \bar{x}^2 / s^2 = 1/CV^2$, where $CV = s/\bar{x}$ is the sample coefficient of variation.

Excel: In Excel, the density and distribution functions are GAMMADIST(x, k, β, FALSE) and GAMMADIST(x, k, β, TRUE).

Excel simulation: In an Excel simulation, Erlang random variates can be generated with the inverse transformation method with $x = $ GAMMAINV(RAND(), k, β, TRUE). Alternatively, Erlang random variates can be generated by taking advantage of the fact that the Erlang is the sum of k independent exponential variates, e.g., $x = -\sum_{j=1}^{k} \beta \ln(r_j)$, where r_j is a random number.

Graph: The following graph is the Erlang density function with parameters $\beta = 1$ and $k = 1, 2$, and 3.

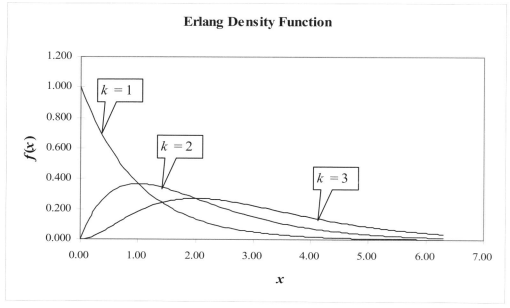

The Excel workbook "Distributions.xls" is on the ***OMWW CD*** available from www.ClamshellBeachPress.com. ◉

See *coefficient of variation, exponential distribution, gamma distribution, inverse transform method.*

ERP – See *Enterprise Resources Planning (ERP).*

error proofing – The process of identifying the likely causes of a failure and preventing the failure or at least mitigating the impact of the failure; also known as mistake proofing, fool proofing, idiot proofing, and fail safing. ✪

The Japanese phrase "poka yoke" (ポカヨケ) means "avoid mistakes." Error proofing principles can improve both product design and process design in all types of organizations – manufacturing, distribution, service, etc.

Error proofing is the application of risk management concepts and techniques applied to product design and process design to improve quality, efficiency, and safety. Failure Mode and Effects Analysis (FMEA) is a more formal approach to the error proofing process. FMEA is a process used to identify possible causes of failures (failure modes) and score them, helping establish which failure modes should be addressed first. Business continuity planning applies error proofing concepts at more strategic level.

Steps in error proofing

The error proofing process for both product design and process design involves the following steps:

1. **Identify error modes** – Identify what could go wrong (an error).
2. **Find prevention methods** – Determine ways that this type of error can be prevented before it occurs.
3. **Find detection/warning methods** – Determine ways that this type of error can be detected before it occurs (to warn the operator) or after it has occurred (to stop the process and fix the problem). Of course, it is best to detect the problem as early as possible. This is known as detection/warning.
4. **Evaluate, select, and implement the best error proofing methods** – Evaluate the potential prevention and detection/warning methods on cost, quality, efficiency, and safety and then select the best ones to implement. Of course, implementation of detection/warning methods require a process for how to handle warning signal has been sent or an fix an error that has been detected.

This process is very similar to Failure Mode and Effects Analysis (FMEA) mentioned above. The sections below will explain the prevention and detection/warning methods in more detail.

Types of error proofing applications

As mentioned above error proofing concepts can be applied to both product design and process design. Product design applications seek to prevent errors in the assembly process and/or in the use of the product. Process design applications seek to prevent error in the process that produces a good or service.

Error proofing applications can also be classified as either prevention or detection/warning. Prevention makes it impossible (or nearly impossible) for the error to occur. Detection/warning signals that an error is about to occur or has already occurred. For example, a microwave will not work if the door is open (a prevention device) and many cars will sound an alarm if the key is left in the ignition (a detection/warning device). A few years ago, some cars were designed not to start until the passengers had buckled their seat belts (a prevention device); but this prevention mechanism was too intrusive and was replaced by a warning beep (a detection/warning device).

The following two sections describe error proofing in both the product and process design context. The next two sections then describe the prevention and detection/warning methods for error proofing.

Error proofing for product design

A better product design can reduce errors to improve quality, efficiency, and safety in the manufacturing process and also in the use of the product by the customer. Error proofing principles can be used to help design products that can be assembled easier (in the factory or by the customer), learned quicker, and used more safely.

For example, many cars will not allow the gear shift to move to the drive position unless the driver's foot is on the brake. Extending an example from Professor John Grout, the gas fueling system in a typical automobile integrates many different error proofing devices (see the photo on the right.) The plastic tether keeps the gas cap from getting lost, the gas cap has a ratchet to signal proper tightness and prevent over-tightening (prevention), the filler hole is too small for the leaded-fuel nozzle, the gas cap has warning messages on it, and the fuel pump will shut off when the tank is full. (Professor Grout has many other interesting examples of error proofing on his website at csob.berry.edu/faculty/jgrout/everyday.html.)

Error proofing for process design

For process design, error proofing principles can be powerful tools for helping improve quality, efficiency, and safety.

Error proofing can be applied to all types of processes to improve safety. Safety is a major issue in nearly all industries in all countries. In 2006 in the United States, OSHA recorded 4,085,400 non-fatal workplace injuries and 5,703 fatal workplace injuries. (Source: www.bls.gov/iif/home.htm#News, December 7, 2007.) Application of error proofing principles is the key to improving these sad statistics.

Error proofing can also be applied to assembly operations to improve efficiency. For example, indicator lights with integrated sensors (see photo on right) can be used to show an assembler which bin to pick a part from. This is a Pick-to-Light solution from Banner Engineering Corp., the K50L. (Photo contributed by Banner Engineering, Minneapolis, Minnesota). A control system turns on the light showing the assembler which part bin to go to next. The integrated sensor detects if the part is picked from the correct bin, providing a signal to the control system to then move onto the next step or turn on an alarm signal or light.

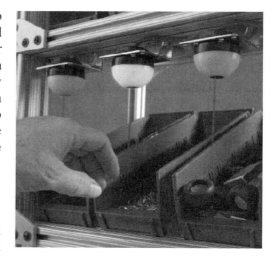

Error proofing – Prevention methods

The basic types of error proofing methods include prevention and detection/warning. Prevention methods can be further broken into three types:

1. **Control** – An action that self-corrects the problem, such as an automatic spell-checker that automatically corrects a misspelled word.
2. **Shutdown** – A device that shuts down the process when the error condition occurs, such as a home iron that shuts off after ten minutes of non-use is a good example.
3. **Human factors** – Use colors, shapes, symbols, sizes, sounds, and checklists to simplify a process to make it less error-prone for human operators. An example here is a "shadow-board" for a tool, which is an outline of the tool painted on a pegboard to signal to the worker where the tool belongs. Another example is the use of symbols for hazardous materials. For example, the symbol on the right is for radioactive materials.

Error proofing – Detection/warning methods

Detection/warning methods detect a problem and warn the operator when an error is about to occur or has already occurred. Unlike prevention methods, detection/warning methods do not control or shutdown the system. A car's oil light is a good example. The pick-to-light solution described above is also a good example. If the part is drawn from the wrong bin, a signal alerts the user (and the control system) that a mistake has been made so the user can quickly correct the problem. Prevention is almost always better than detection/warning because detection/warning relies on human intervention and warnings can be ignored, whereas prevention is automatic and without any human intervention.

Conclusions on error proofing

Error proofing principles can be a powerful way to improve both product design and process design. Prevention methods are generally better than detection/warning methods, but both types of methods can add value by improving quality, efficiency, and safety. Ideally, error proofing devices are simple, cheap, close to where the work is being done (visible), and result in what Shingo calls "100%" inspection – so that the end results is zero errors.

A tutorial on error proofing written by John R. Grout and Brian T. Downs can be found at www.campbell.berry.edu/faculty/jgrout/tutorial.html.

Acknowledgments: CEMBA 09 student Neal Schumacher (Vice President, Engineering, Banner Engineering Corporation) contributed to this entry.

The paper entitled "Error proofing" is available on the *OMWW CD* available from www.ClamshellBeachPress.com. ◉

See *andon light, autonomation, Business Process Re-engineering (BPR), check sheet, ergonomics, fail-safe, Failure Mode and Effects Analysis (FMEA), fault tree analysis, jidoka, muda, multiple-machine handling,*

Pareto's Law, process design, process improvement program, risk mitigation, Root Cause Analysis (RCA), shadow board, work simplification.

ESI – See *Early Supplier Involvement (ESI).*

ethnographic research – An approach for gathering qualitative cultural and behavioral information about a group of people.

Ethnography is based almost entirely on fieldwork where the ethnographer goes to the people who are the subject of study. The ethnographer lives among the people for a year or more, learning the local language and participating in everyday life while striving to maintain a degree of objective detachment. The ethnographer usually cultivates close relationships with "informants" who can provide specific information on aspects of cultural life. While detailed written notes are the mainstay of fieldwork, ethnographers may also use tape recorders, cameras, or video recorders. Ethnography is closed related to anthropology.

Businesses have found ethnographic research very helpful in understanding how people live, use products and services, and/or need potential products or services. Ethnographic research methods provide a systematic and holistic approach is valued by product and service developers as well as by marketing researchers. Ethnography studies what people actually say and do, which avoids many of the pitfalls that come from relying on self-reported, focus-group and survey data.

Acknowledgments: CEMBA 09 students David Moe, Cynthia Benson, Mark Thompson, Joel Hanson, Brenda Schramm, and Ashfaq Khan contributed to this entry.

ETO – See *Engineer to Order.*

EurOMA – See *European Operations Management Association.*

European Operations Management Association (EurOMA) – Europe's leading professional society for Operations Management scholars and practitioners.

EurOMA was originally formed as a UK group in 1984, and rapidly grew into Europe's leading professional association for those involved in Operations Management. The Europe-wide European Operations Management Association was in October 1993. EurOMA is an international network of academics and managers from around the world interested in developing Operations Management. It is a European-based network, with rapidly developing international links, where people can get together to communicate experience and ideas. It is also a network that bridges the gap between research and practice.

EurOMA publishes the ***International Journal of Operations & Production Management*** (***IJOPM***).

The website for EurOMA is www.euroma-online.org.

See *Operations Management (OM).*

EVA – See *Economic Value Added (EVA).*

expediting – The process of assigning a higher priority to a job so it gets started sooner.

Many firms have found that expediting can be counter productive. When many jobs in a factory are given a high priority, the expediting system becomes completely worthless. De-expediting is the process of assigning a lower priority to a job. Schedulers must realize that expediting one job is equivalent to de-expediting another. For example, when an ambulance comes down a highway, all other vehicles must move to the side. Expediting the ambulance, therefore, de-expedites all other vehicles on the road at that time.

See *dispatching rules, job shop scheduling.*

experience curve – See *learning curve.*

experience economy – See *experience engineering.*

experience engineering – The process of understanding and improving customer sensory and emotional interaction and reaction to a service or a product.

Two quotes highlight the main point of experience engineering:
- "Consumer preference and motivation are far less influenced by the functional attributes of products and services than the subconscious sensory and emotional elements derived by the total experience." – Professor Gerald Zaltman, Harvard University, Procter & Gamble's Future Forces Conference, Cincinnati, Ohio 1997. (Source: Berry, Carbone, and Haeckel, 2002.)
- "We need to look at our business as more than simply the building and selling of personal computers. Our business is the delivery of information and lifelike interactive experiences." – Andrew Grove, Chairman, Intel, COMDEX computer show, 1996. (Source: Pine and Gilmore, 1998.)

B. Joseph Pine II and James Gilmore, founders of the management consulting firm Strategic Horizons, wrote many of the early articles on this subject (Pine & Gilmore, 1998). They argue that economies go through four phases: Agriculture → Manufacturing → Service → Experiences.

Each phase is a step-up in economic value and a strategy for producers to differentiate their products and services in a competitive market. The experiences phase is the most interesting. As services become commoditized, organizations are looking for the next higher value (experiences) to differentiate their products and services. Many of the best organizations have learned from the Walt Disney Company and have found that they can differentiate their services by staging experiences. Pine and Gilmore (1998, 1999) talk about how organizations can "stage an experience" with services as the stage and goods as the props. The goal is to engage individuals in a way that creates a memorable event. While experiences have always been at the heart of the entertainment business, Pine and Gilmore argue that all organizations "stage an experience" when they engage customers in a personal and memorable way.

Pine and Gilmore (1999) offer five design principles that drive the creation of memorable experiences:

1. Create a consistent theme that resonates throughout the entire experience.
2. Reinforce the theme with positive cues (e.g., easy-to-follow signs).
3. Eliminate negative cues, those visual or aural messages that distract or contradict the theme (e.g., dirty floors, dim lights).
4. Offer memorabilia that commemorate the experience for the user (toys, dolls, etc.).
5. Engage all five senses (sight, sound, smell, taste, and touch) to heighten the experience and make it more memorable (e.g., the fragrant smell of a great restaurant).

Clued In (Carbone 2004) builds on Pine and Gilmore's work and presents two types of "clues" customers pick up in their customer experience – functional clues and emotional clues. These are compared below.

Experience engineering – functional and emotional clues

Functional clues	Emotional clues
• Actual functioning of the good or service. • Interpreted primarily by the logic part of the brain. • The minimum requirement to enter the game. • Example: Did the plumber fix the leak?	• Smells, sounds, sights, tastes, and textures. • The environment in which it is offered. • Two types of emotional clues: *Mechanics* – Clues emitted by things (signs, facilities, etc.) *Humanics* – Clues emitted by people (gestures, comments, dress, voice tone) • Examples: Feel of leather upholstery, sound and smell of a steak on a grill, tone of the service rep.

Carbone argues that emotional clues can work synergistically with functional clues to create customer value. He further proposes that customer value is equal to the functional benefits plus the emotional benefits less the financial and non-financial costs. He concludes that organizations should manage the emotional component of their products and services with the same rigor that they bring to managing product and service functionality.

See *mass customization, service, service blueprinting, service quality.*

exponential distribution – The exponential distribution is a continuous probability distribution often used to model the time between arrivals for random events such as a machine breakdown or customer arrival to a system; also known as the negative exponential distribution.

Density and distribution functions: The exponential distribution has only one parameter (β), which is the mean. The density and distribution functions for $x > 0$ are $f(x) = (1/\beta)e^{-x/\beta}$ and $F(x) = 1 - e^{-x/\beta}$.

Statistics: Range $[0, \infty)$, mean β, variance β^2, mode 0. A good indicator of an exponentially distributed random variable is a sample coefficient of variation (sample mean/sample standard deviation) close to one.

Excel: In Excel, the exponential density and distribution values are $=(1/\beta)\text{EXP}(-x/\beta)$ and $=1-\text{EXP}(-x/\beta)$ respectively.

Excel simulation: In a simulation in Excel, exponentially distributed random variates can be generated with $-\beta \ln(\text{RAND}())$. Notice that the negative sign in this equation is correct. The natural log of a random number in the range $(0,1]$ will be negative.

Graph: The following is a graph of the exponential density function with mean of 1.

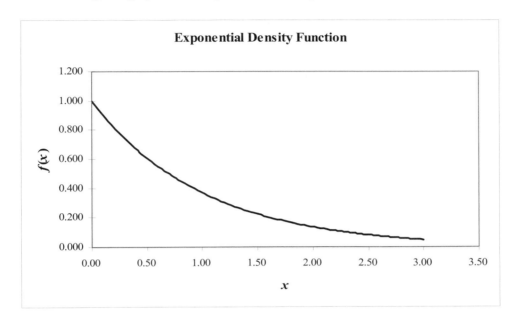

The exponential is a special case of the gamma, Erlang, and Weibull distributions. The exponential distribution is the only continuous distribution that has the memory-less property (e.g., $P(X > t + s \mid X > t) = P(X > s)$ for all $t, s > 0$).

The Excel workbook "Distributions.xls" is on the **OMWW CD** available from www.ClamshellBeachPress.com. ◉

See *coefficient of variation, Erlang distribution, gamma distribution, inverse transform method, Poisson distribution, queuing theory, Weibull distribution.*

exponential smoothing – A time-series forecasting method based on a weighted moving average where the weights decline geometrically with the age of the data; a procedure that smoothes graphical times series data. ✪

Overview

Exponential smoothing is probably the most popular time-series extrapolation forecasting technique. It can also be used as a data smoothing technique. The focus here will be on the use of exponential smoothing for forecasting.

An "exponentially smoothed" average is a moving average that puts much more weight on recent demand (sales) data. The weights decline geometrically back in time. (Note: Exponential smoothing should have been called geometric smoothing.) The average at the end of a period is used as the forecast for every period into the future. Exponential smoothing can be extended to include both trend and seasonal patterns.

Simple exponential smoothing (with no trend and no seasonality)

With simple exponential smoothing, the forecast for the demand in the next period is just the exponentially smoothed average at the end of period t. In other words, the one-period ahead forecast is $F_{t+1} = A_t$ and the n-period ahead forecast is just $F_{t+n} = A_t$.

Simple exponential smoothing uses a simple equation to update the exponentially smoothed average at the end of period t. The exponentially smoothed average at the end of period t is the exponentially smoothed average at the end of period $t-1$ plus some fraction (α) of the forecast error. The constant α (alpha) is called the smoothing constant and is in the range $0 < \alpha < 1$. The updating equation can be written as $A_t = A_{t-1} + \alpha E_t$ where the forecast error is $E_t = D_t - F_t$ and D_t is the actual demand (sales) in period t. The updating equation can be rewritten algebraically as:

$$A_t = A_{t-1} + \alpha E_t$$
$$= A_{t-1} + \alpha(D_t - A_{t-1})$$
$$= \alpha D_t + (1-\alpha)A_{t-1}$$

This suggests that the new exponentially smoothed average is linear combination of the new demand and the old average. For example, when $\alpha = 0.1$, the new average is 10% of the new demand plus 90% of the old average.

The A_{t-1} term in the above equation can be defined in terms of the average at the end of period $t-2$, e.g., $A_{t-1} = \alpha D_{t-1} + (1-\alpha)A_{t-2}$. The equation for A_{t-2} can be further expanded to show that:

$$A_t = \alpha D_t + (1-\alpha)A_{t-1}$$
$$= \alpha D_t + \alpha(1-\alpha)D_{t-1} + \alpha(1-\alpha)^2 D_{t-2} + \cdots + \alpha(1-\alpha)^k D_{t-k}$$

This means that A_t, the exponentially smoothed average at the end of period t, is a weighted average with the weight for demand at lag k of $\alpha(1-\alpha)^k$. For example, when $\alpha = 0.1$, the weight for the demand $k = 5$ periods ago is $0.1(1-0.1)^5 = 0.059$. These weights decline geometrically as the time lag k increases, which suggests that exponential smoothing should probably have been called geometric smoothing.

Exponential smoothing with trend

When a trend component is included, the one-period ahead forecast is $F_{t+1} = A_t + T_t$, where T_t is the exponentially smoothed trend at the end of period t. The n-period ahead forecast is then $F_{t+n} = A_t + nT_t$. The apparent trend in period t is the change in the exponentially smoothed average $A_t - A_{t-1}$. The trend, therefore, can be smoothed in the same way as the average demand was smoothed using the following equation:

$$T_t = \beta(A_t - A_{t-1}) + (1-\beta)T_{t-1}$$

where β (beta) is the smoothing constant for the trend with $0 < \beta < 1$. When a trend component is included, the updating equation for the exponentially smoothed average should be $A_t = \alpha D + (1-\alpha)(A_{t-1} + T_{t-1})$.

The exponential smoothing with trend model is sometimes called "double exponential smoothing" because it is smoothing the difference between the smoothed averages. Gardner (2005) suggests that the trend be "damped" (reduced) for multiple period ahead forecasts. The damped one-period ahead forecasting equation is $F_{t+1} = A_t + \phi T_t$, where $0 \le \phi \le 1$ is the dampening factor. For multiple period head forecasts, the equation is

$F_{t+n} = A_t + T_t \sum_{k=1}^{n} \phi^k$. The damping parameter ϕ can be estimated from historical data.

Exponential smoothing with seasonality

Exponential smoothing can be extended to handle seasonality by using a multiplicative seasonal factor. The one-period ahead forecast is the underlying average times the seasonal factor (e.g., $F_{t+1} = A_t \cdot R$, where R is the multiplicative seasonal factor). The seasonal factors are generally in the range (0.3 to 3.0), indicating the that the lowest demand period is about 30% of the average and the highest demand period is about 300% of the average.

The one-period ahead forecast is defined as $F_{t+1} = A_t R_{t+1-m}$, where A_t is the underlying deseasonalized average and the multiplicative seasonal factor (R_{t+1-m}) inflates or deflates this average to adjust for seasonality. The seasonal factor for the forecast in period $t+1$ has the subscript $t+1-m$ to indicate that it was last updated m periods ago, where m is the number of periods in a season. For example, m = 12 for monthly forecasts. The seasonal factor for a forecast made in January 2008 for February 2008 uses the seasonal factor that was last updated in February 2007.

The n-period ahead equation for forecasting with seasonality is then $F_{t+n} = A_t R_{t+n-m}$, where F_{t+n} is the forecast n periods ahead and R_{t+n-m} is the exponentially smoothed multiplicative seasonal factor for period $t+n$.

The updating equation for the deseasonalized smoothed average is $A_t = \alpha D_t / R_{t-m} + (1-\alpha)A_{t-1}$. Multiplying by R_{t+n-m} adjusts for seasonality so dividing by R_{t+n-m} deseasonalizes the demand. The term D_t / R_{t-m}, therefore, is the deseasonalized demand in period t. The seasonal factors can be smoothed using the equation $R_t = \gamma D_t / A_t + (1-\gamma)R_{t-m}$, where D_t / A_t is the apparent deseasonalized demand in period t and γ (gamma) is the smoothing constant for seasonality with $0 < \gamma < 1$.

Exponential smoothing with trend and seasonality

Exponential smoothing with trend and seasonality is known as the Winters' Model (Winter 1960), the Holt-Winters model, and as triple exponential smoothing. The forecast equation is $F_{t+n} = (A_t + nT_t)R_{t+n-m}$, where F_{t+n} is the forecast n periods ahead, T_t is the exponentially smoothed trend at the end of period t, and R_{t+n-m} is the exponentially smoothed multiplicative seasonal factor for period $t + n$.

The equations for the Winters' model are as follows. These equations should be implemented in this order.

$$A_t = \alpha D_t / R_{t-m} + (1-\alpha)(A_{t-1} + T_{t-1})$$ Smoothed de-seasonalized average

$$T_t = \beta(A_t - A_{t-1}) + (1-\beta)T_{t-1}$$ Smoothed trend

$$R_t = \gamma D_t / A_t + (1-\gamma)R_{t-m}$$ Smoothed seasonal factor

$$F_{t+n} = (A_t + nT_t)R_{t+n-m}$$ Forecast for period $t + n$

Initializing the smoothed average

When implementing any type of exponential smoothing model, the question arises of how to initialize the smoothed average for the first period. The easiest approach for the smoothed average is to use the first value as the smoothed average (i.e., $A_1 = D_1$). A recent moving average is probably a better approach. Exponential smoothing will discount this initial value fairly quickly depending, of course, on the value of alpha.

Initializing the smoothed trend

The easiest approach for initializing the trend (T_0) is to fit a trend line through the last n periods of historical data. The following equation can be used to do this:

$$T_0 = \frac{6}{n(n-1)}\left(\frac{2}{n+1}\sum_{t=1}^{n}tD_t - \sum_{t=1}^{n}D_t\right)$$

When the demand has seasonality, it is better to estimate the overall average slope from the slope between each successive season. This is shown in the following equation where each season has m periods:

$$T_0 = \frac{1}{n-m}\left(\sum_{t=m+1}^{n}(D_t - D_{t-m})/m\right)$$

Initializing and updating seasonal factors

The centered moving average is probably the best approach for initializing seasonal factors. Conceptually, the centered moving average approach for period t estimates the seasonal factor for period t by taking an average with period t as the center. Mathematically, the centered moving average for period t is:

$$CMA_t = \begin{cases} \left(\frac{1}{2}D_{t-m/2} + \frac{1}{2}D_{t+m/2} + \sum_{k=t-m/2+1}^{t+m/2-1} D_k\right)/m & \text{when } m \text{ is even.} \\ \sum_{k=t-\lfloor m/2 \rfloor}^{t+\lfloor m/2 \rfloor} D_k / m & \text{when } m \text{ is odd.} \end{cases}$$

where D_t is the historical demand (sales) in period t, m is the number of periods in a season, and $\lfloor x \rfloor$ is the round-down function (e.g., $\lfloor 3.9 \rfloor = 3$). For example, for monthly forecasts, m is even ($m=12$ months/year), and the centered moving average for July ($t = 7$) is the sum of one-half of the demand in January last year plus one-half the demand in January this year plus the total demand from February to December last year, all divided by 12. For another example, for daily forecasts m is odd ($m = 7$ days/week), sum the demand from three days before t to three days after t and then divide by 7.

The Winters' model updates the seasonal factors for each item independently of all other items. However, the variability of individual item forecast errors is usually high, which can lead to poor updates of the seasonal factors each period. It is a good idea, therefore, to take advantage of the fact that many items have a similar seasonal pattern and create just one set of seasonal factors for all items in the set. This suggests that exponential smoothing should not be used for individual seasonal factors. Instead, seasonal factors should either be smoothed for an entire group of items or not smoothed at all.

Estimating the model parameters

The average age of the data for simple exponential smoothing can be proven to be $1/\alpha$ periods. For an N-period moving average, the average age of the data can be proven to be $(N+1)/2$ periods. Equating these two expressions, the relationship between the α parameter for simple exponential smoothing and the N parameter for an N-period moving average is given by $\alpha = 2/(N+1)$ or $N = 2/\alpha - 1$. While this might be an interesting fact to some, it is not very helpful when estimating the best value for the α parameter.

The forecasting company i2 recommends that the parameters for exponential smoothing with trend use the relationship $\beta = \alpha/2$ and that for exponential smoothing with trend and seasonal use the relationships $\beta = \alpha/2$ and $\gamma = \alpha + \beta$. Using these relationships dramatically simplifies the search procedure.

The Winters' model has three parameters (α, β, γ) that must be estimated. If the user has sufficient historical data, a direct search procedure can be used to find the values for these parameters that minimize the mean squared error (MSE) or the mean absolute errors (MAD). The MAD approach is probably better given that time series data often has outliers that could unduly influence the results. A univariate search can be done for one parameter at a time using Excel's goal seek tool (or with Brent's method) or a response surface approach can be done to optimize all of the parameters simultaneously using Excel's solver or some other response surface search tool.

Extensions

Some authors have suggested that the smoothing parameters should be adaptive and change automatically based on an analysis of the forecast error; however, some research has found that adaptive smoothing approaches to forecasting can be unreliable. The best approach is probably to have an exception report (demand filter or tracking signal) communicate the need for review by an analyst.

Exponential smoothing does a poor job of forecasting when the demand is "lumpy" (e.g., has lots of zeros between demands). A good rule of thumb is that any item with a demand that has a coefficient of variation greater than 1 has "lumpy" demand and therefore should not be forecasted with exponential smoothing methods. Croston (1972) suggested a method for forecasting the time between "lumps" and the size of the lumps, but few firms have used this approach. This author has experimented with Croston's method and found it to be unreliable. The only practical approach for lumpy demand is to increase the size of the time buckets.

The paper "Forecasting with Exponential Smoothing" and the Excel workbook "winters.xls" are on the ***OMWW CD*** available from www.ClamshellBeachPress.com. ◉

See *Box-Jenkins forecasting, centered moving average, coefficient of variation, demand, demand filter, forecast error metrics, forecasting, lumpy demand, Mean Absolute Percent Error (MAPE), moving average, Relative Absolute Error (RAE), seasonal factor, seasonality, time-series forecasting, tracking signal, trend.*

eXtensible Markup Language – See *XML*.

external setup – Another name for an off-line setup.
See *setup reduction methods.*

extranet – The use of Internet/intranet technology to serve an extended enterprise, including defined sets of customers or suppliers or other partners.

An extranet is typically behind a firewall, just as an intranet usually is, and closed to the public (a "closed user group"), but is open to the selected partners, unlike a pure intranet. More loosely, the term may apply to mixtures of open and closed networks.

See *corporate portal, e-business, intranet.*

F

facility layout – The physical organization of processes in a facility. ✪

The layout problem is to locate processes (workcenters) in a facility in order to minimize the total cost. The total cost in a factory is primarily the handling cost to move materials between processes. The total cost in non-factory settings such as banks and hospitals is usually the cost of people traveling between processes. The optimization problem is constrained by the size, shape, and number of floors for the facility and the size and shape of each of the processes. Some processes must be located next to each other and others cannot be located next to each other due to heat, sound, or vibration issues. Other issues to consider include total cycle time, waste, space efficiency, communications, safety, security, quality, maintenance, flexibility, customer waiting time, aesthetics for workers, and aesthetics for customers.

The layout problem is not unique to manufacturing. Service businesses such as hospitals and banks have the same issues. Retailers use planogram methods to help determine the layout within a retail store. Similar layout problems are common in other design contexts such as laying out an integrated circuit.

The three basic types of facility layouts include the process layout (functional layout), the product layout, and the fixed-position (project) layout. Each of these is discussed briefly below.

Process layout (functional layout) – A layout that groups similar activities together in departments or workcenters according to the process or function that they perform. For example, all of the drills might be located together in the drill workcenter. The process layout is generally used in operations that are required to serve a wide variety of customer needs. In order to handle the variety of needs, the equipment must be able to serve many purposes and the workforce needs to be highly skilled. While process layouts offer high flexibility, they are relatively inefficient because of long queues, long cycle times, and high materials handling costs.

The best example of a process layout is a job shop. The major concerns in a process layout are cycle times, utilization, order promising, and scheduling.

Traditional industrial engineering approaches to this process layout include process analysis, simple graphical methods, computer simulation, and computer optimization. CRAFT (Computerized Relative Allocation of Facilities Technique) is a heuristic approach developed by Buffa, Armour, and Vollmann (1964) that uses a heuristic (non-optimal) approach to solving a quadratic assignment formulation of the facility layout problem.

Product layout – A product layout arranges activities in a line according to the sequence of operations that need to be performed to manufacture or assemble a particular product. Each product usually has its own dedicated line. Product layouts are suitable for mass production or repetitive operations in which demand is steady and volume is high. Product layouts tend to be relatively efficient, but not very flexible.

The best example of a product layout is an assembly line. The major concern in a product is balancing the line. In designing an assembly line, many tasks (elements) need to be assigned to workers. These assignments are constrained by the target cycle time for the product and precedence relationships between the tasks (e.g., some tasks need to be done before others). The line balancing problem is to assign tasks to workstations in order to minimize the number of workstations required while satisfying the cycle time and precedence constraints. Many operations researchers have developed sophisticated mathematical computer models to solve this problem. The webpage www.wiwi.uni-jena.de/Entscheidung/alb provides an overview of the research on the problem. The line balancing problem becomes less important when the organization can use cross-trained workers who can move between stations as needed to maximize flow.

Cellular manufacturing is a powerful approach for converting some equipment in a process layout into a product layout for families of parts. See the entry on *cellular manufacturing*. Mixed model assembly allows some firms to justify having a product layout that is not dedicated to any one particular product. See the entry on *mixed model assembly*.

Fixed-position layout (project-layout) – A fixed-position layout is used in projects where the workers, equipment, and materials go to the production site because the product is too large, fragile, or heavy to move. This type of layout is also called a project layout because the work is usually organized around projects. The equipment is often left on-site because it is too expensive to move frequently. Due to the nature of the work, the workers in a fixed position layout are usually highly skilled.

The best example is the construction of a large office tower. Other examples include ship building and machine repair. The major concerns with a fixed-position layout are finishing the project within specifications, within budget, and within schedule. See the entry on *project management*.

The Theory of Constraints literature suggests that the focus for all layouts should be on the bottleneck process. See the entry on *Theory of Constraints*.

See *5S, assembly line, cellular manufacturing, CRAFT, cross-training, flowshop, focused factory, job order costing, lean thinking, line balancing, mixed model assembly, planogram, plant-within-a-plant, process design, process layout, process map, product layout, product-process matrix, project management, spaghetti chart, Theory of Constraints (TOC), workcenter.*

facility location – The physical site for a building. ✪

The facility location problem is to find the best locations for the organization's facilities (e.g., warehouses, stores, factories, offices). The facility location problem is often defined in terms of minimizing the sum of the incoming and outgoing transportation costs. In a retail context, the problem is often defined in terms of maximizing revenue. In the service context, the problem is defined in terms of meeting some service criterion, such as customer travel time or response time for customer needs.

Facility location theory suggests that the problem can be broken into finite and infinite set location models. The finite set location models evaluate a limited number of locations and determine which one is best. The infinite set location models find the best x-y coordinates (or latitudes and longitudes) for a site (or sites) that minimize some mathematical objective function. The center-of-gravity and numeric-analytic location models are both infinite set location models. The gravity model for competitive retail store location and the Kepner-Tregoe Model are both finite set location models.

Some location models assume that vehicles can travel directly across any geography, while others assume that vehicles are constrained to existing transportation networks. Some models assume that cost is simply proportional to the distance or time traveled, whereas others include all of the relevant costs including tariffs, duties, tolls, etc.

See *center-of-gravity model for facility location*, *gravity model for competitive retail store location*, *great circle distance*, *greenfield*, *Kepner-Tregoe Model*, *numeric-analytic location model*, *process design*, *process map*.

factor analysis – See *cluster analysis*.

Fagan Defect-Free Process – A method of reviewing products that incorporates a formal process and encourages continuous improvement.

Michael Fagan created the method when he was a product manager working for IBM. Products are reviewed by a team of four people who are assigned roles: Moderator, Reader, Author, and Tester. At least three of the four team members must have sufficient knowledge of the product to allow them to decide whether the material violates a predefined set of rules. The team members individually review the product for two uninterrupted hours. After individually reviewing the product the team meets to inspect the material. The inspection consists of the reader introducing the material to the team in appropriately sized pieces. Documents are introduced one paragraph at a time. The other team members ask questions about potential rule violations they think they have identified. The author answers questions raised by other team members. The moderator keeps the inspection moving and either records the problems found or delegates this to another team member. The tester can be a member of the quality team in the organization or someone who is involved in product testing.

Participants learn about mistakes that are being made when a product is produced. When the author learns about mistakes they have made, they have an opportunity for continuous improvement. Team members are not restricted to workers that produce the product. In fact, management personnel are encouraged to be team members. However, all team members must play an active role. The process expressly prohibits observers.

The process provides a way to identify systemic problems with work products. These lessons learned can then be applied to other, similar products that have not been subjected to the inspection process.

The process allows early detection of problems before the product is used as an input for other activities. This process is usually applied to software products such as source code, but it can also be applied to other work products such as documents and drawings.

Companies that have implemented the Fagan Defect-Free Process have reported significant benefits with respect to:
- Cycle time (mostly due to reducing test time and effort).
- Customer-reported defects.
- Schedule and budget achievement.
- Productivity.
- Customer satisfaction.

The Fagan Defect-Free Process is explained in greater detail in the Michael Fagan Associates website www.mfagan.com.

Acknowledgments: Brian Dye MOT 04 contributed to this entry.

See *New Product Development (NPD)*.

fail-safe – See *error proofing*.

Failure Mode and Effects Analysis (FMEA) – A process that identifies the possible causes of failures (failure modes), scores them to create a risk priority number, and then mitigates risk starting with the most important failure mode. ✪

Background on FMEA

Failure Mode and Effects Analysis was invented by NASA early in the US Apollo space program. NASA created the tool to alleviate the stress between two conflicting mottos; "failure is not an option" and "perfect is the enemy of good." The first meant successfully completing the mission and returning the crew. The second meant that failure of at least some components was unavoidable.

FMEA is a simple process that identifies the possible causes of failures (failure modes), scores them on three dimensions (severity, occurrence, and detection) to create a risk priority number, and then mitigates risk starting with the most important failure mode. The first step in an FMEA is to identify all potential failure modes where a failure might occur. Once these failure modes have been identified, FMEA then requires that each one be scored on three dimensions: severity, occurrence, and detection. All three dimensions are scored on a 1 to 10 scale where 1 is low and 10 is high. These three scores are then multiplied to produce a Risk Priority Number (RPN). The failure models can then be prioritized based on the RPNs and risk mitigation efforts can then be designed for the more important failure modes.

FMEA was created as a proactive approach before a failure occurs. Root cause analysis is a more appropriate tool to use after a failure has occurred.

The three dimensions of FMEA

The scoring part of an FMEA requires the subjective evaluation of three dimensions for each failure mode, where each dimension is scored on a 1 to 10 scale:

Severity – Impact of the failure. If failure occurred, what is the significance of the harm of this failure in terms of cost, time, quality, customer satisfaction, etc.?

Occurrence – Frequency of occurrence. What is the probability that this failure will occur? (This is sometimes called the probability of occurrence.)

Detection – Ability to detect the problem and avoid the impact. Can the failure be detected early enough that it does not have a severe impact? (Important note: A 10 on detection means that it is hard to detect.)

Risk Priority Number (RPN) = (Severity) x (Occurrence) x (Detection)

It is easy to create an Excel workbook for FMEA. The following is a typical format. These actions usually target the likelihood of occurrence, but should also seek to make detection easier and reduce severity. After creating the workbook, the user can sort the rows by the RPN to prioritize the "actions to reduce risk."

Process step	Failure Mode	Failure causes	Failure effects	Severity (1-10)	Likelihood of occurrence (1-10)	Likelihood of detection (1-10)	Risk priority number (RPN)	Actions to reduce risk
Diagnosis	Incorrect diagnosis	Tests not performed	No treatment given					
		Tests not read correctly	Improper treatment given					

Severity: 1-10 (10 = Very severe)
Likelihood of occurrence: 1-10 (10 = Very likely to occur)
Likelihood of detection: 1-10 (10 = Very unlikely to detect)

Scales for the three dimensions of the risk priority number

One of the criticisms of FMEA is that none of the three scales is well anchored, which makes it hard for respondents to know what a 1, 5, or 10 means. This problem allows for a wide variety of interpretations. Isixsigma.com offers scales at main.isixsigma.com/forum/showmessage.asp?messageID=15024. However, those scales are confusing. The following scales make more sense to this author:

Score	Severity	Occurence[1]		Detectability
10	Absolutely catastrophic impact	Absolutely will fail	$p \approx 100\%$	Absolutely will not detect
9			$p \approx 50\%$	
8	Very severe impact	Very likely will fail	$p \approx 25\%$	Very unlikely to detect
7			$p \approx 12\%$	
6	Severe impact	Likely to fail	$p \approx 6\%$	Unlikely to detect
5	Minor impact	Unlikely to fail	$p \approx 3\%$	Likely will detect
4			$p \approx 1\%$	
3	Very minor impact	Very unlikely will fail	$p \approx 1/1000$	Very likely will detect
2			$p \approx 1/10,000$	
1	Absolutely no impact at all	Absolutely will not fail	$p \approx 1/100,000$	Absolutely will detect

[1] This is the probability of a failure over a defined planning horizon.   Source: Professor Arthur V. Hill

Steps in an FMEA

The following steps can be used to conduct an FMEA:

1. Identify each part or process step – For example, preparation for an MRI-magnetic resonance imaging in a hospital.
2. Identify potential failure modes – Identify all possible ways that the part or process could fail.
3. Identify the potential effects for each failure model – These are the consequences on other systems, parts, or people and could involve issues such as noise, smell, injury, and death.
4. Rank severity of the effect using a 1-10 scale.
5. Evaluate the potential causes for each failure – List every potential cause and/or failure mechanism such as incorrect material, improper maintenance, fatigue, or wear.
6. Rank the possibility of occurrence (1-10) – Remote to high.
7. List current design controls – List prevention and detection activities to assure design adequacy and prevent or reduce occurrence.
8. Rank ability to detect a failure using these controls (1-10) – From almost certain to absolute uncertainty. (Be careful with the direction of this scale.)
9. Calculate the risk-priority number for failure mode – RPN = (severity) x (occurrence) x (detection)
10. Design recommended improvement actions – Design additional actions to reduce severity, occurrence, and detection ratings. Severity of 9 or 10 requires special attention.
11. Assign responsibility and target completion date for implementing designed improvements.
12. Monitor actions taken and effects on RPN.

Criticisms of FMEA

Detectability – FMEA is a simple process, but it is not very scientific. Many users struggle with understanding and scoring the detection dimension. Detection is a type of risk mitigation. When scoring detection, the person doing the scoring must make a number of assumptions about how quickly the failure will be identified and how it will be addressed. These assumptions can lead to inconsistent delectability scores. As a result, some firms report that they are only using the first two dimensions. If detectability is used, the scale should be clearly defined and anchored at three points.

Occurrence – Some decision theorists are troubled by the 1 to 10 scoring for probabilities and suggest that estimating subjective probabilities would be easier to understand and more precise. The word "occurrence" is a little vague and the scale is often poorly defined. Again, if a 1-10 scale is used it should be clearly defined and anchored at three or more points.

Severity – Decision theorists suggest that severity be changed from a subjective 1-10 scale to an economic scale measured in money lost. The scale should at least be clearly defined and anchored at three points.

Prioritizing risk mitigation efforts – FMEA implies that the only issue to consider in ranking (prioritizing) risk mitigation projects is the Risk Priority Number (RPN). However, other issues such as the cost of the risk mitigation effort should also play an important role in setting priorities for allocating risk mitigation resources.

Conclusions for FMEA

Despite the above criticisms, many organizations have found FMEA to be a powerful tool for helping them prioritize risk mitigation efforts. At 3M and other firms, FMEA is a required tool for all Six Sigma projects. Whereas Root Cause Analysis (RCA) identifies contributors to an adverse event after the fact, FMEA is intended to be a proactive (before the fact) tool. Ideally, FMEA anticipates all adverse events before they occur.

See the entry on *Design Failure Mode and Effects Analysis (DFMEA)* for information about how FMEA can be applied to design activities.

The Excel workbook "FMEA.xls" is on the **OMWW CD** available from www.ClamshellBeachPress.com. ⊙

See *Business Continuity Management (BCM), causal map, critical path, Design Failure Mode and Effects Analysis (DFMEA), error proofing, fault tree analysis, Hazard Analysis & Critical Point Control (HACCP), operations performance metrics, Pareto Chart, Pareto's Law, risk, risk assessment, risk mitigation, robust, Root Cause Analysis (RCA), Six Sigma, work simplification.*

FAS – See *Final Assembly Schedule (FAS)*.

fault tree analysis – A graphical management tool for describing the cause and effect relationships that result in major failures; a causal map usually used to identify and solve the causes for a specific actual historical problem.

Fault tree analysis is a causal map drawn from the top down. The actual historical fault or major failure being analyzed is identified as the "top event." All of the possible causes of the top event are identified in a tree. The only distinctive of a fault tree is the use of "OR" nodes for independent causes and "AND" nodes for multiple causes that must exist concurrently for a failure to occur.

See *causal map, error proofing, Failure Mode and Effects Analysis (FMEA), root cause analysis.*

faxban – A pull signal for a kanban system that is sent via fax.

Faxban uses fax communication rather than physical kanban cards to send a pull signal. Faxban can reduce the delay between the time that pull is needed and the time that the pull signal is sent. An e-kanban is very similar except that the signal is sent via email, EDI, or through the web.

See *kanban.*

fuel surcharge – An extra charge added to the cost of a shipment to cover the variable cost of fuel.

FIFO – See *First-in-First-out (FIFO)*.

fill rate – An inventory service level metric that measures the percent of the customer demand that is filled immediately from inventory. ✪

Retailers, distributors, and manufacturers that sell products from stock need a good service level measure related to their inventory investment. The terms "fill rate" and "service level" are often used synonymously in many Make to Stock firms. One of the best measures of the inventory service level is the unit fill rate, which is the percent of units demanded (ordered) that are filled immediately from stock. Some firms modify this slightly by defining it as the percent of units that are shipped within X hours from the time the order was received.

While the unit fill rate is often considered the easiest to use from a mathematical point of view, many firms use similar measures such as the line fill rate, the order fill rate, and the perfect order fill rate. The line fill rate is the percent of lines on purchase orders that are filled immediately from stock. (Note that each item ordered on a purchased order is called a "line.") An order fill rate is the percent of orders filled immediately from stock. The perfect order fill rate is the percent of orders that are perfect in every way – available on-time, with perfect quality, perfect quantity, perfect billing, perfect packaging, etc. The perfect order fill rate is the most demanding standard and will always be lower than the others. The cycle service level is a simple but inaccurate measure of service level that measures the probability of a stockout event on one order cycle. The *service level* and *safety stock* entries have much more detail on this subject.

See *in-stocks, operations performance metrics, perfect order fill rate, reorder point, safety stock, service level.*

Final Assembly Schedule (FAS) – A schedule for the assemble-to-order portion of a manufacturing process.

Assemble-to-order firms will build and/or buy materials, sub-assemblies, and components and keep them in inventory until a customer order arrives. At that point, they will assemble the product to the customer's specifications. Many manufacturing firms will use an MRP system to plan the production and purchase of all major components and then use the FAS to schedule the final assembly for specific customer orders after those orders arrive. The FAS is a short term schedule with a horizon of only a week or two.

See *Master Production Schedule (MPS)*.

financial performance metrics – Economic measures of success. ✪

Operations managers need to have a good understanding of financial performance metrics in order to make good decisions regarding capital investments such as new plants and equipment and also for process improvement projects. In most organizations, the financial performance metrics are the main goal, but the operations performance metrics are often the "drivers" of the financial metrics. The cross-references below include most of the metrics that operations managers need to know.

See *Balanced Scorecard, break-even analysis, Compounded Annual Growth Rate (CAGR), DuPont Analysis, EBITDA, Economic Value Added (EVA), Internal Rate of Return (IRR), Net Present Value (NPV), operations performance metrics, payback period, performance management system, Return on Assets (ROA), Return on Capital Employed (ROCE), Return on Investment (ROI), Return on Net Assets (RONA), sunk cost, total cost of ownership, Y-tree*.

finished goods inventory – The inventory units (or dollars) that are "finished" (completed) and ready for shipment and/or sale to a customer. ✪

Other types of inventory include raw materials, Work-in-Process (WIP), MRO (Maintenance-Repair-Operations), and pipeline (in-transit) inventory.

See *Work-in-Process (WIP) inventory*.

finite loading – See *finite scheduling*.

finite population queuing model – See *queuing theory*.

finite scheduling – Creating a sequence of activities with associated times so that no resource (person, machine, tool, etc.) is assigned more work time than the time available.

The opposite of finite scheduling is infinite loading, which ignores capacity constraints when creating a schedule. Professor Sum Chee Chuong at the National University of Singapore developed some useful language for understanding finite scheduling:

Due-date feasible schedule – A schedule that satisfies all due date requirements for all tasks (orders or operations).

Start-date feasible schedule – A schedule that does not have any tasks (orders or operations) scheduled before the current time.

Capacity feasible schedule – A schedule that does not require any resource to work more time than is available in any period.

Most finite scheduling systems begin with the current due date and therefore will always create start-date feasible schedules. However, if the capacity is insufficient, these systems will not be able to create due-date feasible schedules.

In contrast, MRP systems plan backwards from the due date and therefore always create due-date feasible schedules. However, MRP systems are infinite loading systems and ignore capacity when creating a schedule, which means that they will often create schedules that are not capacity feasible. MRP systems also often create schedules that are not start-date feasible and schedule work in the "past-due" time bucket.

While many ERP systems and project management tools have finite scheduling capabilities, few firms use these tools. Most firms use infinite loading for both ERP and project management and then resolve resource contention issues after the plan (schedule) has been created. Finite scheduling was one of the main needs that motivated the development of Advanced Planning and Scheduling (APS) systems.

See *Advanced Planning and Scheduling (APS), backward loading, closed-loop MRP, forward scheduling, load leveling, Materials Requirements Planning (MRP), project management*.

first mover advantage – The benefit that is sometimes gained by the first significant company to enter a new market.

Amazon is good example of a firm that gained significant advantage from being the first significant firm to enter the market. Although other firms sold books on the internet before Amazon, Amazon was the first firm to do so with appropriate systems and capitalization. Now that Amazon has established itself as the largest internet book retailer, it has the economies of scale to have low transaction costs (through good information systems and good order fulfillment operations) and the economies of scope to offer superior value to publishers and authors. The same arguments can be made for eBay in the on-line auction market.

Of course, the first firm in a market is not always able to establish a long-term competitive advantage. Dell Computer currently has the highest market share for personal computers, but many other firms such as IBM, Apple, and Compaq, entered this market long before Dell.

See *operations strategy*.

first pass yield – See *yield*.

first pick ratio – During order picking, the percentage of orders or lines for which 100% completion was achieved from the primary location or picking face.

See *picking*.

First-In-First-Out (FIFO) – Using the arrival date as the priority for processing or as an accounting rule.

First-In-First-Out (FIFO) has several similar meanings:

Service priority – The customer who arrived first is serviced first. This is a common practice in medical clinics and restaurants.

Production scheduling – The customer order that was received first is processed first. Most lean systems use the FIFO rule. While FIFO is the "fairest" rule, it can be shown that other dispatching rules often have better shop performance in terms of the average time in system.

Stock rotation – The method of picking goods from inventory that have been in inventory for the longest time.

Stock valuation – The method of valuing stocks which assumes that the oldest stock is consumed first and thus issues are valued at the oldest price.

See *dispatching rules*, *Last-in-First-Out (LIFO)*.

fishbone diagram – See *causal map*.

five S – See *5S*.

fixed order quantity – The policy of using a constant (fixed) lotsize in an inventory management or MRP system.

The Economic Order Quantity (EOQ) is a special case of a fixed order quantity. SAP and most other ERP/MRP systems will order in multiples of the fixed order quantity if the net requirements require more than the fixed order quantity.

See *Economic Order Quantity (EOQ)*, *lotsize*, *lotsizing methods*.

fixed storage location – The practice of storing items in a storage area that is labeled with the item ID.

In other words, each item has a home location with the item's identification (part number, item number, SKU) on the shelf. Fixed storage locations are generally inefficient and hard to maintain because the space requirements for products in storage usually change over time as the demand patterns change. These changes require that the organization frequently reallocate the fixed location assignments or have excessive amounts of extra space allocated to each product.

On the positive side, fixed storage locations make it easy for people to find products. Most firms find that a mixture of fixed and random storage locations systems makes sense. The fixed storage locations are used for high volume products where people are frequently picking items. These locations are replenished often from random storage locations that hold larger bulk quantities of items.

See *random storage location*, *supermarket*, *Warehouse Management System (WMS)*, *zone storage location*.

fixture – A device used to hold a work piece securely in the correct position relative to the tool while work is being done on the work piece.

Unlike a fixture, a jig can guide the tool.

See *jig*.

flexibility – The ability to change (adapt) quickly and efficiently in response to a change in the internal or external environment. ✪

While the term "flexibility" is used very commonly in business, it is often used inconsistently and has several very different definitions. A major contributing factor to this ambiguity is that organizations face a wide variety of uncertainties and therefore need to have many different types of flexibility. However, when managers and researchers use the term flexibility, they often fail to specify which type of flexibility they have in mind.

Flexibility can be viewed at different levels in the organization -- from strategic levels (e.g., the ability to double production capacity in two months) to tactical levels (e.g., the ability to change the routing for a part when needed). From a strategic point of view, flexibility can be defined in at least four different ways:

Volume flexibility – The ability to efficiently increase or decrease the production rate. This is sometimes called scalability and is about having economies of scale or at least avoiding diseconomies of scale.

Mix flexibility – The ability to efficiently increase the number of products in one facility. This is sometimes called product range.

Customization flexibility – The ability to efficiently provide a wider range of "Respond to Order" products. This is sometimes called mass customization and is fundamentally about having economies of scope or at least avoiding diseconomies of scope.

New product development flexibility – The ability to efficiently and quickly bring new products to market.

All four of the above strategic flexibilities require that the organization be efficient. Unless the organization can "flex" efficiently it is not truly flexible.

The following website summarizes flexibility issues: www.research.ibm.com/journal/sj/423/shi.html. A good research review article on the subject is Sethi and Sethi (1990).

See *aggregate production planning*, *mass customization*, *New Product Development (NPD)*, *Respond to Order (RTO)*, *scalability*.

Flexible Manufacturing System (FMS) – An integrated set of machines that have automated materials handling between them and an integrated information system.

See *automation*, *cellular manufacturing*, *product-process matrix*.

floater – A direct labor employee used to fill in on a production line when the regular worker is absent.

floor planning – An arrangement used by a retailer to finance inventory where a finance company buys the inventory, which is then held in trust for the user.

flow – The movement of products and/or customers through a process with the minimum time wasted in waiting, processing, and non-value adding activities such as rework or scrap.

In the lean philosophy, one of the main goals is to improve flow by reducing lotsizes, queues, and rework. Improving flow reduces cycle time, which increases visibility and exposes waste.

See *lean*, *time-based competition*.

flowchart – A diagram showing the movement of information and/or objects over time; also called a flow chart and a process flowchart.

The term flowchart has historically been used primarily for information flow. Most process improvement leaders now use the term "process map" when creating a diagram to show the steps in a process. See the *process map* entry for much more detail.

See *process map*, *seven tools of quality*.

flow time – See *cycle time*.

flowshop – An academic research term used to describe a process that involves a sequence of machines where jobs move directly from one machine to the next.

Dudek *et al.* recognized that "there is no precise definition of a flowshop," but point out that "the following general assumptions are common in the literature. Jobs (work orders) are to be processed in *m* stages sequentially. There is one machine at each stage. Machines are available continuously. A job is processed on one machine at a time without preemption and a machine processes no more than one job at a time." Source: Dudek, Panwalkar, and Smith (1992).

See *facility layout*, *job shop*, *job shop scheduling*.

FMEA – See *Failure Mode and Effects Analysis (FMEA)*.

FMS – See *Flexible Manufacturing System*.

FOB – A common freight/shipping acronym meaning "free on board."

When a buyer purchases something and pays for it with terms "FOB origin," the responsibility of the seller stops when the goods are delivered to the transporting company in suitable shipping condition. It is the buyer's responsibility to pay for transportation. In addition, if something gets lost or is damaged during transport, it is settled between the buyer and the transportation company.

See *Cash on Delivery (COD)*, *terms*, *waybill*.

focused factory – A process that is "aligned with its market" and therefore requires a limited range of operations objectives. ✪

The concept of a focused factory was originally developed by Harvard Business School Professor Wickham Skinner (1974) in his seminal article entitled "The Focused Factory." Skinner argued that, "The focused factory will out-produce, undersell, and quickly gain competitive edge over the complex factory." Skinner's article argued that a factory can excel at no more than one or two operations tasks such as quality, delivery reliability, response time, low cost, customization, or short life cycle products.

"You can't be everything to everyone" is an old phrase which suggests that people (and firms) cannot do everything well, at least not in one process. A focused factory is a means of implementing a strategic direction for an operation. A firm can have several "focused factories" in any one factory building or location.

Schroeder and Pesch (1994) defined a focused factory as one with "a limited and consistent set of demands that originate from its products, processes, and customers, enabling the factory to effectively support the business strategy." They state that "many manufacturing executives define focus simply as having a limited number of products ... but this definition is too narrow ... the key is to limit the demands placed on manufacturing by limiting the number of processes and customers as well as the number of products." Schroeder (2008) notes that types of focus could be based on products, processes, technologies, sales volume, customer interface (e.g., make-to-stock versus make-to-order), or product maturity.

A focused factory, therefore, is not a factory that produces only one product, but a factory that reduces the "variability" of the process requirements so the factory can excel at its key operations tasks. Focused factories align their processes to their market and to the operations tasks required for that market. This approach has implications for many process design issues such as workforce (skill levels, salaried versus direct, customer-facing skills, etc.), performance metrics, customer interface, planning and control systems, cost accounting systems, facility layout, supplier relationships, etc. For example, the table below compares an operationally excellent make to stock "focused factory" making high volumes of standard products to an engineer to order "focused factory" developing innovative new products to customer order.

	Operationally Excellent Focused Factory	Product Leadership Engineer to Order Focused Factory
Workforce	Mostly direct labor, low wages	Many salaried workers, high wages
Performance metrics	Inventory, cost, cycle time	Time to market, on-time delivery
Customer interface	Make to Stock/Assemble to Order	Engineer to Order/Make to Order
Planning and control	Pull systems, MRP	Project management
Cost accounting	Throughput accounting, standard costs	Job-order costing, project costing
Facility layout	Product layout	Project layout, process layout
Supplier relationships	Many suppliers for commodities purchased at lowest cost.	Few strategic "partners" who supply technologies as well as components.
Main concern	Cost reduction, reliable delivery	Innovation, time to market
Main strategy	Lean manufacturing	Innovation, technology leadership

When a factory focuses on just a few key manufacturing tasks, it will be smaller, simpler, and more successful than a factory attempting to be all things to all customers. The main benefits of focus are that the focused factory will be able to deliver superior customer satisfaction to a vertical market and be able to dominate that market segment.

Some factories are unfocused originally because designers fail to recognize the limits and constraints of technologies and systems. Other factories are highly focused at first but lose focus over time. Several forces and factors diffuse the original focus. Among these are product and market proliferation. In a sense, losing focus is "scope creep" for a factory.

See *cellular manufacturing, core competence, facility layout, functional silo, handoff, operations strategy, plant-within-a-plant, scope creep.*

fool proofing – See *error proofing.*

force-field diagram – A simple diagram that shows the pros and cons for a decision.

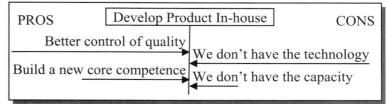

The lengths of the arrows represent the forces for each pro or con on the decision. Once a decision is made, the impact of the forces in favor can be strengthened and those against can be reduced. The figure above is a simple example.

See *Analytical Hierarchy Process (AHP), decision tree, Kepner-Tregoe Model, Pugh Matrix.*

force majeure – Events (or forces) beyond the control of the parties of a contract that prevent them from complying with the provisions of the contract; from French meaning superior force.

Typical forces that might be included in such a contract include governmental actions, restraints by court, war or national emergency, acts of sabotage, acts of terrorism, protests, riots, civil commotions, fire, arson, explosion, epidemic, lock-outs, strikes or other labor stoppages, earthquakes, hurricanes, floods, lightning, epidemics, embargos, blockades, archeological site discoveries, electrical outage, and interruption of supply. The term force majeure is often used as the title of a standard clause in contracts exempting the parties for non-fulfillment of their obligations as a result of conditions beyond their control. In some cases, an industry shortage is considered a justifiable reason for a supplier to declare a force majeure and put customers on allocation.

Here is an example of a force majeure paragraph from naturalproductsinsider.com/ibg/terms.asp (November 27, 2005): "Neither party shall be deemed in default of this Agreement to the extent that performance of their obligations or attempts to cure any breach are delayed or prevented by reason of any act of God, fire, natural disaster, accident, act of government, shortages of materials or supplies, or any other causes beyond the control of such party, provided that such party gives the other written notice thereof properly and, in any event, within fifteen days of discovery thereof and uses its best efforts to cure the delay (force majeure). In the event of such force majeure, the time of performance or cure shall be extended for a period equal to the duration of the Force."

See *leadtime syndrome.*

forecast accuracy – See *forecast error metrics.*

forecast bias – The average forecast error over time, defined mathematically as $\frac{1}{T}\sum_{t=1}^{T} E_t$, where E_t is the forecast error in period t and T is the number of observations available.

The ideal forecasting system has a zero forecast bias, which means that is has an average forecast error of zero. When the forecast bias is zero, the positive and negative forecast errors "balance each other out." Bias is not the same as forecast accuracy. It is possible that a forecasting system with low accuracy (e.g., high Mean Absolute Percent Error (MAPE)) has a low forecast bias, and conversely, that a forecasting system with a high Mean Absolute Percent Error (MAPE) has a low forecast bias. Forecast bias is a measure of the average performance of the forecasting system whereas forecast accuracy is a measure of the reliability of the forecast.

Good forecasting systems have built-in exception reporting systems that trigger a "tracking signal" report when the forecast bias is large. See the *tracking signal* entry.

In practice, forecast bias can be tracked with three approaches: the moving average, the running sum of the errors, or the exponentially smoothed average error. The moving average approach defines the forecast bias as the average over the last T periods. The running sum of the errors approach uses the simple equation $R_t = R_{t-1} + E_t$, where R_t is the running sum of the forecast error at the end of period t. With this approach, a small consistent bias will become large over many periods. The exponentially smoothed average uses the equation $SE_t = SE_{t-1} + \alpha E_t$, where SE_t is the smoothed average error at the end of period t and α is the smoothing constant ($0 < \alpha < 1$). This is probably the best approach because it puts more weight on the most recent data.

See *alignment, demand filter, forecast error metrics, Mean Absolute Deviation (MAD), Mean Absolute Percent Error (MAPE), Mean Squared Error (MSE), tracking signal.*

forecast error metrics – Mathematical measures used to evaluate forecast bias and accuracy. ✪

Forecast error is defined as the actual demand minus the forecast in a period. Using standard mathematical notation, $E_t = D_t - F_t$, where E_t is the forecast error in period t, D_t is the demand in period t, and F_t is the forecast made for period t. Given that the demand is rarely known, most organizations use actual sales as an estimate of the demand. The following table is a summary of many forecast error metrics. Many of these are described in more detail in this encyclopedia.

Purpose	Metric	Expression
Forecast bias metrics for a single item	Average error	$\bar{E}$ ◄
	Smoothed error	SE_t
	Mean Percent Error	MPE
	Mean Error Scaled by the Mean Demand	$\bar{E} / \bar{D}$
	Running sum of the forecast errors	RSE_t
	Tracking Signal	TS_{1t}, TS_{2t} ◄
Forecast accuracy metrics for a single item	Mean Absolute Deviation (Mean Absolute Error)	MAD
	Smoothed Mean Absolute Deviation	$SMAD_t$
	Mean Absolute Deviation as percent of average demand	$MADP$
	Mean Absolute Percent Error (Winsorized 1)	$MAPE$ ◄
	Smoothed Mean Absolute Percent Error	$SMAPE_t$
	Relative Absolute Error – Random Walk	RAE_{rw}
	Relative Absolute Error – Exponential Smoothing	RAE_{es}
	Mean Absolute Scaled Error	$MASE$ ◄
	Thiel's U	U_1, U_2, U_3
	Mean Squared Error	MSE
	Smoothed Mean Squared Error	$SMSE_t$
	Root Mean Squared Error	$RMSE$
	Forecast Attainment	FA
	Demand Filter	DF_t ◄
Forecast bias metrics for a group of items	Count or percentage of items with positive forecast error	$PPFE$
	Weighted average forecast error	$WAFE$
	Forecast attainment	FA ◄
Forecast accuracy metrics for a group of items	Weighted Mean Absolute Percent Error (Winsorized at 1)	$WMAPE$ ◄
	Median $MAPE$	$MdMAPE$
	Geometric Mean of the $MAPE$	$GMMAPE$
	Weighted Relative Absolute Error	$WRAE$
	Median RAE	$MdRAE$
	Geometric Mean RAE	$GMRAE$
	Weight Mean Absolute Scaled Error	$WMASE$ ◄
	Forecast attainment	FA
	Weighted Absolute Percent Error	$WAPE$
	Percent Better	PB
Other forecast error metrics	Variance and standard deviation	$\hat{\sigma}^2, \hat{\sigma}$
	Correlation and coefficient of determination	r, r^2
	Regression	a, b, r^2
	Autocorrelation at lag k	$\hat{\rho}_k$

◄ Indicates recommended metrics.   Source: Professor Arthur V. Hill

The papers "Forecast Error Metrics" and "Forecast Error Economics" can be found on the **OMWW CD** available from www.ClamshellBeachPress.com.

See *Box-Jenkins forecasting, demand filter, exponential smoothing, forecast bias, forecast horizon, forecast interval, forecasting, geometric mean, Mean Absolute Deviation (MAD), Mean Absolute Percent Error (MAPE), Mean Absolute Scaled Error (MASE), Mean Squared Error (MSE), Median Absolute Percent Error (MdAPE), operations performance metrics, Relative Absolute Error (RAE), standard deviation, Thiel's U, tracking signal, Winsorizing.*

forecast horizon – The number of time periods into the future that are forecasted.

For example, if a firm regularly makes forecasts that cover the next six months, it has a six-month forecast horizon. If a firm has a six-month manufacturing leadtime, it should clearly forecast at least six months into the future. Forecast error increases rapidly with the forecast horizon. It is often more practical and more economical to spend money to reduce the manufacturing leadtime (and the corresponding forecast horizon) than it is to find a better forecasting method to improve the forecast error for a given forecast horizon.

See *all-time demand, forecast error metrics, forecast interval, forecasting, forward visibility.*

forecast interval – The highest and lowest reasonable values for a forecast.

This is usually set as the forecast (which is usually an expected value) plus or minus z standard deviations of the forecast error. A reasonable value is $z = 3$. A forecast interval is very similar to a confidence interval, but it is not exactly the same. It is important to understand that the forecast interval is strongly influenced by the forecast horizon, where the forecast interval increases with the forecast horizon.

See *forecast error metrics, forecast horizon, forecasting, forward visibility, geometric mean.*

forecasting – Predicting the future values of a variable. ✪

Almost all organizations need to forecast sales or demand on a regular basis. Organizations also need to forecast the cost of materials, the availability of labor, the performance of a technology, etc. Three main types of forecasting methods are time series methods, causal methods, and qualitative methods. Each of these is discussed briefly below.

Time series methods try to find historical patterns in the sales data and then extrapolate those into the future. The most popular time series method is the exponential smoothing with trend and seasonality (usually called the Winters' or Holt-Winters' Model) (Winters 1960). The Box-Jenkins method is a much more sophisticated model for time series forecasting.

Causal methods are nearly always multiple regression methods where the model predicts one variable (the dependent variable) from one or more other independent lagged variables. See the entries on *linear regression* and on *econometric forecasting* for more information on causal models.

Qualitative methods are subjective methods such as sales force feedback, Delphi, or some other formal or informal means of collecting estimates from people. See the entries on *Delphi* and *technological forecasting* for more information on qualitative models.

Demand forecasting best practices

Demand forecasts are better when:
- Expressed as an interval rather than a point estimate.
- Aggregated across products, regions, etc.
- Made for a short horizon.
- Based on lots of historical data.
- Supplemented by human intelligence.
- Clearly differentiated from a plan.
- Carefully aligned with reward systems.
- Created collaboratively by the supply chain.
- Used by everyone without modification.

Demand forecasting principles

The following are important forecasting principles (with a little humor):
- Understand that forecasting is difficult (especially if about the future) -- and that forecasts are nearly always wrong. (The only thing that we know for certain about a forecast is that it is almost always wrong.)
- Separate forecasting and planning – forecast ≠ plan.
- It is easier to fit a model to historical data than it is to create accurate forecasts.
- Use lean to reduce cycle times and forecast horizons. (See *lean thinking*.)
- Use information systems to replace inventory and improve service.

- Use leading indicators to reduce forecast error. (See *econometric models*.)
- Use demand management to balance supply and demand. (See *demand management*.)
- Use yield management to maximize revenue. (See *yield management*.)
- Use demand filters and tracking signals to control forecasts. (See *demand filter* and *tracking signal*.)
- Use the Bass Model for product lifecycle forecasting. (See *Bass Model*.)
- Use the geometric time series model for end-of-life forecasting. (See *all-time demand*.)
- Use supply chain coordination to share demand information to reduce forecast error. (See *supply chain management*.)

Common misunderstandings

Two misunderstandings of forecasting are common. These include confusing forecasting and planning, and confusing sales and demand history. Each of these misunderstandings is discussed below.

Confusing forecasting and planning – Many firms use the term "forecast" for their production plan. As a result they lose important stockout (opportunity cost) information and create confusion and muddled thinking throughout the organization. In a typical business context, the firm needs a forecast of the demand for its product without consideration of the firm's capacity or supply. In response to this "unfettered" (unconstrained) demand forecast, the firm should make its production and inventory plans. In some periods, the firm might plan to have inventory greater than demand; in other periods the firm might plan to have inventory short of demand.

Confusing sales and demand history – Many people use the terms sales and demand interchangeably. However, they are not the same. Technically, demand is sales plus lost sales. Most firms keep a sales history, which they sometimes call the demand history. (SAP uses the term "consumption" history.) This is a "censored" time series because sales will be less than demand when sales are lost due to lack of inventory. This distinction is important when using historical sales (not demand) to forecast future demand. Some retailers try to use information on their "in-stock position" to inflate the sales history in order to estimate the demand history.

The website www.forecastingprinciples.com/welcome.html is an excellent website with a dictionary, bibliography, and lots of other valuable information on forecasting. ***The Principles of Forecasting*** is a free web-based book edited Scott Armstrong that can be found on Google Books (www.Books.Google.com).

See *all-time demand, Anchoring, Bass Model, Box-Jenkins forecasting, censored data, coefficient of variation, Collaborative Planning Forecasting and Replenishment (CPFR), Delphi forecasting, demand, demand filter, demand management, econometric forecasting, elasticity, exponential smoothing, forecast error metrics, forecast horizon, forecast interval, forward visibility, inventory management, leading indicator, linear regression, lumpy demand, Mean Absolute Deviation (MAD), Mean Absolute Percent Error (MAPE), moving average, Sales & Operations Planning (S&OP), seasonal factor, seasonality, supply chain management, technological forecasting, Theta Model, time-series forecasting, tracking signal, trend, vertical integration.*

forecasting lifetime demand – See *all-time demand*.

for-hire carrier – A common carrier or contract carrier trucking firm that transports goods for monetary compensation.
> See *logistics*.

forward buy – The practice of purchasing raw materials, components, etc. ahead of the need, usually in anticipation of a price increase.
> See *bullwhip effect*.

forward integration – See *vertical integration*.

forward loading – See *forward scheduling*.

forward scheduling – A finite scheduling method that begins with the start date (which could be the current time) and plans forward in time, never violating the capacity constraints; also called forward loading.
> The planned completion date is an output of the process. This is quite different from backward scheduling which starts with the due date (planned completion date) and plans backwards to determine the planned start date. The entry on finite scheduling explains this concept in more detail.
> See *backward scheduling, finite scheduling*.

forward visibility – Giving information on future demand and production plans to internal and external suppliers.

Customers can give their suppliers forward visibility by sharing their forecasts and production plans. This allows suppliers to plan their production to better meet their customer's requirements.

See *Electronic Data Interchange (EDI)*, *Enterprise Resources Planning (ERP)*, *forecast horizon*, *forecast interval*, *forecasting*.

Fourth Party Logistics (4PL) provider – See *Third Party Logistics (3PL) provider*.

Free-on-Board (FOB) – See *FOB*.

freight bill – Invoice for the transportation charges of goods shipped or received. See *logistics*

freight forwarder – An independent business that handles export shipments for compensation.

See *logistics*.

FTE – See *Full Time Equivalent*.

Full Time Equivalent (FTE) – A labor staffing term used to equate the salary or work hours for a number of part-time people to the number of "equivalent" full-time people.

For example, three people working half-time is equal to 1.5 FTEs.

functional build – A design and manufacturing methodology that de-emphasizes individual part quality and focuses on system quality.

Conventional design and manufacturing processes sequentially check each part being produced against design specifications utilizing C_p and C_{pk} metrics. This requires that all critical dimensions of a part be within specification limits. An example is an auto manufacturer checking 1,400 points on a door die. If any of these are out of tolerance, they would be re-worked to achieve proper specifications. With functional build, if the part is close to passing, it is used in the assembly and the overall assembly is held to tighter tolerances. In contrast, the functional build process checks fewer points and fixes only the ones necessary to bring the door assembly (system) into tolerance. The result is a higher quality assembly, which is what the customer really cares about, at a substantially lower cost.

A study conducted by CAR found that Japanese automobile manufacturers had the lowest quality doors as measured by C_{pk} for individual parts, but had high customer scores for the door assembly, while American manufacturers had higher door component C_{pk}'s, but lower customer scores. (Adapted from "The Quest for Imperfection," Charles Murray, **Design News** 10.10.05, www.designnews.com.)

See *process capability and performance*, *Taguchi methods*.

functional silo – A functional group or department in an organization such as marketing, operations, accounting, and finance that is overly focused on its own point of view which results in inefficient and/or ineffective processes.

In rural America, a silo is a tall cylindrical tower used for storing grain, animal feed, or other material. The photo on the right shows a series of six silos on a farm. The metaphor here is that firms have "silos" or islands where people in a group do not coordinate or communicate with the other silos, which results in bad processes.

The term functional silo is a pejorative (negative) term used to describe organizations that are so focused on business functions (marketing, operations, finance, etc.) that they have poor service and inefficient processes. The functional departments (functional silos) are usually drawn as vertical lines and processes to serve any one market segment are usually drawn as horizontal lines that cross two or more silos.

For example, a customer order begins with a salesperson who hands it off to order entry, but neglects to include all of the information. The order entry person enters the sales order data into the information system, but accidentally enters the promise date incorrectly. The manufacturing organization makes the product to the customer's requirements, but misses one important unusual customer need. The shipping people accidently ship the product to the billing address rather than to the point of need. It is easy for information to get lost in this process due to the fact that each "silo" (department) has different goals and information systems. It is hard for any one process to "own" this customer order because the process is too far from the voice of the customer.

The lean answer to this issue is to create organizations around value streams. In the operations strategy literature, this is called creating focused factories aligned with each customer segment.

See *Deming's 14 points*, *focused factory*, *lean thinking*.

fuzzy front end – The process for determining customer needs or market opportunities, generating ideas for new products, conducting necessary research on the needs, developing product concepts, and evaluating product concepts up to the point that a decision is made to proceed with development.

This process is called the fuzzy front end because it is the most unstructured part of product development. Preceding the more formal product development process, it generally consists of three tasks: strategic planning, concept generation, and, especially, pre-technical evaluation. These activities are often chaotic, unpredictable, and unstructured. In comparison, the subsequent new product development process is typically structured, predictable, and formal, with prescribed sets of activities, questions to be answered, and decisions to be made.

Adapted from www.pdma.org/library/glossary.html.

See *New Product Development (NPD)*.

G

Gage R&R – See *Gauge R&R*.

gainsharing – An incentive program that provides financial benefits to employees based on improvements in quality and/or productivity.

See *Balanced Scorecard, socio-technical design*.

game theory – A branch of mathematics that models the strategic interactions among competitors to determine the optimal course of action.

Business can be viewed as a "game" between the competitors in a market. A decision (move) by one player motivates a move by another player. Historically, game theory can be traced back to the Talmud and Sun Tzu's writings. John von Neumann and Oskar Morgenstern are credited with the mathematical development of modern-day game theory in their book ***Theory of Games and Economic Behavior*** (Von Neumann & Morgenstern, 1944). In the early 1950s, John Nash generalized these results and created the basis for the modern field of mathematical game theory. (John Nash was made famous by the movie the Brilliant Mind.)

A major issue with game theory is the tradeoff between realism and simplicity. The most common assumptions in game theory are:

- Rationality – People take actions likely to make them happier, and they know what makes them happy.
- Common knowledge – Everyone else is trying to make themselves as happy, potentially at our expense.

The most widely known example of game theory is probably the prisoners' dilemma.

Adapted from http://www.valuebasedmanagement.net/methods_game_theory.html, January 3, 2005.

See *co-opetition (co-competition), Prisoners' Dilemma, zero sum game*.

gamma distribution – A continuous probability distribution used to model task times.

Important special cases of the gamma distribution include the exponential distribution (when $\alpha = 1$), the k-Erlang distribution (for integer $\alpha = k$), and the chi-square distribution.

Gamma density and distribution functions:

The gamma density function is defined for $x > 0$ as $f(x) = \beta^{-\alpha} x^{\alpha-1} e^{-x/\beta} / \Gamma(\alpha)$, where $\Gamma(\alpha)$ is called the gamma function, which is defined as $\Gamma(\alpha) = \int_{t=0}^{\infty} t^{\alpha-1} e^{-t} dt$. Neither the Gamma distribution function nor the gamma function has a closed-form, but both can be approximated numerically.

Statistics: Mean $\alpha\beta$, variance $\alpha\beta^2$, and mode $\beta(\alpha-1)$ if $\alpha \geq 1$ (0 otherwise).

Excel: In Excel, the natural log of the gamma function is GAMMALN(α), which means that the gamma function is EXP(GAMMALN(α)). The gamma density and distribution functions are GAMMADIST(x, α, β, FALSE) and GAMMADIST(x, α, β, TRUE). The inverse distribution function is GAMMAINV(p, α, β).

Excel simulation: An Excel simulation can generate Gamma distributed random variates with the inverse transform method using x = GAMMAINV(RAND(), α, β).

Graph: The following graph shows a gamma density function with a range of α parameters and β = 1. See Law and Kelton (2000) for more details.

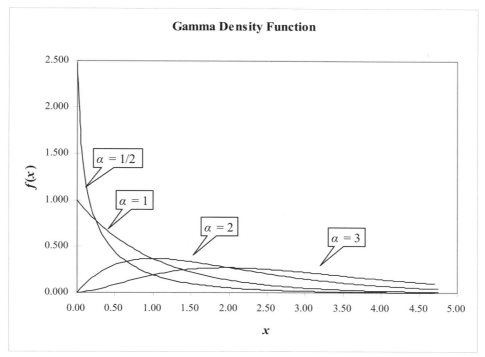

The Excel workbook "Distributions.xls" is on the **OMWW CD** available from www.ClamshellBeachPress.com. ●

See *beta distribution*, *Erlang distribution*, *exponential distribution*, *gamma function*, *inverse transform method*.

gamma function – A mathematical extension of the factorial function to real and complex numbers.

The gamma function is used in probability distributions such as the beta, gamma, and chi-square and is also useful for evaluating ratios of factorials. The factorial for a positive integer n is $n! = n \cdot (n-1) \cdot (n-2) \cdots 1$, where $0! \equiv 1$. The gamma function generalizes this to all real numbers and is defined as $\Gamma(\alpha) = \int_{t=0}^{\infty} t^{\alpha-1} e^{-t} dt$. When α is an integer, $\Gamma(\alpha) = (\alpha+1)!$

The gamma function provides a practical tool for evaluating ratios of factorials such as $n!/m!$ found in probability and statistics. When n and/or m are large, this calculation results in computer overflow problems. (The largest factorial that Excel can handle is 69!) Given that $n!/m! = \Gamma(n+1)/\Gamma(m+1)$, we know that $\ln(n!/m!) = \ln(\Gamma(n+1)) - \ln(\Gamma(m+1))$. Define the natural log of the gamma function as $GLN(x) = \ln(\Gamma(x))$, which means that $n!/m! = GLN(n+1) - GLN(m+1)$ and finally $n!/m! = \exp(GLN(n+1) - GLN(m+1))$. This procedure can be done in double precision and does not risk integer overflow problems. The natural log of the gamma function is found in Excel (GAMMALN(x)) and is a useful tool when factorials get large.

The gamma function has no closed form, but efficient and accurate numerical methods are available to approximate $\ln(\Gamma(\alpha))$. The following VBA code was written by the author based on the algorithm in Press *et al.* (2002). This was tested in Excel and found to be virtually identical to the Excel function gammaln(x).

```
Function gamma_ln(xx As Double) as double
Dim x As Double, y As Double, tmp As Double, ser As Double, j As Integer
Static cof(0 To 5) As Double
    cof(0) = 76.1800917294715: cof(1) = -86.5053203294168
    cof(2) = 24.0140982408309: cof(3) = -1.23173957245015
    cof(4) = 1.20865097386618E-03: cof(5) = -5.395239384953E-06
    x = xx: y = x
    tmp = x + 5.5: tmp = tmp - (x + 0.5) * Log(tmp)
    ser = 1.00000000019001
    For j = 0 To 5
        ser = ser + cof(j) / (y + j + 1)
    Next j
    gamma_ln = -tmp + Log(2.506628274631 * ser / x)
End Function
```

See *beta distribution, gamma distribution, hypergeometric distribution.*

Gantt Chart – A graphical project planning tool that shows horizontal bars that depict the beginning and ending times (dates) for each task. ✪

The following simple example of a Gantt Chart shows the starting and ending dates for each task. While a Gantt Chart is a useful tool for communicating a project schedule (plan), it does not show precedence relationships between tasks and therefore is not a good project planning tool for large projects. Microsoft Project uses a Gantt Chart to communicate a project schedule, but the data structures inside Microsoft Project consider the precedence constraints between tasks. The diagram below shows a simple Gantt Chart with five tasks.

Gantt Chart example

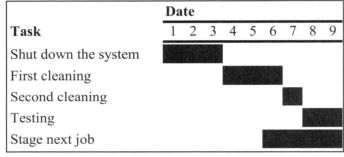

The Excel workbook entitled "Project schedule template.xls" is available on the **OMWW CD** available from www.ClamshellBeachPress.com. This is a simple project scheduling tool. ◉

See *Critical Path Method (CPM), project management, waterfall scheduling.*

gap model – See *service quality.*

gate – See *project management, stage-gate process.*

Gauge R&R – A statistical tool that measures the variation in measurements that arises from (a) measurement device variability (repeatability) and (b) operator variability (reproducibility); also called Gage R&R.

Note that the word "gauge" is often spelled "gage," but according to the **New Merriam-Webster Pocket Dictionary** (G. & C. Merriam Co., 1971), "gauge" is the proper spelling.

An old management proverb says, "You cannot manage what you cannot measure." This is particularly true for managing process improvement. It is impossible to reduce variation in a process (and the products that are produced by that process) without a reliable measurement system.

Before presenting more of the details behind Gauge R&R, it is important to define a "gauge." Many people assume that the term "gauge" is confined to mean a micrometer, but in the context of Gauge R&R, the term "gauge" can mean any measurement device. In fact, "Gauge R&R" can be used for any measurement tool and can even be used for surveys and other non-factory measurement tools. The following list of common measurement and test equipment includes a broad range of measuring devices:

- Hand tools (e.g., calipers, micrometers, linear scales)
- Gauges (e.g., pins, thread, custom gages)

- Optical tools (e.g., comparators, profiles, microscopes)
- Coordinate measuring machines (CMM)
- Electronic measuring equipment (e.g., digital displays, output)
- Weights, balances and scales
- Hardness testing equipment (e.g., Brinell, Rockwell)
- Surface plate methods and equipment
- Surface analyzers (e.g., optical flats, roughness testers)
- Force measurement tools (e.g., torque wrenches, tensiometers)
- Angle measurement tools (e.g., protractors, sine bars, angle blocks)
- Color measurement tools (e.g., spectrophotometer, color guides, light boxes)
- Gage maintenance, handling, and storage

The measurement system is a key part of understanding and improving process capability -- and Gauge R&R is a key part of the measurement system. In many Six Sigma and lean manufacturing applications, Measurement System Analysis (MSA) is conducted in the Measure step of the DMAIC process. Of course, MSA is also a key part of the control plan, the "C" step in DMAIC.

Gauge R&R measures two different types of variation in the measurement process:

- **Repeatability** – The ability of a device (gauge) to produce consistent results. It is a measure of the "within" variability between repeated measurements for one device, with one operator, on one part.
- **Reproducibility** – The ability of the appraiser (operator) to produce consistent results. It is the variation between different operators who measure the same part with the same device.

In addition, most Gauge R&R studies also measure the interaction between gauge and operator. For example, out of several inspectors, one might have a tendency to read one gauge differently than others. Gauge R&R can be applied to any kind of measurement.

The two most common methods used for Gauge R&R are the (1) Average and Range method and (2) Analysis of Variance (ANOVA). The Average and Range method, like many classical SPC methods, is based on ranges, which are easy to calculate manually. ANOVA is more accurate but the Range and Average method is simpler and therefore has been more widely used. With the increased availability of statistical software tools for ANOVA, it is likely that ANOVA-based Gauge R&R will become the method of choice in the future.

Some of the material above was adapted from email correspondence with Mr. Gary Etheridge, Staff Engineer, Seagate and from the website for the AIAG Automotive Industry Action Group (http://www.aiag.org). A reference on Gauge R&R can be found in DeMast and Trip (2005).

See *Design of Experiments (DOE), measurement system analysis, metrology, Six Sigma.*

gemba – A Japanese term for the place where the "actual" or "real" work takes place; sometimes written as genba.

The Japanese word "gemba" is frequently used for the shop floor or any place where value-adding work actually occurs. The main idea communicated by the term is that improvement really only takes place with (1) engagement of the people who work the process and (2) direct observation of the actual current conditions. For example, standardized work cannot be documented in the manager's office, but must be defined and revised in the "gemba."

The Japanese characters are 現場 (from http://www.fredharriman.com/resources/documents/FHcom_Kaizen _Terminology_03.pdf, January 27, 2009.

See *kaizen event, lean thinking.*

geometric decay – See *all-time demand.*

geometric mean – A measure of the central tendency appropriate for the product of two or more values.

The arithmetic mean (i.e., the average) is relevant for quantities that are added together and answers the question, "If all quantities had the same value, what is the value needed to achieve the same total?" In the same way, the geometric mean is relevant any time several quantities that are multiplied together to produce a product. The geometric mean answers the question, "If all quantities had the same value, what is the value needed to achieve the same product?"

The mathematical definition of the geometric mean is $G_n = (x_1 \cdot x_2 \cdots x_n)^{1/n} = \left(\prod_{i=1}^{n} x_i \right)^{1/n}$, where x_i is the i-th value and n is the number of values.

For example, suppose you have an investment which earns 10% the first year, 50% the second year, and 30% the third year. What is its average rate of return? It is not the arithmetic mean, because what these numbers mean is that on the first year your investment was multiplied (not added to) by 1.10, on the second year it was multiplied by 1.60, and the third year it was multiplied by 1.20. The relevant quantity is the geometric mean of these three numbers.

Any time you have a number of factors contributing to a product, and you want to find the "average" factor, the answer is the geometric mean. Interest rates are probably the most common application. The geometric mean is also a useful summary when we expect that changes in the data occur in a relative fashion. Filters will trap dust in an amount relative to the amount of air flowing through them. Adjustments in salary are often a percentage amount. Kidney enzymes usually metabolize drugs in proportion to the amount of drug in the blood. Geometric means are often useful summaries for highly skewed data. They are also natural for summarizing ratios. Caution: Do not use a geometric mean with negative or zero values in the data.

Example 1 – The volume of a room can be found by multiplying the length (L), depth (D), and height (H) together. In other words, $V = LDH$. Assuming that $L = 10$, $D = 12$, and $H = 8$, then $V = 960$ cubic feet. What are the dimensions of a room that is a perfect cube (with $L = D = H$) that has the same volume? The answer is the geometric mean which is equal to $G_n = \left(\prod_{i=1}^{n} x_i \right)^{1/n} = (LDH)^{1/3} = (10 \cdot 12 \cdot 8)^{1/3} = 960^{1/3} \approx 9.87$ feet.

Note that the arithmetic mean for this problem is $(10+12+8)/3 = 10$ feet and that $G_n < A_n$ (e.g., $9.87 < 10$).

Example 2 – The geometric mean is an appropriate measure of central tendency when averages of rates or index numbers are required. For example, suppose that in three successive years the return on an investment is 5%, 20% and -4%. The average rate of return can be found as the geometric mean: $G2 = (1.05 \cdot 1.20 \cdot 0.96)^{1/3} = 1.065$. Therefore, the average rate of return (compound annual growth rate, CAGR) is 6.5%.

The geometric mean is closely related to the Compound Annual Growth Rate or CAGR. If sales grow from s_i to s_j over $n = j - i + 1$ years, the CAGR during this period is $(s_j / s_i)^{1/n} - 1$. For example, if sales grew from \$10 to \$16 million over a five-year period, the CAGR during this period is $(16/10)^{1/5} - 1 = 0.10$ or 10%.

The question about finding the average rate of return can be rephrased as: "By what constant factor would your investment need to be multiplied by each year in order to achieve the same effect as multiplying by 1.10 one year, 1.60 the next, and 1.20 the third?" The answer is the geometric mean. If you calculate this geometric mean you get approximately 1.283, so the average rate of return is about 28% (not 30% which is what the arithmetic mean of 10%, 60%, and 20% would give you).

Here are some basic mathematical facts about the arithmetic and geometric mean. Suppose that we have two quantities, A and B. Taking the arithmetic mean we get the number $(A+B)/2$ which can be interpreted in a number of ways. One interpretation (probably the most common) is that this quantity is the midpoint of the two numbers viewed as points on a line. Now suppose that we have a rectangle with sides of lengths A and B. The arithmetic mean can also be interpreted as the length of the sides of a square whose **perimeter** is the same as the rectangle. Similarly, the geometric mean is the length of the sides of a square that has the same **area** as the rectangle.

The arithmetic mean (i.e., the average) is defined as $A_n = (1/n) \sum_{i=1}^{n} x_i$. The geometric mean is always less than or equal to the arithmetic mean (e.g., $G_n \le A_n$). The proof for this can be found at cut-the-knot.com/pythagoras/corollary.html. $G_n = A_n$ if and only if $x_1 = x_2 = \ldots = x_n$. The logarithm of the geometric mean is the arithmetic mean of the log transformed data (e.g., $\log(G_n) = (1/n) \sum_{i=1}^{n} \log(x_i)$).

Excel uses the function GEOMEAN(*number1, number2,...*) for the geometric mean. The Compounded Annual Growth Rate (CAGR) can be computed with the Excel function XIRR(*values, dates*).

See *Compounded Annual Growth Rate (CAGR), forecast error metrics, Internal Rate of Return (IRR)*.

Getting Things Done (GTD) – A philosophy for managing a personal task list, filing system, and emails in a disciplined way; the name of a popular book on personal time management by David Allen (Allen, 2001).

See the entry for the *two minute rule* for what is probably Allen's most famous principle.

The book *Personal Operations Management* (Hill 2010) expands Allen's framework by applying lean perspective to self-leadership problems such as the problems of purpose, priorities, margins, boundaries, task list, e-mail, interruptions, paper, and meetings. This book integrates many principles not included in Allen's book included margins, boundaries, interruptions, and meetings.

This book is available from Clamshell Beach Press website, www.ClamshellBeachPress.com. ◉

See *personal operations management, two minute rule, tyranny of the urgent*.

Global Data Synchronization Network (GDSN) – An initiative designed to overcome product data inaccuracies and increase efficiencies among trading partners and their supply chains.

GDSN is a network of certified data pools that enable product information to be captured and exchanged in a secure environment conforming to global standards. Different versions of product information in the supply chain can cause serious business issues. Global Data Synchronization (GDS) ensures that trading partners always use the same version of the data. This empowers the supplier to manage the information flow in the supply chain and not rely on the trading partner or other third-parties to manipulate their data. The foundational principles of GDS include:

- Product data is updated consistently between trading partners.
- Data is validated against standards and business rules ensuring its accuracy.
- Trading partners classify their products in a common, standardized way.
- Trading partners have a single point of entry through their chosen data pool, reducing the cost of using multiple vendors.
- The uniqueness of items, such as products, cases, pallets etc, is guaranteed through the GS1 Global Registry.

The standards body that governs the GDSN is GS1, an organization dedicated to the design and implementation of global standards and solutions to improve the efficiency and visibility of supply and demand chains globally and across sectors. The GS1 system of standards is the most widely used supply chain standards system in the world. GS1 has over 30 years of experience in global standards and operates in multiple sectors and industries.

Adapted from http://www.gs1.org/docs/what_is_gs1.pdf.

Acknowledgments: CEMBA 10 students Ami Ebel, Molly Litechy, Lee Petersen, Jeff Schmitz, Raju Thotakura, and Mark Thurbush contributed to this entry.

Global Positioning System (GPS) – A satellite-based technology that can be used to determine the current latitude and longitude for a device.

GPS technology can be a very helpful tool for collecting information in a transportation system.

global sourcing – See *sourcing*.

goal tree – See *Y-tree*.

gold parts – A phrase used in the Theory of Constraints for parts that have passed through the bottleneck.

These parts are much more valuable because we have invested time in them from our most valuable resource (the bottleneck).

See *inspection, Theory of Constraints (TOC)*.

golden zone – A designated area in a warehouse located next to the dock doors for the highest volume inventory.

This area usually has fixed storage locations.

See *Warehouse Management System (WMS)*.

Goldratt – See *Theory of Constraints (TOC)*.

Gompertz Curve – See *logistic curve*.

goodness-of-fit tests – See *chi-square goodness of fit test, Kolmogorov-Smirnov test (K-S test)*.

GPS – See *Global Positioning System (GPS)*.

gravity model for competitive retail store location – A mathematical model for locating one or more new retail stores relative to the competing stores in a region.

The basic concept of the gravity model is that the "gravitational pull" for a store on a customer is directly proportional to the size of the store and inversely proportional to the travel time squared. In other words, big stores that are close to a customer will have a large attraction for a customer; conversely, small stores that are far away will have almost no attraction at all. This model is an application of Newton's Law, which states that the gravitational pull between two heavenly bodies is directly proportional to the mass of the bodies and inversely proportional to the square of the distance between them.

The goal is to find the best location for one or more new stores from a set of potential locations assuming that the new stores will have to compete for customers with the other stores in the region. The model allocates the revenue in the market to each of the stores based on the "pull," which is a function of store size (bigger is better) and travel time (closer is much better). The model can be used to evaluate all reasonable alternatives and select the store locations that maximize the total expected revenue.

The goal is to allocate all of the revenue in a region to m stores. Store j is characterized by its size S_j and by a competitive index c_j, which is used to adjust for weak and strong competitors in the market. The region has n population areas (census blocks). The travel time from census block i to store j is t_{ij}. The "pull" for store j with competitive index c_j on census block i is directly proportional to the size of the store and inversely proportional to the travel time to the ρ power. Pull, therefore, is defined as $pull_{ij} = c_j S_j / t_{ij}^\rho$. The ρ parameter can be determined empirically, but is usually close to $\rho = 2$.

The probability that a resident of census block i will shop at store j is the normalized pull, which is given by:

$$p_{ij} = \frac{pull_{ij}}{\sum_{k=1}^{m} pull_{ik}}$$

Census block i has m_j customers with average revenue per customer of r_i. The expected revenue for store j, therefore, is $R_j = \sum_{i=1}^{n} p_{ij} r_i m_i$. The best location for a store (or set of stores) can be found by using the model to evaluate all reasonable alternative configurations and selecting the one that has the largest expected revenue.

The paper "Location Theory" and the Excel workbook "Gravity.xls" are on the ***OMWW CD*** available from www.ClamshellBeachPress.com. ◉

See *center-of-gravity model for facility location, facility location, great circle distance, numeric-analytic location model.*

great circle distance – The shortest distance between any two points on a sphere.

Given that the earth is approximately spherical, the great circle distance can be used to estimate the distance between any two points defined by their latitude and longitude coordinates on the earth. With the easy availability of Global Positioning Systems (GPS), this is a practical means to approximate distances for a variety of logistics problems.

Define (x_i, y_i) as the latitude and longitude for location i in radians. If the latitude and longitude are defined in hours, minutes, and seconds (h:m:s), convert to degrees (d) with $d = h + m/60 + s/60/60$. Convert degrees to radians by multiplying by $2\pi / 360$. The great circle angle between points i and j is:

$$GCA_{ij} = \sin(x_i)\sin(x_j) + \cos(x_i)\cos(x_j)\cos(y_j - y_i)$$

and the great circle distance is $GCD_{ij} = \left(\dfrac{C}{2\pi}\right)\arcsin(GCA_{ij})$, where $C \approx 24{,}902$ miles is the circumference of the world. The absolute value of the GCA should be bounded to less than one. The following equation is more accurate for short distances:

$$GCD_{ij} = \left(\frac{C}{2\pi}\right) \arctan\left(\frac{\sqrt{(\cos(x_j)\sin(y_2 - y_1))^2 + (\cos(x_1)\sin(x_2) - \sin(x_1)\cos(x_2)\cos(y_2 - y_1))^2}}{\sin(x_1)\sin(x_2) + \cos(x_1)\cos(x_2)\cos(y_2 - y_1)}\right)$$

When this equation is implemented in a computer program, Wikipedia recommends using the atan2 function for the arctangent function to avoid dividing by zero. See Wikipedia for more details on this function.

Love, Morris, and Wesolowsky (1988) suggest that intra-city travel distances should be inflated by a factor of 1.18 to account for the fact that the path between two points is rarely a straight line due to road structures. Yellow Cab and other firms estimate that intra-city travel speeds average about 30 miles per hour for most cities.

The following is test problem data from Love, Morris, and Wesolowsky (1988) that can be used to validate a computer implementation of the above equations. The distance in land miles between Seattle (47:36:00,122:20:00) and Miami (25:45:00, 80:11:00) is 2735.590 miles.

Some of the concepts above were adapted from http://en.wikipedia.org/wiki/Great_circle_distance, November 23, 2006

See *facility location*, *gravity model for competitive retail store location*, *Manhattan square distance*, *numeric-analytic location model*.

green belt – See *Six Sigma*.

green manufacturing – Manufacturing that is environmentally conscious and ideally more profitable; sometimes referred to as "sustainability."

The number of computers and other electronic devices on our planet appears to be increasing according to Moore's Law and are having a negative impact on our environment. According to Greenpeace, demand for new technology creates 4,000 tons of e-waste an hour, which often ends up on dead-hardware mountains in India, Africa, and China.

With take-back programs, customers return used technology to manufacturers that recycle the parts for new products. Many European nations have legal requirements for return logistics. The United States has few such laws, but many firms are voluntarily implementing such programs. For example, in 2004, Dell Computer recovered 40,000 tons of unwanted equipment for recycling -- up 93% from 2005.

Ideally, organizations can improve the environment and improve their profits at the same time. Here are several good examples adapted from the article fastcompany.com/magazine/120/50-ways-to-green-your-business .html, October 25, 2007:

- General Mills – In the past two years, General Mills has turned its solid waste into profits. Take its oat hulls, a Cheerios by-product. The company used to pay to have them hauled off, but realized they could be burned as fuel. Now customers compete to buy the waste. In 2006, General Mills recycled 86% of its solid waste, earning more selling the waste than it spent on disposal. In 2006, General Mills redesigned packaging and shaved off 20% of the paperboard box without shrinking contents. The result was 500 fewer distribution trucks on the road each year.
- General Electric – Trains were already the cleanest way to move massive amounts of freight long distances, but General Electric raised the game with its Evolution locomotives, diesel engines launched in 2005 that cut fuel consumption by 5% and emissions by 40% compared to locomotives built just a year earlier. GE has plans for a GE hybrid diesel-electric locomotive that captures energy from braking (like the Toyota Prius) and improves mileage by another 10%. According to GE, the energy dissipated in braking a 207-ton locomotive during the course of a year is enough to power 160 homes for the same period.
- Wal-Mart – Wal-Mart is providing funding to the biggest truck manufacturers (ArvinMeritor, Eaton, International, and Peterbilt) to develop the first heavy-duty diesel-hybrid 18-wheeler. Wal-Mart, which operates the second-largest truck fleet in the country, will test the prototypes next year. Wal-Mart has pushed the liquid-laundry-detergent industry to cut bottle sizes by 50% or more by concentrating the liquid. Thus, Unilever's triple-concentrated All Small & Mighty detergent has saved 1.3 million gallons of diesel fuel, 10 million pounds of plastic resin, and 80 million square feet of cardboard since 2005. This fall, Procter & Gamble is converting its entire collection of liquids to double concentration.
- C3 Presents – Austin-based concert promoter C3 Presents made news when it banned Styrofoam cups from the sixth annual Austin City Limits Music Festival this year. Following the model the company created for

Lollapalooza, C3 took a holistic approach to greening nearly every aspect of ACL, from bamboo-based concert T-shirts to gel sanitizer in the bathrooms to bio-diesel power generators.

- Philadelphia Eagles – Starting in 2006, the team's "Go Green" environmental campaign has its stadium cleaning crew making two full sweeps after each game with one to pick up recyclables and another for trash.
- Tesco – Some retailers have introduced product labels that encourage customers to weigh their carbon. The British grocery giant Tesco has a program to label all 70,000 of its products with carbon breakdowns.
- Unilever – Unilever has reconfigured the plastic bottles for its billion-dollar Suave shampoo brand, saving the plastic equivalent of about 15 million bottles a year.

See *Moore's Law*, *remanufacturing*, *reverse logistics*, *sustainability*, *triple bottom line*.

greenfield – The concept of building a new plant (or other facility) in a new location, which is often a field with no existing buildings on it.

This is often an opportunity for the firm to start with a fresh perspective on facility layout, process technology, and organization.

In contrast, older facilities and land are sometimes called "brownfields." These are often abandoned, idled, or under-used industrial or commercial facilities. Some brownfield locations have problems with industrial contamination.

See *facility location*.

grey market reseller – A broker that sells products through distribution channels other than those authorized or intended by the manufacturer.

Grey market resellers typically buy used equipment or "clearance" products on the open market and resell them to end user customers at a price lower than that desired by the manufacturer. These resellers sell outside of the normal distribution channels and typically have no relationship with the manufacturer and typically provide no service.

Acknowledgments: CEMBA 09 students Mark Anderson, Paul Beswetherick, Tiffany Grunewald, Perry McGahan, Caitlyn Rosendahl, Sara Rottunda, and Yarden Wolfe contributed to this entry.

gross profit margin – An ambiguous term that relates gross profit to sales, measured as either (1) Revenue − Cost of Goods Sold or (2) 100(Revenue − Cost of Goods Sold)/Revenue; also called gross margin.

The first definition is the margin in dollars, while the second definition is the margin as a percentage. The second definition above is sometimes called the gross margin percentage.

See *cost of goods sold*.

gross requirement – The total demand for an item, including both independent and dependent demand.

See *Materials Requirements Planning (MRP)*.

group technology – This term has two similar meanings. First, it has to do with the classification of parts (items) based on similar production processes and resources required. Second, it is used to describe a cell or group of people with a high level of cross training so they can produce a complete product or assembly. The cell is considered as one workcenter for capacity planning purposes.

See *cellular manufacturing*.

groupware – A type of software that provides functions to aid workgroups with communication, collaboration, and coordination.

Emphasis is on computer-based augmentation of human communications and information sharing, and support of generic workgroup tasks such as scheduling and routing of message-based workflow tasks.

GTD – See *Getting Things Done (GTD)*.

H

HACCP – See *Hazard Analysis & Critical Point Control (HACCP)*.

half-life curve – A mathematical model that shows the relationship between a performance measure (such as defects) and the time required to reduce (cut) the performance measure in half. ✪

The half-life concept suggests that the performance measure will be cut in half every h periods, where h is a constant. For example, if the unit cost at time zero is $100 and the half-life is six months, the unit cost will be $50 at six months, $25 at 12 months, etc.

Background on the half-life curve

Time-based learning with exponential decay is sometimes called the half-life curve, a term popularized by Ray Stata, founder of Analog Devices, Inc. (Stata 1989). Whereas the learning curve assumes that learning is driven by production volume, the half-life curve assumes that learning is driven by time. The half-life is the time required to cut the performance variable in half. Any performance variable with an ideal point of zero can be used in this model. For example, the performance variable could be cost/unit, time/unit, defects, cycle time, percent on-time delivery, etc.

The model

The basic equation for the half-life curve is $y(t) = ae^{bt}$, where $e \approx 2.718281$. The performance variable $y(t)$ is the performance at time t. The constants are $a = y(0)$ and $b = -\ln(2)/h$, where the half-life (in periods) is $h = -\ln(2)/b$. For example, if the half-life is 6 months, and the defect rate is 10% at time zero, at month 6 the defect rate should be 5%, and at month 12 the defect rate should be 2.5%. The following graph is an example of a half-life curve with parameters $h = 2$, $y(0) = 100$, and $b = -0.347$. Note that unlike the learning curve, the half-life curve is continuous and is defined for all values of t.

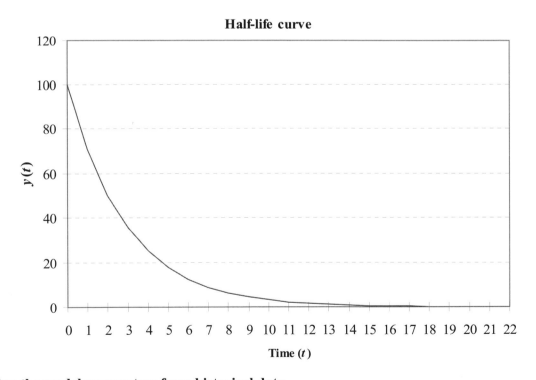

Half-life curve

Estimating the model parameters from historical data

The easiest way to estimate b is to find the value that fits the first and last historical points $b = \ln(y(t)/y(0))/t$. A more accurate (but more complicated) approach for estimating b is to apply linear regression on transformed historical data. To apply linear regression, take the natural log transform of both sides of the basic equation to find $\ln(y(t)) = \ln(a) + bt$, use linear regression to estimate the $\ln(a)$ and b parameters, and then use the model to estimate the performance variable at some time t in the future. We can use the equation $h = -\ln(2)/b$ to estimate the half-life from the b parameter. However, the regression approach is complicated by the fact that it does not work if $y(t)$ is ever zero and also by autocorrelation in the data.

The paper "Learning Models" and the Excel workbook "learning models.xls" are on the ***OMWW CD*** available from www.ClamshellBeachPress.com. ●

See *learning curve, learning organization, Moore's Law, operations performance metrics.*

handoff – A point in a process where work or information is transferred from one individual or organization to another.

From a lean manufacturing perspective, handoffs can lead to waste because each handoff has the potential to lose information and create a queue of materials waiting to be picked up. Reducing the number of handoffs will usually reduce the amount of information that is lost, reduce the number of queues, and reduce queue time, which results in better quality, better service, and cycle time.

Handoffs can also present problems due to the fact that the reward systems between the individuals or organizations might be different. For example, in a service organization, the customer-facing organization is usually rewarded based on customer satisfaction, but the "back-office" operations might be rewarded based on efficiency. Work enlargement seeks to combine these jobs into one job so that proper tradeoffs can be made between customer service and efficiency.

Acknowledgments: CEMBA 09 students Brian Clark, Brent Niccum, Tushar Patel, Rebecca Savoie, and Kate Walker contributed to this entry.

See *cellular manufacturing, focused factory, job enlargement.*

hard currency – A freely convertible currency that is not expected to depreciate in value in the foreseeable future.

Hawthorne Effect – The concept that the act of showing attention to people often spurs them to better job performance.

The Hawthorne Studies (or experiments) were conducted from 1927 to 1932 at the Western Electric Hawthorne Works in Chicago, where Harvard Business School professor Elton Mayo examined productivity and work conditions. The studies grew out of preliminary experiments at the plant from 1924 to 1927 on the effect of light on productivity. Those experiments showed no clear connection between productivity and the amount of illumination but researchers began to wonder what kind of changes would influence output. The basic concept is that the mere act of showing concern for people often spurs them to better job performance. (Note: Many different interpretations of the Hawthorne Effect can be found in the literature.)

For example, if the leadership of an organization gives management training to a new employee, the employee will feel valued and will likely be motivated to work harder. The motivation is independent of the particular skills or knowledge gained from the training. That is the Hawthorne Effect at work.

The Hawthorne Effect has been called the "Somebody Upstairs Cares syndrome." When people spend a large portion of their time at work, they must have a sense of belonging and being part of a team. When they do, they produce better. That is the Hawthorne Effect.

Historical notes: Professor Elton Mayo wanted to find out what effect fatigue and monotony had on job productivity and how to control them through such variables as rest breaks, work hours, temperature and humidity. In the process, he stumbled upon a principle of human motivation that would help to revolutionize the theory and practice of management.

Mayo took six women from the assembly line, segregated them from the rest of the factory, and put them under the eye of a supervisor who was more of a friendly observer than a disciplinarian. Mayo made frequent changes in their working conditions, always discussing, and explaining the changes in advance. He changed the hours in the work week, the hours in the work day, the number of rest breaks, and the time of the lunch hour. Occasionally, he would return the women to their original, harder working conditions. The investigators selected two women for their second series of experiments and asked them to choose another four women, thus making a small group of six. The group was employed in assembling telephone relays - a relay being a small but intricate mechanism composed of about forty separate parts which had to be assembled by the women seated at a lone bench and dropped into a chute when completed. The relays were mechanically counted as they slipped down the chute. It was intended that the basic rate of production should be noted at the start, and that subsequently changes would be introduced, the effectiveness of which would be measured by increased or decreased production of the relays. Throughout the series of experiments, an observer sat with the women in the workshop noting all that went on, keeping the women informed about the experiment, asking for advice or information, and listening to their complaints.

The experiment began by introducing various changes, each of which continued for a test period of four to twelve weeks. The results of these changes are as follows:

- Under normal conditions with a 48-hour week, including Saturdays, and no rest pauses, the women produced 2,400 relays a week each.
- They were then put on piece-work for eight weeks and output went up.
- Two five-minute rest pauses, morning and afternoon, were introduced for a period of five weeks, and output went up once more.
- The rest pauses were lengthened to ten minutes each, and output went up sharply.
- Six five-minute pauses were introduced, and the women complained that their work rhythm was broken by the frequent pauses, and output fell slightly.
- Return to two rest pauses, the first with a free hot meal supplied by the company, and output went up.
- The women were dismissed at 4:30 pm instead of 5:00 pm, and output went up.
- They were dismissed at 4:00 pm and output remained the same.

Finally, all the improvements were taken away, and the women went back to the physical conditions of the beginning of the experiment: work on Saturday, 48-hour week, no rest pauses, no piece work and no free meal. This experiment continued for 12 weeks. Output was the highest ever recorded averaging 3000 relays a week.

What happened was that six individuals became a team and the team gave itself wholeheartedly and spontaneously to cooperation in the experiment. The consequence was that they felt they were participating freely and without afterthought and were happy in the knowledge that they were working without coercion from above or limitation from below. They were satisfied with the consequence because they felt they were working under less pressure than ever before. In fact, regular medical checks showed no signs of cumulative fatigue and absence from work declined by 80 percent. It was noted that each woman had her own technique of putting the component parts of the relay together. Some women varied this technique in order to avoid monotony, and it was found that the more intelligent the woman, the greater the number of variations. The experimental group had considerable freedom of movement. They were not pushed around or bossed by anyone. Under these conditions, they developed an increased sense of responsibility. Instead of discipline being imposed from a higher authority, discipline came from within the group itself. (Adapted from accel-team.com /human_relations August 23, 2004.)

See *socio-technical design*.

Hazard Analysis & Critical Point Control (HACCP) – Regulations issued by the US Food and Drug Administration (FDA) to drive standardization in food safety.

Concepts center on building quality into food manufacturing processes rather than relying only on inspections and sampling. HACCP involves seven principles:

1. **Analyze hazards** – Potential hazards associated with a food and measures to control those hazards are identified. The hazard could be biological, such as a microbe; chemical, such as a toxin; or physical, such as ground glass or metal fragments.
2. **Identify critical control points** – These are points in food production from the raw state through processing and shipping to consumption by the consumer at which the potential hazard can be controlled or eliminated. Examples are cooking, cooling, packaging, and metal detection.
3. **Establish preventive measures with critical limits for each control point** – For a cooked food, for example, this might include setting the minimum cooking temperature and time required to ensure the elimination of any harmful microbes.
4. **Establish procedures to monitor the critical control points** – Such procedures might include determining how and by whom cooking time and temperature should be monitored.
5. **Establish corrective actions to be taken when monitoring shows that a critical limit has not been met** – For example, reprocessing or disposing of food if the minimum cooking temperature is not met.
6. **Establish procedures to verify that the system is working properly** – For example, testing time-and-temperature recording devices to verify that a cooking unit is working properly.

7. **Establish effective recordkeeping to document the HACCP system** – This includes records of hazards and their control methods, the monitoring of safety requirements and action taken to correct potential problems. Each of these principles must be backed by sound scientific knowledge. For example, published microbiological studies on time and temperature factors for controlling food borne pathogens.
Adapted from www.cfsan.fda.gov/~lrd/haccp.html.
See *Failure Mode and Effects Analysis (FMEA)*.

hazmat – A hazardous material.

Hazmat or HAZMAT is any solid, liquid, or gas that can harm people, other living organisms, property, or the environment. The term hazardous material is used in this context almost exclusively in the United States. The equivalent term in the rest of the English-speaking world is Dangerous Goods. A hazardous material may be radioactive, flammable, explosive, toxic, corrosive, biohazardous, an oxidizer, an asphyxiant, an allergen, or may have other characteristics that make it hazardous in specific circumstances. Source: http://en.wikipedia.org/wiki/HAZMAT, October 1, 2006.

headhaul – A carrier's primary trip, bringing a shipment to its destination. See *logistics*.

hedging – Any transaction designed to reduce financial risk.

Hedging usually deals with reducing the risk of loss from price fluctuations. Hedging is usually done for defensive purposes. Hedging is often a combination of "bets" (transactions) such that if one bet loses another wins (e.g., taking two positions that will offset each other if prices change). In operations, hedging is commonly used to reduce the risk of a price increase for raw materials. For example, Southwest Airlines, the only major airline to remain consistently profitable since the 9/11 tragedy, used a hedging strategy that allowed it to buy jet fuel for 38% less than the market price (Schlangenstein, 2005). Unlike arbitrage, a "hedge" does not carry the implication of having an edge. Note that the word "hedge" can be used as a noun or a verb.

See *arbitrage*.

heijunka – A Japanese technique used to smooth production over time.

平準化
HEI JUN KA
Production Smoothing

Dennis (2002) defined Heijunka as "distribution of volume and mix evenly over time." The Japanese word "heijunka" (pronounced "hey-june-kah") literally means to "make flat and level." Taiichi Ohno (1978) at Toyota defined heijunka as "production leveling."

Heijunka is considered to be one of the main pillars of the Toyota Production System (TPS) and is closely related to lean production. Heijunka is similar to the concept of production smoothing, which has been in the academic literature for over 30 years.

Customer demand must be met with the customer's preferred delivery times, but customer demand is "bumpy," while factories prefer "level" or stable production. Therefore, a manufacturer needs to try to smooth out these bumps in production. One of the main concepts for smoothing production is frequent changing of the model mix to be run on a given line. Instead of running large batches of one model after another, TPS advocates small batches of many models over short periods of time. This is called "mixed model" assembly in the United States. This requires quick changeovers, but results in smaller lots of finished goods that are shipped frequently.

Simple example of production smoothing

Week	Demand		Weekly production
1	900		500
2	200	Average = 500 units/week →	500
3	700		500
4	200		500
5	500		550
6	500	Average = 550 units/week →	550
7	400		550
8	800		550
9	400		450
10	400	Average = 450 units/week →	450
11	200		450
12	800		450

The main tool for heijunka is a visual scheduling board known as a heijunka box. The heijunka box is generally a wall schedule, which has rows dedicated to each product (or product family) and columns for each time period (say 20 minute periods). Colored production control kanban cards representing individual jobs are placed in the slots created, in proportion to the number of items to be built of a given product type during a time interval. The heijunka box makes it easy to see what types of jobs are queued for production. Workers remove the kanban cards from the front of the schedule as they process the job.

The heijunka box consistently levels demand by short time increments (20 minutes in this example). This is in contrast to the mass-production practice of releasing a work for one shift, day, or even a week to the production floor. Similarly, the heijunka box consistently levels demand by mix. For example, it ensures that Product C and Product D are produced in a steady ratio in small batch sizes.

Production process stability introduced by leveling makes it considerably easier to introduce lean techniques ranging from standard work to continuous flow cells. Muda (waste) declines as mura (unevenness in productivity and quality) and muri (overburden of machines, managers and production associates) decline.

When every process is leveled by volume and mix, it is a different world for employees -- who are no longer overburdened; for customers -- who get better products on the date promised; and for manufacturers -- who get to keep the money saved when muda, mura and muri are all reduced.

Some of the above concepts are from www.sme.org/cgi-bin/get-newsletter.pl?LEAN&20061010 &3&, October 26, 2006.

See *dispatching rules, job shop scheduling, lean thinking, mixed model assembly, takt time.*

heijunka box – See *heijunka.*

Herbie – The bottleneck in a process.

The question, "Where's your Herbie?" is asking, "Where is your bottleneck?" This is based on the popular Goldratt Institute film and book entitled ***The Goal*** (Goldratt, 1992), where one boy (Herbie) in the Boy Scout troop slowed down the entire troop on a long march through the woods. The teaching point here was that organizations need to "go find their Herbie and help him with his load."

See *bottleneck, Theory of Constraints (TOC).*

heuristic – A simple rule of thumb (procedure) that is used to solve a problem.

For example, when a vehicle schedule is created, the next location selected for the vehicle might be the one closest to the last one selected. This is called the "closest customer" heuristic.

See *algorithm.*

hidden factory – A term for the vast amount of rework and other non-value added activities often done in a factory or some operation.

Armand Feigenbaum, a well-known quality expert, emphasized the "hidden factory" that corrected the mistakes made by others and estimated that the hidden factory might be as much as 40% of the total cost.

Miller and Vollmann (1985) defined a slightly different type of hidden factory when they pointed out that many factories had a large number of non-value-added transactions. This is particularly true in firms that reduce lotsizes and move towards lean production without using lean (e.g., visual) control systems.

Finding and eliminating the hidden factory is a key part of process improvement.

See *Activity Based Costing (ABC)*, *lean thinking*, *yield*.

High Performance Work Systems (HPWS) – A form of workgroup that typically emphasizes high employee involvement, empowerment, and self-management.

HPWS generally incorporate some or all of the following features:
- More job complexity, multi-tasking, and multi-skilling.
- Increased employee qualifications.
- Ongoing skill formation through enterprise training.
- A minimum of hierarchy.
- Greater horizontal communication and distribution of responsibility (often through teams).
- Compensation incentives for performance and skill acquisition.
- Increased focus on "core activities."
- More horizontal inter-firm links for subcontracting and outsourcing.

This was adapted from industrialrelationscentre.com/infobank/current_issues_series/rethinking_ high-performance_work_systems.pdf, September 19, 2005.

Firms that use High Performance Work Systems often seek to improve organization performance through six synergistic strategies:
- Leadership that empowers others.
- A relentless focus on strategy and results.
- Open sharing of relevant information.
- Borderless sharing of power.
- A team-based design.
- Teamwork reinforced through rewards.

Unfortunately, the definition of HPWS is ambiguous and practices vary widely between firms. HPWS is closely related to employee involvement, employee empowerment, high involvement, people involvement, high commitment systems, mutual gains enterprises, socio-technical systems, participative management, self-management, boss-less systems, self-directed work teams, and empowered work teams.

Source: Adapted from a contribution by Aleksandar Kolekeski, a graduate student at ISPPI Institute, Skopje, Macedonia, kolekeski@msn.com, September 19, 2005.

See *New Product Development (NPD)*, *productivity*, *socio-technical design*.

histogram – A graphical approach for displaying frequency data as a bar chart. Histograms can be shown both vertically and horizontally.

The histogram is one of the seven tools of quality. See the *Pareto Chart* entry to see an example of a histogram.

See *Pareto Chart*, *seven tools of quality*.

hockey stick effect – A pattern of sales or shipments that increase dramatically at the end of the week, month, or quarter.

This pattern looks like a hockey stick because it is low at the beginning of the period and high at the end. The hockey stick effect is nearly always a logical result of reward systems based on sales or shipments. The large changes cause variance in the system, which often results in increased inventories, stockouts, overtime, idle capacity, frustrated workers, and other significant problems. Clearly, the best solution is to change the reward system to motivate workers to produce and sell at the market demand rate.

One creative potential solution is to have different sales regions with offset quarters so one region has a quarter ending in January, another ending in February, etc. Another creative solution is to shorten the reporting reward period from quarters to months or even weeks. This gives the organization less time to change between the extreme priorities, and therefore motivation to avoid the hockey stick.

See *aggregate production planning*, *carrying charge*, *carrying cost*.

holding cost – See *carrying charge, carrying cost.*

hoshin –A systematic planning methodology developed in Japan for setting goals and aligning the organization to meet those goals; also called hoshin kanri, hoshin planning, and policy deployment. 方針 管理

Hoshin is short for hoshin kanri. The word hoshin is from "ho," which means direction and "shin," which means needle. Therefore, the word hoshin could translate into direction needle or compass. The word kanri is from "kan," which means control and "ri," which means reason or logic. Taken altogether, hoshin kanri means management and control of the organization's direction needle or focus. Hoshin planning is like a management compass that points everyone in the organization toward a common goal.

The purpose of hoshin kanri is to help the organization improve performance by studying current problems, defining management policies, setting targets, and implementing change to achieve these targets. The process passes (deploys) policies and targets down the management hierarchy. At each level, the policy is translated into policies, targets and actions for the next level down.

Hoshin operates at two levels: (1) strategic planning level to define long-range objectives and (2) daily management level to address routine aspects of business operations.

Hoshin plans should be regularly reviewed against actual performance. This review can be organized in a "hoshin review table," which should show the owner, timeframe, performance metrics, target, and results. Any difference between the target and actual results should be explained. The review tables should cascade upwards.

Hoshin is similar to Management by Objectives, except that it focuses more on organizational rather than individual goals. Hoshin is also similar to the balanced scorecard, the Y-tree, and the PDCA concepts.

See *balanced scorecard, lean thinking, PDCA (Plan-Do-Check-Act), Y-tree.*

house of quality – See *Quality Function Deployment (QFD).*

hub-and-spoke system – A distribution system used by railroads, motor carriers, and airlines to consolidate passengers or shipments to maximize equipment efficiency.

Many passenger airlines such as Delta and United have a hub-and-spoke network where the hub is a central airport and the spokes are the routes that bring passengers to and from the hub. In contrast, the direct route (or point to point) system does not use a central hub airport. In North America, Southwest Airlines is an example of a direct route system.

The hub-and-spoke system is an important distribution strategy. For example, FedEx, a delivery service, has a hub in Memphis for all of its shipments. Virtually all FedEx shipments go through this hub.

See *logistics.*

hypergeometric distribution – A discrete probability distribution widely used in quality control and auditing.

The hypergeometric distribution is useful for determining the probability of exactly x defective units found in a random sample of n units drawn from a population of size N that actually contains m defective units. It is a particularly useful distribution for acceptance sampling and auditing. The normal, Poisson, and binomial are often used as approximations for the hypergeometric.

The hypergeometric distribution can be used to create confidence limits on the number of errors in a population based on a sample. For example, an auditor can take a sample and then conclude with a 95% confidence level that the true percentage of errors in the population is no more than p percent. The auditor can also use this distribution to estimate the sample size required to achieve a desired confidence limit. Most statistics textbooks recommend using the normal distribution for the proportion defective; however, this is an approximation for the hypergeometric and will be inaccurate when the error rate is small.

Probability mass function: $p(x) = \binom{m}{x}\binom{N-m}{n-x} \Big/ \binom{N}{n}$, where x is the number of successes in the sample, n is the size of the sample, m is the number of successes in the population, and N is the size of the population.

Statistics: Range $\{0, 1, \ldots, n\}$, mean πn, variance $\pi(1-\pi)n(N-n)/(N-1)$, where $\pi = m/N$.

Excel: In Excel, the probability mass function is HYPGEOMDIST(x, n, m, N), where x is the number of successes in the sample, n is the size of the sample, m is the number of successes in the population, and N is the size of the population. Excel does not have an inverse function for hypergeometric. The natural log of the gamma function (GAMMALN(x)) is useful for software implementation of the hypergeometric.

Graph: A jar has a population of $N = 100$ balls, with $m = 20$ red balls and $(N - m) = 80$ white balls. Samples of $n = 5$ balls are drawn randomly from the jar. The following graph is the hypergeometric probability mass function for x, the number of red balls found in a sample.

When the population size is large compared to the sample size (i.e., $N \gg n$), the hypergeometric distribution can be approximated reasonably well with a binomial distribution with parameters n (number of trials) and $\pi = m / N$, which is the probability of failure on a single trial. The Poisson distribution is often used as an approximation for the hypergeometric in the auditing profession. The normal distribution can be used as an approximation for the Poisson when the mean is large (say greater than 9).

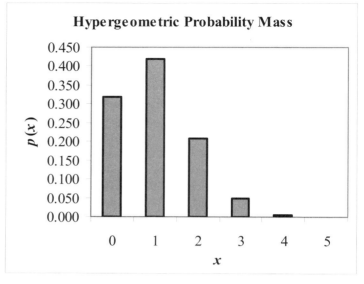

The paper "Audit Sampling" and the Excel workbooks "Audit Sampling" and "Distributions.xls" present extensive discussions and examples of how the hypergeometric distribution can be implemented for quality control purposes. These documents and Excel workbooks are on the **OMWW CD** available from www.ClamshellBeachPress.com. ◉

See *binomial distribution, gamma function, Poisson distribution, Statistical Quality Control (SQC)*.

hypothesis – In the operations management context, a suggested explanation for a problem; a statement of what could be true; a proposition for how a problem might be solved.

A hypothesis consists of a statement of what could be true, often with some accompanied explanation and justification. A hypothesis requires more work by the investigator to attempt to disprove it. When attempting to address an operations problem, the best consultants work with their clients to quickly generate a large number of hypotheses about how the problem might be solved. Much of the remainder of the consulting engagement is then dedicated to testing to see if the hypotheses are true.

Most scientists require that a hypothesis be falsifiable, which means that it is possible to test if the statement is false. Failing to falsify a hypothesis does not prove that the hypothesis is true. A hypothesis cannot ever be accepted or confirmed because no human will ever have infinite knowledge. However, after a hypothesis has been rigorously tested and not falsified, it may form the basis for theory and for reasonable action.

See *issue tree, Minto Pyramid Principle, strategy map*.

I

I2 – A software vendor of Advanced Planning and Scheduling (APS) systems.

See *Advanced Planning and Scheduling (APS)*.

ideation – A group brainstorming process that seeks to generate innovative thinking for new product development from of a group of people.

Ideation is done in the conceptual phase (the fuzzy front end) of the design process. Ideation has strict disciplines but allows for free-wheeling imagination. The process identifies the specific issue in need of rethinking, rethinks it in a fresh way, and evaluates the practical advisability of the resulting ideas. Source: Graham, Douglas, and Thomas Bachmann (2004).

See *brainstorming, causal map, Kano Analysis, New Product Development (NPD), Nominal Group Technique (NGT), Triz*.

IDOV – See *Design for Six Sigma (DFSS), Six Sigma*.

IIE – See *Institute of Industrial Engineers.*

impact wheel – A graphical brainstorming tool that can be used to help groups identify and address all of the effects of a decision, action, or potential event.

The world is a highly interdependent economic, social, and technologic system, where every decision and event has cascading impacts through many subsystems. Managers often fail to clearly identify all of the potential impacts of a decision and also often fail to conduct proper risk mitigation for those impacts.

The impact wheel is a simple structured brainstorming approach designed to help managers fully explore the potential consequences of specific events and decisions. The impact wheel can help managers uncover and manage unexpected and unintended consequences of a decision. It is a powerful tool for exploring the future that will be created by decisions that they make today.

The impact wheel process begins with the facilitator writing down the name for a change (event or decision) on a Post-it™ note and placing it on the wall. The facilitator then engages the participants in a discussion of (1) the "impacts" extending out from the change (drawn like the spokes of a wheel), (2) the likelihood for each impact, and (3) implications of each impact (costs, benefits). The group then focuses on each of the critical impacts and repeats the process around each one. This approach can be supported by environmental scanning (to consider external issues), scenario development (to consider best-case, worst-case, status-quo, and wild-card scenarios), and expert interviews (to gain insights from subject matter experts). More detailed risk analysis might follow with a formal Failure Mode and Effects Analysis (FMEA) for each impact.

The following diagram is a simple application of an impact wheel in a bank considering adding more workers. The first round identified "more difficult scheduling" as one impact of hiring more workers. The second round further identified the need to buy new software and hire a new scheduler.

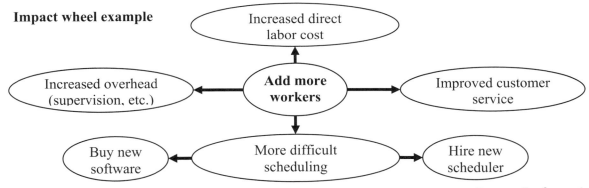

Impact wheel example

Source: Professor Arthur V. Hill

Some of the above content is from www.davidpearcesnyder.com/the_impact_wheel.htm, February 4, 2004.

See *5 Whys, brainstorming, causal map, Failure Mode and Effects Analysis (FMEA), issue tree, Nominal Group Technique (NGT), Root Cause Analysis (RCA), Six Sigma.*

Incoterms – See *terms.*

independent demand – This term that has two meanings: (1) demand from external customers, rather than a higher-level assembly or warehouse; (2) demand that must be forecasted rather than planned.

This concept is no longer very helpful given that many firms can now get detailed long-range demand information from their customers. Typical examples of independent demand include retail inventory demand, demand for an item sold from a distributor's warehouse, and demand for an end-item for a manufacturing firm. Demand for a component that goes into an end-item would be considered dependent demand, because this demand is planned based on the plan for the end-item.

See *demand, dependent demand.*

inductive reasoning – Inductive reasoning is making inferences about a larger subject based on specific examples.

In contrast, deductive reasoning begins with a general "theory" or concept which makes inferences about specific applications or situations. Arguments based on experience or observation are best expressed inductively, while arguments based on laws, rules, or other widely accepted principles are best expressed deductively. Consider the following pair of examples:

John: I've seen that when I throw a ball up in the air, it comes back down. So I guess that the next time I throw the ball up, it will come back down too.

Steve: I know from Newton's Law that everything that goes up must come down. And so, if you throw the ball up, it must come down.

John is using inductive reasoning, arguing from observation, while Steve is using deductive reasoning, arguing from the Law of Gravity. Steve's argument is clearly from the general (the Law of Gravity) to the specific (this throw); John's argument may be less obviously from the specific (each individual instance in which he has observed balls being thrown up and coming back down) to the general (the prediction that a similar event will result in a similar outcome in the future) because he has stated it only in terms of the next similar event (e.g., the next time he throws the ball).

As you can see, the difference between inductive and deductive reasoning is mostly in the way the arguments are expressed. Any inductive argument can also be expressed deductively, and any deductive argument can also be expressed inductively.

Even so, it is important to recognize whether the form of an argument is inductive or deductive because each requires different types of support. John's inductive argument is supported by his previous observations, while Steve's deductive argument is supported by his reference to the Law of Gravity. Thus, John could provide additional support by detailing his observations, without any recourse to books or theories of physics, while Steve could provide additional support by discussing Newton's law, even if Steve himself had never seen a ball thrown.

Adapted from chelationtherapyonline.com/PreventCancer/p59.htm, June 8, 2005.

industrial engineering – The branch of engineering that deals with the design, implementation, and evaluation of integrated systems of people, knowledge, equipment, energy, and material to produce products and services in the most efficient way. ✪

Industrial engineers draw upon the principles and methods of engineering analysis and synthesis, operations research, and the physical and social sciences to design efficient methods and systems. Industrial engineers work to eliminate wastes of time, money, materials, energy, and other resources. Typical industrial engineering issues include plant layout, analysis and planning of workers' jobs, economical handling of raw materials, flow of materials through the production process, and efficient control of the inventory. Industrial engineers work not only in manufacturing, but also in service organizations such as hospitals and banks. The field of industrial engineering has expanded in recent years to consider many issues across the supply chain.

See *Institute of Industrial Engineers (IIE)*.

infinite loading – Creating a production plan based on planned manufacturing leadtimes without regard to available production capacity.

If the planned leadtime is two weeks, the plan is two weeks if the factory has no work at all, two weeks if the factory is working 24 hours per day, and two weeks if all of the workers are on strike.

See *Advanced Planning and Scheduling (APS)*, *finite loading*, *Materials Requirements Planning (MRP)*, *project management*.

INFORMS – See *Institute for Operations Research and the Management Sciences (INFORMS)*.

in-sourcing – See *outsourcing*.

inspection – The process of checking units to make sure they were done correctly. ✪

Inspection can be done for either (1) an accept/reject decision for a batch of parts (batch control), or (2) to check if a process is still in control (process control). Inspection can be done by (1) the operator (self-check, source inspection), (2) the next person in the process (successive check), (3) the last step (final inspection), or some combination of the above.

Ideally, inspection is done at the source (quality at the source) so the process has immediate feedback and has a sense of ownership of quality. Most firms conduct final inspection before a product is delivered to a customer. Inspection should be done just before a bottleneck so valuable bottleneck time is not wasted on a bad part. (More attention should be given to the "gold parts" that have gone through the bottleneck because valuable bottleneck capacity has been invested in these parts.)

Many firms are eliminating incoming inspection by having the supplier certify that the parts meet certain quality standards. This saves money and time for both parties. An ideal process has no inspection because products and processes are so carefully designed that inspection, a non-value adding activity, is not needed.

See *acceptance sampling*, *Computer Aided Inspection (CAI)*, *cost of quality*, *Deming's 14 points*, *gold parts*, *supplier qualification and certification*, *Total Quality Management (TQM)*.

Installation Qualification (IQ) – See *process validation*.

instantaneous replenishment – Instantaneous replenishment is a situation in which the entire lotsize is received all at one time.

This is the normal situation when ordering from an outside supplier that ships the entire order quantity at one time. This is also the situation when a distribution center places an order to an internal plant because the entire order is shipped at one time.

However, if we were to study the inventory for a batch chemical process, the inventory grows when the chemical is being produced, but declines at the demand rate when the chemical is not being produced. When the chemical is being produced, the inventory grows at the rate $p - d$, where p is the production rate and d is the demand (sales) rate. When the chemical is not being produced, the inventory declines at the rate d. This is called non-instantaneous replenishment.

See *cycle stock*, *lotsizing methods*.

Institute for Operations Research and the Management Sciences (INFORMS) – The largest professional society in the world for professionals in the field of operations research (O.R.).

INFORMS was established in 1995 with the merger of the Operations Research Society of America (ORSA) and The Institute for Management Sciences (TIMS). The society serves the scientific and professional needs of O.R. educators, investigators, scientists, students, managers, and consultants, as well as the organizations they serve, by such services as publishing 12 scholarly journals that describe the latest O.R. methods and applications and a membership magazine with news from across the profession. The society organizes national and international conferences for academics and professionals, as well as members of the society's special interest groups. The Institute serves as a focal point for O.R. professionals, permitting them to communicate with each other and reach out to other professional societies, as well as the varied clientele of the profession's research and practice.

INFORMS publishes twelve scholarly journals, including **Management Science**, **Operations Research**, and **Manufacturing & Service Operations Management** (**MSOM**). Other INFORMS journals include **Decision Analysis**, **Information Systems Research**, **INFORMS Journal of Computing**, **Interfaces**, **Marketing Science**, **Mathematics of OR**, **Organizational Science**, and **Transportation Science**.

The INFORMS website is www.informs.org.

See *Operations Management (OM)*, *Operations Research (OR)*.

Institute for Supply Management (ISM) – A professional society for purchasing management professionals.

Founded in 1915, the Institute for Supply Management (ISM) claims to be the largest supply management association in the world. ISM's mission is to lead the supply management profession through its standards of excellence, research, promotional activities, and education. ISM's membership base includes more than 40,000 supply management professionals with a network of domestic and international affiliated associations.

Formerly known as the National Association of Purchasing Management, the organization changed its name to The Institute for Supply Management in May 2001 to reflect the increasing strategic and global significance of supply management. ISM has a certification process for the Certified Purchasing Manager (C.P.M.) designation. The process requires a passing grade on the CPM exam.

ISM provides many publications to its members, including the **Journal of Supply Chain Management**, a publication for purchasing professionals and educators.

The ISM website is www.ism.ws.

See *Operations Management (OM)*.

Institute of Industrial Engineers (IIE) – The world's largest professional society dedicated solely to the support of the industrial engineering profession and individuals involved with improving quality and productivity.

Founded in 1948, IIE is an international, non-profit association that provides leadership for the application, education, training, research, and development of industrial engineering.

IIE publishes two academic journals (*IIE Transactions* and *The Engineering Economist*), a monthly news magazine (*IE Magazine*), and a practitioner management journal (*Industrial Management*).

The IIE website is www.iienet2.org.

See *industrial engineering, Operations Management (OM)*.

in-stocks – The percentage of retail stores that have sufficient inventory on-hand; also called in-stock position.

In-stocks is defined as the percentage of retail stores in a retail chain that have an on-hand inventory that is at or above the required presentation minimum inventory on the shelves. The calculation of the in-stock for an item is equal to (number of stores that have at least the presentation minimum on-hand)/(Total number of stores stocking that item).

See *fill rate, service level*.

Integer Programming (IP) – A type of linear programming where the decision variables are restricted to integer values.

The term integer programming is short for integer linear programming. Mixed Integer Programming (MIP) has some decision variables that are continuous and some that are integer.

See *assignment problem, knapsack problem, Linear Programming (LP), Mixed Integer Programming (MIP)*.

Integrated Product Development (IPD) – The practice of systematically forming teams of functional disciplines to integrate and concurrently apply all necessary processes to produce an effective and efficient product that satisfies the customer's needs.

IPD is nearly synonymous with simultaneous engineering and concurrent engineering. Benefits claimed for IPD include less development time, fewer engineering changes, less time to market, higher quality, and higher white collar productivity.

See *concurrent engineering, New Product Development (NPD), simultaneous engineering*.

intellectual capital – The sum of an organization's collective knowledge, experience, skills, competences, and ability to acquire more.

At least one source defined intellectual capital as the difference between book value and market value. While this might be too strong, most management experts agree that the balance sheet and other financial statements do not reflect intellectual capital and that intellectual capital is the most valuable asset for many firms. Also called knowledge capital.

See *knowledge management, learning organization*.

inter-modal shipments – The movement of consumer goods and light industrial products by a railroad in a trailer or container that originates and terminates with either a motor carrier or ocean shipping line.

See *logistics, multi-modal shipments*.

Internal Rate of Return (IRR) – The discount rate at which the present value of the future cash flows of an investment equal the cost of the investment.

The IRR has to be found by trial and error (numerical) methods. It is the discount rate at which the net present value is zero. The entry Compounded Annual Growth Rate (CAGR) provides much more information on this subject.

See *Compounded Annual Growth Rate (CAGR), financial performance metrics, geometric mean*.

interpolated median – A measure of central tendency that is equal to the median plus or minus a correction factor that adjusts for a non-symmetrical (skewed) distribution when many observations are equal to the median.

Many experts consider the median to be a better measure of central tendency than the mean because the median, unlike the mean, is not influenced by extremely low or high values. Some people consider the interpolated median to be a better measure of central tendency than the median when many values are equal to the median (computed in the standard way) and the distribution is non-symmetrical (skewed). However, one of my statistical consultants asserts that the interpolated median does not have a good theoretical basis and was just "made up by someone who could not decide between the mean and the median."

The interpolated median is used for low resolution data (such as surveys, student grades, and frequency data) where several values fall at the median. When the distribution is skewed, the interpolated median adjusts the median upward or downward according to the number of responses above or below the median. A right-skewed distribution will have a positive correction factor and a left-skewed distribution will have a negative correction factor.

Define the following parameters for a data set:

N Number of observed values.

im Interpolated median.

m Median (computed in the standard way).

n_b Number of values below (less than) m.

n_e Number of values equal to m.

n_a Number of values above (greater than) m.

If $n_b = n_a$, the distribution is not skewed, the correction factor is zero, and the interpolated median will be equal the median (e.g., $im = m$). (Note: $n_b = n_a$ will always be true when $n_e \leq 1$.) If $n_b < n_a$, the distribution is right-skewed, the correction factor is positive, and the interpolated median is greater than the median; conversely, if $n_b > n_a$, the distribution is left-skewed, the correction factor is negative, and the interpolated median is less than the median. If the number of values equal to the median (n_e) is equal to zero or one, the number of values above and below the median will always be equal and the correction factor will be zero.

The equation for the interpolated median is then:

$$im = \begin{cases} m & \text{for } n_e = 0 \\ m + (n_a - n_b)/(2n_e) & \text{for } n_e > 0 \end{cases}$$

For example, the following is a sample of $N = 7$ responses for a five-point Likert survey: $x_i = \{1,3,3,3,5,5,5\}$ with a median of $m = 3$. The number of observations below the median is $n_b = 1$, the number above the median is $n_a = 3$, and the number equal to the median is $n_e = 3$. The interpolated median is then $im = 3.33$, which is higher than the median because $n_a > n_b$. The right-skewed distribution "pulls" the interpolated median above the median. The graph below shows the frequency distribution for this data with more observations above than below the median and the interpolated median that is "corrected" so that it is slightly higher than the median.

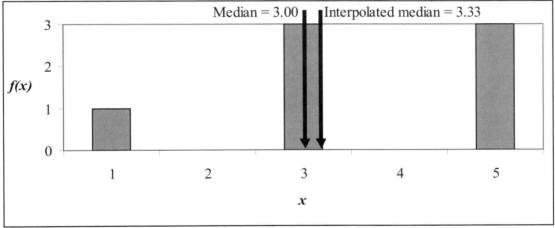

See *median*.

interval notation – A mathematical convention for writing the range for a variable.

The interval notation uses a closed parentheses [ ] when endpoints are included, open parentheses ( ) when end points are not included, positive infinity ∞, negative infinity $-\infty$, and the union sign U. For example, $[0, a)$ means the range includes all values from 0 to a, with 0 included but a not included. The range $(-\infty, -2] \cup (1, \infty)$ includes all values less than or equal to –2 and all values greater than 1.

intranet – A private application of the same Internetworking technology, software, and applications within a private network, for use within an enterprise.

An intranet is a private network as opposed to the Internet, which is the public network. An intranet may be entirely disconnected from the public Internet, but is usually linked to it and protected from unauthorized access by security firewall systems. More loosely, the term may include extranets as well. An intranet involves web-based technologies and is typically used within an organization's internal network to centralize applications or data. An intranet is usually segmented into data or applications that all employees have access to and data or applications that are restricted to only authorized users.

See *corporate portal*, *e-business*, *extranet*.

Inventory Dollar Days (IDD) – A Theory of Constraints (TOC) measure of investment in inventory.

The Theory of Constraints (TOC) promotes Inventory Dollar Days (IDD) as a measure of things done ahead of schedule and Throughput Dollar Days (TDD) as a measure of things done behind schedule. A dollar-day is one dollar held in inventory for one day. When you borrow money from a bank, your interest payment is based on how many dollars you borrowed and for how long, which means that interest is based on dollar-days. When a department is holding inventory, it should be charged for the dollar-days of inventory it is holding. The Inventory Dollar Days can be calculated as IDD = (unit cost) x (quantity on hand) x (days on hand). For example, if a manufacturing order for 100 units has been waiting at a workcenter for 5 days and the unit cost is $2, the workcenter has 100x5x2=$1000 dollar days for that order.

Similarly, when a department is late, it delays the receiving payment and loses the time value of money during the delay, and therefore should be based on the dollar-days late. This is called Throughput Dollar Days (TDD). Throughput dollar days measures the value of each late shipment multiplied by the number of days it was late (e.g., a one million dollar order that is five days late becomes five million dollar days).

Mr. Phil Brooks, President of H. Brooks and Company (www.hbrooks.com), a St. Paul, Minnesota distributor of fresh fruits and vegetables, shared the following quote with the author: "We began measuring dollar days of inventory last winter, with an item ranking and overall totals by buyer and vendor. You will find that this number will be surprisingly large and will create an insight followed by instant action -- and focus on inventory items that are unneeded. In the last eight months, we have cut this measure by about 50%."

Dollar-days is neither a measure of time or money. It is similar to a measure of the carrying cost of inventory.

Much of the above discussion was adapted from ciras.iastate.edu/library/toc/measurements.asp and mcts.com/Theory-of-Constraints.html, October 11, 2008.

See *inventory turnover*, *operations performance metrics*, *periods supply*, *Theory of Constraints (TOC)*, *Throughput Dollar Days (TDD)*.

inventory management – Inventory management involves planning and control of all types of inventories. ✪

This often includes forecasting demand, purchasing materials, and fulfilling sales orders. Inventory management involves two decisions that must be made frequently: when to order, and how much to order. A less frequent inventory management decision is deciding if an item should be stocked or not. If an item is not stocked, the firm must make, assemble, or buy the item to satisfy the customer demand.

The papers "Inventory Management" and "To Stock or Not to Stock: That is the Question" can be found on the **OMWW CD** available from www.ClamshellBeachPress.com. ✪

See *aggregate inventory management*, *distribution*, *forecasting*, *inventory turnover*, *joint replenishment*, *logistics*, *lotsizing methods*, *Materials Requirements Planning (MRP)*, *periods supply*, *reorder point*, *supply chain management*, *Warehouse Management System (WMS)*, *zero inventory*.

inventory position – The on-hand plus on-order minus allocated inventory quantities. ✪

On-hand inventory is the material that is physically located in the plant or warehouse. On-order inventory includes the materials that have been ordered but not yet received. Allocated inventory is material that has been promised to customers or other orders and therefore is not available for sale.

See *allocated stock*, *continuous review system*.

inventory shrink – See *shrinkage*.

inventory turnover – The number of times that the inventory is replaced during a time period (usually a year). ✪

The standard accounting measure for inventory turnover is the cost of goods sold divided by the average inventory investment. For example, if a firm has an annual cost of goods sold of $10 million and an average inventory investment of $5 million, the firm has two turns per year. Inventory turnover (T) can be rewritten in units as $52d/I$, where d is the average demand per week and I is the average inventory in units.

The inverse of the inventory turnover ratio for any inventory is the periods supply. The inverse of the inventory turnover ratio for work-in-process inventory (WIP) is an estimate of the dollar-weighted cycle time for a product.

Some students confuse inventory turnover with other turnover measures. Employee turnover is the number of times that employees are replaced during a period (usually a year). In most of the world outside of the United States, "turnover" means sales or revenue.

The six "fallacies" of inventory turnover

The inventory turnover metric is often misused by operations managers and others. The six "fallacies" regarding inventory turnover include:
- The ratio fallacy
- The end-of-period inventory fallacy
- The different numerator/denominator units fallacy
- The different demand fallacy
- The industry average fallacy
- The common turnover (days supply) fallacy

Each of these fallacies is discussed briefly below.

The ratio fallacy

An old adage from mathematics says that "The sum of ratios is not the same as the ratio of a sum." This plays out in important ways when working with inventory turnover ratios. For example, a firm has only two items, A and B, with the following characteristics:

Item	Unit Cost	Average demand/ week (units)	Average demand/ week ($)	Inventory (units)	Inventory ($)	Inventory turnover	Days supply
A	$10	1,000	$10,000	1,000	$10,000	52.0	7
B	$1	10	$100	260	$2,600	2.0	182
Totals	$11	1,010	$10,100	1,260	$12,600	54	189
Averages	$5.50	505	$5,050	630	$6,300	27	94.5

Many people would conclude from the example above that this firm has 27 turns and a days supply of 94.5 days. However, this conclusion is incorrect. This firm has a total weekly cost of goods sold of $10,000 and a total inventory investment of $12,600, which means that the correct measures for this firm are 42 turns per year and nine days supply. The incorrect approach gives far too much weight to the unimportant items and far too little weight to the important items.

The end-of-period inventory fallacy

Many firms compute inventory turnover based on the end-of-year (or end-of-quarter) inventory investment rather than the average inventory investment. However, this end-of-period inventory is often much lower than the average because of seasonal demand and/or reward systems that drive sales people (and others) to sell more at the end of the year. As a result, these firms have the incorrect denominator in the ratio and therefore tend to overstate their true inventory turnover. The solution to this problem is to collect data on the average inventory at more frequent intervals such as every month or every week.

Many sources suggest that the correct approach is to define the average inventory as (beginning inventory + ending inventory)/2. However, this approach does not really address the root problem because the beginning inventory for the period (year or quarter) is the ending inventory from the previous period.

The different numerator/denominator units fallacy

Many textbooks, authors, and even Dun & Bradstreet, define inventory turnover as sales divided by the average inventory investment. The sales/I and CGS/I metrics are the same only if the organization values its inventory at the sales price, which is a common practice in retailing.

More generally, it is important to have comparable values in the numerator and denominator of the inventory turnover ratio. If the numerator is in terms of the sales price, the denominator should also value inventory at the sales price. If the cost of goods sold includes labor or other charges necessary for producing or assembling finished goods inventory, the average inventory value should also include the same non-inventory charges. If the cost of goods does not include any labor or non-material charges, the average inventory value should only include the actual cost of the components or raw materials.

The different demand fallacy

It can be proven mathematically that if demand is increasing over time, turnover should go up and if demand is decreasing, turnover should go down. For example, if sales double, the turnover ratio should increase by a factor of $\sqrt{2} \approx 1.41$, an increase of about 41%.

More generally, the relationship between demand and inventory turnover can be expressed as $T = A\sqrt{D}$, where, A is a constant and D is the demand rate. This means that when demand changes by a factor of D_t / D_{t-1}, the inventory turnover should change by a factor of $\sqrt{D_t / D_{t-1}}$.

For example, last quarter a firm had a cost of goods sold of $100, an average inventory investment of $10, and $100/10 = 10$ turns, which was viewed as an acceptable inventory turnover ratio by the executive team. This quarter, demand was up 25% (to $125) and average inventory went up to $12.5, which was again 10 turns, and the operations organization was again commended for achieving 10 turns. However, the firm's inventory turnover should have increased by a factor of $\sqrt{125/100} - 1 = 11\%$, which means that turns should have increased turns from 10 to 11.8 and that operations should have been reprimanded rather than commended.

The industry average fallacy

Most accounting texts suggest that the inventory turnover ratio should be compared against industry averages. Many firms also compare inventory turnover between divisions and products. The problem with this method is that firms, divisions, and products have different demands and also have different strategies with respect to customer service and product mix. As mentioned above with the "different demand fallacy," inventory turnover should be higher for higher demand products. In addition, a high customer service firm and/or a firm with a broad mix of products will likely have a lower inventory turnover ratio.

The common turnover (days supply) fallacy

Many well-intentioned managers set a policy dictating that all products, product families, business units, or purchased materials have the same turnover ratio (or the same days supply). For example, many manufacturing executives set a policy that all items should have exactly 30 days supply and reward (and punish) employees whenever the days supply is greater than X days above or below 25 days. This policy has several problems:

First, all items have different demand and cost parameters and therefore should have different inventory levels. The average turnover (days supply) is based on the average inventory level, which is the sum of the lotsize and safety stock inventories. The lotsize inventory should be a function of the relationship between the demand, ordering (setup) cost, and carrying cost per unit and will not be the same for all items. The safety stock inventory should be a function of the standard deviation of the demand, the replenishment leadtime, the number of order cycles per year, and the target service level. Neither the lotsize inventory nor the safety stock inventory should be the same for all items; therefore, neither the inventory turnover nor the days supply should be the same for all items. Dictating a common target value for all items, therefore, is poor management.

Second, the inventory turnover and days supply for any one item will change dramatically during an order cycle. When an item is first purchased, the lotsize inventory (also called the cycle inventory) will be high. At the end of the order cycle just before the receipt of a new order, the lotsize inventory should be very close to the safety stock inventory. Of course, when the firm is faced with special opportunities to buy, the purchased materials inventory could be much larger. Therefore, monitoring inventory turnover and days supply for an individual item on a short-term basis is often a poor control mechanism. It is important to take an average on a time horizon that is consistent with the leadtimes. For example, if the firm's replenishment leadtimes are around two months on average, the average demand and average inventory for the turnover and periods supply metrics should be based on something more than two months of data.

It is good management to have a target turnover or periods supply for a group of items. However, this well-intended policy can easily cascade down the organization and become the target for each plant, product, and raw material. Good managers should not allow this to happen.

Thanks to Professor Jack Wacker (formerly at Iowa State University now at ASU) for his insights into conceptual definitions, particularly with respect to this definition.

The paper "Inventory Turnover" is on the **OMWW CD** available from www.ClamshellBeachPress.com. ⊙

See *aggregate inventory management, balanced scorecard, carrying charge, carrying cost, cycle time, DuPont Analysis, employee turnover, Inventory Dollar Days (IDD), inventory management, operations performance metrics, periods supply, turnover*.

inventory turns – See *inventory turnover*.

inventory/order interface – See *push-pull boundary*.

inverse transform method – A procedure for generating random variates from a particular theoretical or empirical cumulative probability distribution.

The distribution function $F(x)$ for a random variable x is defined such that $F(x_0) = P(x < x_0)$. The inverse distribution function is defined such that $x = F^{-1}(p)$ is the x value associated with the probability p for this distribution function. In other words, if $p = F(x)$, then $x = F^{-1}(p)$. The inverse transform method generates random variates using $x = F^{-1}(r)$, where r is a uniformly distributed random variable in the interval $(0, 1)$.

See *Erlang distribution, exponential distribution, gamma distribution, lognormal distribution, normal distribution, random number, simulation, Weibull distribution*.

IPD – See *Integrated Product Development*.

Ishikawa Diagram – See *causal map*.

ISO 14001 – Certification standards created by the International Organization for Standardizations related to environmental impact.

The ISO 14001 standards specify the requirements for an environmental management system to enable an organization to formulate a policy and objectives, taking into account legislative requirements and information about significant environmental impacts. It applies to those environmental aspects that the organization can control and over which it can be expected to have influence.

ISO 16949 quality standard – See *TS 16949 quality standard*.

ISO 9000 – Certification standards created by the International Organization for Standardizations in 1987 that now play a major role in setting process documentation standards for global manufacturers.

Originally developed from the British Standards Institution BS 5750, the ISO 9000 standards are now recognized in over 100 countries. Some people summarize ISO as an external motivation to "document what you do -- and do what you document." Some criticize ISO 9000 as a non-value added activity that focuses on documentation rather than on process improvement. Others argue that the primary value for North American firms is to help them sell products in Europe.

ISO 9000 provides general requirements for various aspects of a firm's operations, including Purchasing, Design Controls, Contracts, Inspection, Calibration, etc. For example, ISO9001 requires that Statistical Process Control (SPC) be applied to a firm's operations. This is more than simply documenting activities. The most recent standard is ISO9001:2000, which is a bit different than the older ISO9001:1994 standard in its emphasis on SPC and process flow diagrams.

Acknowledgments: David Learner, MOT 04, contributed to this entry.

See *standardized work, TS 16949 quality standard*.

issue tree – A mapping tool that can be used to break down a problem into its major component issues in order to prove or disprove a hypothesis.

In their book **The McKinsey Mind**, Rasiel and Friga (2001) define an issue tree as "the series of questions or issues that must be addressed to prove or disprove a hypothesis." Issue trees are used by many consulting firms to structure their thinking and analysis for addressing a client's problem. Like detective work, the process starts with a set of hypotheses that the investor believes are likely solutions to of the problem. These hypotheses are expressed as questions. For each of the main questions (hypotheses), the issue tree starts with the question on the far left and identifies the questions that need to be answered to address that question. The process continues with more detailed questions on the right. Ideally, the issues at any one level in the tree are "mutually exclusive and collectively exhaustive" (MECE) so that all possibilities are explored. If the answer is "no" to any question, further inquiry along that branch of the tree is usually not needed. Issue trees are usually drawn from left to right and are often created in Excel.

Consulting organizations commonly use issue trees to break down the main issue (usually written on the left) into smaller issues on the right (Rasiel, 1998). The figure below is a simple issue tree example that analyzes a production improvement hypothesis. This example "explodes" the waiting line problem into a set of sub-issues that the consulting project should consider. Issues should be MECE (Mutually Exclusive and Collectively Exhaustive). This concept is very closely related to the Minto Pyramid Principle (Minto 1996) that is used by almost all major consulting firms to structure arguments in a consulting presentation. Issue trees are also similar to the concept of a mindmap.

The figure below shows an issue tree example adapted from **The McKinsey Mind** by Rasiel and Friga (2001). Rasiel and Friga note that an issue tree is a special case of a logic tree.

Issue tree example

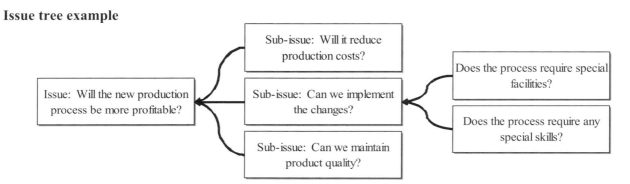

See *causal map, decision tree, hypothesis, impact wheel, MECE, mindmap, Minto Pyramid Principle, Root Cause Analysis (RCA), Y-tree.*

item number – A unique identifier for an item or material.

See *check digit, EPC (Electronic Product Code), Stock Keeping Unit (SKU), Universal Product Code (UPC).*

J

JCAHO – See *Joint Commission (JCAHO).*

jidoka – The Toyota Production System practice of designing processes and empowering workers to shut down a process when an abnormal condition occurs. ✪

The Japanese word "jidoka" is often translated as "autonomation," which is a contraction of the words "autonomous" and "automation." Jidoka is sometimes translated as "automation with a human touch (or human mind)." According to Ohno (1978), the original Jidoka device was a loom developed by Sakichi Toyoda (1867-1930), the founder of the Toyota Motor Company. This loom stopped instantly if any one of the threads broke so that defective products were not built and so that the problems could be seen immediately. According to Ohno

(1979), Toyota sold the patent for his loom in 1930 to the Platt Brothers in England for $500,000, and then invested this money in automobile research, which later led to the creation of the Toyota Motor Company.

Originally, jidoka focused on automatic methods for stopping a process when an error condition occurs; however, it is now used to describe both automated and human means for stopping a process when a problem occurs. For example, a process can use limit switches or devices that will automatically shut down the process when the required number of pieces have been made, a part is defective, or the mechanism jams. This same process can be operated with policies that allow the operators to shut down the machine when a warning light goes on.

Jidoka has two main benefits:

Quality benefits of Jidoka – Jidoka causes work to stop immediately when a problem occurs so that defective parts are never allowed to move from one workstation to the next. This highlights the causes of problems, forces constant process improvement, and therefore improves quality. The production process itself should ensure quality. The goal is quality, not quantity. Whereas automation focuses on labor reduction, Jidoka (autonomation) focuses on quality improvement. Note that Jidoka is closely related to Shigeo Shingo's concept of Poka yoke.

Cost benefits of Jidoka – Jidoka frees equipment from the necessity of constant human attention and makes it possible to separate people from machines and allows workers to handle multiple operations. Ideally, the machine or line is able to stop automatically, which reduces the burden of workers to monitor the process. In fact, many sources define Jidoka as stopping production automatically when a problem occurs.

According to the Nummi website (www.nummi.com/prodsyst.htm), the objectives of jidoka can be summed up as (1) ensuring quality 100% of the time, (2) preventing equipment breakdowns, and (3) using labor efficiently.

Jidoka is often implemented with a signal to communicate the status of a machine. For example, a production process might use Andon lights with a green light if everything is okay, a yellow light to signal an abnormal condition, and a red light if the process is stopped.

Acknowledgments: Mr. Eishi Kimijima, CSOM MBA 02, contributed to this entry. The Japanese characters are from fredharriman.com.

See *andon light, automation, autonomation, error proofing, lean thinking, multiple-machine handling, Toyota Production System (TPS)*.

jig – A mechanical device that holds a work piece securely in the correct position and/or has the capability of guiding the tool during a manufacturing operation.

See *fixture*.

JIT – See *Just-in-Time (JIT)*.

JIT II – A practice of having supplier representatives work at a customer location in order to better facilitate product design and/or production coordination activities.

The term and concept were developed by Lance Dixon at Bose Corporation who wrote a book by the same name. JIT II is essentially Vendor Managed Inventory (VMI), early supplier involvement, and co-location of personnel. The term does not appear to be widely used.

See *co-location, Early Supplier Involvement (ESI), lean thinking, Vendor Managed Inventory (VMI)*.

job enlargement – Adding more tasks to a job; increasing the range of the job duties and responsibilities. ✪

Job enlargement can have many benefits for an organization such as:

Develop worker skills – This gives workers a broader base of experience that can help the firm "learn" faster. Workers with a broader base of experience can help the organization improve those processes.

Reduce cycle time – When workers have broader skills, they can be moved to where the work is. This reduces queue time and cycle time.

Improve worker morale and retention – Enlarged jobs are often more interesting, which improves worker morale and retention. When enlarging a job, management can add more tasks, add more task significance, or both.

Adding more tasks – This is usually called job enlargement or "horizontal job enlargement" and adds similar tasks to the job description. The worker gets more of a co-worker's job. For example, the worker is the job of cleaning the sinks in addition to cleaning the floors.

Adding more task significance – This is usually called job enrichment or "vertical job enlargement" and adds more authority to the job. The worker gets some of the boss' job. For example, the worker might be given the added responsibilities of planning, organizing, and inspecting the cleaning of the sinks and the floors.

Note that the management literature does not have consistent definitions of the terms "job enlargement" and "job enrichment."

See *addition principle, Business Process Re-engineering (BPR), cross-training, handoff, division of labor, job rotation, learning organization, socio-technical design, standardized work, work simplification.*

job enrichment – See *job enlargement.*

job order costing – A cost accounting approach that allocates costs to a job as it passes through the system.

The direct labor, direct materials, and overhead costs are accumulated as the job passes through each step in a process. This type of costing system makes the most sense for a process layout such as a job shop.

See *backflushing, facility layout, process layout, target cost.*

job rotation – The movement of workers between different jobs in an organization.

This policy can be an effective method for cross training and can improve communications, increase process understanding, and reduce stress and boredom. Job rotation can also prevent muscle fatigue and reduce workplace injuries.

Job rotation also makes sense for managers. The VP of Rosemount in Eden Prairie, Minnesota had been the VP of Engineering, the VP of Manufacturing, and the VP of Marketing before being given the role as the head of a division. This executive was very well prepared for that general management role.

See *cross-training, job enlargement, learning organization, socio-technical design, workforce agility.*

job shop – A factory (or department in a factory) that has a number of general-purpose machines and makes products based on customer orders. ✪

Job shops have a Make to Order process, where each customer order is fairly unique. As a result, job shops typically have long customer leadtimes, long queues, highly skilled workers, and fairly general purpose machines. One of the main issues in a job shop is promising completion dates to customers and then scheduling the orders through the machines to reliably deliver the jobs before the promised dates.

See *discrete manufacturing, dispatching rules, flowshop, job shop scheduling, makespan.*

job shop scheduling – The process of creating a schedule (or sequence) for jobs (orders) that will be processed in a job shop.

Job shops must make order date promises to customers when the jobs arrive. However, the uncertainty in queue times, setup times, and run times makes it difficult to predict when an order will be completed. One of the main performance metrics used in most job shops is the percent of orders that are on-time with respect to the original promise date. While many managers agree that it would be better to measure against the original customer request date, few firms use this policy. Some firms follow the poor management practice of allowing the promise date to be changed after the promise was made to the customer, and then measure their performance against the revised promised date.

Academic research in job shop scheduling divides problem into the static and dynamic classes of problems. In the static problem, the set of jobs is given and does not change. The static problem is usually defined as minimizing the average flow time or the makespan (the ending time for the last job). Historically, the academic research in job shop scheduling has focused on simulation experiments that compare dispatching rules and developing both exact and heuristic finite scheduling algorithms that create schedules that do not violate the available capacity. The exact methods require inordinate amounts of computing time, but guarantee the optimal (mathematically best) solution; the heuristic methods are computationally fast, but do not guarantee the optimal solution.

Most Advanced Planning and Scheduling (APS) systems such as I2, Manugistics, and SAP APO have scheduling capabilities for job shop scheduling. However, in this author's experience, these are sometimes hard to understand, implement, and maintain because of the data requirements, the complexity of the problems, and the complexity of the systems.

See *Advanced Planning and Scheduling (APS), dispatching rules, expediting, flowshop, heijunka, job shop, makespan, service level, slack time.*

Joint Commission (JCAHO) – An independent, not-for-profit organization that sets healthcare quality standards and accredits healthcare organizations in the USA; formerly called the Joint Commission on Accreditation of Healthcare Organizations.

JCAHO is an independent, not-for-profit organization in the United States that is governed by a board of physicians, nurses, and consumers. JCAHO evaluates and accredits more than 15,000 health care organizations and programs in the United States.

JCAHO's mission is "To continuously improve the safety and quality of care provided to the public through the provision of health care accreditation and related services that support performance improvement in health care organizations." The JCAHO "positioning statement" is "Helping Health Care Organizations Help Patients."

JCAHO standards address an organization's performance in key functional areas. Each standard is presented as a series of "Elements of Performance," which are expectations that establish the broad framework that JCAHO surveyors use to evaluate a facility's performance.

The homepage for JCAHO is www.jointcommission.org.

See *adverse event, sentinel event.*

joint replenishment – The practice of ordering a number of different products on a purchase or manufacturing order to reduce the ordering (setup) cost.

In the purchasing context, the in-coming shipping cost can often be reduced by ordering many items from a supplier on the same purchase order. One simple way to manage this situation is to trigger a purchase order when one item reaches a reorder point, and then reorder all items sourced from that supplier on that same purchase order. The lotsizing policy can be an "order-up-to" policy with constraints on the order size (e.g., minimum order size). In other words, set the lotsize Q to the "order-up-to" level minus the current inventory position. If Q is less than the minimum order quantity, do not include that item on the purchase order.

In a manufacturing context, joint replenishment is important when the process has major (family) setups between families of products and minor setups between products within a family. In this type of joint replenishment situation, when one product needs to be made, the firm considers making many or all of the products in the family.

See *inventory management, lotsizing methods, major setup cost, setup cost.*

Just-in-Time (JIT) – A philosophy developed by Toyota in Japan that emphasizes manufacturing and delivery of small lotsizes only when needed by the customer. ✪

Just-in-Time primarily emphasized the production control aspects of lean manufacturing and the Toyota Production System (TPS). For all practical purposes, the term Just-in-Time manufacturing has disappeared from common usage. The concept of "lean manufacturing" is now considered more current and larger in scope.

See *lean thinking, Toyota Production System (TPS).*

K

kaikaku – A Japanese word meaning radical change, transformation, or revolution.

Some experts argue that the Japanese word kaikaku is synonymous with kaizen blitz. However, a closer look suggests that while kaizen is the steady, long-term continuous improvement, kaikaku is best described as a paradigm shift that occurs once every so often. Kaizen is essential for a long-term Lean transformation but at the beginning and at several critical phases kaikaku is necessary to break paradigms and elevate the awareness of people to a higher level of understanding. According to isixsigma.com, Kaikaku is revolutionary whereas kaizen is evolutionary in small increments.

See *Business Process Re-engineering (BPR), kaizen, kaizen event.*

kaizen – A Japanese word meaning gradual and orderly continuous improvement or "change for the better." ✪

The English translation is usually "continuous improvement" or "continual improvement." Kaizen is usually associated solely with quality improvement (e.g., reducing defects) but it can be used to make any type of process improvement.

According to the kaizen philosophy, everyone in an organization should work together to make improvements. It is a culture of sustained continuous improvement focusing on eliminating waste in all systems and processes of an organization. Kaizen is often implemented through kaizen events.

The Lean Enterprise Institute dictionary notes that kaizen has two levels:
1. System or flow kaizen focusing on the overall value stream. This is kaizen for management.
2. Process kaizen focusing on individual processes. This is kaizen for work teams and team leaders.

The Japanese characters for kaizen (改善) mean change for the good. Source: en.wikipedia.org/wiki/Kaizen, October 9, 2006.

See *kaikaku, kaizen event, lean thinking*.

kaizen event – A kaizen event (or kaizen process) is typically a short-term (3-5 work days) activity with a number of people working as a team to make significant process improvements; also known as a kaizen blitz, rapid process improvement workshop (RPIW), and Kaikaku. ✪

The kaizen process uses various lean tools and methods to make the problem visible, and then uses formal root cause analysis and other means to identify and correct the problem at the source. The result is rapid process improvement including lower costs, higher quality, lower cycle time, and better products and services. While kaizen has historically been applied in manufacturing, many service businesses are now applying kaizen as well. One notable example is the Park Nicollet Health Systems.

A kaizen event is not a business meeting or a typical process improvement project. It is a hands-on, on-the-job, action learning and improvement activity led by a skilled facilitator. The process involves identifying, measuring, and improving a process. Unlike many approaches to process improvement, kaizen is a method to achieve rapid process improvement.

Kaizen teams include people who work the process and also heavily involve other people who work the process. Therefore, workers usually feel consulted and involved, which goes a long way in overcoming resistance to change. On this same theme, kaizen events often try many different small "experiments," again with the workers involved, which drives rapid learning and system improvement, while maintaining strong "buy-in" from the people who work the process everyday.

Compared to a typical process improvement approach (such as DMAIC), a kaizen event has a number of advantages and disadvantages as noted in the table below.

Advantages	Disadvantages
• Quick business results	• Disruption of business, customers
• Order-of-magnitude changes	• Not enough time for data-based decision making
• Disruption limited to the event	• Items on the "30-day list" for more than 30 days
• Team involvement	• Can make people angry
• Ownership of the results	• Sometimes hasty decisions are bad ones

Source: Professor Arthur V. Hill

One issue with kaizen events is managing the activities before and after the event. It is fairly common for items on the "30-day list" to be on the list for over 30 days.

See *5 Whys, 5S, gemba, kaikaku, kaizen, lean thinking*.

kanban – A simple device that sends a pull signal. ✪

Kanban is the Japanese word for sign, signboard, card, instruction card, visible record, doorplate, or poster. In manufacturing, a kanban is usually a card, cart, container, or square marked with tape on a table or on the floor. An empty container gives a factory worker permission to fill the box. If a worker does not have an empty box to fill, the worker is "blocked" from doing any more work and should be re-assigned somewhere else where their work is needed.

A kanban control system uses a signaling device to regulate JIT flows. The cards or containers make up the kanban pull system. A kanban is a card that is attached to a storage and transport container. The authority to produce or supply additional parts comes from downstream operations. It identifies the part number and container capacity, along with other information. A kanban system is a pull-system, in which the kanban is used to pull parts to the next production stage when they are needed. In contrast, an MRP system (or any schedule-based system) is a push system, in which a detailed production schedule for each part is used to push parts to the next production stage when scheduled.

The weakness of a push system (MRP) is that customer demand must be forecast and production leadtimes must be estimated. Bad guesses (forecasts or estimates) result in excess inventory and long leadtimes. Long leadtimes leave more room for error. The weakness of a pull system (kanban) is that following the JIT production philosophy is essential, especially concerning the elements of short setup times and small lot sizes.

The characters for kanban in kanji are 看板 and in katakana are カンバン. Source: en.wikipedia.org/wiki/Kanban.

See http://www.ashland.edu/~rjacobs/m503jit.html.

See *blocking, faxban, lean thinking, starving.*

Kano Analysis – A quality measurement tool used to categorize and prioritize customer requirements based on their impact on customer satisfaction; also called the Kano Model, Kano Diagram, and Kano Questionnaire.

Kano Analysis was developed by the Japanese quality expert Dr. Noriaki Kano of Tokyo Rika University to analyze customer needs and their relationship to customer satisfaction. He defined three types of customer perceptions of product characteristics:

- **Must haves** – The basic functions and features that customers expect of a product or service. For example, an airline that cannot meet airport noise regulations will not succeed in the marketplace.
- **More the better** – Generally, the better the performance the greater the customer satisfaction. For example, an airline that provides more entertainment options will be perceived as having better service.
- **Delighters** – These are the unexpected "extras" that can make a product stand out from the others. For example, an airline that offers free snacks in the waiting area would be a welcome surprise. Delighters vary highly between customers and tend to change over time. A popular service quality expression is that "Today's delight becomes tomorrow's expectation."

For example, when customers pick up a rental car at an airport, they will likely have different attitudes about seats, checkout speed, and global positioning systems. Customers will always expect seats in the car and will be completely dissatisfied with a car without seats. Seats, therefore, are a "must have" feature. Customers expect the check-in process to take about 15 minutes, but are happier if it takes only 10 minutes. Satisfaction, therefore, increases with check-in speed. Lastly, many customers are delighted if their rental car has a Global Positioning System (GPS). A GPS, therefore, is a "delighter" feature.

Kano Analysis uses a graphical approach as shown in the Kano Diagram below. The x-axis ("dysfunctional/functional") of the diagram measures the level of a particular product attribute (i.e., checkout speed) and the y-axis ("delight/dissatisfaction") measures customer satisfaction. For example, checkout speed is a "more the better" feature and is drawn as a 45 degree straight line. Must-have features (such as seats) are drawn so that high functionality (e.g., having seats) brings satisfaction up to zero. When a "delighter" feature such as a global positioning system is not present, satisfaction is still at or above zero, but increasing a "delighter" can significantly increase satisfaction.

Kano Diagram

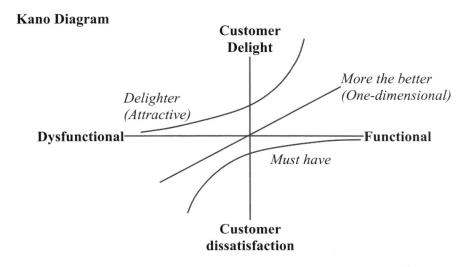

Kano Analysis begins by identifying all possible customer requirements and uses a survey instrument to measure customer perceptions about each requirement. The following is a simple example of the Kano Questionnaire:

If the radio antenna automatically retracts when the radio is turned off, how do you feel? (Note: This is the functional form of the question.)	1. I like it that way. 2. It must be that way. 3. I am neutral. 4. I can live with it that way. 5. I dislike it that way.
If the radio antenna automatically does not retract when the radio is turned off, how do you feel? (Note: This is the dysfunctional form of the question.)	1. I like it that way. 2. It must be that way. 3. I am neutral. 4. I can live with it that way. 5. I dislike it that way.

Each question has two parts (1) "How do you feel if that feature is present in the product?" and (2) "How do you feel if that feature is not present in the product?" Respondents are asked to respond on the following scale: I like it, I expect, I'm neutral, I can tolerate it, I dislike it. The responses for the two questions are then translated into curves on the graph.

Kano Analysis can be used to classify and prioritize customer needs. This is useful because customer needs are not all the same kind, do not all have the same importance, and are different for different subpopulations. The results of a Kano Analysis can be used to identify customer segments, prioritize customer segments, design products for each segment, and guide process improvement efforts.

Walden *et al.* (1993) have written a good review article on Kano Analysis.

See *Analytical Hierarchy Process (AHP)*, *ideation*, *New Product Development (NPD)*, *Pugh Matrix*, *service quality*, *Voice of the Customer (VOC)*.

Keiretsu – A Japanese term for a set of companies with interlocking business relationships and shareholdings.

The "Big Six" keiretsu are Mitsui, Mitsubishi, Sumitomo, Fuyo (formed primarily from the old Yasuda zaibatsu), Sanwa, and Dai–Ichi Kangyo. The keiretsu were established after World War II, following the dissolution of the family-owned conglomerates known as Zaibatsu by the American Occupation authorities. It was the belief of many Americans that they could hasten the spread of democracy in Japan by reducing the concentration of wealth and hence economic power. Shares of companies owned by the Zaibatsu were distributed to employees and local residents, with the result that in 1949 when the stock market reopened, 70% of all listed shares were held by individuals.

The zaibatsu dissolution was done in a haphazard manner, however. Often a single factory that merely assembled products for its group found itself an independent company, lacking a finance department, marketing department or even procurement department. To deal with this precarious situation, companies within the former Zaibatsu banded together through a system of cross-shareholding, whereby each company owned shares in all other group members' companies. Within this structure, the major shareholders tend to be a bank, a general trading company, and a life insurance company. The "Big Six" keiretsu are all led by their respective banks, which are the largest in Japan.

Because listed companies bought and held onto shares in other listed companies, the ratio of shares owned by individuals in Japan steadily declined to around 20% by 2003. There has also never been a hostile takeover of a listed Japanese company simply because its shareholders refuse to sell at any price. This has made management rather complacent and greatly reduced shareholders' rights. Annual shareholders' meetings in Japan tend to be held on the exact same day, and usually end quickly without any questions.

In the 1990s, when the Japanese stock market showed a relentless decline, stable shareholding began to decline. Banks needed to sell their shareholdings in order to realize gains to cover their credit costs. Life insurers had to sell in order to realize higher returns to pay their policyholders. Even corporations are selling shares because the original rationale for holding them has disappeared.

The term is rarely used by Western companies; one notable exception is the venture capital firm of Kleiner, Perkins, Caufield & Byers, which encourages transactions among companies in which it holds a stake.

Much of the above is adapted from www.free-definition.com/Keiretsu.html, November 11, 2004.

In terms of supply chain management and Just-in-Time, the characteristics of Keiretsu in Toyota are:

- Pressure on suppliers to reduce prices.
- Compensation to suppliers for suggestions.
- Early involvement of suppliers in design – drawings approved as opposed to drawings supplied.
- Commitment of suppliers to supply high quality parts.
- Evaluation and competition of suppliers: Two-vendor policy
- Propagation of Just-in-Time to suppliers
- Sustainable monthly master schedule with kanban as a signal for the adjustment
- Leveled production

See *Just-in-Time, lean thinking*.

Kepner-Tregoe Model – A type of systematic scoring approach for evaluating alternatives to assist in a decision making process and for winning organizational approval for those decisions.

The Kepner-Tregoe (KT) Model is a structured methodology for gathering information and prioritizing and evaluating it. It was developed by Charles H. Kepner and Benjamin B. Tregoe in the 1960s. The KT Model is particularly effective when the organization has to evaluate a number of qualitative issues that have significant trade-offs between them. KT Model has been "discovered" by many different people and is very similar to Criteria Based Matrix, Pugh Matrix, and Multi-Attribute Utility Theory (MAUT), and other methodologies.

The typical steps in the Kepner-Tregoe approach include:

1. Clearly define the problem at a high level.
2. Establish strategic requirements (musts), operational objectives (wants), and constraints (limits).
3. Rank objectives and assign relative weights.
4. Generate alternatives.
5. Assign a relative score for each alternative on an objective-by-objective basis.
6. Calculate weighted score for each alternative and identify top two or three.
7. List adverse consequences for each top alternative and evaluate probability (high, medium, low) and severity (high, medium, low).
8. Make a final, single choice between top alternatives.

Adapted from www.valuebasedmanagement.net/methods_kepner-tregoe_matrix.html, January 3, 2005.

The Kepner-Tregoe entry in Wikipedia provides a paired-comparison approach for developing the weights for the KT Model. Each of the criteria is listed on both the columns and the rows. Experts are then asked to independently compare all pairs of criteria in the matrix and to put a "1" when the row criterion is more important than the column. Ties are not allowed. The main diagonal of the matrix is filled with all "1"s. The rows are then summed and divided by the sum of the values in the matrix, which will always be $s = n + n(n-1)/2$, where n is the number of criteria that are evaluated. For example, a location decision has three criteria which are cost, distance to markets, and availability of suppliers. The matrix is then:

	Cost	Markets	Suppliers	Sum	Sum/s	Rank
Cost	1	1	1	3	50%	1
Markets	0	1	1	2	40%	2
Suppliers	0	0	1	1	10%	3
		Sum (s)		6	100%	

Note: Given that $n = 3$, $s = n + n(n-1)/2 = 6$. This is a good check to help avoid data entry errors.

It can be seen in this analysis that the cost dimension clearly dominates the other two criteria. This matrix is only used to compute the weights for the criteria that are used for inputs to the KT model.

The following is an example of the KT method used for a new plant location decision where management has collected both quantitative and qualitative data and needs to make difficult decisions regarding trade-offs between costs, risks, quality, etc. A simple example is presented in the table below without the "X" values filled in. Of course, many other criteria could also be used in this analysis.

Kepner-Tregoe example

Factors	Weight	China	Mexico

Quantitative			
Capital cost		X	X
Raw material cost		X	X
Labor cost		X	X
Transportation cost		X	X
Total cost	50%	X	X
Qualitative			
Distance to markets	40%	X	X
Availability of suppliers	10%	X	X
		Weighted Score	Weighted Score

The final score seldom "makes" the final decision. The scoring process only informs the process and helps stimulate useful debate that supports the final decision, which must be made (and owned) by the management team. It is wise to have the people who make the decision to create the weights and to score the alternatives so that they own the inputs as well as the results.

Some have criticized the KT model because it does not explicitly consider risk and uncertainty issues. It is a good practice to have a risk dimension included as one of the qualitative factors. In addition, KT tends to focus on consensus, which can lead to group-think and limit creative and contradictory points of view.

The Kepner-Tregoe Model appears to be nearly identical to the Pugh Matrix. The Kepner-Tregoe consulting firm's website is kepner-tregoe.com.

See *affinity diagram, Analytical Hierarchy Process (AHP), C&E Matrix, decision tree, facility location, force-field diagram, Nominal Group Technique (NGT), Pugh Matrix, Triz.*

Key Performance Indicator (KPI) – A metric of strategic importance.

See *balanced scorecard, dashboard, Key Process Output Variable (KPOV), operations performance metrics.*

Key Process Input Variable (KPIV) – See *Key Process Output Variable (KPOV).*

Key Process Output Variable (KPOV) – A term commonly used in Six Sigma programs to describe an important output variable controlled by one or more Key Process Input variables (KPIVs); also called Critical To Quality (CTQ).

All processes have both inputs and outputs. Key Process Input Variables (KPIVs) include both controlled and uncontrolled variables. Controlled input variables can be changed by organization whereas uncontrolled variables are currently outside of the organization's control. An example of a controlled input variable is the temperature of an oven; an example of an uncontrolled input variable may be the humidity of the room. Many uncontrolled KPIVs can become controlled if the organization should decide to make the investment. For example, room humidity can be controlled with investment in humidity control equipment.

Key Process Output Variables (KPOVs) are variables that are affected by the KPIVs. KPOVs are usually variables that either internal or external customers care about, such as units produced per hour, defects per million opportunities, and customer satisfaction.

See *C&E Matrix, Critical To Quality (CTQ), Key Performance Indicator (KPI), Six Sigma.*

kitting – Grouping individual items together for future use such as assembly, typically in boxes or bags.

Kitting parts is often a good way to make sure that all parts are available and easy to reach. In a manufacturing context, "kits" of parts are often put together in boxes and given to workers to assemble. In a distribution context, kits of parts are prepared to be packed and shipped. If inventoried, kits should have their own part numbers.

Some manufacturing consultants argue that kitting is a bad idea because it tends to increase inventory, increase cycle times, and is often a non-value-added step in a process. They advocate that firms should have "logical" kitting where they use their computer-based MRP system to make sure that all of the parts are available before being released for assembly.

KJ Method – A technique for building affinity diagrams named after Kawakita Jiro; also known as KJ Analysis.

The key principle of the KJ Method is that everyone works together in silence. The idea is that this allows the more creative right brain to come into play. In practice, it also has the significant benefit that it keeps people focused on sorting out the problem, rather than getting sidetracked in discussion.

The website www.rmaf.org.ph/Awardees/Biography/BiographyKawakitaJir.htm provides extensive information on Mr. Kawakita Jiro and on how and why he developed this method.

See *affinity diagram*.

knapsack problem – An important operations research problem that derives its name from the problem of finding the best set of items that can fit into a knapsack (backpack).

The knapsack problem is to select the items to put into a knapsack (now known as a backpack) that will maximize the total value subject to the constraint that the items must fit into the knapsack with respect to the knapsack's maximum weight or volume. The knapsack problem is a well-known and highly studied combinatorial optimization problem in the operations research discipline.

Given a set of *n* items that each have value v_i and weight (or volume) w_i, the knapsack problem is to find the combination of items that will fit into the knapsack to maximize the total value. Stated mathematically, the knapsack problem is to maximize the total value, $\sum_{i=1}^{n} v_i x_i$, subject to the constraint that the items fit into the knapsack, e.g., $\sum_{i=1}^{n} w_i x_i < W$, where W is the maximum weight (or volume) for the knapsack and the decision variables x_i are restricted to either zero or one (e.g., $x_i \in \{0,1\}$ for all i). The "bounded knapsack problem" allows for up to c_i copies of each item. The mathematical statement of the problem is the same except that the domain for the decision variables changes to $x_i \in \{0,1,...,c_i\}$. The "unbounded knapsack problem" places no upper bound on the number of copies for each kind of item.

The knapsack problem can be solved to optimality with dynamic programming. Although no polynomial-time algorithm is known, fairly large knapsack problems can be solved to optimality quickly on a computer.

See *Integer Programming (IP)*, *Operations Research (OR)*.

knock-down kit – A kit or box of parts that can be used to assemble a product; also known as a Complete, Knocked Down (CKD) or Semi Knocked Down (SKD).

Knock-down kits are commonly used in the automotive industry. The manufacturer sells knock-down kits to a foreign affiliate to avoid paying high import taxes and/or receive tax preferences for having higher local content.

The General Motors factory in northern Hungary receives knockdown kits in large wooden boxes from Opal in Germany and then assembles them into cars using Hungarian workers.

knowledge capital – See *knowledge management*.

knowledge management – A range of practices used by organizations to identify, create, represent, and distribute knowledge for reuse, awareness, and learning across the organization.

Hansen, Nohria, and Tierney (1999) defined two knowledge management strategies. These include:

Codification strategy – In some organizations, knowledge management centers on the computer. Knowledge is carefully codified and stored in databases where it can be accessed and used easily by anyone in the company. This is called a codification strategy.

Personalization strategy – In other organizations, knowledge is closely tied to the person who developed it and is shared mainly through direct person-to-person contact. The purpose of the computer for these companies is to help people communicate knowledge, not just store it. This is called the personalization strategy.

Good information systems infrastructure is an important success factor for a good knowledge management system. However, the biggest problem in knowledge management is usually not the information system but rather the lack of proper incentives for people to add knowledge to the knowledge database. People are busy and often do not have time to add new information that might be valuable to others. Some people are also concerned that if they put their private information into the knowledge management system their jobs could be at risk and they might, in fact, diminish their value to the firm.

See *business intelligence, intellectual capital, knowledge capital, knowledge worker, learning organization, tribal knowledge*.

knowledge worker – A person whose primary job is use their intellectual capability to acquire, accumulate, process, analyze, synthesize, create, develop, use, manage, distribute, and/or communicate information.

The term knowledge worker was first used by Professor Peter F. Drucker in his book *Landmarks of Tomorrow* (1959) to describe people who use their intellectual capacities rather than their manual or physical skills in their work.

Knowledge workers are typically involved in tasks such as planning, acquiring, searching, analyzing, organizing, storing, programming, distributing, marketing, or otherwise adding value by transforming information into more valuable information. Knowledge workers include those in the information technology fields, such as programmers, systems analysts, technical writers, academic professionals, and researchers. The term is also used to for people with information intensive jobs such as lawyers, teachers, scientists, engineers, and medical professionals.

See *knowledge management*.

Kolmogorov-Smirnov test (K-S test) – A non-parametric statistical test that is usually used to determine if a set of observations differs from a hypothesized continuous probability distribution.

The K-S test can be used to determine if a particular continuous theoretical distribution (such as the beta, exponential, gamma, lognormal, or Weibull) is a good fit with the data. The K-S test compares the empirical cumulative distribution with the hypothesized cumulative distribution function. More generally, the K-S test can be used to determine if any two datasets differ significantly. The K-S test makes no assumption about the distribution of data.

The KS test is based on the largest "error" between the actual and theoretical cumulative distribution functions. Given n independent samples arranged in numerical order $x_1 \leq x_2 \leq \ldots \leq x_n$, define $F_s(x)$ as the cumulative distribution for the sample. $F_s(x_j) = (j+1)/n$, therefore, is the fraction of the n observations that are less than or equal to x. Define $F(x)$ as the hypothesized theoretical cumulative distribution. The "one-sided" K-S statistics are then $D_n^+ = \max(F_s(x_j) - F(x_j))$ and $D_n^- = \max(F(x_j) - F_s(x_j))$.

Critical values for the D_n statistic are tabulated in many statistics textbooks and are available in many statistical software packages. Unfortunately, Excel does not support the K-S test without add-ins software such as Crystal Ball. For large sample sizes, $P(D_n > x/\sqrt{n}) \approx 1 - 2\sum_{i=1}^{\infty}(-1)^{i-1}e^{-2i^2x^2}$.

Technically, the K-S test is only appropriate when all of the parameters of the distribution are known with certainty. However, in nearly all cases, it is necessary to estimate the parameters from the data. The chi-square test is more appropriate than the K-S test for discrete distributions.

Failure to reject the null hypothesis of no difference should not be interpreted as "accepting the null hypothesis." For smaller sample sizes, good-of-fit tests are not very powerful and will only detect major differences. On the other hand, for a larger sample size, these tests will almost always reject the null hypothesis because it is almost never exactly true. As Law and Kelton (2002) state, "This is an unfortunate property of these tests, since it is usually sufficient to have a distribution that is "nearly" correct."

The K-S test was developed by Russian mathematicians Andrey Nikolaevich Kolmogorov (Андрей Николаевич Колмогоров, 1903-1987) and Vladimir Ivanovich Smirnov (Владимир Иванович Смирнов, 1887-1974).

See *chi-square goodness of fit* test.

KPI – See *Key Performance Indicator (KPI)*.

KPOV – See *Key Process Output Variable (KPOV)*.

L

labor intensive – Requiring or having a large expenditure of labor in comparison to capital.

A process or industry that requires large amounts of human effort to produce goods. Good examples include consulting firms and accounting firms because they generally have high labor costs relative to their capital investment.

See *capital intensive*.

labor management systems – See *work measurement*.

labor standards – See *work measurement*.

LAI – See *Lean Advancement Initiative (LAI)*.

Last-In-First-Out (LIFO) – A priority or accounting rule that is based on the last arriving item, unit, or customer.

In inventory management with LIFO, the unit that was put into inventory last will be the first to go out. This practice will likely result in some inventory never being used.

In accounting, LIFO is used to determine the cost of goods sold where the most recent units purchased from suppliers are assumed to be sold first and are assigned their corresponding unit cost.

See *First-in-First-Out (FIFO)*.

Law of Large Numbers – A fundamental concept in probability and statistics that describes how the average of a randomly selected sample from a large population is likely to grow closer to the true average of the whole population as the number of observations increases.

For example, the average weight of 10 apples randomly selected from a barrel of 100 apples is probably closer to the true average weight of all 100 apples than the average weight of 3 apples taken from that same barrel.

The weak Law of Large Numbers states that as the sample size grows larger, the difference between the sample mean and the population mean will approach zero. The strong Law of Large Numbers states that as the sample size grows larger, the probability that the sample and population means will be equal approaches 1.

One of the most important conclusions of the Law of Large Numbers is the Central Limit Theorem which describes how sample means tend to occur in a Normal Distribution around the mean of the population regardless of the shape of the population distribution, especially as sample sizes get larger.

See *Central Limit Theorem*

layout – See *facility layout*.

LCL (Less than Container Load) – See *Less than Container Load (LCL)*.

leading indicator – A variable that can be used to predict another variable one or more periods ahead.

Examples of leading indicators include building permits, non-residential housing, mobile phones shipped, unemployment insurance claims, money supply, and inventory changes. The Fed watches many of these indicators when it decides what to do about interest rates.

In contrast, coincident indicators change at the same time as the variable of interest and lagging indicators change after the variable of interest. These variables, therefore, are of no use for predictive purposes.

See *balanced scorecard, econometric forecasting, forecasting*.

leadtime – The planned replenishment time for an order; often written two words (e.g., lead time); also called production leadtime, manufacturing leadtime, and planned leadtime. ✪

The planned leadtime is a planning factor used in both MRP and reorder point systems for the planned time required to replenish inventory from a supplier (a purchase order) or from a plant (a manufacturing order). This planning factor is called the "replenishment leadtime" in SAP.

Ideally, the planned leadtime is a reliable forecast of the expected (average) actual replenishment time in the future. In other words, the planned leadtime should not include any cushion or buffer to handle situations where the actual leadtime is longer than average. The buffer should be handled by the safety stock and should not be imbedded in the planned leadtime.

The planned leadtime for a manufacturing order is the sum of the planned leadtimes for all of the steps in the routing for the order. For each operation, this typically includes (a) the queue time before the operation begins, (b) the setup time to get the machine ready for production, (c) the run time to process the order, and finally (d) the post-operation time to wait for the order to be picked up and moved to the next workcenter.

The term leadtime is often used as a synonym for throughput time, cycle time, flow time, and customer leadtime. However, the prefix "lead" suggests that the term leadtime should be used primarily as a planning factor for the time to "lead" the event, rather than as the actual throughput time. It is better, therefore, to use the terms throughput time, cycle time, or flow time rather than leadtime when describing actual throughput times. (See the *cycle time* entry to better understand the two conflicting definitions of cycle time.)

The planned leadtime is a constant, but the actual throughput time (sometimes called cycle time) is a random variable. Over a given period of time for data collection, the actual throughput time is a random variable and has a minimum, maximum, mean, standard deviation, median, etc. Note that the safety stock calculation should use either an estimate of the longest leadtime or use the more complicated safety stock equation that includes both the mean and standard deviation of the leadtime. (See the *safety stock* entry for more details.)

The promised customer leadtime is the promised customer wait time for an order. The actual customer leadtime is the actual wait time (a random variable) experienced by the customer.

It is important to understand that the planned leadtime, actual leadtime (throughput time, flow time), promised customer leadtime, and actual customer leadtime might all be different. Therefore, it is important for managers, engineers, and students of operations management to be very clear when they use these terms. When a manager reports that the factory has a leadtime of two weeks, this could mean a two-week planned leadtime, two-week average leadtime, two-week minimum leadtime, two-week modal leadtime, two-week promised customer leadtime, etc.

The *cycle time* entry provides more insights into these and other closely related issues.

See *cumulative leadtime, customer leadtime, cycle time, demand during leadtime, purchasing leadtime, push-pull boundary, reorder point, run time, takt time.*

leadtime syndrome – A vicious cycle where a supplier's quoted leadtime gets longer, which results in customers ordering more to cover their planned leadtime, which results in the supplier making the quoted leadtime even longer.

The cycle can be described as follows:

1. A manufacturer increases the quoted leadtime. This could be for any reason such as a vacation, a machine problem, a slight increase in demand, etc.
2. The customer learns about the increased leadtime and releases orders earlier to cover the demand during the planned leadtime. Note that the customer's true average demand did not change in this scenario.
3. The manufacturer receives the larger order, adds it to the order backlog, and further increases the quoted leadtime. The leadtime syndrome continues back to step 1.

The solution to the leadtime syndrome is for customers to communicate their true demand to their suppliers to give their suppliers forward visibility of their true demand and for suppliers to avoid increasing quoted leadtimes, even when the demand increases. The leadtime syndrome is closely related to the bullwhip effect. Historical note: George Plossl discussed the leadtime syndrome in books and seminars in the 1980s.

See *bullwhip effect, force majeure, Parkinson's Laws.*

Lean Advancement Initiative (LAI) – A learning and research community that brings together key aerospace stakeholders from industry, government, and academia; formerly called the Lean Aerospace Initiative.

LAI is a consortium-guided research program headquartered at the Massachusetts Institute of Technology (MIT) Department of Aeronautics and Astronautics, in close collaboration with the Sloan School of Management. LAI is managed under the auspices of the Center for Technology, Policy and Industrial Development, an interdisciplinary research center within the Engineering Systems Division. LAI was born out of practicality and necessity. Declining procurement budgets, rising costs, and overcapacity prompted the defense acquisition strategy to stress affordability rather than just performance at any cost. The Initiative was formally launched in 1993 when leaders from the U.S. Air Force, MIT, labor unions, and defense aerospace businesses forged a trail-blazing partnership to transform the industry, reinvigorate the workplace, and reinvest in America by applying lean manufacturing principles. LAI's website is http://lean.mit.edu. Much of this content is from that website.

Lean Aerospace Initiative – See *Lean Advancement Initiative (LAI).*

lean design – Lean design is a set of tools for reducing the new product development cost and time with a focus on reducing variation, addressing bottlenecks, eliminating rework, and managing capacity.

See *lean thinking, New Product Development (NPD).*

Lean Enterprise Institute (LEI) – A nonprofit education and research organization founded by Jim Womack in 1997 to promote and advance the principles of lean thinking in every aspect of business and across a wide range of industries.

Led by Jim Womack, LEI develops and teaches lean principles, tools, and techniques designed to enable positive change. A major LEI objective is to create a complete toolkit for Lean Thinkers to use in transforming businesses. The lean toolkit is intended to be a dynamic and continually evolving means of sharing knowledge among Lean Thinkers.

One of the more important publications of the LEI is the **Lean Lexicon** edited by Chet Marchwinski and John Shook (2006).

The LEI website is www.lean.org.

See *7 Wastes*, *lean thinking*.

lean manufacturing – See *lean thinking*.

lean production office – See *lean promotion office*.

lean promotion office – The program "office" (team) that manages the lean implementation.

This team provides leadership, training, and support for implementing a lean manufacturing program.

See *lean thinking*, *program management office*.

lean sigma – A combination of lean manufacturing and Six Sigma programs; also called Lean Six Sigma. ✪

Many experts disagree about how lean and Six Sigma principles should be "married" in an organization. George, Rowlands, and Kastle (2003) argue that Six Sigma focuses on reducing variation whereas lean focuses on reduce the average cycle time. However, this dichotomy seems too simplistic given that many organizations use Six Sigma to reduce the average cycle time rather than just the variation of the cycle time. Also, many organizations apply lean principles such as foolproof devices and small lotsizes are designed to reduce variation.

Paul Husby, retired Senior VP at 3M, and many other thought leaders argue that Six Sigma is more of a methodology that tends to rely on statistical methods, whereas lean is more of a philosophy of how a firm should be managed, with emphasis on simplicity, visibility, standardized work, and accountability. He suggests the following simple rule: If the cause is unknown or difficult to determine, use DMAIC; otherwise use lean.

One of the best ways to combine lean and Six Sigma principles is to use the Six Sigma program framework to provide an organizational structure for process improvement projects. This structure helps the firm align projects with the organization's strategies and goals, are staffed appropriately, and have proper accountability. Many Six Sigma projects use lean manufacturing principles and tools (cycle time reduction, lotsize reduction, etc.). The Six Sigma DMAIC approach can be used for all projects, but experts such as Husby argue that DMAIC is not needed for many lean projects because the problem and the solution are already well-defined.

At Medtronic the program is called "Lean Sigma Solutions." Evidently, Michael George has trademarked the term lean sigma, which means that some firms might have legal problems using the term. According to Scot Webster, VP of Quality Shared Services at Medtronic, "Six Sigma makes a science of process capability and lean makes a science of process flow process flow and both are implemented with the DMAIC approach."

Mr. Webster argues that the standard Six Sigma equation $Y = f(x_1, x_2, …, x_N)$ works for both Six Sigma and for Lean. The only difference is that for Six Sigma, the challenge is to find the vital few x_i variables among a large number of possible variables; for lean, the challenge is to find the vital few from only 18 potential tools. He lists eleven of the eighteen tools in his publicly available talk. These include transfer lot size, process lot size, options, rework, downtime, external set up, internal set up, attended machine, unattended machine, move, and labor. He summarized his talk on lean sigma by arguing that both Six Sigma and Lean are about leadership development and asserted that lean sigma was 70% leadership development and 30% process improvement.

See *cross functional team*, *DMAIC*, *lean thinking*, *Six Sigma*, *stakeholder analysis*, *Voice of the Customer (VOC)*.

Lean Six Sigma – See *Lean Sigma*.

lean thinking – A philosophy and set of practices originally developed at Toyota that seeks to eliminate waste; also known as lean manufacturing or just lean. ✪

Overview

Lean manufacturing is based on the Toyota Production System. The term "lean" and the most widely known discussion of lean manufacturing can be found in **Lean Thinking** by Womack and Jones (2003). Central to the lean manufacturing approach is a focus on waste reduction and a high level of engagement of all company personnel in implementing and improving the manufacturing process. After many years of studying lean, this author concludes that lean thinking can be summarized in just five words: simple, visual, error proof, wasteless, and standard. Lean manufacturing offers many benefits such as reductions in cycle time and inventory and improvements in quality and customer responsiveness.

Lean concepts were first introduced at Toyota by Taiichi Ohno in Japan (Ohno 1978). Richard Schonberger played an important role in popularizing lean concepts in the United States, with an emphasis on the material flow aspects of lean (Schonberger 1982, 1986). More recently, Jim Womack at LEI has led a resurgence of interest in lean thinking with a view of lean that goes well beyond materials flow (Womack & Jones 2003)

The figure below is the popular "house of lean," which is often used to teach the fundamentals of lean thinking. A similar figure appears in the Ohno (1978) book. This figure is adapted from Pascal (2002).

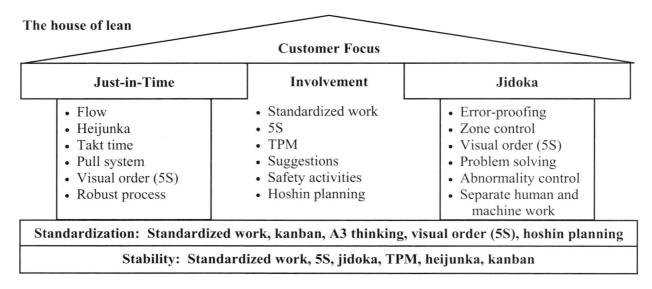

All of the terms shown in this figure can be found in this book. Note that the left side focuses on managing materials where the right side focuses more managing the equipment.

Lean manufacturing can be implemented by following the five shown in the framework illustrated below:

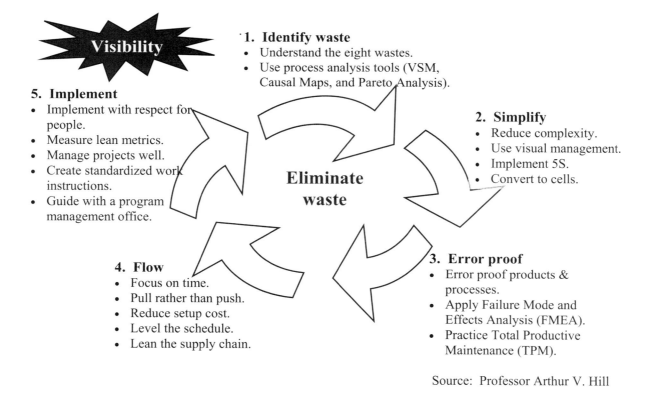

Source: Professor Arthur V. Hill

Lean manufacturing and the eight wastes

One of the key ideas of lean manufacturing is to identify and eliminate waste. The following tables define each of the eight wastes and propose a solution to each one.

Waste 1. Overproduction

Definition	Producing before need.
Results	Large inventory, long cycle times, poor quality, poor visibility of defects.
Solution	Maximize flow, simplify, setup reduction (SMED), heijunka (level loading), TPM, forecasting, improve yields, calculate safety stocks, use pull systems (blocking and starving), improve yield through error proofing and kaizen events
Example	A large plastics-injection molding firm had millions in excess inventory due to large setup costs, poor planning, and excess safety stocks. A large medical device firm had millions of excess inventory in trunk stock (sales rep vehicles) because of reward systems that rewarded sales people for sales without any accountability for inventory.
Notes	When manufacturing managers are held responsible for utilization, Overall Equipment Effectiveness (OEE), and absorbed overhead, they will tend to build inventory before it is needed. Similarly, when sales people are rewarded for sales without being held accountable for inventory, they will tend to fill the pipeline with inventory. Firms tend to overproduce because they start an order too early and/or produce in large lotsizes. Order timing is driven by the safety stock. Safety stocks can be improved by conducting a safety stock analysis, reducing the variability of demand, and reducing the variability of the leadtime. Firms often order too much because of ordering cost (perceived or real) and/or uncertain yields. Lotsizes can be improved by reducing the setup/ordering cost. Yield can often be improved with setup methods, error proofing, process capability measurement, and statistical process control. It is hard to distinguish this type of waste from unnecessary inventory (Waste 5).

Waste 2. Waiting

Definition	Time wasted when materials, customers, workers, equipment, or orders have to wait for another resource such as a machine.
Results	Long cycle times, about 90% of time is waiting. Unnecessary cost.
Solution	Maximize flow, pull systems, takt time, jidoka, kaizen, TPM, value stream map
Example	One firm had six months of work-in-process waiting for a process that required only about five days of labor.
Notes	Take a "waste walk" to look for waiting, waiting rooms, work-in-process, idle machines and idle people. WIP inventory is often a function of the lotsize. Carefully reducing lotsizes can sometimes reduce WIP inventory. One of the key concepts here is managing the bottleneck, which is the one process that has the lowest capacity.

Waste 3. Transporting

Definition	Movement of parts, products, transactions, and/or customers that does not add value.
Results	Long cycle times, long travel times, damaged products, high materials handling cost, dissatisfied customers.
Solution	Maximize flow, better factory layout, better factory location, better supplier location, pull systems, value stream mapping
Example	• Having services come to patients at Park Nicollet Health Services has reduced patient travel from an average of 736 feet per visit to 126 feet. • Many manufacturing firms build subassemblies, move them to storage for months, and then move back out to the factory for final assembly. This is often not the best approach. • Factory layouts can often be the cause of excess transportation. Many firms have found that changing the layout from a process (functional) layout to a cellular layout reduces

	transportation waste and also reduces WIP and queue time.
Notes	Many managers are quite surprised when they measure how far the product, workers, and customers travel. Excess inventory levels can also lead to excess handling.

Waste 4. Inappropriate processing (also known as over-processing)

Definition	Effort that adds no value to the customer. Using the wrong equipment or process.
Results	Poor layout, high transportation, overproduction (to keep utilization high), high setups, high capital costs.
Solution	Maximize flow, standardize, flow lines, one-piece pull, lean design
Example	• A firm bought a huge complicated machine to run parts much more efficiently. In the process, it discarded the old, almost fully-depreciated machine that could make the same parts. The argument was that this would get the depreciation off the books. However, the old machine could have added significant flexibility to the plant at zero incremental cost. • One t-shirt printing factory counted the shirts six times in the process.
Notes	Small, cheap, simple, dedicated machines are better than large, expensive, complex, shared machines. These machines can be old!

Waste 5. Unnecessary inventory

Definition	More inventory than needed.
Results	Too much inventory, inventory carrying cost, hidden quality problems, space tied up with inventory.
Solution	Maximize flow, error proof, kanban/pull system, supplier development, one-piece flow set-up reduction (SMED)
Example	See overproduction for examples.
Notes	(1) Too much safety stock, (2) too much lotsize (cycle) inventory. Safety stock inventory is due to ordering too early. Lotsize inventory is due to ordering too much. We often order too much because of ordering cost (perceived or real) and/or uncertain yields.

Waste 6. Unnecessary/excess motion

Definition	Movement of people that does not add value. This can include poor ergonomics and wasted motion to pick-up or stack parts, look for items, tools, or people.
Results	High cost, long processing times, poor health, poor safety, too much bending, stretching, walking, lifting, and reaching.
Solution	Simplify, standardize, error proof, 5S, point of use storage, water spider, one-piece flow, workstation design
Example	• The analysis of an assembly process found that about half of the steps were unnecessary. • An analysis of a banking process found that the number of steps taken by workers could be reduced dramatically without spending any money to make the improvement.
Notes	Jobs with excess motion should be redesigned with involvement of workers. Automation is best for work that is Dangerous, Dirty, or Dull (D3). Simple housekeeping can be an effective way of reducing wasted movement for direct labor and materials. 5S is a technique used by many companies to keep the workplace organized, which results in less time wasted searching for tools and/or parts. Re-laying out the factory can also help reduce waste of motion.

Waste 7. Defects

Definition	Any undesired outcome in quality, time, or meeting customer expectations.
Results	High materials cost, high labor cost, rework, poor customer satisfaction, lost capacity.
Solution	Error proof, standardize, one-piece pull, jidoka
Example	Many years ago, a Hungarian light bulb factory tried to improve a high defect rate by increasing inspection. They did 100% inspection, throwing away all defective light bulbs without learning from their errors. They were trying to "inspect quality into the product."

Notes	Any word beginning with "re" is usually a bad idea − retest, recheck, repair, rework, retype, reenter, repack, recount, reassemble, resend, return, revisit, reinstall, restart, etc.

Waste 8. Underutilization of employees
(Note that Jim Womack of LEI added this eighth waste. This sometimes called the waste of human potential.)

Definition	Not using employees' minds, creativity, and human potential.
Results	Lost opportunity to eliminate waste, bored workers, and employee turnover.
Solution	Implement with respect for people, cross-training, job rotation, and suggestions systems.
Example	Many years ago, Citibank had a process that involved a 14-part form. Many of the employees knew that only a few of the parts of the form were being used, but no one in leadership took the time to ask the employees how the process might be improved.
Notes	Jim Womack added this eighth waste to Ohno's original list of seven wastes. One way to engage human potential is to attack the first seven wastes. Customer-facing processes should also study underutilization of customers' minds, creativity, and human potential. Similarly, the best firms also engage their suppliers in improving their products and processes.

Source: Professor Arthur V. Hill

The DNA of the Toyota Production System

Steven Spear and Kent Bowen (1999) wrote an important **HBR** article that defines five rules that capture much of the lean philosophy used at Toyota. They emphasize that lean is more of a philosophy a set of tools.

Rule 1. Specifications document all work processes and include content, sequence, timing and outcome − At Toyota, each process is specified with detailed instructions. For example, when assemblers install seats with four bolts, the bolts are inserted and tightened in a precise sequence. Every worker installs them in the same way every time. This regimentation increases the linkage between the way work is done and the results. If everyone worked in different ways, the link would be broken or obscure. How do we reconcile such regimented work with the experimentation and concern for individuals that is supposed to be a part of the system? The answer is that while individual workers cannot vary the process, teams are required to actively analyze, experiment, change and improve the process. Rule 1 links closely with the widespread use of TQM, SPC and associated problem-solving skills. If workers do not possess those skills, Rule 1 is pretty much worthless and even counterproductive. This is often seen in an insistence on detail work instructions. Detailed work instructions are all very well if the process is stable and/or workers have an adequate TQM background. What usually happens is that engineers write unrealistic instructions with little input from workers. Nobody involved has an adequate TQM background. Workers cannot follow the instructions and they are promptly ignored. There is little feedback to the authors. The authors are busy writing new work instructions for other parts that will also be ignored. As a result the processes appear to have documentation, but, in practice, do not. Processes are inconsistent with inconsistent results. Nobody recognizes the inconsistencies or responds to them. Quality problems continue, pretty much as before. the whole thing is, at best, a waste of time. At worst it diverts efforts from a serious attack on problems.

Rule 2. Connections with clear YES/NO signals directly link every customer and supplier − This implicit rule gave rise to kanban, Direct Link and other lean scheduling. It tells us that every operation should send its products to subsequent "customers" directly using methods and algorithms that are clear and precise. It precludes separate warehouses and separate people or departments whose only function is inventory management.

Rule 3. Every product and service travels a single, simple and direct flow path − Toyota's U-shaped workcells are the ultimate manifestation of this rule. It means that every piece of finished product has been through the same equipment and precisely the same process. It improves consistency, makes trouble-shooting easier and simplifies material handling and scheduling.

Rule 4. Workers at the lowest feasible level, guided by a teacher (Sensei), improve their own work processes using scientific methods − Rule 4 ties closely with Rule 1. It prevents Work Instructions from becoming moribund memorials rather than living guides. It enlists the entire workforce in the improvement (Kaizen) efforts.

Rule 5. Integrated failure tests automatically signal deviations for every activity, connection and flow path – This is the concept of Jidoka or Autonomation. It prevents products with unacceptable quality from continuing in the process. Examples are detectors for missing components, automatic gages that check each part and visual alarms for low stocks.

Many lean experts argue that promoters of lean sigma programs "just don't get it." The argument is that lean sigma programs use some lean tools but miss out on the lean philosophy, which means they do not understand lean. Clearly, lean is much more than a set of tools.

See *5S, 7 Wastes, A3 Report, agile software development, andon light, batch-and-queue, blocking, Capability Maturity Model (CMM), cellular manufacturing, champion, continuous flow, cross-training, demand flow, Drum-Buffer-Rope (DBR), facility layout, flow, functional silo, gemba, heijunka, hidden factory, hoshin, jidoka, JIT II, Just-in-Time (JIT), kaizen, kaizen event, kanban, Keiretsu, lean design, Lean Enterprise Institute (LEI), lean promotion office, lean sigma, muda, one-piece flow, overhead, pacemaker, pitch, process improvement program, program management office, project charter, pull systems, Quick Response Manufacturing, red tag, Shingo Prize, Single Minute Exchange of Dies (SMED), Six Sigma, socio-technical design, stakeholder analysis, standardized work, supermarket, takt time, Theory of Constraints (TOC), Toyota Production System (TPS), transactional process improvement, two-bin system, value added ratio, value stream map, visual control, water spider, zero inventory.*

learning curve – A mathematical model that relates a performance variable (such as cost per unit) to the number of units produced, where the performance variable decreases as the cumulative production increases, but decreases at a slower rate; also called *experience curve*. ✪

The philosophy of the learning curve

All systems that involve people can improve and the rate of improvement can and should be measured. This learning can take place at any level – the machine, individual, department, plant, business unit, firm. Some authors use the term "experience curve" for more complex systems such as factories or firms; however, there is no practical difference between the learning curve and experience curve concepts.

The performance variable

The performance variable is usually the cost per unit or time per unit, but could be any variable that has an ideal point of zero. For example, other possible variables could be the defect rate (defects per million opportunities, DPMO), customer leadtime, etc. Variables such as yield and productivity are not appropriate performance variables for the learning curve because they do not have an ideal point of zero.

Example

The following graph is an example of a learning curve with $k = 80\%$, $y_1 = 100$, and a learning parameter of $b = 0.322$. Note that the graph is only defined for integer values of n.

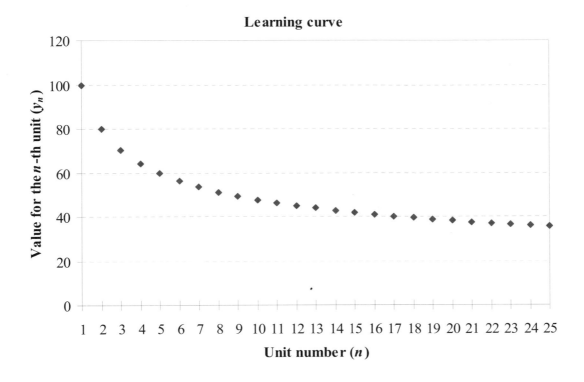

The learning curve and goal setting

People tend to "satisfice" if not given an appropriate goal. The learning curve, therefore, can be used to set appropriate goals for improvement. The learning rate can also be used to benchmark organizational learning across organizational boundaries. Every measure in a balanced scorecard could have a complementary measure for its rate of learning.

Learning curve model

With the learning curve, every time production is doubled, the cost goes down by a fixed percentage. (The remainder of this discussion will assume that the performance variable is cost.) For example, with an 80% learning curve, the cost goes down by 20% every time the cumulative production doubles. If the unit cost for the first unit is $100, the unit cost for the second unit is $80, the unit cost for the fourth unit is $64, etc.

The equation for the learning curve model is $y_n = y_1 n^{-b}$ where n is the unit number, y_n is the cost for the n-th unit, y_1 is the value for the first unit, and b is the learning parameter. The model requires that $b \geq 0$ and uses a negative sign in the model. Many textbooks present the model without a negative sign and have $b \leq 0$.

For a k-percent learning curve, the cost goes down by $(1-k)\%$ every time the cumulative production doubles. If the learning rate parameter k is known, the learning curve is given by $b = -\ln(k)/\ln(2)$. Conversely, if the learning parameter b is known, learning rate parameter is $k = 2^{-b}$.

For example, for an 80% learning curve, $k = 0.8$ and $b = 0.322$. With $y_1 = 100$, the unit cost for the first 8 units is 100, 80, 70, 64, 60, 56, 53, and 51. (Note these values are rounded to the nearest integer.)

The cumulative cost through the n-th unit is given by the following approximation (Camm, Evans, & Womer, 1987; Badiru, 1992) $Y_n = \sum_{i=1}^{n} y_i \cong \frac{y_1}{1-b}\left((n+\tfrac{1}{2})^{(1-b)} - (\tfrac{1}{2})^{(1-b)}\right)$. This approximation was tested for $k = 0.8$ and was found to have an absolute percent error of less than 2% when $n = 1$. The error approaches zero as n

increases, with an error of less than 0.03% for $n > 100$. This equation can be used to estimate the average cost through the n-th unit as $A_n = Y_n / n$. (See the paper *Learning models* for the derivation of this approximation.)

Estimating the parameters for the learning curve

The easiest approach for estimating the learning parameter from historical data is to find the value that fits the curve to the first and last observed historical values $b = -\ln(y_n / y_1) / \ln(n)$. The parameter y_1 for this model is set to the first observed historical value. However, this approach places too much weight on the first and last values and ignores all of the historical data in between.

Another approach recommended by some is to estimate the model parameters b and y_1 with linear regression on log transformed historical data. We first apply the natural log transform to both sides of the basic learning curve equation to find $\ln(y_n) = a - b \ln(n)$, where $a = \ln(y_1)$. We then apply linear regression to the transformed data to estimate the intercept ($a = \ln(y_1)$) and slope (b) for the line. We then estimate the intercept $y_1 = \exp(a)$ and learning rate $k = 2^{-b}$. However, linear regression poses some serious technical problems due to autocorrelation in the data. Several methods such as first differences can be used to try to compensate for the autocorrelation problem, but that is beyond the scope of this document. Note that the required transformation is not possible if the performance variable is zero for any historical observation.

It is not clear which method is more accurate for estimating the parameters for the model. Most practitioners find the first method much easier to apply, but most academics recommend the regression method.

The paper "Learning Models" and the Excel workbook "learning models.xls" are on the **OMWW CD** available from www.ClamshellBeachPress.com. ●

See *balanced scorecard, half-life curve, learning organization, linear regression, Moore's Law, operations performance metrics, satisficing*.

learning organization – An organization that has the ability to learn from its environment and improve its ability to compete over time. ✪

Most organizations today find that their current products and processes will become obsolete in a fairly short period of time. It is necessary, therefore, for managers to lead their organizations in such a way that the organization has built-in systems for improving over time. Learning organizations have the ability to transform experience into improved work processes and knowledge that is accessible to the whole organization and relevant to its core purpose. Specifically, organizations need to learn from many sources:

- **Customers** – To learn about customer's needs and desires as they change over time,
- **Suppliers** – To learn about new materials, technologies, and processes.
- **Research labs/technology suppliers** – To learn about new product and process technologies being developed by research labs universities, and suppliers
- **Workers** – To learn about and document new processes as they are developed by workers (to make implicit knowledge explicit)

Organizations can nurture learning in many ways. Some of the more effective approaches for accelerating learning include:

- **Knowledge management systems** – Using information systems to codify and share knowledge.
- **Measure learning** – Use the learning curve (and the closely related half-life curve) to measure and reward learning based on performance.
- **Service guarantees** – To reward customers for sharing their complaint information.
- **Early supplier involvement** – To get suppliers more involved in product design.
- **Benchmarking** – To capture standards and processes to use as a basis of comparison.
- **Cross-training/job rotation/job enrichment** – To disseminate learning within the firm.
- **Co-location** – To improve learning across different functions and firms.
- **Cycle-counting** – To find the source of data integrity problems.

See *balanced scorecard, business intelligence, co-location, cross-training, half-life curve, intellectual capital, job enlargement, job rotation, knowledge management, learning curve, Moore's Law, operations performance metrics, satisficing, workforce agility.*

Less than Container Load (LCL) – A shipment of a container that is not full. Note: Containers are usually 20 feet long.

See *Less than Truck Load (LTL), logistics, shipping container, truck-load.*

Less than Truck Load (LTL) – A shipment that does not fill the truck or a shipment with sufficient weight to qualify for a truck-load quantity discount.

LTL is usually used to designate shipments weighing between 100 and 10,000 pounds. These shipments are usually not economical to ship via parcel shippers or Full Truck Load carriers and fall somewhere in between. This quantity of freight involves more intermediate handling than does truck-load freight.

A typical LTL carrier collects freight from various shippers, consolidates that freight onto trailers, and sends the shipment for line-haul. For delivery, a similar process is followed, where the freight from the line-haul trailer is unloaded, re-sorted, and sent for delivery. In most cases, drivers make deliveries first and then pickup from shippers once the trailer is empty. Therefore, most pickups are made in the afternoon and most deliveries are performed in the morning.

The main advantage to using an LTL carrier is that a shipment may be transported for a fraction of the cost of hiring an entire truck and trailer for an exclusive shipment. A number of additional services are also available from LTL carriers that are not typically offered by FTL or parcel carriers. These services include liftgate service at pickup or delivery, residential (also known as "non-commercial") service at pickup or delivery, inside delivery, notification prior to delivery, freeze protection, and others. These services are usually billed at a predetermined flat fee or for a weight based surcharge calculated as a rate per pound or per hundred-weight.

Acknowledgments: CSOM MBA 09 students Puneet Gupta, Randolph Cooper, and Ravi Kiran contributed to this entry.

See *Less than Container Load (LCL), logistics, shipping container, truck-load.*

leverage the spend – Combine purchasing from multiple units in an organization in order to justify negotiation for a lower price from a supplier.

An organization can "leverage the spend" with a supplier by combining all purchases across multiple departments, plants, and divisions into one negotiated contract. This allows the organization to buy in larger quantities, which gives it the power to bargain for a lower price. One common example is for Maintenance, Repair and Operations (MRO) items, such as office supplies, purchased by a large multi-divisional organization. Many of these organizations used to allow each department, location, plant, and division to buy its own MRO supplies. The firm can often get a much better price from suppliers by combining "the spend" (all purchases) across all divisions and all departments. The same concept can often be used for many direct materials (non-MRO items) as well. Many consulting firms have made this concept a major part of their consulting services.

See *MRO (Maintenance-Repair-Operations), purchasing.*

level production – See *Heijunka.*

life-cycle planning – See *product lifecycle management.*

lifetime demand – See *all-time demand.*

LIFO – See *Last-In-First-Out (LIFO).*

Likert scale – A psychometric scale commonly used in survey instruments.

When responding to a Likert-scaled item on a survey, respondents typically specify their level of agreement to a statement. The following is an example of a Likert scale used by Professor Hill and his research colleagues.

1. Disagree strongly
2. Disagree
3. Neutral
4. Agree
5. Agree strongly

The scale is named after Rensis Likert who published a report describing its use (Likert, 1932). The proper pronunciation is "lick-urt" and not "lie-kurt."

line balancing – The problem of assigning tasks to workstations in order to minimize the number of workstations required while still satisfying the cycle time and precedence constraints.

In designing an assembly line, many tasks (elements) need to be assigned to workstations. These assignments are constrained by the cycle time for the line (i.e., one completion every five minutes) and the precedence relationships between the tasks (e.g., some tasks need to be done before others). Many operations researchers have developed sophisticated mathematical computer models to solve this problem. The webpage www.wiwi.uni-jena.de/Entscheidung/alb provides a good review of the research on this problem. The line balancing problem is less important when the organization can use cross-trained workers who can move between workstations as needed to maximize flow.

See *assembly line, cross-training, facility layout*.

line extension – A new product that is a variation of an existing product.

Line extensions are not significantly different from the original product and almost always share the same brand. Examples include a new package size, a new flavor, or a new ingredient. For example, Cheerios breakfast cereal now comes in many variants with different flavors and package sizes.

See *New Product Development (NPD)*.

line fill rate – See *fill rate*.

line of visibility – The line that separates a service operation into back office operations (that take place without the customer) and front office operations (that are in direct contact with the customer).

See *service blueprinting, service quality*.

Linear Programming (LP) – A mathematical approach for finding the optimal value of a linear function of many variables constrained by a set of linear equations of the same set of variables.

LP has been applied to many operations problems. The most important problems are listed as follows:

The assignment problem – Match the items needing assignment with the possible assignments (locations) in order to minimize the total cost subject to the constraint that each item must have exactly one location and each location must have exactly one item. See the *assignment problem* entry for more detail.

The transportation problem – Find the amount of a product to send from plant i to market j in order to minimize total cost. Constraints include (a) the need to exactly satisfy the market demand and (b) the requirement that all available product be shipped someplace. This problem can easily be extended to handle multiple periods (where the product is "shipped" from one period to the next) and multiple products (commodities). Special-purpose algorithms called network algorithms can solve the multiple-period single-commodity problem very efficiently. See the *transportation problem* entry for more detail.

The blending problem – Find the optimal blend of ingredients to minimize the total cost while still meeting the nutritional requirements.

The product mix problem – Find the optimal product mix to maximize contribution to profit while still meeting the capacity constraints.

Related techniques include integer programming, mixed integer linear programming, and many others.

Mathematically, a linear program is expressed as: Minimize $\sum_{j=1}^{n} c_j x_j$ subject to the constraints $\sum_{j=1}^{N} a_{ij} x_j \le b_i$

for constraints $i=1, 2, \ldots, M$. The x_j are the decision variables, the c_j are the coefficients of the objective function, and the b_i are the "right hand side" constraint coefficients.

The solution to a linear program provides the optimal values for each of the decision variables (the x_i variables). In addition, the solution also provides "shadow prices" for each constraint. The shadow price is the value added by relaxing a constraint by one unit.

Efficient computer code is available to solve linear programs with tens of thousands of variables. Closely related tools include integer programming (IP), mixed-integer programming (MIP), zero-one programming, network optimization, stochastic programming, chance constrained programming, and goal programming.

See *aggregate production planning, assignment problem, Integer Programming (IP), Mixed Integer Programming (MIP), network optimization, Operations Research (OR), sensitivity analysis, transportation problem, Traveling Salesperson Problem (TSP)*.

linear regression – A standard statistical technique that is used to find an approximate linear relationship between one or more independent (predictor) variables and a single dependent variable. ✪

Linear regression is a powerful tool for both forecasting and for understanding the relationships between two or more variables. Linear regression fits a linear equation to a set of historical data points in order to minimize the sum of the squared errors between the fitted linear equation and the historical data points.

Trend lines

The simplest type of regression is a trend line that relates the time period t to the dependent variable y_t. The parameters for the linear model $y_t = a + bt + \varepsilon_t$ can be estimated to minimize the sum of the squared errors $\sum_{t=1}^{n} \varepsilon_t^2$ with the following two equations:

$$\hat{b} = \frac{6}{n(n-1)} \left(\frac{2}{n+1} \sum_{t=1}^{n} t y_t - \sum_{t=1}^{n} y_t \right) \quad \text{and} \quad \hat{a} = \frac{1}{n} \sum_{t=1}^{n} y_t - \hat{b}(n+1)/2$$

Note that the equation for $\hat{b}$ must be solved before the equation for $\hat{a}$.

For simple linear regression, the input data consists of n observations on a single independent variable (x_i, x_i, ..., x_n) and a single dependent variable (y_i, $i = 1, 2, ..., n$). The parameters for the linear model $y_i = a + bx_i + \varepsilon_i$ can be estimated to minimize the sum of the squared errors $\sum_{i=1}^{n} \varepsilon_i^2$ with the following two equations:

$$\hat{b} = \frac{n \sum_{i=1}^{n} (x_i y_i) - \sum_{i=1}^{n} x_i \sum_{i=1}^{n} y_i}{n \sum_{i=1}^{n} x_i^2 - \left(\sum_{i=1}^{n} x_i \right)^2} \quad \text{and} \quad \hat{a} = \frac{1}{n} \sum_{i=1}^{n} y_i - \frac{\hat{b}}{n} \sum_{i=1}^{n} x_i$$

Note that the equation for $\hat{b}$ must be solved before the equation for $\hat{a}$.

The Excel function TREND(*range*) is a useful tool for projecting trends into the future. Excel charts also have the capability of showing a trend line. The Excel formula INDEX(LINEST(*range*),1,1) calculates the trend and the formula INDEX(LINEST(*range*),1,2) calculates the intercept for a trend line.

Multiple regression

For multiple regression, the input data consists of M observations on a single dependent variable (y_i, $i = 1, 2, ..., M$) and the N independent variables ($x_{i1}, x_{i2}, ..., x_{iN}$). The goal is to estimate the β_j parameters for the linear model $y_i = \beta_0 + \beta_1 x_{1i} + \beta_2 x_{2i} + ... + \beta_N x_{Ni} + \varepsilon_i$ that minimize the sum of the squared errors, where ε_i is the error term for the i-th observation. In other words, the least squares fit minimizes the sum of the squared errors $\sum_{i=1}^{M} \varepsilon_i^2$. Multiple regression uses matrix algebra to estimate the β_j parameters and to evaluate the goodness of fit for the model.

Simple and multiple linear regression can also be done in Excel with Tools/Data analysis/Regression. (If Data Analysis is not listed under Tools, then go to Add-ins and check the Analysis ToolPak to load this feature into your version of Excel.) A more direct approach for simple linear regression is to use INDEX(LINEST(*yrange, xrange*),1,1) to return the slope and INDEX(LINEST(*yrange, xrange*),1,2) to return the intercept. It is easy to extend this approach to access all of the parameters and statistics for both simple and multiple regression. See Excel Help for more details.

One challenge of Excel's multiple regression capability is that the input range (*xrange*) must consist of contiguous (side by side) columns of observations on the x variables. Most people involved in serious statistical analysis use products such as Minitab, SPSS, and SAS that are dedicated to statistical applications.

See any standard statistics textbook for more information on regression, multiple regression, and econometric models.

See *discriminant analysis, econometric forecasting, forecasting, logistic regression, scatter diagram, Six Sigma, Theta Model, time-series forecasting.*

line-haul – The longest leg of a shipment; also, the movement of freight between terminals.

See *logistics.*

Little's Law – A fundamental queuing theory principle developed by MIT Professor John D.C. Little in 1961 that shows that the relationship between the average time in system (W_s), the average arrival rate (λ), and the average number in system (L_s) is given by $L_s = \lambda W_s$ for a queuing system in steady state. ✪

In other words, the average number of customers (units, calls, etc.) in the system (in steady state) is equal to the product of the average arrival rate and the average time in system. For example, if a bank has an average arrival rate of $\lambda = 10$ customer/hour and the average time in system is $W_s = 1$ hour, the average number in system is $L_s = 10$ customers.

Similarly, the relationship between the average time in queue, average arrival rate, and average number in queue is given by $L_q = \lambda W_q$, which means that the number of customers waiting in queue is the average arrival rate times the average time in queue. Both forms of the equation are considered Little's Law.

Little's Law can also be written as $W_s = L_s / \lambda$ to find the average time in system. For example, if a factory has an average demand rate (λ) of 10 orders per day and the current work-in-process inventory (L_s) is 100 orders, the average time in system (W_s) for an order will be $W_s = L_s / \lambda = 100/10 = 10$ days.

Note that the average time in system can be defined as the average time in queue plus the average service time. Mathematically, this can be written as $W_s = W_q + 1/\mu$, where μ is the mean service rate and $1/\mu$ is the mean service time.

See *capacity, periods supply, queuing theory, wait time, Work-in-Process (WIP).*

load leveling – In both project planning and manufacturing contexts, the goal is often to have a level (even) workload for resources (machines, people, etc.) over time.

Some finite planning systems attempt to create schedules that require about the same amount of a resource in every period. This is called level loading.

See *finite scheduling, project management.*

location analysis – See *facility location.*

logistic curve – A growth curve that has an "S" shape as the market demand reaches a saturation point.

The simple logistic curve is given by $y(t) = a/(1 + c\exp(-bt))$, where t is the time since introduction, $y(t)$ is the cumulative sales until time t, a is the saturation point (the maximum total market demand), and b is the coefficient of imitation.

The Richards curve is a generalization of the logistic curve and is given by $y(t) = d + a/(1 + c\exp(-b(t-m)))^{1/c}$, with the additional parameters d the lower asymptote, b the average growth rate, and m time of maximum growth.

The Gompertz curve has a similar shape and is given by $y(t) = a\exp(-ce^{-bt})$, where t is the time since introduction and a is the upper asymptote.

Many researchers consider the Bass Model to be superior to any of the above mentioned models. Although the above models have a simpler mathematical form than the Bass Model, the Bass Model only requires the estimation of three parameters, which suggests that it is no more difficult to use than the above models.

Note that the logistic curve has nothing to do with the field of logistics.

See *Bass Model.*

logistic regression – Logistic regression is an approach for creating a model for predicting a dependent binary (e.g., 0-1) variable (the y response variable) based on a set of independent variables (the x variables).

The y variable is binary, which means that the y variable can be either a zero or a one. The model can also be used to estimate the probability that $y = 1$ for a given set of x values. Logistic regression can be a useful tool in the area of quality for understanding the impact of certain variables on defects. Other applications include credit scoring (determining which customers are worthy of credit), donor screening (determining which potential donors might be more likely to give money), and niche marketing (determining which customers should receive a mailing).

For a single x variable, the logistic regression model has the form:

$$\hat{p}(x) = \frac{e^{\beta_0 + \beta_1 x}}{1 + e^{\beta_0 + \beta_1 x}}$$

where, $\hat{p}(x)$ is the estimated probability that $y = 1$ for the given x value. The parameters β_0 and β_1 are usually estimated using a Maximum Likelihood Estimation approach to provide the best fit with historical data. The model can be extended to handle multiple x variables.

Logistic regression is also called Binary Logistic Regression and is closely related to Probit Analysis. Many statistical packages such as SPSS, SAS, and MINITAB have logistic regression capabilities. Note that logistic regression has nothing to do with logistics.

See *cluster analysis, data mining, data warehouse, discriminant analysis, linear regression.*

logistics – Logistics is the organizational function that is responsible for managing a company's total distribution, transportation, and warehousing needs. ✪

Logistics is responsible for managing the flow of materials between facilities (suppliers, warehouses, plants, distributors, and customers) and the associated flows of information and cash. Logistics is closely associated with transportation, warehousing, inventory management, and customer services activities. The logistics function is often responsible for negotiating contracts with a large number of suppliers of transportation and other services. For any one facility, logistics involves the planning and control of the inbound and outbound materials flow plus the inventory at the facility. In the military, logistics also involves the movement of personnel.

Logistics plays a major role in delivering the "nine rights" to customers:

- The right product
- The right quantity
- The right time
- The right quality
- The right place

- The right form
- The right price
- The right packaging
- The right information

See *backhaul, bonded warehouse, Boxcar, common carrier, cross-docking, deadhead, distribution, distribution center (DC), distribution channel, Distribution Requirements Planning (DRP), dock-to-stock, drop ship, for-hire carrier, freight bill, freight forwarder, headhaul, hub-and-spoke system, inter-modal shipments, inventory management, Less than Container Load (LCL), Less than Truck Load (LTL), line-haul, materials management, milk run, multi-modal shipments, private carrier, purchasing, reverse logistics, supply chain management, Third Party Logistics (3PL) provider, ton-mile, transportation problem, Traveling Salesperson Problem (TSP), truck-load, Warehouse Management System (WMS).*

lognormal distribution – A continuous probability distribution used to model random variables that are always non-zero and have a long right tail, such as the time to perform a task for the demand for a product.

The shape of the lognormal distribution is similar to the Gamma and Weibull distributions, but tends to have a larger spike for low values of x. The lognormal is appropriate for random variables that are the product of other variables. If a random variable x_i is lognormally distributed, the random variable $\ln(x_i)$ will be normally distributed. It is important to note that the parameters (μ, σ) are for the underlying normal distribution and not of the lognormal distribution itself.

Density function: The lognormal density function for $x > 0$ is $f(x) = \frac{1}{x\sigma\sqrt{2\pi}} \exp\left(\frac{-(\ln x - \mu)^2}{2\sigma^2}\right)$.

Partial expectation function: $g(z) = \exp(\mu + \sigma^2 / 2)F\left(\dfrac{-\ln(z) + \mu + \sigma^2}{\sigma}\right) - zF\left(\dfrac{-\ln(z) + \mu}{\sigma}\right)$

(Source: http://en.wikipedia.org/wiki/Log-normal_distribution#Partial_expectation.)

Distribution function: Like the normal, the lognormal distribution function has no closed form.

Statistics: Range $[0, \infty)$, mean $\exp(\mu + \sigma^2 / 2)$, median $\exp(\mu)$, mode $\exp(\mu - \sigma^2)$, variance $\exp(2\mu + \sigma^2)(\exp(\sigma^2) - 1)$. (Note: the function $\exp(x) = e^x$.)

Parameter estimation: With n observations on a lognormally distributed random variable x_i, the maximum likelihood estimators for the parameters of the underlying normal distribution are $\hat{\mu} = \dfrac{1}{n}\sum_{i=1}^{n} \ln(x_i)$ and $\hat{\sigma} = \sqrt{\dfrac{1}{n}\sum_{i=1}^{n} (\ln(x_i - \hat{\mu})^2}$. When given the mean and variance of the lognormal distribution (μ_{LN}, σ_{LN}), the parameters for the underlying normal distribution are $\sigma = \sqrt{\ln(1 + \sigma_{LN}^2 / \mu_{LN}^2)}$ and $\mu = \ln(\mu_{LN}) - \sigma^2 / 2$. Also note that the lognormal becomes degenerate when $\sigma_{LN} \leq \mu_{LN} / \sqrt{e}$.

Excel: In Excel, the function LOGNORMDIST(x, μ, σ) can be used for the cumulative lognormal. Excel does not have a function for the lognormal density function, but it can be calculated with $1/(x*\sigma*\text{SQRT}(2*\text{PI}()))*\text{EXP}(-((\text{LN}(x)-\mu)\char`\^2/(2*\sigma\char`\^2)))$. Note that all of the parentheses in this formula are required. The cumulative inverse function in Excel is LOGINV(p, μ, σ). The Excel functions LOGNORMDIST(x, μ, σ) and LOGINV(p, μ, σ) use the mean and standard deviation of the underlying normal distribution rather than the mean (μ_{LN}) and standard deviation (σ_{LN}) of the lognormal distribution itself.

Excel simulation: In an Excel simulation, lognormally distributed random variates can be generated with the inverse transform method with $x = $ LOGINV(RAND(), μ, σ).

Graph: The graph below is the lognormal density function with $\mu_{LN} = 1.6487$ ($\mu = 0$) and $\sigma_{LN} = 1.6487$ ($\sigma = 1$). The median for this distribution is 1. At the tails, $F^{-1}(0.05) = 0.193$ and $F^{-1}(0.95) = 5.180$.

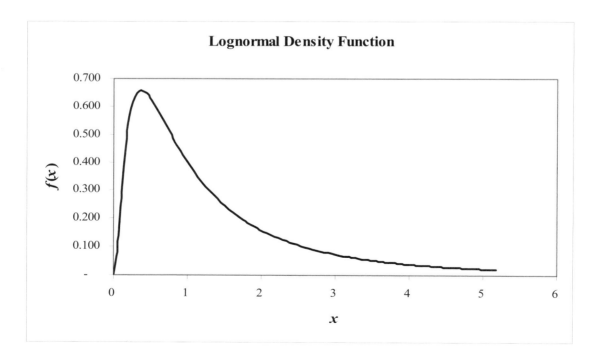

Lognormal Density Function

The Excel workbook "Distributions.xls" is on the **OMWW CD** available from www.ClamshellBeachPress.com. ◉

See *inverse transform method, normal distribution.*

loss leader – A product offered at a low price in order to attract customers; known as a "key value item" in the United Kingdom.

A loss leader is a product sold at a low price (even at a loss) in order to stimulate profitable sales of other products. A loss leader is a kind of sales promotion. In the United States, loss leaders are restricted by state minimum-price laws.

Some automobile dealerships use the loss leader as a "bait and switch" strategy. They offer an automobile for a very low price (the loss leader), but might have only one vehicle available for sale. Some dealers follow the unscrupulous practice of having no vehicles available at the low price. When customers arrive, they lie to the customer by telling them that "it was already sold."

The following statements are generally true about loss leaders:

- In a retail store context, loss leaders such as milk are often placed at the back of a store to force shoppers to walk past other more profitable products on the way.
- Loss leaders are often products that customers purchase frequently so they are aware that the loss leader price is a good value. This leads customers to believe the entire store has good prices.
- Items offered as loss leaders are often limited and/or have a short product life, which discourages stockpiling by customers.

A closely related strategy involves using a loss leader to make it hard for customers to switch to other systems or standards. In other words, the loss leader reduces the initial cost for the customer, but increases their switching cost, which "locks" them into a particular technology or service provider. Examples in this category include:

- Razor given away or sold below cost in order to sell highly profitable disposable razor blades.
- Game consoles sold below cost in order to sell games.
- Inkjet printers sold below cost in order to sell consumables.
- Cell phones offered for free in order to sell cell phone contracts.

In summary, a loss leader strategy is a common marketing strategy to increase customer traffic and revenue at the cost of lost gross margin on just a few products.

Some of the above concepts are adapted from the Wikipedia entry for loss leader.

Lot Tolerance Percent Defective (LTPD) – The maximum level of percent defective that is acceptable in a production batch.

The LTPD of a sampling plan is the level of quality routinely rejected by the sampling plan. It is generally defined as the percent defective that the sampling plan will reject 90% of the time. In other words, this is also the percent defective that will be accepted by the sampling plan at most 10% of the time. This means that lots at or worse than the LTPD are rejected at least 90% of the time and accepted at most 10% of the time.

See *Acceptable Quality Level (AQL), acceptance sampling, consumer's risk.*

lot-for-lot – A simple lotsizing rule that sets the lotsize quantity equal to the net requirement in a period; also known as a "discrete lotsize."

When planning using lot-for-lot order quantity, the system uses the exact net requirement quantity (i.e., requirements minus available stock) as the order quantity for the period. The system will group requirement quantities from the same period (usually one day) together in one lotsize.

Contrary to some sources, lot-for-lot does not necessarily match the production lotsize with an individual customer order. Lot-for-lot is equivalent to a periods supply of one period.

See *lotsize, lotsizing methods, periods supply.*

lotsize – The quantity that is ordered; also called batch size and order size. ✪

When dealing with suppliers, this is typically called the order size; when dealing with manufacturing orders placed on an internal factory, this is typically called the lotsize or batchsize. The optimal lotsize is generally called the Economic Order Quantity (EOQ). See the *EOQ* entry for more information on that subject.

See *cycle stock, Economic Order Quantity (EOQ), fixed order quantity, lot-for-lot, lotsizing methods, periods supply.*

lotsize inventory – See *cycle stock*.

lotsizing methods – Techniques for determining the number of units to be ordered on a purchase or manufacturing order.

The basic lotsizing methods include the following:

- **Fixed lotsize** – A constant quantity is ordered every time. Note that multiples of the fixed lotsize may be required if the net requirements exceed the fixed lotsize.
- **Economic Order Quantity (EOQ)** – Order the economic order quantity every time. The EOQ is a special case of a fixed lotsize. Again, multiples of the fixed lotsize may be required if the net requirements exceed the EOQ.
- **Period order quantity** – The lotsize is set equal to a fixed number of periods of net requirements (e.g., 4 week's supply).
- **Lot-for-lot** (discrete lotsize) – The lotsize is set to what is needed for the next period. Lot-for-lot is a special case of the period order quantity where the number of periods is one.
- **Dynamic lotsizing procedures** – These procedures are similar to the period order quantity in that they define the lotsize in terms of the number of periods of net requirements that will be added to define the lotsize. However, the number of periods used in the lotsize can change for each order. The procedures attempt to find the optimal (e.g., minimum cost) lotsizes for the net requirements over the planning horizon. Examples of dynamic lotsizing procedures include Least Unit Cost, Least Period Cost, Least Total Cost (also called Part Period Balancing), and Wagner-Whitin.

Most ERP systems such as SAP require that users define both a lotsizing rule and a rounding value. The rounding value is appropriate when the lotsizes are constrained by delivery, packaging or shipment units. This is useful, for example, if deliveries can only be made in lots of 10 pieces or if the quantity produced can only be packed and transported in full pallets.

Many firms such as retailers and distributors often buy many different products from a single supplier. Many items can be ordered on one order and therefore can share the ordering cost. See the entry on *joint replenishment* for discussion on this issue.

Many firms have found that the analysis of a single item in an inventory has little value, but that an aggregate analysis of a large set of items can have a significant impact. See the entry on aggregate inventory analysis.

The paper "Lotsizing" and the Excel workbooks "lotsizing.xls" and "EOQ.xls" are on the **OMWW CD** available from www.ClamshellBeachPress.com. ◉

See *aggregate inventory management, Economic Lot Scheduling Problem (ELSP), Economic Order Quantity (EOQ), fixed order quantity, instantaneous replenishment, inventory management, joint replenishment, lot-for-lot, lotsize, Period Order Quantity (POQ), safety stock, time-varying demand lotsizing problem, transfer batch, Wagner-Whitin lotsizing algorithm.*

LP – See *Linear Programming (LP)*.

LTL – See *Less than Truck Load (LTL)*.

LTPD – See *Lot Tolerance Percent Defective (LTPD)*.

lumpy demand – An intermittent sales pattern that has sales separated by many periods with no sales.

For example, the following demand stream is said to be lumpy: 2000, 0, 0, 0, 0, 0, 0, 0, 1000, 0, 0, 0, 5000. Lumpy demand is often caused by having a small set of customers who often have large lotsizes. For example, one of 3M's international operations in Europe would only order from a plant in North America once every six months. The demand stream for this was (0, 0, 0, 0, 0, B), where "B" was a big number.

Lumpy demand often creates significant problems for forecasting, inventory management, and scheduling. The coefficient of variation is a practical way to measure lumpiness. A good rule of thumb is that demand with a coefficient of variation greater than 1 is considered to be lumpy demand. Exponential smoothing forecasting methods do a very poor job in forecasting lumpy demand. The only practical way to handle this is to increase the size of the time "buckets" (e.g., increase the time period from week to months or from months to quarters).

See *coefficient of variation, exponential smoothing, forecasting*.

M

MAD − See *Mean Absolute Deviation (MAD)*.

maintenance − The work of keeping something in proper condition, upkeep, or repair.

See *autonomous maintenance, availability, bathtub curve, emergency maintenance, Mean Time Between Failure (MTBF), Mean Time To Repair (MTTR), MRO (Maintenance-Repair-Operations), predictive maintenance, preventive maintenance, reliability, Total Productive Maintenance (TPM)*.

Maintenance-Repair-Operations − See *MRO*.

major setup cost − The changeover cost from one family of products to another family of products; the "between-family" changeover cost.

A minor setup cost is the "with-in" family setup cost, which is the cost of changing over from one product to another in the same family of products. Both major and minor setup costs can be sequence-dependent.

See *sequence-dependent setup time, setup cost*.

Make to Order (MTO) − A process that produces products in response to a customer order. ✪

Make to Order (MTO) processes typically produce products that (1) are built in response to a customer order, (2) are unique to a specific customer's requirements, and (3) are not held in finished goods inventory. However, the last two statements are not always true.

MTO products are not always unique to a customer − It is possible (but not common) to use an MTO process for standard products. For example, the publisher for this book (Clamshell Beach Press) could have used an MTO process called "Print on Demand" that prints a copy of the book after the customer order is received. This is an example of a "standard product" that is produced in response to a customer order.

MTO products are sometimes held in finished goods inventory − Many descriptions of MTO state that MTO never has any finished goods inventory. However, an MTO process may have a small amount of temporary finished goods inventory waiting to be shipped. An MTO process may also have some finished goods inventory when the customer order size is smaller than the minimum order size. In this case, the firm might hold residual finished goods inventory speculating that the customer will order more at a later date.

The *Respond to Order (RTO)* entry discusses these issues in much more depth.

Acknowledgments: CSOM MBA 08 student Hillary Drake provided helpful edits for this entry.

See *Build to Order (BTO), Engineer to Order (ETO), mass customization, Pack to Order, push-pull boundary, Respond to Order (RTO)*.

Make to Stock (MTS) − A process that produces standard products to be stored in inventory. ✪

These can be delivered quickly to the customer. The performance metric for MTS is usually the unit fill rate, line fill rate, order fill rate, or perfect order fill rate. See the *Respond to Order (RTO)* entry for more detail.

See *Assemble to Order (ATO), Engineer to Order (ETO), perfect order fill rate, push-pull boundary, Respond to Order (RTO), service level*.

make versus buy decision − The decision to either manufacture an item internally or purchase it from an outside supplier. ✪

Managers in manufacturing firms often have to decide between making a part (or product) internally or buying it (outsourcing it) from a supplier. These decisions require careful analysis of accounting data and often have strategic implications. The guiding slogan is that "a firm should never outsource its core competence."

One of the most difficult aspects of this decision is how to handle overhead. If overhead is completely ignored and the focus is on only direct labor and materials, the decisions will generally go in the direction of "in-sourcing." If overhead is fully allocated (including overhead that will not go away when you outsource), decisions tend to go in the direction of outsourcing and can lead the firm into the "death spiral" where everything is outsourced. In the death spiral, the firm outsources and finds itself with the same overhead but fewer units, which means that the overhead per unit goes up, which leads the firm to more outsourcing. A figure depicting the death spiral is below.

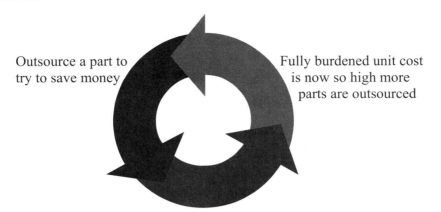

Outsource a part to try to save money

Fully burdened unit cost is now so high more parts are outsourced

Allocate same overhead to fewer direct hours

Source: Professor Arthur V. Hill

See *Business Process Outsourcing, outsourcing, supply chain management, vertical integration*.

makespan – The time that the last job finishes for a given set of jobs.

The static job shop scheduling problem involves scheduling a set of jobs on one or more machines. One of the common objectives used in the static job shop scheduling problem is to minimize the makespan. This means to minimize the maximum completion time for all of the jobs. In other words, the goal is to assign jobs to machines and sequence (or schedule) them so that the completion time for the last job is minimized.

See *job shop, job shop scheduling*.

Malcolm Baldrige National Quality Award (MBNQA) – This annual award was established in 1987 to recognize Total Quality Management in American industry. ✪

The MBNQA represents the US Government's endorsement of quality as an essential part of successful business strategy. The MBNQA is based on the premise that competitiveness in the United States economy is improved by (1) helping to stimulate American companies to improve quality and productivity, (2) establishing guidelines and criteria in evaluating quality improvement efforts, (3) recognizing quality improvement achievements of companies, and (4) making information available on how winning companies improved quality. The award was named after Malcolm Baldrige, the United States Secretary of Commerce from 1981 to 1987. The MBNQA scoring system is based on the following seven categories:

Category	Weight
Leadership	120
Strategic planning	85
Customer and market focus	85
Measurement, analysis, and knowledge management	90
Workforce focus	85
Process management	85
Results	450
Total	1000

The figure below presents the Baldrige Criteria for Performance Excellence framework:

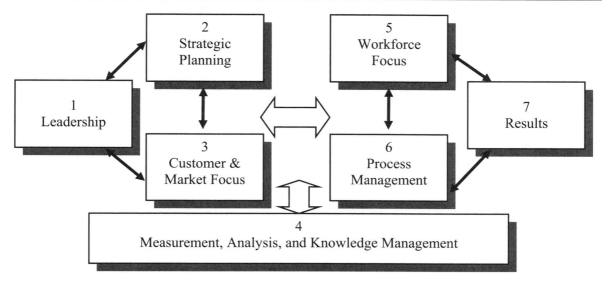

See www.baldridge.org for more information.

See *Shingo Prize, Total Quality Management (TQM)*.

Manhattan square distance – A distance metric on an x-y plane that limits travel to the x and y axes.

The Manhattan square distance is a good estimate for many intra-city travel distances where vehicles can only travel in certain directions (e.g., north/south or east/west) due to the layout of the roads. The equation for the Manhattan square distance is $d_{ij} = |x_i - x_j| + |y_i - y_j|$. This metric is named after the densely populated Borough of Manhattan in New York City that is known for its rectangular street layout. The Minkowski distance metric is a general form of the Manhattan square distance.

See *cluster analysis, great circle distance, Minkowski distance metric*.

MANOVA (Multivariate Analysis of Variance) – See *ANOVA (Analysis of Variance)*.

Manufacturing and Service Operations Management Society (MSOM) – A professional society that is a division of INFORMS that "promotes the enhancement and dissemination of knowledge, and the efficiency of industrial practice, related to the operations function in manufacturing and service enterprises."

According to the MSOM website, "the methods which MSOM members apply in order to help the operations function add value to products and services are derived from a wide range of scientific fields, including operations research and management science, mathematics, economics, statistics, information systems and artificial intelligence. The members of *MSOM* include researchers, educators, consultants, practitioners and students, with backgrounds in these and other applied sciences."

The website for MSOM is http://msom.society.informs.org/.

MSOM publishes the ***M&SOM Journal***, which is an INFORMS publication.

See *Institute for Operations Research and the Management Sciences (INFORMS), Operations Management, Operations Research*.

manufacturing cell – See *cellular manufacturing*.

Manufacturing Cycle Effectiveness (MCE) – See *value added ratio*.

Manufacturing Execution System (MES) – A system that provides real-time information on manufacturing operations from the time an order is started until it is completed in a factory.

Unlike ERP and MRP systems, manufacturing execution systems do not plan order launch dates or order sizes; instead they focus on collecting data and planning the detailed operations after an order has been started. MES functions include resource allocation and status, dispatching production orders, data collection/acquisition, quality management, maintenance management, performance analysis, operations/detail scheduling, document control, labor management, process management, and product tracking and genealogy. In many systems, document control includes systems for providing work instructions, videos, and drawings to operators on the shop floor at the time of need. A well-developed MES allows production planners to create work instructions that contain appropriate buyoffs and data collection forms embedded in the work instructions. Some of the benefits claimed for an MES include (1) reduces manufacturing cycle time, (2) reduces data entry time, (3) reduces Work-in-Process (and increases inventory turns), (4) reduces paper between shifts, (5) reduces leadtimes, (6) improves product quality (reduced defects), (7) eliminates lost paperwork and blueprints, (8) improves on-time delivery and customer service, (9) reduces training and changeover time, and, as a result, (10) improves gross margin and cash flow performance.

The related concept of a shop floor control system has been around for many years; the term "MES" was first used in 1990. An MES has features that go well beyond the traditional shop floor control system. The MES Association website http://www.mesa.org has lots of useful information on this subject.

See *shop floor control, Total Productive Maintenance (TPM).*

manufacturing leadtime – See *leadtime.*

Manufacturing Resources Planning (MRP) – See *Materials Requirements Planning (MRP).*

Manugistics – A software vendor of Advanced Planning and Scheduling (APS) systems.

See *Advanced Planning and Scheduling (APS).*

MAPD (Mean Absolute Percent Deviation) – See *Mean Absolute Percent Error (MAPE).*

MAPE (Mean Absolute Percent Error) – See *Mean Absolute Percent Error (MAPE).*

Maquiladora – A Mexican corporation that operates under a maquila program approved for it by the Mexican Secretariat of Commerce and Industrial Development (SECOFI).

First, a maquila program entitles the company to foreign investment participation in the capital and in management of up to 100% without need of any special authorization. Second, it entitles the company to special customs treatment, allowing duty free temporary import of machinery, equipment, parts and materials, and administrative equipment, such as computers and communications devices, subject only to posting a bond guaranteeing that such goods will not remain in Mexico permanently.

Ordinarily, all of a maquiladora's products are exported, either directly, or indirectly, through sale to another maquiladora or exporter. The type of production may be the simple assembly of temporarily imported parts; the manufacture from start to finish of a product using materials from various countries, including Mexico; or any conceivable combination of the various phases involved in manufacturing, or even non-industrial operations, such as data-processing, packaging, and sorting coupons.

The nuts and bolts legislation now governing the industry's operation is the "Decree for Development and Operation of the Maquiladora Industry," published by the Mexican federal Diario Oficial on December 22, 1989. This decree describes application procedures and requirements for obtaining a maquila program and the special provisions that apply only to maquiladora.

Source: http://www.udel.edu/leipzig/texts2/vox128.htm, October 22, 2005.

See *outsourcing, supply chain management.*

market share – The percent of the overall sales (dollars or units) of a market (local, regional, national, or global) that is controlled by one company.

One insightful question to ask a senior executive is "What is your market share?" When they answer, then ask, "Of what?" Many managers are caught by this trick question and report their market share for their regional or national market instead of the global market. This question exposes a lack of global thinking.

mass customization – A business model that uses a routine approach to efficiently create high variety in products and/or services in response to customer-defined requirements. ✪

The word "routine" here means "a prescribed, detailed course of action to be followed regularly; a standard procedure."

Many people mistakenly assume that mass customization is only about increasing variety. However, some of the best examples of mass customization focus on reducing cost while maintaining the same variety. For example, AbleNet (www.ablenetinc.com) manufactures a wide variety of products for disabled people such as the button shown on the right. The product comes in a number of different colors and with a wide variety of features (e.g., push once, push twice, etc.). AbleNet was able to create a modular design that provided customers with the same variety, while at the same time dramatically reducing the number of products that it produced and stored. It was able to "mass customize" by postponing the customization to decals and cover plates that could be attached to the top of the button. It also moved much of the feature customization to the software, allowing the hardware

to become more standard. As a result, AbleNet was able to significantly improve service, reduce inventory, and reduce cost while keeping the same variety for its customers.

Pine (1993) argues that mass customization should be considered in a market that already has many competitors and already has significant variety. In other words, the market has already proven that it wants variety. According to Kotha (1995), the competitive challenge in this type of market is to provide the needed variety at a relatively low cost.

Products and services can be mass customized for a channel partner (e.g., a distributor), a customer segment (the high end of the market), or an individual customer (personalization). One of the primary approaches for mass-customization is postponement, where customization is delayed until after the customer order is received. For example, IBM in Rochester, Minnesota, builds the AS400 using "vanilla boxes," which are not differentiated until after the customer order has been received. IBM customizes the vanilla boxes by inserting hard-drives, modems, etc. into slots on the front of the box.

Eight strategies for mass customization include:

1. Design products for MC – Make the products customizable.
2. Use robust components – Commonality is a great way to improve customization.
3. Develop workers for MC – Mass customization and flexibility is fundamentally a function of the flexibility and creativity of the workers.
4. Apply lean/quality concepts – Lean thinking (and short cycle times) and high quality are essential prerequisites to a good system for mass customization.
5. Reduce setup times – Long setup times (and large lotsizes) are the enemy of mass customization.
6. Use appropriate automation – Many people equate mass customization with automation; however, many of the best mass customization concepts have little to do with automation.
7. Breakdown functional silos – Functional silos contribution to long cycle times, poor coordination, and high costs – all of which present obstacles to mass customization.
8. Manage the value chain for MC – The best examples of mass customization leverage the entire value chain (and the supply chain too).

Source: Professor Arthur Hill's lecture on mass customization.

Pine and Gilmore (1999) have extended mass customization concepts to "experiences," where the goal is to create tailored memorable experiences for customers.

Acknowledgments: Kevin Thayer (CEMBA 06) helped write the above definition for mass customization.

See *Assemble to Order (ATO), commonality, configurator, economy of scope, Engineer to Order (ETO), experience engineering, flexibility, Make to Order (MTO), modular design (modularity), operations strategy, Pack to Order, postponement, Print to Order, product-process matrix, push-pull boundary, Respond to Order (RTO)*.

Master Production Schedule (MPS) – A time-phased plan specifying the requirements for end items by time period. ✪

The MPS is derived from the three sources – (1) firm customer orders (order that have already been received from customers), (2) stock transfer orders (orders to ship material from one location such as a plant to another such as a regional warehouse), and (3) the high-level plan that comes out of the Sales & Operations Planning (S&OP) process.

For example, the high-level production plan (aggregate plan) for a furniture company may specify the total volume of mattresses it needs over each month of the next year. The MPS goes the next step down and identifies the exact size mattresses and also states period by period (usually weekly) how many of each of these mattress types are needed. Further down this process is MRP, which calculates all raw materials, parts, and supplies needed to make the mattress specified by the MPS.

See *aggregate production planning, Available-to-Promise (ATP), Business Requirements Planning (BRP), Capacity Requirements Planning (CRP), Final Assembly Schedule (FAS), Materials Requirements Planning (MRP), Resource Requirements Planning (RRP), Rough Cut Capacity Planning (RCCP), Sales & Operations Planning (S&OP)*.

master schedule – See *Master Production Schedule (MPS)*.

material delivery routes – See *water spider*.

Material Review Board (MRB) – A standing committee that determines the disposition of items that have questionable quality.

materials management – Materials management is the organizational unit that coordinates the flow of inventory through a system by means of production and/or purchase orders.

Materials management must balance the conflicting objectives of marketing and sales (have lots of inventory, never lose a sale, maintain a high service level) and finance (keep inventories low, minimize working capital). The term materials management often includes manufacturing planning and control, distribution management, transportation, and inventory management. Supply chain management is viewed by many as taking materials management disciplines to the supply and distribution networks.

See *logistics, supply chain management*.

materials plan – See *Materials Requirements Planning (MRP)*.

Materials Requirements Planning (MRP) – A comprehensive computer-based planning system for both factory and purchase orders; a major module within Enterprise Resources Planning Systems; also called Manufacturing Resources Planning. ✪

MRP is an important module within Enterprise Requirements Planning systems for most manufacturers. MRP was originally called "Materials Requirements Planning" and only planned purchase orders for outside suppliers. MRP was then expanded to also handle orders sent to the shop floor (manufacturing orders) and the name was changed to "Manufacturing Resources Planning."

Planning is done level by level down the bill of material. MRP begins by netting out (subtracting) any on-hand and on-order inventory from the gross requirements. It then schedules backwards from the need date using fixed planned leadtimes to determine the order start dates. Lotsizing rules are then applied to determine order quantities. The lotsizes are often defined in terms of the number of periods (days) of net requirements.

MRP creates planned orders (the materials plan) for both manufactured and purchased materials. Each order is defined by an order number, a part number, an order quantity, a start date, and a due date. MRP systems use the planned order start date to determine priorities for both shop order and purchase orders. MRP, therefore, is said to be "a priority planning system" and not a true scheduling system.

Nearly all MRP systems create detailed materials plans for an item using a "time-phased order point" and fixed planned leadtimes. Contrary to some textbooks, MRP systems rarely consider available capacity when creating a materials plan. Therefore, MRP systems are called "infinite" loading systems rather than "finite" loading systems." However, MRP systems can create load reports that help managers identify situations when the plant load (planned hours) exceeds the capacity available. Advanced Planning and Scheduling (APS) systems are capable of creating detailed materials plans that take into account available capacity; unfortunately, these systems are hard to implement because of the requirements for data accuracy and availability.

See *Advanced Planning and Scheduling (APS), aggregate production planning, Bill of Material (BOM), closed-loop MRP, Distribution Requirements Planning (DRP), Enterprise Resources Planning (ERP), finite scheduling, gross requirements, infinite loading, inventory management, Master Production Schedule (MPS), net requirements, pegging, purchasing, time fence, time-phased order point*.

maximum inventory – See *periodic review system*.

maximum stocking level – An SAP term for the target inventory.

See *periodic review system*.

MBNQA – See *Malcolm Baldrige National Quality Award*.

MCE (Manufacturing Cycle Effectiveness) – See *value added ratio*.

Mean Absolute Deviation (MAD) – A common measure of forecast accuracy defined as $MAD = \frac{1}{T}\sum_{t=1}^{T}|E_t|$, where E_t is the forecast error in period t and T is the number of periods in the forecast history.

In the 1960s, computers were not able to take square roots, and many authors recommended approximating the standard deviation as $\sigma = \sqrt{\pi/2}MAD \approx 1.25MAD$. This approximation is accurate as long as the demand is normally distributed and the mean forecast error is close to zero (i.e., the forecasts are unbiased). However, when either of these two assumptions is not true, this approximation can be quite inaccurate.

An extensive Monte Carlo experiment compared the $1.25MAD$ approximation to the standard deviation for a large set of normally distributed forecast errors generated for the experiment. The experiment covered a wide range of factor level settings for both the forecast bias (μ) and the standard deviation (σ) of the forecast error. The results found that the average percent error in the $1.25MAD$ approximation, $(1.25MAD - \sigma)/\sigma$, could be predicted from the coefficient of variation (*CV*), which is the standard deviation divided by the mean. The average error in the approximation grows dramatically as *CV* approaches zero. When *CV* = 1, the average percent error is 46.32%. *CV* has to be greater than 3.21 to reduce the average percent error to less than 5%. On the positive side, the *MAD* is less sensitive to outliers than is the standard deviation of the forecast error and is considered by some to be a more robust measure of forecast error.

Like most time series forecasting statistics, the *MAD* can be smoothed at the end of each period with the updating equation $SMAD_t = \alpha|E_t| + (1-\alpha)SMAD_{t-1}$. The smoothed *MAD* is sometimes called the smoothed absolute error or *SAE*.

See *forecast bias, forecast error metrics, forecasting, Mean Absolute Percent Error (MAPE), Mean Squared Error (MSE), Median Absolute Percent Error (MdAPE), Relative Absolute Error (RAE), standard deviation, tracking signal.*

Mean Absolute Percent Deviation (MAPD) – See *Mean Absolute Percent Error (MAPE).*

Mean Absolute Percent Error (MAPE) – A commonly used measure of forecast accuracy defined mathematically as $MAPE = \dfrac{1}{T}\sum_{t=1}^{T}\dfrac{|E_t|}{D_t}$, where E_t is the forecast error in period t, D_t is the actual demand (or sales) in period t, and T is the number of observed values. ✪

The MAPE is also called the *MAPD*, the Mean Absolute Percent Deviation. Many firms will multiply by 100 to rescale this as a percentage. The *MAPE* is the average of the ratios (forecast error)/(actual demand). The *MAPE* is not the *MAD* divided by the average demand.

The *MAPE* has two significant problems: instability and dividing by zero. First, when the demand is abnormally small, the *APE* values can be quite large. For example, when the demand is 10 and the forecast is 100, the *APE* (absolute percent error) for that period is 90/10 = 900%. These very large values can have an undue influence on the average in the *MAPE* calculation. Second, when the demand (D_t) is zero in any period, the *MAPE* is undefined and the equation cannot be implemented. These data points, therefore, should be either bounded by a reasonable value or omitted. A common approach is to bound the *APE* at 100%. For example, if the demand is zero and the forecast error is 20 units, $|E_t|/D_t$ should be set to 1. This means that *MAPE* is defined in the range (0, 100%).

One firm addressed the divide-by-zero problem by defining an adjusted *MAPE* based on the error divided by the forecast rather than the error divided by the actual demand. In other words, they defined the absolute percent error in any period as $|E_t|/F_t$ rather than $|E_t|/D_t$. Given that the forecast is almost never zero, this usually avoids the divide-by-zero problem. This adjusted *MAPE* is defined as the error as percent of the forecast rather than the error as a percent of demand, and therefore is not easy for most people to interpret or explain.

Makridakis (1993) and Collopy and Armstrong (2006) suggest an approach that helps avoid the above problems called the Unbiased Absolute Percent Error (*UAPE*). The *UAPE* defines the denominator as the average of the demand and forecast. In other words, the absolute percent error in any period is defined as $|E_t|/(D_t/2 + F_t/2)$ rather than $|E_t|/D_t$. One advantage of this metric is that it is constrained to the interval between 0 and 200. Given that the sum of the forecast and demand is almost never zero, this approach also tends to avoid the divide-by-zero problem. This adjusted *MAPE* can be interpreted as a lower bound on the forecast error and will always be less than the *MAPE*. However, interpretation is difficult because the result is not the error as percent of demand, but the error as a percent of the midpoint between the demand and the forecast.

Still another way to adjust the *MAPE* to try to avoid the divide-by-zero problem is to define the denominator as the maximum of the forecast and the demand. In other words, use $|E_t|/\max(D_t, F_t)$ rather than $|E_t|/D_t$. This can be interpreted as a lower bound on the forecast error and will always be less than the *MAPE*. However, when both the demand and the forecast are both zero, this method will still have the divide-by-zero problem.

Like most time series forecasting statistics, *MAPE* can be smoothed with the updating equation $SMAPE_t = \alpha |E_t| / D_t + (1 - \alpha) SMAPE_{t-1}$. Of course, implementation of this equation should be sure to handle the divide-by-zero problem mentioned above.

The *MAPE* can be misleading as an aggregate measure for a group of items with both low and high demand. For example, a firm has just two items, one very important item with high demand, high unit cost, and low *MAPE* (say 10%), and another very unimportant item with low demand, low unit cost, and high MAPE (say 90%). When these two *MAPE* values are average, the overall *MAPE* is 50%. However, this gives too much weight to the low demand item and not enough to the important item. The weighted *MAPE* avoids this problem.

The weighted *MAPE* is defined as $\sum_{i=1}^{N} w_i MAPE_i / \sum_{i=1}^{N} w_i \overline{D}_i$, where w_i is the importance weight for item i.

In the opinion of many experts, the Mean Absolute Scaled Error (*MASE*) is a better metric than the *MAPE* because it does not have any of the above problems. Unfortunately, it is harder to understand than the *MAPE*.

See *demand filter, exponential smoothing, forecast bias, forecast error metrics, forecasting, Mean Absolute Deviation (MAD), Mean Absolute Scaled Error (MASE), Mean Squared Error (MSE), Median Absolute Percent Error (MdAPE), Relative Absolute Error (RAE), Thiel's U, tracking signal, Winsorizing.*

Mean Absolute Scaled Error (MASE) – The relative absolute error metrics described above compare the forecast error in one period with the forecast error for a simple benchmark forecasting method (such as the random walk) in the same period. While this idea of comparing the forecast error to a simple benchmark is appealing, these procedures can often have a divide-by-zero problem. For the random walk forecast, the relative absolute error will have a divide-by-zero problem every time the demand is the same in any two periods, e.g., $D_t = D_{t-1}$.

Hyndman and Koehler (2006) proposed an appealing and simple forecast error metric that usually avoids the divide-by-zero problem by scaling the errors by the Mean Absolute Deviation (Mean Absolute Error) for the random walk forecasting procedure. In other words, instead of dividing by the error for the simple forecast each period, it divides by the *MAD* for the random walk forecast over a number of periods.

The *MAD* for the random walk is:

$$MAD_{RW} = \frac{1}{T} \sum_{t=1}^{T} |D_t - F_t| = \frac{1}{T} \sum_{t=1}^{T} |D_t - D_{t-1}|$$

The forecast for the random walk is simply the actual demand in the previous period (e.g., $F_t = D_{t-1}$). This assumes a one-period ahead forecast, but it could be easily modified for a *k*-period ahead forecast by replacing the term $|D_t - D_{t-1}|$ in the numerator with the term $|D_t - D_{t-k}|$. Note the above equation requires $T + 1$ demand values starting at D_0. The Mean Absolute Scaled Error, therefore, is defined as:

$$MASE = \frac{MAD}{MAD_{RW}} = \frac{\frac{1}{T} \sum_{t=1}^{T} |E_t|}{\frac{1}{T} \sum_{t=1}^{T} |D_t - D_{t-1}|} = \frac{\sum_{t=1}^{T} |D_t - F_t|}{\sum_{t=1}^{T} |D_t - D_{t-1}|}$$

This *MASE* approach has all of the advantages of a relative measure without the divide-by-zero problem. The *MASE* will only have a divide-by-zero problem when the demand does not change over the entire horizon, which is an unlikely situation.

The *MASE* expresses the mean absolute error (the *MAD*) as a percentage of the random walk forecast mean absolute error. A *MASE* less than one indicates that the forecasts are better than the random walk forecast; a *MASE* greater than one indicates that the forecasts are worse than the random walk forecast. A forecasting model with a *MASE* of 20% has a forecast error that is 20% of the forecast error of the simplistic random walk forecast, which would generally be considered a good forecast. A *MASE* of 95% is only slightly better than a simplistic random walk forecast.

The Mean Absolute Scaled Accuracy (*MASA*), is the companion accuracy measure for the *MASE*, and is defined as $1 - MASE$. *MASA* can be interpreted as the percent accuracy of the forecast relative to the random walk forecast. A *MASA* of 0 means that the forecasts are no better than the random walk forecast; a *MASA* of 60% means that the average absolute forecast error is 60% of the random walk forecast. *MASA* is a good measure of forecast accuracy for a forecasting system because it measures the forecast accuracy against an objective standard (the random walk forecast) and is not very hard to understand.

Dan Strike at 3M has suggested a very similar metric that uses a 12-month moving average as the scaling factor. This metric is even simpler than *MASE* to explain, but slightly harder to implement.

This simple scaling concept can be extended to the mean squared error and the root mean squared error. In fact, Thiel's U_3 metric (described in the next section) is the mean squared error scaled by the mean squared error for the random walk forecast.

The *MASE* can be implemented with exponential smoothing for both the numerator (the smoothed MAD) and the denominator (the smoothed MAD for a random walk forecast).

Hyndman and Koehler (2006, p. 13) assert that measures based on scaled measures (such as the *MASE*) "should become the standard approach in comparing forecast accuracy across series on different scales." This makes sense to this author. However, the *MASE* has two significant organizational challenges. First, it is not always easy to explain the *MASE* to managers. Their description "the mean absolute percent error relative to a random walk forecast" makes sense to this author, but may not be readily understood by some managers. Second, when changing from the *MAPE* to the *MASE*, those responsible for forecasting will have to explain why the reported forecast errors increase dramatically. Assuming that about half of the variation is explained by the random walk forecasts, the reported forecast error will double with a change from the *MAPE* to the *MASE*.

See *forecast error metrics, Mean Absolute Percent Error (MAPE)*.

Mean Squared Error (MSE) – A measure of forecast error that is the average of the squared forecast errors and is defined mathematically as $MSE = \dfrac{1}{T}\sum_{t=1}^{T} E_t^{\,2}$, where E_t is the forecast error in period t and T is the number of observed values. ✪

The *MSE* is an estimate of the variance of the forecast error and is approximately equal to the variance when the forecast bias is close to zero. Like most time series statistics, the *MSE* can be smoothed with the updating equation $SMSE_t = (1-\alpha)SMSE_{t-1} + \alpha E_t^{\,2}$.

The Root Mean Square (*RMSE*) is the square root of the MSE and is an estimate of the standard deviation of the forecast error. Variances are additive but standard deviations are not; therefore, the *RMSE* should not be smoothed.

See *forecast bias, forecast error metrics, Mean Absolute Deviation (MAD), Mean Absolute Percent Error (MAPE), standard deviation*.

Mean Time Between Failure (MTBF) – The average time that a component is expected to work without failing.

The MTBF is a good measure of the reliability of a product. The MTBF is often modeled with the bathtub curve that has higher failure rates at the beginning and ending of the product lifecycle.

See *availability, bathtub curve, maintenance, Mean Time To Repair (MTTR), reliability, Total Productive Maintenance (TPM)*.

Mean Time To Repair (MTTR) – Measure of the average time required to fix something such as a machine.

The *MTTR* is a measure of the complexity and cost of a repair job. Schroeder (2007) states that *MTTR* is a measure of the "maintainability" of a product. e careful about using the *MTTR* as performance evaluation measure for service techs. The best service techs are often assigned to the most difficult repair jobs, which means they will have the highest *MTTR*. The same is true for doctors.

See *availability, maintenance, Mean Time Between Failure (MTBF), Total Productive Maintenance (TPM)*.

Measurement System Analysis – An approach for verifying the accuracy and precision of data measurement system using statistical analysis tools such as Gauge R&R, attribute Gauge R&R, and the P/T ratio; sometimes abbreviated MSA.

See *Gauge R&R, metrology*.

MECE – The concept that an analysis should define issues and alternatives that are mutually exclusive and collectively exhaustive.

The MECE concept is most often applied in analyzing business problems. Mutually exclusive means that each idea or alternative is distinct and separate and does not overlap. Collectively exhaustive means that the set of ideas or alternatives covers all of the possibilities and includes every issue relevant to the problem.

This concept is widely used at McKinsey and other consulting firms where it is used to define both issues and the alternative courses of action (Rasiel, 1998). Note that the issues can be represented in an issue tree and the courses of action can be represented in a decision tree.

See *causal map, decision tree, issue tree, Minto Pyramid Principle, story board, y-tree*.

median – The middle value of a set of sorted values. ✪

The median, like the mean, is a measure of the central tendency. The calculation of the median begins by sorting the values in a list. If the number of values is odd, the median is the middle value in the sorted list. If the number of values is even, the median is the average of the two middle values in the sorted list. For example, the median of $\{1, 2, \mathbf{3}, 9, 100\}$ is 3 and the median of $\{1, 2, \mathbf{3}, \mathbf{9}, 100, 200\}$ is (3+9)/2=6.

The median is often a better measure of central tendency than the mean when the data is highly skewed. For example, consider the following house selling prices: $175, $180, $200, $240, $241, $260, $800, and $2400. The mean is $562, but the median is only $240.5. In this case the mean is "pulled up" by the two high prices.

Excel provides the function median(*range*) for computing the median of a range of values.

The interpolated median is better than the median when the data is skewed and many values are at the median. This is often true for Likert survey questions on the 1-5 or 1-7 scale and also for grades that are translated from A, A-,B+, etc. to a 4.0 scale.

Acknowledgments: CEMBA 09 students Leslie Bronk, Terry Collier, Rick Mann, and Adam Podbelski contributed to this entry.

See *interpolated median, Median Absolute Percent Error (MdAPE), trimmed mean*.

Median Absolute Percent Error (MdAPE) – The middle value of all the percent errors for a data set when the absolute values of the errors (negative signs are ignored) are ordered by size.

See *forecast error metrics, Mean Absolute Deviation (MAD), Mean Absolute Percent Error (MAPE), median*.

Methods Time Measurement (MTM) – See *work measurement*.

metrology – The science of measurement.

Metrology attempts to validate the data obtained from test equipment and considers precision, accuracy, traceability, and reliability. Metrology, therefore, requires an analysis of the uncertainty of individual measurements to validate the accuracy of a given instrument. The dissemination of traceability to consumers (both internal and external) is often performed by a dedicated calibration laboratory with a recognized quality system.

Metrology has been an important topic in commerce since people started measuring length, time, and weight. For example, according to ***New Unger's Bible Dictionary***, the cubit was an important measure of length among the Hebrews in the Bible (Exodus 25:10; 1 Kings 7:24; Ezekiel 40:5) and other ancient nations. It was commonly measured as the length of the arm from the point of the elbow to the end of the middle finger, about eighteen inches.

The scientific revolution required a rational system of units and made it possible to apply science to measurement. Metrology became a driver of the Industrial Revolution and was a critical precursor to systems of mass production.

Modern metrology had its roots in the French Revolution and was based on the concept of establishing units of measurement based on constants of nature, and thus making measurement units available "for all people, for all time." For example, the meter was based on the dimensions of the Earth and the kilogram was based on the mass of a cube of water. This led to the creation of the Système International d'Unités (International System of Units or SI), which has gained worldwide acceptance as the standard for modern measurement. The SI is maintained under the auspices of the Metre Convention and its institutions, the General Conference on Weights and Measures, or CGPM, its executive branch the International Committee for Weights and Measures, or CIPM, and its technical institution the International Bureau of Weights and Measures, or BIPM. The U.S. agencies holding this responsibility are the National Institute of Standards and Technology (NIST) and the American National Standards Institute (ANSI).

See *Gauge R&R, Measurement System Analysis, Six Sigma*.

milk run − The practice of having a manufacturer send a vehicle to multiple local suppliers to pick up materials on a frequent schedule (often daily) in small quantities.

The traditional approach is a customer firm to send fairly large orders to suppliers on an infrequent basis and for the suppliers to ship orders to the customer via a common carrier. With a milk run, the customer firm sends its own truck to pick up small quantities from a number of local suppliers on a frequent basis (say once every week). Milk runs speed delivery and reduce inventory. Hill and Vollmann (1986) developed an optimization model for this problem.

See *logistics*.

min/max inventory system − An inventory control system that orders enough to bring the inventory position up to the maximum inventory level (target inventory level) when the inventory position falls below the reorder point (the "min" or minimum). ✪

The min/max system is also known as the (R,T) and the (S,s) system. The min/max system triggers an order when the inventory position falls below the reorder point (the "min" or minimum). The order size is defined as the "max" (maximum, or target inventory) less the current inventory position. In other words, when the inventory position goes below the minimum, the system orders order enough to bring the inventory position up to the maximum.

A special case of this is the $(S,S-1)$ system where orders are placed on a "one-for-one" basis. In other words, every time a unit is consumed, another unit is ordered. The $(S,S-1)$ policy is particularly practical for low demand items such as repair parts.

See *reorder point*.

mindmap − A diagram used to show the relationships between concepts, ideas, and words that are connected to a central concept or idea at one or more levels.

A mindmap is a very useful graphical tool that can be used by an individual or a group to capture, refine, and share information about the relationships between concepts, ideas, words, tasks, and/or objects that are connected to a central concept or idea at one or more levels in a hierarchy. Some of the uses of mindmaps include:

- Generate ideas
- Capture ideas
- Take course notes
- Provide structure to ideas
- Review and study ideas
- Visualize and clarify relationships
- Help plan meetings and projects
- Organize ideas for papers
- Create the storyboard for a presentation
- Stimulate creativity
- Create a shared understanding
- Create the agenda for a meeting
- Communicate ideas with others
- Teach concepts to others
- Document ideas
- Help make decisions
- Create a work breakdown structure
- Create a task list
- Prioritize activities
- Solve problems

The term "mindmap" suggests that a mindmap represents the way that people think about a subject. The spatial organization on the paper (or screen) communicates the relationship between the nodes (ideas, concepts, objects, etc.) in the creator's mind. Mindmaps create value for the users in both the creation and the communication process. Creating a mindmap helps the creator(s) translate their thinking about a subject into more concrete ideas. Once created, a mindmap is often an excellent way to communicate the concepts to others.

Methods − The concepts on a mindmap are drawn around the central idea. Subordinate concepts are than drawn as branches from those concepts. Some experts suggest that the mindmaps should only be drawn by hand, using multiple colors and icons (drawings) and possibly supplemented with photos. This makes the mindmap easier to remember, more personal, and more fun. These same experts argue that the mindmap should be able to fit on one piece of paper; however, they allow it to be a large piece of paper. Many powerful software packages are now available for helping create Mindmaps. These include Mind Manager (mindjet.com), Inspiration (inspiration.com), and many others. (Wikipedia has a nice list of available mindmapping software.)

Relationship to other diagramming tools – A mindmap is similar to a causal map except that the links in a mindmap usually infer similarity rather than causality. A strategy map is a special type of causal map. A project network shows the time relationships between the nodes and therefore is not a mindmap. However, a mindmap is a good way to help people brainstorm to create the work breakdown structure (the hierarchical list) of all of the tasks that need to be done to complete a particular project. Mindmaps are similar to issue trees since both issue trees and mindmaps show subordinate concepts. Issue trees are more structured that mindmaps in that they are usually drawn from left to right where mindmaps do not have to follow any set format.

Mindmap example – The example on the next page was created by the author with Mindjet Mind Manager software from Mindjet to brainstorm both the work breakdown structure and the issue tree for a productivity improvement project. The symbol (+) indicates that additional nodes are currently hidden from view. The user can click this icon to expand these.

In conclusion, mindmaps are a powerful tool for visualizing, structuring, and communicating the concepts related to a central idea. This author expects that mindmapping software in the future will be as popular as Microsoft's popular process mapping tool (Visio) and project management tool (Microsoft Project Manager).

More information on this subject is available in the "Mindmapping" paper available from www.ClamshellBeachPress.com. ●

See *causal map*, *issue tree*, *strategy map*, *Work Breakdown Structure (WBS)*.

Mindmap example

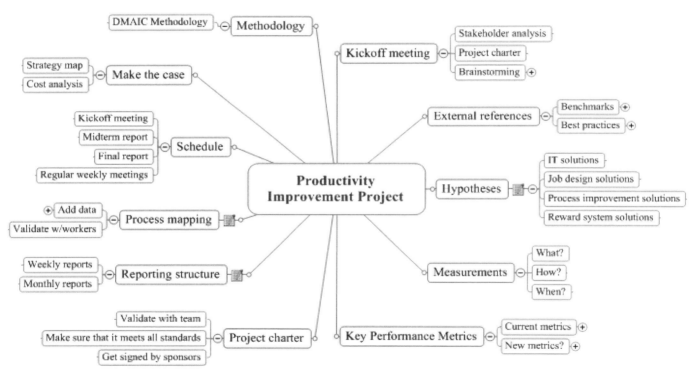

Source: Arthur V. Hill

Minkowski distance metric – A generalized distance metric that can be used in both logistics and in cluster analysis.

If location i has coordinates (x_i, y_i), the Minkowski distance between locations i and j is given by $d_{ij} = (| x_i - x_j |^r + | y_i - y_j |^r)^{1/r}$. The Minkowski distance metric is equal to the Euclidean distance when $r = 2$ and the Manhattan square distance when $r = 1$.

This same concept can be applied in cluster analysis and multidimensional scaling where item i has K attributes $(x_{i1}, x_{i2}, \ldots, x_{iK})$. The distance between item i and item j is then $d_{ij} = (\sum_{k=1}^{K} |x_{ki} - x_{kj}|^r)^{1/r}$. Again, the Minkowski distance metric is equal to the Euclidean distance when $r = 2$ and the Manhattan square distance when $r = 1$.

See *cluster analysis, Manhattan square distance.*

minor setup cost – See *major setup cost, setup cost.*

Minto Pyramid Principle – A structured approach to building a persuasive argument and presentation developed by Barbara Minto (1996), a former McKinsey consultant.

Most professors will agree that many (if not most) MBA student PowerPoint case study presentations are disorganized and unpersuasive. Most of them could benefit from the Minto Pyramid Principle (MPP) developed by Barbara Minto (1996), a former McKinsey consultant. This approach to structured thinking can improve almost any presentation and almost any form of persuasive speech.

The core idea of the MPP is that the arguments should be presented in a pyramid structure, starting with the fundamental question (or hypothesis) at the top and then cascading down the pyramid with arguments at one level supported by arguments at the next level. At each level the author asks the questions, "How can I support this argument" and "How do I know that this is true?" The presentation mentions all of the arguments at one level, and then drills down to the next level for one of the arguments.

For example, a firm is considering moving its manufacturing operations to China. At the top of the pyramid is the hypothesis that, "We should move part of our manufacturing to China." From this, the team doing the analysis and making the presentation asks, "Why is it a good idea to move to China?" The answer comes at the next level with three answers: (1) We will have lower labor cost in China, (2) We can better serve our customers in Asia, and (3) Locating in China will eventually open new markets for the company's products in China. The team then asks "why" for each of these three items and breaks these out in more detail at the next level. This example is illustrated in the figure below. The "enable us to lower our direct labor cost" argument is fully developed before the "better able to serve our customers in Asia" is started.

Minto recommends that the pyramid be started with an introduction that should be presented as a story with an opening statement of the thesis that consists of a factual summary of the current situation, a complicating factor or uncertainty that the audience should care about, and the explicit or implied question that this factor or uncertainty raises in the audience's mind, and which the presenter's thesis answers. The closing consists of a restatement of the main thesis and the key supporting arguments (usually the second row of the pyramid), a reminder of why it is important, and finally an action plan.

Example of the Minto Pyramid Principle

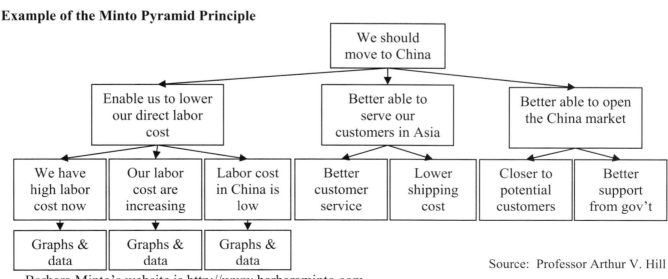

Source: Professor Arthur V. Hill

Barbara Minto's website is http://www.barbaraminto.com.

See *hypothesis, issue tree, MECE, story board.*

mission statement – A short statement of an organization's purpose and aspirations, intended to provide direction and motivation.

Most organizations have a vision and/or mission statement that is intended to define their purpose and their *raison d'être*[4]. However, for the vast majority of organizations, creating a vision and/or mission statement is a waste of time. Vision and mission statements are published in the annual report and displayed prominently on the walls, but are understood by few, remembered by none, and have almost no impact on anyone's thinking or behavior. However, this does not have to be the case. Vision and mission statements can be powerful tools for aligning and energizing an entire organization.

While scholars do not universally agree on the difference between vision and mission statements, most view the vision statement as the more strategic statement. A vision statement should be a short, succinct, and inspiring statement of what the organization intends to become and to achieve at some point in the future. It is the mental image that describes the organization's aspirations for the future without specifying the means to achieve those aspirations. The table below presents some examples of vision statements that have worked.

Examples of vision statements

Worked	Would not work
Put a man on the moon by the end of the decade – J.F. Kennedy	To be an aeronautical leader and apply ingenuity and innovation in our work as we value our taxpayers and government employees.
Put a computer on every desk in America – Bill Gates	Be a leader in the field of software development in the American market by making software that is easy to use. We also will provide a good return on investment for our shareholders.
Be number one or number two in every market we compete in. – Jack Welch, CEO, GE	Be an industry leader providing quality products to our customers, using the talents of our employees and providing above average returns to our shareholders.

The mission statement translates the vision into more concrete and more detailed terms. Many organizations also have a values statement dealing with integrity, concern for people, concern for the environment, etc., where the values statement defines constraints rather than aspirations. Of course, the leadership must model the values. Enron's values statement was excellent, but the leadership did not live up to it (cf., www.thesmokinggun. com/enron/enronethics3.html). Goals and objectives are a means of implementing the vision and mission. While used interchangeably by many, most people define goals as longer term and less tangible, with objectives being the means to implement the goals.

Of course, having a vision, mission, goals, and objectives is not enough. Organizations further need to further define competitive strategies and projects to achieve them. A competitive strategy is a plan of action to achieve a competitive advantage. Projects are a means of implementing strategies. Projects require goals and objectives, but also require a project charter, a team, and a detailed schedule. Both strategies and projects should be driven by the organization's vision and mission. The following figure shows a comprehensive model for tying these concepts together.

---

[4] *Raison d'être is a French phrase that means reason to be or justification for existence. This phase is often written in English as raison d'etre without the ê.*

Values – Our core beliefs that constrain all that we do.
▼
Vision – What we want to become in the future.
▼
Mission – What we want to achieve with our vision.
▼
Strategies – How we will achieve our mission, with clearly defined goals.
▼
Projects and priorities – How we implement strategies with clearly defined objectives.
▼
Alignment – How individuals will contribute to the mission.

The figure below shows the Kaplan and Norton (2004) model, which starts with the mission, then follows with values and vision. Many authors argue that the vision and mission should be derived from values. Some authors argue that the vision is a longer term view and that the mission should be derived from this vision.

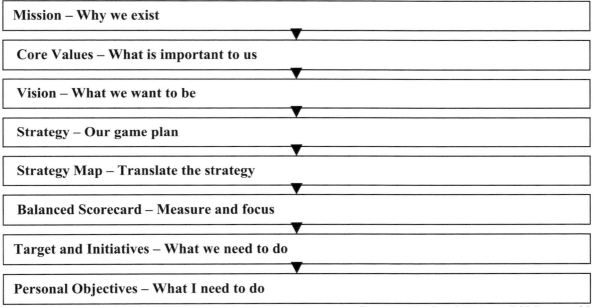

Source: Kaplan & Norton (2004), page 33.

In conclusion, vision and mission statements can be powerful tools to define the organization's desired end state and to energize the organization to make the vision and mission a reality. In order to be successful, these statements need to be clear, succinct, passionate, shared, and lived out by the organization's leaders. They should be supported by a strong set of values that are also lived out by the leadership. Lastly, the vision and mission need to be supported by focused strategies, which are implemented through people and projects that are aligned with the strategies and the mission.

The paper "How to Create a Mission Statement" is on the ***OMWW CD*** available from www.ClamshellBeachPress.com. ⦿

See *Balanced Scorecard*, *SMART*.

mistake proofing – See *error proofing*.

Mixed Integer Programming (MIP) – A type of linear programming where some decision variables are restricted to integer values and some are continuous.

The term mixed integer programming is short for mixed integer linear programming.

See *Integer Programming (IP), Linear Programming (LP), Operations Research (OR)*.

mixed model assembly – The practice of assembling more than one product during any period of time using one assembly process.

For example, an assembly worker might see three units of product A, then two units of product B, then four units of product A, etc. The alternative to this policy is to make large batches of each product and then switch over to the other product. The advantages of mixed model assembly are that it reduces inventory, improves service levels, and smoothes the production rate; the disadvantages are that it requires frequent changeovers from one product to another and adds complexity to the manufacturing task.

See *assembly line, facility layout, heijunka, setup reduction methods*.

mizusumashi – See *water spider*.

modular design (modularity) – Organizing a complex system (such as a large program, an electronic circuit, or a mechanical device) as a set of distinct components that can be developed independently and then plugged together. ✪

Although this may appear to be a simple idea, experience shows that the effectiveness of the technique depends critically on the manner in which systems are divided into components and the mechanisms used to plug components together. (Source: www-unix.mcs.anl.gov/dbpp/text/node40.html, October 27, 2000.)

Modularity is a general systems concept and is a continuum describing the degree to which a system's components can be separated and recombined. It refers both to the tightness of coupling between components and to the degree to which the "rules" of the system architecture enable (or prohibit) the mixing and matching of components. Since all systems are characterized by some degree of coupling (whether loose or tight) between components, and very few systems have components that are completely inseparable and cannot be recombined, almost all systems are, to some degree, modular (Schilling 2000).

See *commonality, mass customization*.

modularity – See *modular design*.

moment of truth – Any time that a firm "touches" its customers or employees. ✪

A moment of truth is an opportunity for the firm's customers (or employees) to find out the truth about the firm's employees and its true character – to find out "who they really are." This is a chance for employees to show the customers that they really do care about them and to ask customers for feedback on how products and services might be improved. These are special moments and should be managed carefully.

When creating a process map, it is important to highlight the process steps that include the customer. A careful analysis of a typical service process often uncovers many more moments-of-truth than management truly appreciates such as a call for a quick question, a question posed to a salesperson, a contact regarding a billing problem, etc.

Pine and Gillmore's book (2007) on "Authenticity" argues that in a world increasingly filled with deliberately staged experiences and manipulative business practices (frequent flyer miles comes to mind here), consumers choose to buy based on how real and how honest they perceive a service provider. This is very close to the concept of moments of truth.

See *service blueprinting, service quality*.

Monte Carlo simulation – See *simulation*.

Moore's Law – A prediction made by Intel cofounder Dr. Gordon E. Moore in 1965 that states that the number of components on an integrated circuit will double every 12 months (or 24 months or 18 months).

In 1975 Moore revised his 12 months to 24 months. Other people have revised the law to the widely quoted number of 18 months, which is an average of the 12 and 24 months. Moore's Law is really not a "law." It is an observation that the number of components on a circuit was growing at an exponential rate.

This observation is not a new one. Benjamin Franklin noted in his 1751 essay "Observations concerning the Increase of Mankind, peopling of Countries, etc.," that the population doubled in the English colonies in America about every 25 years. Franklin observed that "This million doubling, suppose but once in 25 years, will, in another century, be more than the people of England, and the greatest number of Englishmen will be on this side the water."

Moore's Law is an exponential growth model of a continuous variable that can be applied to many fast-growth contexts, such as millions of instructions per second (MIPS) for the fastest computer, the number of Internet users, the mosquito population in Minnesota, etc.

The mathematical model for exponential growth is the identical to the half-life "time-based learning" model, $y(t) = ae^{bt}$, except that with exponential growth the performance variable increases (exponential growth) instead of decreases (exponential decay) over time. Whereas the performance variable for exponential growth doubles every h time periods, the performance variable for the half-life curve "halves" every h time periods. The constants for Moore's Law are $a = y(0)$, $b = \ln(2)/h$, and $h = \ln(2)/b$. Note that the signs for b and h here are opposite those of the half-life model. Note that unlike the learning curve model that has discrete time periods, the exponential growth (or decay) model relates two continuous variables – time and performance.

The paper "Learning Models" and the Excel workbook "learning models.xls" are on the *OMWW CD* available from www.ClamshellBeachPress.com. ⬤

See *green manufacturing, half-life curve, learning curve, learning organization.*

moving average – A rolling average over a specified number of recent periods used to smooth data for charting and/or make forecasts. ✪

The moving average is often used to make forecasts based on the most recent data. Exponential smoothing is a similar approach that calculates a weighted average, with the weights declining geometrically with the age of the data. An *N*-period moving average can be proven to be mathematically equivalent to simple exponential smoothed average with the smoothing constant $\alpha = 2/(N+1)$.

See *Box-Jenkins forecasting, centered moving average, exponential smoothing, forecasting, time-series forecasting.*

MPS – See *Master Production Schedule.*

MRB – See *Material Review Board.*

MRO (Maintenance-Repair-Operations) – Purchased "non-production" items not used directly in the product.

MRO is typically divided between manufacturing MRO (cutting oil, sandpaper, etc.) and non-manufacturing MRO (travel, office supplies, etc.). Manufacturing MRO categories include Electrical and mechanical, Electronic, Lab equipment and supplies, and Industrial supplies. These items are generally not handled by the firm's ERP system, but are often a significant expense for many firms. Note that "MRO" has various (but similar) meanings, including "Maintenance, Repair, and Operating supplies," "Maintenance, Repair, and Operations," and "Maintenance, Repair, and Overhaul."

General and Administrative expenses generally include computer related capital equipment, travel and entertainment, and MRO (Maintenance, Repair and Operations). MRO is usually the most significant and most mission-critical of these.

Many consulting firms have been able to significant success in helping large multi-division firms to "leverage their MRO spend" across many divisions. They save the firm large amounts of money by getting all of the divisions to buy from the same MRO suppliers. For example, they get all of the divisions to use the same airline and negotiate a significantly lower price. Deloitte Consulting uses the term "operating resource management" (ORM) for "the strategic purchase of non-production goods through the effective use of aggregate buying, volume discount, lowered transaction costs, and decision support techniques to identify vendor discount operations."

See *Business Process Outsourcing, leverage the spend, maintenance, purchasing, Total Productive Maintenance (TPM).*

MRP – See *Materials Requirements Planning (MRP).*

MTBF – See *Mean Time Between Failure (MTBF).*

MTM (Methods Time Measurement) – See *work measurement.*

MTO – See *Make to Order (MTO).*

MTS – See *Make to Stock (MTS).*

MTTR – See *Mean Time To Repair (MTTR).*

muda – A Japanese word for waste used to describe any activity that does not add value. ✪

In everyday Japanese, muda means useless, futile, and waste. In popular lean manufacturing terminology, muda is any type of waste. The 7 wastes are examples of muda: over-production, waiting, conveyance, processing, inventory, motion, and correction.

ム ダ

MU DA

According to the Lean Enterprise Institute, Muda, Mura, and Muri are three Japanese terms often used together in the Toyota Production System that collectively describe wasteful practices to be eliminated.

- **Muda** (Non-value added) – Any activity that consumes resources without creating value for the customer.
- **Mura** (Imbalance) – Unevenness in an operation; for example, an uneven work pace in an operation causing operators to hurry and then wait.
- **Muri** (Overload) – Overburdening equipment or operators.

See *7 wastes, error proofing, lean thinking, Toyota Production System (TPS)*.

multi-modal shipments – Moving containers using multiple modes of transportation.

An example of this is a container picked up from the shipper by truck, loaded onto the rail, shipped by rail to a port, and then loaded on a vessel. Multi-modal shipments help optimize supply chain efficiency, but can cause problems for container tracking because of the multiple movements and lack of coordination between the various modes.

See *inter-modal shipments, logistics, shipping container*.

multiple-machine handling – The practice of assigning workers to operate more than one machine at a time.

This is a common Japanese manufacturing practice and is enabled by the application of jidoka and error proofing principles. Chaku-Chaku is an application of this principle.

See *Chaku-Chaku, error proofing, jidoka*.

Mura – See *Muda*.

Muri – See *Muda*.

Murphy's Law – A humorous and pessimistic popular "law" stated as, "If it can go wrong, it will." ✪

Some people argue that Murphy's Law is an expression of the Second Law of Thermodynamics, which suggests that all systems move to the highest state of disorder (the lowest possible state of energy) and tend to stay there unless energy is supplied or order is restore them. This is sometimes called the law of entropy.

See *Parkinson's Laws, project management*.

N

NAPM (National Association of Purchasing Management) – See *Institute for Supply Management (ISM)*.

National Association of Purchasing Management (NAPM) – See *Institute for Supply Management (ISM)*.

NC machine –See *Numerically Controlled (NC) machine*.

near miss – See *adverse event*.

Net Present Value (NPV) – The future stream of benefits and costs converted into equivalent values today.

This is done by assigning monetary values to benefits and costs, discounting future benefits and costs using an appropriate discount rate, and subtracting the sum total of discounted costs from the sum total of discounted benefits. Mathematically, the Net Present Value is defined as:

$$NPV = \sum_{t=1}^{n} \frac{C_t}{(1+r)^t} - C_0$$

where, t is the time period, n is the number of time periods, r is the discount rate, C_t is the net cash flow in period t, and C_0 is the initial cash outlay.

See *financial performance metrics*.

Net Promoter Score (NPS) – A simple but useful loyalty metric based on customer willingness to recommend.

The Net Promoter Score (NPS) is a relatively new loyalty metric developed by Frederick Reichheld (2003). The NPS is derived from the willingness to recommend metric and includes only one simple loyalty question, "How likely is it that you would recommend us to a friend or colleague?"

Customers are asked to respond using a 0 to 10 Likert rating scale with 0 anchored on the extreme negative end and 10 on the extreme positive end. Customers are then divided into three categories: (1) Promoters (9 or

10) are loyal enthusiasts who keep buying from a company and urge their friends to do the same; (2) Passives (7 or 8) are satisfied but unenthusiastic customers who can be easily wooed by the competition; and (3) Detractors (0 to 6) are unhappy customers. The NPS is then defined as the percentage of customers who respond as promoters minus the percentage who respond as detractors.

The advocates of the NPS claim that it is the single best predictor of actual loyalty. They further argue that it is comparable to a financial net worth that takes the assets minus the liabilities, where the assets are the promoters and the liabilities are the detractor. They also argue that the NPS is highly correlated with growth rates and that it is the single most reliable indicator of a company's ability to grow. The consulting firm Satmetrix offers a short white paper on this subject on the web at satmetrix.com/pdfs/NetPromoterWPfinal.pdf.

Hill, Hays, and Naveh (2000) developed a similar concept based on a mathematical/economic model that shows that loyalty is related to the ratio (not the difference) of satisfied and dissatisfied customers, e.g., $\Pi_s / (1 - \Pi_s)$, where Π_s is the percent satisfied (or percent promoters). Combining these two models suggests that loyalty is a function of the ratio Π_p / Π_d, where Π_p is the percent promoters and Π_d the percent detractors. This concept has not yet been tested empirically.

See *service quality*.

net requirements – The number of units still needed to satisfy the materials plan in an MRP system.

The net requirement is an important MRP part of planning. It is calculated as the gross requirements (units needed by higher level items), plus allocations (units already promised to an order), less on-hand inventory (units that are available now), less scheduled receipts (units that will soon be available), and less safety stock (desired number of units on-hand at all times).

See *Materials Requirements Planning (MRP)*.

network effect – An economics term that describes a situation where the value of a product or service increases with the number of adopters, thereby encouraging an increasing number of adopters; also called a network externality.

The network effect can be illustrated with a cell phone. If the world had only one cell phone using a particular communication technology, it would be of no value. However, this cell phone becomes much more valuable when two of them exist, even more valuable when four of them exist, and much more valuable when nearly everyone has one.

Economists call this a network externality because when new consumers join the network, they have a beneficial "external" impact on the consumers already in the network. The network effect produces a self-reinforcing cycle with more buyers attracting more sellers and more sellers attracting more buyers.

Robert Metcalfe noted that the value of a network grows with the square of the number of participants. Metcalfe's Law states that the value of a telecommunications network is proportional to the square of the number of users of the system (n^2). Metcalfe's Law explains many of the network effects of communication technologies and networks such as the Internet, social networking, and Wikipedia. It is related to the fact that the number of unique connections in a network of a number of nodes (n) can be expressed mathematically as $n(n - 1)/2$.

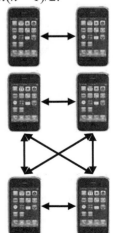

The network effect is often the result of word-of-mouth testimonials. In other words, people may adopt a service because "everyone" uses it. Over time, positive network effects can create a "bandwagon effect" as the network becomes more valuable. This is related to the Bass Model.

The expression "network effect" nearly always refers to positive network externalities as in the case of the telephone. Negative network externalities can also occur where more adopters make a product less valuable. This is sometimes referred to as "congestion."

The economy of scale concept has to do with the size of the business making it more efficient. In other words, economy of scale has to do with the supply side of a business. The network effect is essentially a "demand side" economy of scale that has to do with the "interoperability" of the network.

Acknowledgments: CSOM MBA students Drew Motylinski, Mrinal Shaw, and Brent Herzog contributed to this entry.

See *Bass Model, economy of scale*.

network optimization – An efficient algorithmic approach for modeling and solving a class of linear programming problems.

Most network optimization problems can be represented by a directed graph (a set of notes with arrows connecting them). The user must define the minimum flow, maximum flow, and cost per unit flow that can pass along each arc in the network. The fundamental rule is conservation of flow, which states simply that the flow coming into a node must equal the flow going out of a node.

Many problems can be modeled as a network optimization problem, including the assignment problem, the transportation problem, and the transshipment problem.

The Ford and Fulkerson "out-of-kilter" algorithm is the most famous approach for solving this problem, but primal network algorithms are much more efficient. Several variants of the Ford and Fulkerson algorithm are available in the public domain and are often adequate for practical problems.

The Excel workbooks "Netsolver.xls" and "SPAT.xls" are on the *OMWW CD* available from www.ClamshellBeachPress.com. Netsolver.xls is a general purpose network optimization. SPAT.xls is a network optimization for assigning students to project teams. ◉

See *assignment problem*, *Linear Programming (LP)*, *transportation problem*.

neural network – A type of computer program that has the ability to "learn" over time; often called an "artificial neural network."

A neural network is a program that creates a computer network designed to function in a similar way to natural neural structures such as a human brain. In more practical terms, neural networks are non-linear statistical data modeling tools. They can be used to model complex relationships between inputs and outputs or to find patterns in data.

For example, a neural network approach was used at the University of Minnesota to try to identify how much of a particular polymer was found in a microscopic digitized photo. The program was trained by hundreds of photos that had many variables describing each pixel in the photo. Over time, the neural net program was able to develop a simple set of decision rules that could be used to correctly classify future pixels most of the time.

Neural networks are used sometimes in data mining applications to try to find relationships between inputs and outputs. For example, neural networks might be helpful in identifying which customers might have high credit risk based on past history with other customers.

Acknowledgments: CEMBA 09 students Chris Knapp, Rob Klingberg, Jennifer Lute, Connie Lindor, Amit Ganguly, and Aaron Forbort contributed to this entry.

See *artificial intelligence*, *data mining*.

never event – See *sentinel event*.

New Product Development (NPD) – The process of generating new product concepts, creating the designs, and bringing new products and services to market; also called product development. ✪

The innovation process is often divided into three fundamental steps:

The fuzzy front-end – The front-end activities that precede the new product development in order to generate, evaluate, and select concepts to be started into the new product development process. Clearly, organizations want to only start ideas into new product development that have high probability of market and financial success.

New product development – The process of translating product specifications into specific designs that can be manufactured and brought to market.

Commercialization – The process of managing a new product through pilot production, production ramp-up, and product launch into the channels of distribution.

One of the key issues for new product development is forming the NPD project team. The following four tables compare the new product development team structure for four types of organizations: Functional, lightweight, heavyweight, and autonomous. A good reference on this subject is Clark and Wheelwright (1992).

Functional

Description	• Members are grouped by discipline.
	• Entire project is decomposed into independent function responsibilities.
Advantages	• Good means of evaluating functional performance.
	• Functional managers bring experience and knowledge.

Disadvantages	• Project tends to move sequentially through functional areas • No one directly involved in the project is responsible for results.
Best when	• Need deep expertise.

Lightweight

Description	• Members still reside in their functional areas and are not dedicated to the team. • The team depends on the technical functions for the resources necessary to get the work accomplished. • Liaison person (middle or junior level manager) to coordinate their project committee.
Advantages	• Greater coordination and better scheduling
Disadvantages	• Speed and coordination advantages are seldom realized.
Best when	• Derivative product

Heavyweight

Description	• Dedicated team leader with large responsibility. • Team members report to the team leader. • Core Group is co-located with their heavy weight project leader, but still has a reporting relationship with functional bosses. • Core team "contract."
Advantages	• Focused task objectives. • Handle cross functional integration very well. • Rapid and efficient development of new products and processes.
Disadvantages	• May raise conflicts with the functional management. • Teams want control over secondary activities as well. • May inhibit development of deep functional excellence. • Possibly requires more testing and quality assurance.
Best when	• System solution required.

Autonomous (sometimes called "tiger teams")

Description	• Similar to heavyweight team. • No functional reporting relationships.
Advantages	• Few conflicts with functional management.
Disadvantages	• Teams want control over secondary activities as well. • May inhibit development of deep functional excellence. • Possibly requires more testing and quality assurance.
Best when	• Radical new concept.

Product Development and Management Association (PDMA) and the Product Development Institute (PDI) are two of the leading professional societies for NPD professionals in North America.

The Japanese approach to NPD appears to be quite different than that used in Western Europe and North America. The book ***The Toyota Product Development System: Integrating People, Process and Technology*** by Morgan and Liker (2006) is a good overview of the Toyota process.

See *absorptive capacity, adoption curve, Analytical Hierarchy Process (AHP), breadboard, clockspeed, commercialization, Computer Aided Design (CAD), concurrent engineering, configuration management, Design for Six Sigma (DFSS), disruptive technology, Early Supplier Involvement (ESI), Fagan Defect-Free Process, flexibility, fuzzy front end, High Performance Work Systems (HPWS), ideation, Integrated Product Development (IPD), Kano Analysis, lean design, line extension, phase review, platform strategy, process design, Product Data Management (PDM), project charter, project management, prototype, Pugh Matrix, Quality Function Deployment (QFD), simultaneous engineering, socio-technical design, stage-gate process, technology road map, time to market, time to volume, Triz, Voice of the Customer (VOC), waterfall scheduling.*

newsvendor model – An important decision problem where the decision maker must decide how much to purchase given the distribution of demand, the cost of under buying per unit, and the cost of over buying per unit. ✪

Overview

The newsvendor problem used to be called the "newsboy" problem. The optimal order quantity is the demand associated with the critical ratio (sometimes called the critical fractile), which is defined as $R = c_u/(c_u + c_o)$. The optimal order quantity is $Q* = F^{-1}(R)$ where $F^{-1}(R)$ is the inverse of the cumulative distribution function. In the simplest retail environment, c_u is the sales price minus the unit cost (the gross margin) and c_o is the unit cost minus the salvage value. Solving the problem for a discrete distribution requires a simple search procedure.

Example

For example, a grocery store owner needs to buy newspapers every Monday. If the owner buys one newspaper more than the demand, the store loses the cost of the newspaper (e.g., c_o = unit cost = \$0.10). If the owner buys one newspaper less than the demand, the store loses the margin on the newspaper (e.g., c_u = unit price – unit cost = \$0.50 – \$0.10 = \$0.40). The critical ratio, therefore, is $R = c_u/(c_u + c_o)$ = 0.4/(0.4 + 0.1) = 90%, and the optimal order quantity is at the 90-th percentile of the demand distribution.

Newsvendor model with discrete demand

A discrete random variable only takes on integer (whole number) values. If we assume that demand is discrete, the distribution is defined by a probability mass function $p(D)$. With order quantity Q and a realization of demand D, the cost is:

$$C(D,Q) = \begin{cases} c_o(Q-D) & \text{if } D < Q \\ c_u(D-Q) & \text{if } D \geq Q \end{cases}$$

The equation for the expected (average) Total Incremental Cost, therefore, is given by:

$$TIC(Q) = \sum_{D=0}^{\infty} p(D)C(D,Q) = \sum_{D=0}^{Q} c_o p(D)(Q-D) + \sum_{D=Q}^{\infty} c_u p(D)(D-Q)$$

The first summation is the expected overage (scrap) cost and the second term is the expected underage (shortage) cost. The optimal order quantity $Q*$ can be found at the point where the total incremental cost is about the same for ordering Q and $Q+1$ units, which is when $TIC(Q) \approx TIC(Q+1)$. The optimal order quantity can be found algebraically to be the $Q*$ that is the smallest value of Q where the following relationship holds true:

$$P(D \leq Q*) = \sum_{D=0}^{Q*} p(D) \geq c_u/(c_u + c_o)$$

The value $R = c_u/(c_u + c_o)$ is called the "critical ratio" or "critical fractile" and is always between zero and one. The optimal Q can be found with a simple search procedure starting at $Q=0$ and increasing Q until the above relationship is satisfied. When $c_u = c_o$, the critical ratio is 0.5, which is consistent with intuition that suggests the optimal Q should be at the median of the demand distribution when the two costs are equal.

For example, a buyer for a manufacturer is faced with a decision of how much to make of the last manufacturing run of a service part. The firm currently has zero in stock and the forecast for the lifetime demand for the part is $\lambda = 4$ units. The demand over the lifetime of the product is assumed to be a Poisson distributed random variable (a reasonable assumption). The forecast is the mean of the distribution. The overage cost (c_o) and underage cost (c_u) are estimated to be $100 and $1000 per unit, respectively. The c_u parameter is large because a stockout is very frustrating to customers and because the part will be very difficult to manufacture in the future. The critical ratio is $c_u /(c_u +c_o) = 1000/1100 = 0.91$. Table 1 shows the Poisson probabilities and cumulative Poisson probabilities. The best value of Q can be found by finding the smallest value of Q that satisfies the equation above. The optimal value is $Q* = 7$.

Poisson probabilities with mean $\lambda = 4$.

$$P(D \le Q) = \sum_{D=0}^{D=Q} p(D)$$

Q	$p(Q)$	
0	0.018	0.018
1	0.073	0.092
2	0.147	0.238
3	0.195	0.433
4	0.195	0.629
5	0.156	0.785
6	0.104	0.889
7	0.060	0.949	$\leftarrow Q* = 7;\ P(D \le Q*) \ge c_u /(c_u +c_o) = 0.91$
8	0.030	0.979
9	0.013	0.992
10	0.005	0.997

Note that $p(Q) = P(D = Q)$, the probability that the demand will be equal to Q.

This procedure for Poisson distributed demand can be implemented in Excel fairly easily. The cumulative Poisson distribution can be implemented in Excel with the function POISSON(x, *mean*, TRUE).

The newsvendor model with continuous demand

As with the discrete demand case, the cost associated with demand realization D and order quantity Q is given by:

$$C(D,Q) = \begin{cases} c_o(Q-D) & \text{if } D < Q \\ c_u(D-Q) & \text{if } D \ge Q \end{cases}$$

Assuming that the demand (D) is a continuous random variable with density function $f(D)$ and cumulative distribution function $F(D)$. The total incremental cost function is given by:

$$TIC(Q) = \int_{D=0}^{\infty} C(D,Q)f(D)dD$$

$$= c_o \int_{D=0}^{Q} (Q-D)f(D)dD + c_u \int_{D=Q}^{\infty} (D-Q)f(D)dD$$

To find the optimal Q, take the derivative of the total incremental cost function and set it to zero to find:

$$\frac{dTIC(Q)}{dQ} = c_o F(Q) - c_u(1 - F(Q)) = 0$$

$$\Rightarrow F(Q^*) = c_u / (c_u + c_o)$$

$$\therefore Q^* = F^{-1}[c_u / (c_u + c_o)]$$

Testing the second derivative proves that Q^* is a global optimum. Note that the critical ratio is the same for the discrete and continuous demand cases.

In order to find Q^*, the optimal value of Q, we need to find the Q associated with the cumulative probability $F(Q^*) = c_u / (c_u + c_o)$. Mathematicians write this as $Q^* = F^{-1}[c_u / (c_u + c_o)]$, where F^{-1} is the inverse of the cumulative distribution function. Microsoft Excel includes the inverses for many distributions, including the Normal, Log Normal, and Gamma distributions.

For the normal distribution, the Excel function for the optimal Q^* is given by NORMINV(critical ratio, mean, standard deviation). For example, if we have a newsvendor problem with normally distributed demand with a mean of 4 units, a standard deviation of 1 unit, and with costs $c_o = \$100$ and $c_u = \$1000$, the critical ratio is $R = 0.91$ and the optimal order quantity is $Q^* = $ NORMINV(0.91, 4, 1) = 5.34 units.

When little or no historical demand information is available

When little or no historical demand information is available and/or the demand distribution is not symmetrical, the triangular distribution is a practical approach for modeling the demand distribution. An experienced person (or team) estimates three parameters – minimum demand (D_{min}), modal demand (D_{ml}), and maximum demand (D_{max}). It is a good idea to ask for D_{min} and D_{max} first so that people do not "anchor" on the mode. Excel does not include the triangular distribution or its inverse, but it can be implemented fairly easily in Excel. The entry for the triangular distribution provides equations for both the cumulative and inverse functions.

Estimating the critical ratio when the cost parameters are not known

When the parameters cost-over (c_u) and cost-under (c_o) are not known, the critical ratio can still be estimated from the an estimate of the ratio of the cost parameters $r = c_u / c_o$. It is easy to show algebraically that the critical ratio is given by $R = r / (r + 1)$.

Behavioral issues with the newsvendor problem

Decision-makers (buyers, analysts, managers) facing the newsvendor problem often make bad decisions. The main issue is that the reward systems are not aligned with the economics. In other words, the decision-makers are told to optimize the economics, but are then also told to reduce lost sales or reduce excess inventory. These mixed messages lead the decision-makers to respond to the voice that is "yelling" the loudest and to ignore the economics.

A project at a large music retailer found that the real cost of excess inventory for new releases was quite low due to the fact that the firm could return CDs to the manufacturer for a modest restocking fee (about 15% of the cost). The cost of a stockout was quite high due to high margins (about $10 per CD). Clearly, the buyers should have been aggressively over-buying on a consistent basis. However, excess inventory was easy to measure and lost sales were hard to measure, which led buyers to give more weight to excess inventory and less weight to lost sales in their buying decisions. In other words, it appeared that buyers were being driven by the reward system to under-buy even though the economics should have led them to over-buy. The difference between their decisions and the economics appeared to be an opportunity for profit improvement.

Two recent research papers have addressed the behavioral issues with the newsvendor problem (Schweitzer & Cachon, 2000; Bolton & Katok, 2004). Both of these studies used human experiments that did not consider the reward system issues mentioned above. These authors concluded that subjects would consistently under-buy for high-profit products and over-buy for low-profit products. This pattern could not be explained by risk aversion, risk-seeking preferences, loss avoidance, waste aversion, or understanding opportunity costs. One explanation offered was "anchoring and insufficient adjustment." This explanation is "the subjects anchor around average demand in the early periods of the game and insufficiently adjust in subsequent periods towards the expected profit-maximizing order quantity. In essence, they fail to learn."

Conclusions on the newsvendor model

The newsvendor logic is fundamental to solving many operations problems such as seasonal purchasing problems. The intuition obtained from the newsvendor can also be helpful. Explicitly defining the over-buying cost, under-buying cost, calculating the critical ratio can often lead managers and analysts to much better decisions. The model can help people make decisions based on economic reasoning rather than on politics, power, or personalities.

If managers are willing and able to make some assumptions about the form and the parameters of the demand distribution, they can imbed the newsvendor economic model in their planning and control systems to make better decisions. This is particularly true for "style" goods buying systems and inventory systems, where decisions have to be made routinely and where these decisions have significant financial impact on the firm.

The newsvendor economic logic appears in many different business contexts, such as buying for a one-time selling season, making a final production run, setting safety stocks, setting target inventory levels, and making capacity decisions. All of these contexts have the same problem structure: a single policy parameter, such as the order quantity, in the presence of random demand, and known unit overage and unit underage costs.

The papers "The Newsvendor Problem" and "Seasonal Buying" and the Excel workbook "newsvendor.xls" are on the **OMWW CD** available from www.ClamshellBeachPress.com. ◉

See *Anchoring, capacity, Poisson distribution, safety stock, slow moving demand, stockout, triangular distribution.*

NGT – See *Nominal Group Technique (NGT)*.

no fault receiving – A way of inventory accounting used in retailing where store employees are only required to "count boxes" and put the items away.

Employees are not required to account for the item count in each box. This form of receiving is usually used in conjunction with an annual, formal, inventory count.

Nominal Group Technique (NGT) – A planning tool that helps a group organize and prioritize issues and gain consensus in the process. ✪

Originally developed as an organizational planning technique by Delbecq, Van de Ven, and Gustafson in 1971, the nominal group technique can be used as an alternative to both the focus group and the Delphi techniques. It presents more structure than the focus group, but still takes advantage of the synergy created by group participants. One nice outcome of the NGT is that it helps to build consensus (agreement) on the issues in the process.

Here is one approach for facilitating NGT brainstorming sessions:

1. **Prepare** (Organization) – Define the main question, find a skilled facilitator, select a group of experts, instruct the experts to come prepared to address the main question, arrange for a room with some empty walls, acquire marking pens (to make it hard for people to write too small), and acquire a number of 3M Post-it™ notes (at least 10 per expert). The lined 4x6 Super-Sticky Post-it™ notes with various colors work great.

2. **Kickoff** (Facilitator) – Spend a few minutes to clearly define the main question (e.g., How can we reduce waiting times for our customers?) and the scope for the discussion (e.g., Our scope will not include MIS issues.). Ask the experts if they have any questions about the main question, scope, or process before beginning.

3. **Generate** (Experts) – Spend about 10 minutes to think quietly and creatively about the main question and generate a number of ideas to address the question.

> **MONDAY STAFF**
>
> *We don't have enough workers for the Monday morning rush. Last Monday was the worst ever!*

Write each idea on a separate note. Write a one-word to three-word title in large capital letters on the top half of the note, followed by a longer description in smaller letters on the bottom half. See the example to the right. Notes MUST be readable from the other side of the room.

4. **Share** (Experts) – Each time we go around the room, you will be asked to share just one note at a time. The facilitator will add your note to the wall, putting it in a logical group. Discussion is not allowed during this time, except to ask short clarification questions. Do not repeat a note already on the wall unless your note adds a new thought. Feel free to pass (and also to jump back in) to add a new note. We will continue to go around the room until everyone has shared all their notes.

5. **Group and discuss** (Facilitator) – We will select one expert to come to the wall to rearrange the notes into related groups and another to write a short name on a note in large font for each group. This can be done during a break. If we have time, we will also discuss the ideas further.

6. **Vote** (Experts) – Each expert then votes for exactly two groups that they believe are the most important. We will add the votes to prioritize the groups.

7. **Delegate** (Experts) – In most situations, it is important to decide who has the ownership for a particular issue and to clearly define the next steps for that person. In some cases, it is also a good idea to begin to create a charter for a project to address the issue.

Advantages of the NGT process over typical brainstorming include:

- Shows respect for all participants and their ideas.
- Does not allow "high-verbal" or "high-control" participants to dominate the discussion
- Collects many ideas from the experts.
- Quickly and efficiently groups and prioritizes the ideas
- Efficiently creates a set of notes to document all of the ideas in the meeting
- Results in great ideas.
- Creates a sense of ownership of the results.

As the name suggests, the nominal group technique is only "nominally" a group, since the rankings are provided on an individual basis.

Research on the Nominal Group Technique is extensive and shows that in numerous circumstances the process produces better results than unstructured group interactions (Campbell, 1966; Dunnett, Campbell, and Jaastad, 1963; Vroom, Grant, and Cotton, 1969; Gustafson, Shukla, Delbecq, and Walster, 1973; Van de Ven, 1974; Stumpf, 1978). Data suggest the following three principles for why nominal group process is successful: (1) Ideas should not be evaluated one at a time. Rather the facilitator should collect many ideas before any one of them are evaluated. Postponing evaluation increases creative solutions. (2) In estimating numbers, thinking again improves the accuracy of the numbers. A sort of bootstrapping occurs, where the group members best themselves by listening to other group members and revising their own opinions. (3) Individual generation of ideas leads to more ideas and more creative ones than generating ideas while listening to other group members. (Source: gunston.doit.gmu.edu/healthscience/708/frteam. asp, February 21, 2004.)

While the Nominal Group Technique is widely used, it is not intended for all situations. It is not intended for tasks that require ordering or judging the worth of several alternatives. In these circumstances, this technique may produce judgments that are inferior to the judgment of the most knowledgeable group member (Holloman and Hendrick, 1972; Nemiroff, Pasmore, and Ford, 1976). But by far, the most serious problem with the process is that participants feel awkward about restrictions in their interactions. Therefore, they may not be committed to the group's consensus. Data show that nominal group process is the wrong process when acceptance of the group's conclusions rather than originality is important. Acceptance is crucial as to whether the model is put to use. In these situations, less structured processes produce more widely accepted group decisions than Nominal Group Technique (Stumpf, 1978, Maier and Hoffman, 1964, Miner, 1976). The above paragraph was adapted from gunston.doit.gmu.edu/healthscience/708/frteam.asp, February 21, 2004.

A short paper "Structured Brainstorming with the Nominal Group Technique" is on the *OMWW CD* available from www.ClamshellBeachPress.com. ◉

See *affinity diagram, brainstorming, causal map, ideation, impact wheel, Kepner-Tregoe Model, Root Cause Analysis (RCA)*.

non-instantaneous replenishment – See *instantaneous replenishment*.

normal distribution – A continuous probability distribution commonly used to model forecast errors, regression model errors, and for the sum of a large number of independent random variables.

  Density function: The normal distribution density function has a bell-shape and is written mathematically as $f(x) = \dfrac{1}{\sqrt{2\pi}\sigma} e^{-(x-\mu)^2/(2\sigma^2)}$ where μ is the mean and σ is the standard deviation.

  Distribution function: The distribution function has no closed form, but is tabulated in many books.

  Statistics: Range $(-\infty, \infty)$, mean=mode=median (μ), variance (σ^2). The inflection point for the density function is one sigma away from the mean. The standard normal distribution has mean $\mu = 0$ and standard deviation $\sigma = 1$.

  Excel: In Excel, the standard normal distribution function evaluated at z is NORMSDIST(z). This is the probability that a standard normal random variable will be less than or equal to z. The normal density and distribution functions in Excel are NORMDIST(x, μ, σ, FALSE) and NORMDIST(x, μ, σ, TRUE). NORMINV(p, μ, σ) is the inverse distribution function, which returns the value of x that has cumulative probability p.

  Excel simulation: In an Excel simulation, normally distributed random variates can be generated by the inverse transform method with x = NORMINV(RAND(), μ, σ). The Box-Muller method is a special-purpose approach for generating independent normal random deviates from a stream of random numbers and is far more computationally efficient than the inverse transform method. The VBA code for the Box-Muller method follows:

```
Function normal_rv_bm(mu, sigma)
Const twopi As Double = 6.28318530717959
Dim ncall As Integer, u1 As Double, u2 As Double, z As Double, z2 As Double
  ncall = ncall + 1
  If ncall Mod 2 <> 0 Then
    u1 = Rnd()
    u2 = Rnd()
    z = Sqr(-2 * Log(u1)) * Cos(twopi * u2)
    z2 = Sqr(-2 * Log(u1)) * Sin(twopi * u2)
  Else
    z = z2
  End If
  normal_rv_bm = z * sigma + mu
End Function
```

  Graph: The graph on the right is the normal density function with $\mu = 10$ and $\sigma = 2$.

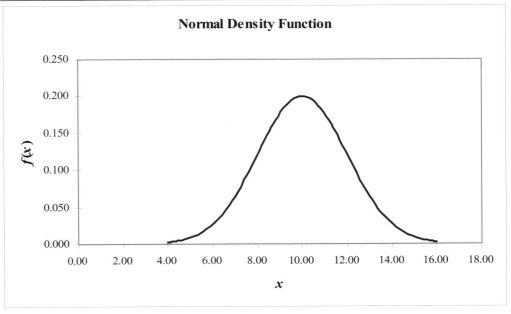

Normal Density Function

Approximation code for $F(z)$: The following VBA code is an accurate approximation for the standard normal distribution function adapted from the Press, Flannery, Teukolsky, and Vetterling (2002) book *Numerical Recipes in FORTRAN*.

```
Function normsdistF(z)
'    standard normal distribution function - approximation.
Const c2 As Double = 0.3989423, p As Double = 0.2316419
Const b1 = 0.31938153, b2 = -0.356563782, b3 = 1.781477937
Const b4 = -1.821255978, b5 = 1.330274429
Dim t As Double, b0 As Double
    t = 1 / (1 + p * Abs(z))
    b0 = c2 * Exp((-z) * (z / 2))
    normsdistF = 1 - b0 * (((( b5 * t + b4) * t + b3) * t + b2) * t + b1) * t
    If z < 0 Then normsdistF = 1 - normsdistF
End Function
```

Approximation for the inverse distribution function $F^{-1}(z)$: The following is an approximation for the inverse of the standard normal distribution function: $x = F^{-1}(p) \approx 5.06329114(p^{0.135} - (1-p)^{0.135})$ or in Excel =5.06329114*(p ^0.135-(1-p)^0.135). This approximation was tested in the range $p = (0.504, 0.99997)$ and found to have a maximum absolute percent error of 4.68% at $p = 0.99997$. In the range $p = (0.504, 0.9987)$ the maximum absolute percent error was 0.67% at $p = 0.10$.

The Excel workbook "Distributions.xls" is on the *OMWW CD* available from www.ClamshellBeachPress.com. ◉

See *central limit theorem, confidence interval, inverse transform method, lognormal distribution, sampling*.

normal time – An industrial engineering term for the time to complete a task as observed from a time study, adjusted for performance ratings. ✪

The steps in estimating the normal time are as follows:

1. The average time from a time study (t_i) is collected for N operators. The time study also collects a subjectively determined performance rating (r_i) for each operator. This is scaled so that $r=100$ for a person working at a normal rate and $r=110$ for someone working 10% faster than normal.

2. Each operator's average time is adjusted by the performance rating. The average of these times is called the normal time for the operation, $NT = \sum_{i=1}^{N} r_i t_i / N$.

3. The normal time is adjusted for percent allowances (A) to compute the standard time, $ST = NT(1 + A)$. The percent allowances (A) is for bathroom breaks, rest time, etc. and is usually on the order of 15%. The standard labor cost is the standard time (ST) times the standard cost per hour.

See *performance rating, standard time, time study, work measurement, work sampling*.

NPD – See *New Product Development*.

numerically controlled (NC) machine – See *Computer Numerically Controlled (CNC) machine*.

numeric-analytic location model – An iterative method that guarantees the optimal solution to the single facility infinite set location problem.

The problem

A firm needs to locate a single warehouse to serve n customers. Each customer (j) has coordinates (x_j, y_j), demand (weight) w_j, and a transportation cost of c_j per unit per mile. The single warehouse facility is to be located at the coordinates (x_0, y_0). The travel distance from the warehouse to customer j is assumed to be Pythagorean (straight-line) distance defined by $d_j = \sqrt{(x_0 - x_j)^2 + (y_0 - y_j)^2}$. The problem is to find the (x_0, y_0) coordinates for the warehouse that minimize the total incremental cost (*TIC*) defined by:

$$TIC = \sum_j^n c_j w_j d_j = \sum_j^n c_j w_j \sqrt{(x_0 - x_j)^2 + (y_0 - y_j)^2}$$

The solution method

The center-of-gravity solution for this problem is $x_0 = \sum_{j=1}^n c_j w_j x_j$ and $y_0 = \sum_{j=1}^n c_j w_j y_j$. This is sometimes called the "center of mass" or the "centroid." While the center-of-gravity method is quite simple, it is not necessarily optimal and is sometimes far from optimal.

The optimal location for the warehouse can be found by taking the first derivative of the total incremental cost function and setting it equal to zero:

$$\partial TIC / \partial x_0 = \sum_j^n c_j w_j (\tfrac{1}{2})[(x_0 - x_j)^2 + (y_0 - y_j)^2]^{-\frac{1}{2}} 2(x_0 - x_j)$$

$$= \sum_j^n c_j w_j [(x_0 - x_j)^2 + (y_0 - y_j)^2]^{-\frac{1}{2}} (x_0 - x_j)$$

Setting this derivative to zero, the optimal x-coordinate for the facility is:

$$x_0 = \frac{\sum_j^n c_j w_j \sqrt{(x_0 - x_j)^2 + (y_0 - y_j)^2} \, x_j}{\sum_j^n c_j w_j \sqrt{(x_0 - x_j)^2 + (y_0 - y_j)^2}}$$

However, this equation cannot be solved because x_0 is on both sides of the inequality. Similar analysis finds that the same is true for y_0. To solve this problem, an iterative approach can be used to find better x-y coordinates with each iteration. Recognize that the term $\sqrt{(x_0 - x_j)^2 + (y_0 - y_j)^2}$ is the current distance from the warehouse to location j. Assume that this does not change very much with each iteration and use the following equations iteratively to find better facility coordinates (x_0, y_0):

$$x_0(new) = \frac{\sum_j^n c_j w_j x_j / d_j(old)}{\sum_j^n c_j w_j / d_j(old)} \quad \text{and} \quad y_0(new) = \frac{\sum_j^n c_j w_j y_j / d_j(old)}{\sum_j^n c_j w_j / d_j(old)}$$

For each iteration, the procedure assumes that d_j is fixed. In other words, the procedure finds the new x-y coordinates based on the old distances. The procedure updates the distances with each step. The center-of-gravity method is a good starting point for the procedure.

Step 1. Start with an initial location. This could be the center-of-gravity solution or a random location. Update the distances (d_j) for each customer.

Step 2. Find new coordinates for the facility with equations above and update the distances (d_j) for each customer using the equations above.

Step 3. Continue iterating with Step 2 until no more improvement can be found.

The paper "Location Theory" and the Excel workbook "AL.xls" are on the **OMWW CD** available from www.ClamshellBeachPress.com. This "Allocation-Location" Excel model extends the above concepts to handle latitude/longitude data. ◉

See *center-of-gravity model for facility location, facility location, gravity model for competitive retail store location, great circle distance.*

O

obsolescence – Stock that can no longer be sold because of lack of market demand, old product technology, spoilage, etc.

Most firms try to remove obsolete inventory from storage in order to free up space and to take a tax write-off earlier rather than later.

See *all-time demand*, *carrying charge*, *shrinkage*, *termination date*.

OC curve – See *operating characteristic curve*.

Ockham's Razor – A rule in science and philosophy stating that entities should not be multiplied needlessly; also called the law of parsimony.

This rule is interpreted to mean that the simplest of two or more competing theories is preferable and that an explanation for unknown phenomena should first be attempted in terms of what is already known.

See *parsimony*.

OEE – See *Overall Equipment Effectiveness*.

OEM (Original Equipment Manufacturer) – See *original equipment manufacturer*.

off-line setup – See *setup reduction*.

offshoring – Developing a source of supply in another country with either vertically integrated suppliers or external suppliers.

Offshoring refers to the location of the source of supply whereas outsourcing refers to the use of another party regardless of their location. The primary issues that managers should consider when they relocate services offshore are (1) expertise in managing remote locations, (2) quality of the workforce, (3) cost of labor, (4) language skills, (5) telecom bandwidth, (6) cost and reliability, (7) infrastructure, (8) political stability, (9) enforceability of intellectual property rights and business contracts, and (10) general maturity of the business environment.

See ebstrategy.com/Outsourcing/default.htm for more information.

See *outsourcing*, *supply chain management*.

one-piece flow – A lean manufacturing practice of making only one part at a time (a batch size of one) before moving the part to the next step in the process; also called single piece flow, make-one-move-one, and one-for-one replenishment.

This is the lean ideal, but it is not always achievable. Single Minute Exchange of Dies and other setup reduction methods are critical to helping organizations reduce setup cost (and ordering cost) and move toward this ideal.

See *batch-and-queue*, *continuous flow*, *lean thinking*, *setup reduction methods*, *Single Minute Exchange of Dies (SMED)*, *zero inventory*.

on-the-job-training (OJT) – An approach for training employees by involving them in the work.

Workers develop skills simply by working, ideally under the watchful eye of a supervisor and/or mentor.

on-time delivery – See *service level*.

open-book management – Sharing key financial information openly with employees and other stakeholders.

Some firms go so far as to share their financial information with their customers and/or suppliers. This concept is no longer talked about very much and seems to be rarely practiced.

operating characteristic curve – A graphical approach for understanding the parameters of a lot acceptance sampling plan.

The operating characteristic curve (OC) plots the probability of accepting a lot on the y-axis and the lot fraction or percent defectives on the x-axis.

See *acceptance sampling*, *consumer's risk*, *producer's risk*, *Statistical Process Control (SPC)*.

Operations Management (OM) – Management of the transformation process that converts labor, capital, materials, information, and other inputs into products and services for customers. ✪

Operations management is one of the core subjects taught in all business schools, along with accounting, finance, marketing, human resources, management information systems, and general management/strategy. The reader is referred to the preface of this encyclopedia for a framework for operations management.

The operations management framework below was developed through an extensive survey of operations management professors and practitioners (Hays, Bouzdine-Chameeva, Meyer Goldstein, Hill, & Scavarda 2007). An organization's operations strategy is derived from its business strategy and should guide and inform decisions in the four "pillars" of operations management: product & process design, capacity & demand management, supply chain management, and process improvement. These four pillars are supported by quality and people management, systems management, analytical tools, and performance metrics.

The reader is encouraged to study the entries in this book for each of the terms in the above framework. The operations management profession is supported by many academic and professional societies including:

Name	Web address
American Society for Quality (ASQ)	www.asq.org
APICS - The Association for Operations Management (APICS)	www.apics.org
Association for Manufacturing Excellence (AME)	www.ame.org
Council of Supply Chain Management Professionals (CSCMP)	www.cscmp.org
Decision Sciences Institute (DSI)	www.decisionsciences.org
European Operations Management Society (EurOMA)	www.euroma-online.org
Institute for Operations Research and the Management Sciences (INFORMS)	www.informs.org
Institute for Supply Management (ISM)	www.ism.ws
Institute of Industrial Engineers (IIE)	www.iienet2.org
International Federation of Operational Research Societies (IFORS)	www.ifors.org
Manufacturing and Service Operations Management Society (MSOM)	http://msom.society.informs.org
Production and Operations Management Society (POMS)	www.poms.org
Project Management Institute (PMI)	www.pmi.org
Society of Manufacturing Engineers (SME)	www.sme.org
Supply Chain Council – SCOR	www.supply-chain.org

The reader can find a short description for each of these societies in this encyclopedia. This list omits many other important professional societies in related disciplines and outside of North America.

See *American Society for Quality (ASQ), APICS (The Association for Operations Management), Association for Manufacturing Excellence (AME), Council of Supply Chain Management Professionals (CSCMP), Decision Sciences Institute (DSI), European Operations Management Association (EurOMA), Institute for Operations Research and the Management Sciences (INFORMS), Institute for Supply Management (ISM), Institute of Industrial Engineers (IIE), Operations Research (OR), Production Operations Management Society (POMS), Project Management Institute (PMI), Society of Manufacturing Engineers (SME), Supply Chain Council.*

operations performance metrics – Variables that are used for setting targets and evaluating the operations function. ✪

As noted in the entry on the balanced scorecard, it is important that the performance metrics be balanced. One way to "balance" metrics is to make sure that the organization uses both financial performance metrics and operations performance metrics. Operations performance metrics are often the key means for achieving the financial performance metrics.

With respect to operations performance metrics, many firms make it a practice of having at least one metric from each of these three categories: Better (a quality related metric), Faster (a time related metric), and Cheaper (a cost related metric). Many operations thought leaders argue that the "cheaper" metrics are often the result of improving the "better" and "faster" metrics. This author has added a four category of metrics called "stronger," which focuses on risk management and mitigation.

See *balanced scorecard, benchmarking, Capability Maturity Model (CMM), cycle time, dashboard, Data Envelopment Analysis (DEA), Failure Mode and Effects Analysis (FMEA), fill rate, financial performance metrics, forecast error metrics, half-life curve, Inventory Dollar Days (IDD), inventory turnover, Key Performance Indicator (KPI), learning curve, learning organization, Overall Equipment Effectiveness (OEE), process capability and performance, productivity, queuing theory, service level, sigma level, strategy map, supplier scorecard, Throughput Dollar Days (TDD), utilization, wait time, work measurement, yield, Y-tree.*

Operations Research (OR) – The science that applies primarily mathematical and computer science tools to support decision making. ✪

Operations Research (OR) draws on many mathematical disciplines such as optimization, statistics, stochastic processes (queuing theory), decision theory, simulation, graph theory (network optimization), and game theory. Optimization can be further broken down into constrained and unconstrained optimization, each of which can be broken down further into linear, non-linear, and discrete optimization. Simulation appears to be a field of growing importance with a number of powerful software tools such as Arena that are available for creating complex stochastic models of real-world systems.

Historically, OR professionals have argued that OR projects should be multi-disciplinary. While this is true, in reality, most OR people are trained as mathematicians, computer scientists, or industrial engineers. Operations research is synonymous with management science. The largest professional organization for operations research is INFORMS (www.informs.org).

Additional information can be found at http://en.wikipedia.org/wiki/Operations_research.

See *decision tree, Institute for Operations Research and the Management Sciences (INFORMS), knapsack problem, Linear Programming (LP), Mixed Integer Programming (MIP), Operations Management (OM), simulated annealing, simulation.*

operations strategy – A set of policies for using the firm's resources to support the business unit's strategy for gaining competitive advantage. ✪

Operations strategy is usually defined in terms of the operations objectives of cost, quality, flexibility, and service. Other variants of this list also include delivery (instead of service), time or speed (as a part of service or flexibility), and customization (as a type of flexibility). Some lists also include safety, sustainability, environmental issues, and development of human capital. This author is currently using the operations objectives better, faster, cheaper, and stronger, where stronger means more robust (error resistant and resilient) and better aligned with strategy.

Firms can often gain competitive strategic advantage by avoiding tradeoffs between these operations objectives. For example, Dell Computer was able to "change the rules of game" and gain significant competitive advantage by being the first to successfully offer low cost assemble-to-order customized computers through direct mail (e.g., providing customization and quality without cost). Similarly, FedEx was one of the first to offer reliable overnight package delivery at a reasonable price (e.g., providing reliable and fast delivery at a reasonable price).

The operations strategy may be explicit or it may be implicit. An implicit strategy is not written down and the senior executive team may not be able to articulate the strategy; however, the implicit operations strategy usually becomes apparent with an objective evaluation of the management's consistent approach to decision making and the firm's position in the market.

Researchers in the operations management field often make a distinction between the operations strategy process and content. The process is the methodology that the organization uses to create its operations strategy, whereas the content is the substance of the strategy.

The entries entitled *balanced scorecard* and *strategy map* discuss process issues in more detail. The strategy map entry presents the time-based competition strategy. The entry on *mass customization* presents customization as a potential component of an operations strategy. Outsourcing to achieve lower cost can also be considered to be a component of an operations strategy.

See *agile manufacturing, balanced scorecard, blue ocean strategy, core competence, first mover advantage, focused factory, mass customization, order qualifier, outsourcing, plant-within-a-plant, resource based view, strategy map, supply chain management, time-based competition, vertical integration, virtual organization.*

opportunity cost – The value of an alternative that was not taken; the value of an opportunity that was foregone because of a decision that was made. ✪

When someone has a choice between two or more alternatives, they will generally choose the best alternative. However, choosing the best alternative means that they cannot choose the next best alternative. The opportunity cost is the value of the next best alternative that must be sacrificed. Opportunity cost, therefore, can be thought of as the value of "the road not taken."

For example, a firm can only make one product in a factory and decides to build product A instead of product B. It makes a profit on product A, but gave up the profit on product B. The profit on product B is said to be the opportunity cost.

For a manufacturing example, consider a factory that has one large machine that constrains the plant's production rate (e.g., the bottleneck). The firm makes $1000 per hour in gross revenue every hour the machine is running. The firm currently has a setup time on this machine of one hour per day, which means that the firm could make $1000 more per day if the setup could be eliminated. The standard costing system assigns direct labor and overhead to this machine at a rate of $200 per hour. However, the true cost of the setup is much more than $200 per hour because of the opportunity cost (i.e., the lost gross margin).

See *carrying cost, setup cost, stockout, Theory of Constraints (TOC).*

order backlog – See *backlog.*

order cost – See *setup cost.*

order cycle service level – See *safety stock.*

order penetration point – See *push-pull boundary.*

order fill rate – See *fill rate.*

order picking – See *picking.*

order point system – See *reorder point.*

order qualifier – A basic screening criterion that permits a firm's products to be considered as possible candidates for purchase.

An order qualifier keeps an organization's products and services in the running whereas an order winner closes the sale. An order qualifier is a criterion that customers use to screen products to be evaluated further.

In contrast, an order winner makes a critical difference in the buyer's decision process. In other words, the order qualifier gets the "salesperson in the door" (to be considered by the potential buyer) and the order winner gets the "salesperson out the door with the order in hand" (seals the deal and beats out the competition). An order qualifier could also be called an order loser.

The terms "order winners" and "order qualifiers" were apparently coined by Professor Terry Hill of the London Business School.

See *operations strategy.*

order size – See *lotsize.*

order winner – See *order qualifier.*

order-to-cash – The time between the receipt of the order from the customer and the receipt of the payment from the customer.

See *cycle time, Respond to Order (RTO).*

order-up-to system – See *periodic review system.*

Original Equipment Manufacturer (OEM) – A manufacturer that sells products made by other companies under its own brand.

The OEM usually offers its own warranty, support, and licensing of the product. The term is confusing because the OEM is not the manufacturer, but rather the re-seller of the equipment to the end user. However, the

OEM is often the customizer and designer of the equipment. More fitting terms are original equipment customizer, original equipment designer, or original concept designer.

In some cases, the OEM does not add value to the equipment, but merely brands it with its own logo. The OEM's name is either placed on the devices by the manufacturer that makes the equipment or by the OEM itself. In other cases, the OEM does add value. For example, an OEM might purchase a computer from a company and combine it with its own hardware and/or software and sell it as a turnkey system (see *Value Added Reseller*).

Some firms specialize in OEM manufacturing but never sell anything under their own brand (see *contract manufacturer*). Many companies both manufacture and sell retail, but also have a separate OEM division for goods that are private labeled.

OEM is pronounced "O.E.M." with each letter being pronounced.

Based loosely on www.pcmag.com/encyclopedia_term/0,2542,t=OEM&i=48291,00.asp, October 25, 2006.

See *contract manufacturer*, *Value Added Reseller (VAR)*.

outsourcing – Buying products and services from a supplier that is not owned by a firm. ✪

Outsourcing versus offshoring

Many popular articles imply that "outsourcing" is buying products and/or services from Asia or from some other part of the world. However, the correct definition of outsourcing is buying product and/or services from any outside firm. Sourcing products and services from a wholly-owned subsidiary on another continent should be called "offshoring" rather than outsourcing; buying products and/or services from another firm on another continent should be called offshore outsourcing.

Examples

A good example of traditional outsourcing is Boston Scientific's clean room gowns. Boston Scientific's core competence is designing, manufacturing, marketing, and selling implantable medical devices – not managing gowns. However, their gown supplier has a clear focus on clean room gowns and is "world class" at this business. Therefore, Boston Scientific outsources its gown management to this firm. An example of outsourcing services is Best Buy, which outsourced nearly all of its Information Technology and human resources functions to other firms.

Outsourcing and core competence

Nearly every consultant, book, and instructor will declare that firms should not outsource their core competence. However, this statement is not always helpful. Many firms find that their definition of their core competence changes over time.

Some penetrating questions that managers should ask with respect to outsourcing include:

- **If this process is a core competency, why are we making it only for ourselves?** If a firm has a truly world-class process, then why not leverage that expertise (and overhead)? The answer to this question is often, "Well, the process is really not that good," which suggests the process is not a true core competence after all.
- **If the process is not a core competency, why not buy it from someone who has this core competency?** Many firms have carefully considered answers to this question, but many others have not.
- **Are we ready to become dependent on others for this process?** When outsourcing manufacturing, management is, in effect, deciding that the process is not a core competency and is creating dependency on other firms. When a firm outsources, it will no longer have those 20-year veterans who know everything there is to know about esoteric materials, equipment, and testing. The firm gives up the equipment, tools, and expertise. Over time, the firm may even erode its ability to talk intelligently to its suppliers and customers. This is not a problem as long as the process is clearly not a core competency and as long as the firm has willing suppliers who do have this cutting edge core competency.

- **Do we understand the switching costs?** Switching is often difficult and costly and involves many systems – machines, tooling, people, expertise, information systems, coordination, transportation, production planning, costing, etc. Of course, switching back may be just as costly if management changes its mind.

Advantages and disadvantages of outsourcing

Many firms find that they can improve both cost and quality if they can find an outside supplier that has a core competence in a particular area. Historically, many firms have outsourced the manufacturing of components. More recently, we have seen firms outsourcing final assembly, new product development, and many services such as IT and human resources.

Given that outsourcing often increases inventories, outsourcing can go against lean principles. For example, if a firm outsources a component to China and dramatically increases leadtimes, inventory and the associated carrying cost will also increase dramatically. An example of successful lean outsource implementation is Dell where they outsourced nearly all their component manufacturing and yet carry nearly zero component inventory. If managed properly, outsourcing, in combination with smart supplier agreements and Vendor Managed Inventories, can sometimes result in a significant decrease in inventories and provide excellent synergies with lean manufacturing.

Many firms fail to understand that overhead costs do not go away (at least not in the short term) with an outsourcing decision. Some of the "surprise" overhead costs that come with an outsourcing decision include:

- Overhead costs allocated to production in the high-wage location, which must be re-allocated to remaining products. In other words, some of the fixed costs do not go away in outsourcing and the internal burden rates go up and the volume goes down. (See the entry on the death spiral.)
- Carrying cost of the additional inventory of goods in transit (the square root law).
- Cost of additional safety stocks to ensure uninterrupted supply.
- Cost of expedited shipments.
- Cost of scrap related quality issues.
- Cost of warranty claims if the new facility or supplier has a long learning curve.
- Cost of engineer visits to set up the operation or to straighten out problems.
- Cost of stockouts and lost sales caused by long leadtimes.
- Cost of obsolete parts.

Outsourcing decisions sometimes also fail to properly account for currency risks, country risks, connectivity risks, and competitive risks when a supplier becomes a competitor.

Few contracts are enforceable across international borders, particularly in countries that do not have a well-developed legal system. Therefore, the manufacturer will assume some risk with both the intellectual property (both product designs and process designs) and also during the order-to-cash cycle for any order. However, all business relationships have risk and come down to developing trust between the business partners. If the supplier wants to keep the manufacturer as a customer, they need to prove themselves to be trustworthy. Firms need to weigh this risk against the risk of global competitors coming to market with a significantly cheaper and better product.

Drivers of increased outsourcing and offshoring

The World is Flat (Friedman, 2005) identified ten forces that have "flattened" the world and made offshore outsourcing much easier:

- The fall of the Berlin wall -- 11/9/89
- When Netscape Went Public -- 8/9/95
- Work Flow Software
- Open-Sourcing
- Outsourcing
- Offshoring
- Supply-Chaining
- Insourcing
- In-forming
- Wireless

See *Activity Based Costing (ABC)*, *burden rate*, *Business Process Outsourcing*, *contract manufacturer*, *co-packer*, *core competence*, *delegation*, *make versus buy decision*, *Maquiladora*, *offshoring*, *operations strategy*, *purchasing, Service Level Agreement (SLA), sourcing, supply chain management, Vendor Managed Inventory (VMI), vertical integration.*

Over/Short/Damaged Report (OSD Report) – A transportation management report that highlights any items that were received but unexpected (e.g., over what was expected), expected but not received (e.g., short of what was expected), or received in damaged condition.

An OSD report is commonly run for a single inbound trailer or for a day's worth of inbound trailers to gauge the quality of the shipments. Ideally, an OSD report would be completely empty with no unexpected, missing, or damaged items.

The OSD report is typically created by the Transportation Management System or Warehouse Management System. It is created by comparing the list of what was expected to be received (typically from the Advanced Shipping Notification, known as the ASN) with the actual receipts as recorded by the warehouse personnel who handled the receiving. Often this OSD report is created by comparing the bar-code scans of the wireless devices used during receiving with the ASN file that outlined what should have been in the trailer.

The OSD report is important to managers for several reasons:

1. **Overage items will probably need manual intervention** – Normally, in a cross-dock or warehousing scenario, each incoming item has an ultimate destination (typically another warehouse or some end shipping point). This destination is indicated in the ASN file. If an unexpected item is received in a high-volume cross-dock or warehousing environment, manual intervention will be required to determine the appropriate ultimate destination of the item.

2. **Missing items will need manual intervention** – Again, in normal circumstances, each item will have an ultimate destination. If items are missing, warehouse managers may need to alert downstream warehouses or customers of missing goods.

3. **Proper recording of damages limits liability** – In many logistics scenarios, the company takes ownership of the items after they are indicated as "received in good condition." Any damage to items after a good receipt will be the legal liability of the recipient, not the originator of the items. Therefore, if items are received as damaged, it may be very important that the damage be noted immediately. Good wireless Transportation Management and Warehouse Management systems will facilitate the recording of this damage by giving warehouse personnel the ability to indicate damaged goods upon receipt. An increase in damage claims from a supplier, without a corresponding increase of damage noted during initial receipt, will almost certainly result in an increased financial liability for items damaged by the recipient.

From a high-level management perspective, the OSD report can be used to gauge overall effectiveness of the relationship between the DC (or originator of the shipment) and the cross-dock (or recipient of the shipment). A baseline accuracy (e.g., what percent of shipments over the last quarter had Over/Short/Damage issues) can be determined. Over time, a shift in the accuracy of the receipts might be a leading indicator of one or more of the following problems: change in procedures at the originating facility, problem with receiving procedures or personnel, or IT problems (relating to the exchange of information).

Acknowledgments: CEMBA 09 students David Collins, Judy Djugash, Kaaren Howe, Kristi Olson, Michael Pynch, Lynn Sellman, and Travis Swenson contributed to this entry.

See *Advanced Shipping Notification (ASN), cross-docking, Electronic Data Interchange (EDI), Transportation Management System (TMS), Warehouse Management System (WMS).*

Overall Equipment Effectiveness (OEE) – A key metric for lean operations used extensively in TPM applications; defined as the product of three variables – the Availability rate, Performance rate, and Yield (or Quality) rate. ✪

Overall Equipment Effectiveness (OEE) is considered by many to be a key metric for lean operations management. OEE is used extensively in Total Productivity Management (TPM) applications, particularly in large firms such as 3M that have large capital intensive operations.

The six big losses

The motivation for the OEE metric is to help the firm identify and manage the "six big losses," which are defined as follows:

- **Breakdown losses:** These are losses from defective products and losses of time due to decreased productivity from equipment breakdowns. (Breakdown losses affect the Availability Rate variable in OEE.)
- **Set-up and adjustment losses:** These are losses from defective units and downtime that may be incurred when equipment is adjusted to shift from producing one kind of product to another. (Set-up losses affect the Availability Rate variable in OEE.)
- **Idling and minor stoppage losses:** These losses result from brief periods of idleness between units or when easy-to-clear jams occur. (Idling and minor stoppage losses affect the Performance Rate variable in OEE.)
- **Reduced speed losses:** These losses occur when equipment is run at less than the design speed (even though the design speed may not be known). Reduced speed losses may occur because materials or tooling may be off spec and require special treatment, or operators may fear running the equipment too fast. (Reduced speed losses affect the Performance Rate variable in OEE.)
- **Quality defects and rework:** These are product related defects and corrections caused by malfunctioning equipment. (Quality defects and rework losses affect the Quality Rate variable in OEE.)
- **Start-up losses:** These are yield losses incurred during early production, i.e., from machine start-up to steady state. (Start-up losses affect the Quality Rate variable in OEE.)

Reasonable target values are availability greater than 90%, performance greater than 95%, and quality greater than 99%. World-class OEE is better than 85%. (Source: www.mfgeng.com/TPM.htm, April 14, 2004.)

The three variables used in the OEE calculation

OEE is the product of three variables defined as follows:

$$OEE = (Availability\ Rate) \times (Performance\ Rate) \times (Yield\ Rate)$$

The **Availability rate** is defined as (operating time less downtime)/(total operating time) and reflects downtime losses due to changeovers, equipment failures, and startup losses.

The **Performance rate** is defined as (total output)/(potential output at rated speed) and reflects speed losses due to idling and minor stoppages or reduced speed operation.

The **Yield (or quality) rate** is defined as (good output)/(total output) and is a function of defects and rework. The yield rate for OEE is sometimes called the quality rate.

The goal of the OEE metric

The goal of measuring OEE is to improve the effectiveness of the equipment. Since equipment effectiveness affects shopfloor employees more than any other group, it is appropriate for them to be involved in tracking OEE and in planning and implementing equipment improvements to reduce lost effectiveness. It is recommended that the operator collect the daily data about the equipment for use in the OEE calculation. Collecting this data will:
- Teach the operator about the equipment.
- Focus the operator's attention on the losses.
- Grow a feeling of ownership of the equipment.

The roll of the shift leader or line manager

The shift leader or line manager is often the one who will receive the daily operating data from the operator and process it to develop information about the OEE. Working hands-on with the data will:
- Give the leader/manager basic facts and figures on the equipment.
- Help the leader/manager give appropriate feedback to the operators and others involved in equipment improvement.
- Allow the leader to keep management informed about equipment status and improvement results.
  However, managers should be careful to never use OEE to build inventory long before it is needed.
  (Much of the above was adapted from www.oeetoolkit.nl/OEEAlgemeen/what_is_oee .htm, November 9, 2001.)

Criticisms of OEE

If OEE is applied to a non-bottleneck machine, care must be taken to avoid maximizing utilization and building inventory that is not needed. It does not make sense to maximize one asset (a machine) in order to create another asset (inventory) that sits idle for a long time.

Conclusions

OEE can be an important metric to help firms better understand and manage the performance of large machines, particularly bottleneck machines. As Goldratt (1992) says, "an hour lost on the bottleneck is an hour lost for the entire plant." However, managers should be careful to never use OEE to build inventory long before it is needed. Maximizing utilization for a non-bottleneck machine will, by definition, build unneeded inventory. Improving asset utilization on one asset (e.g., a large machine) does not justify reducing asset utilization on another asset (e.g., inventory). Therefore, OEE should only be used for bottleneck machines.

Overall equipment effectiveness evaluation form

EQUIPMENT AVAILABILITY		World class target 90%	
A. Total time available		_____	minutes
B. Planned downtime		_____	minutes
C. Net available time			
Total available time – planned downtime	A–B	_____	minutes
D. Unplanned downtime			
Number of breakdowns ___ Total minutes ___			
Number of breakdowns ___ Total minutes ___			
Number of minor breakdowns ___ Total minutes ___	Total	_____	minutes
E. Operating time	C–D	_____	minutes
Net available time – unplanned downtime			
F. Equipment availability	100·E/C		%
100(Operating time)/(Net available time)			
PERFORMANCE EFFICIENCY		World class target 95%	
G. Total parts run (good and bad)		_____	parts
H. Ideal cycle time			min/part
I. Performance efficiency	100·(G·H/E)		%
100 x (Total parts run x ideal cycle time)/(operating time)			
J. Missing in action time	E–(G·H)	_____	minutes
(Operating time) – (Total parts run x ideal cycle time)			
QUALITY RATE World class target 100%			
K. Total defects (rework + scrap)		_____	parts
L. Quality rate	100·(G–K)/G		%
100(Total parts run – total defects)/(Total parts run)			
OVERALL EQUIPMENT EFFECTIVENESS (OEE)		World class target 85%	
Equipment availability x Performance efficiency x Quality rate	100·F·I·L		%

Definitions of terms above:
Total available time = Shift length or planned equipment run time.
Planned downtime = Equipment downtime due to contractual activities such as lunch, breaks, meetings, etc.
Unplanned downtime = Equipment is down due to breakdowns, setups, adjustments, etc.
Ideal cycle time = Design cycle time, best cycle time achieved or estimate.

Acknowledgments: Mr. Tom Meline, Plant Manager, Phillips Temro (CEMBA'04), provided significant help with an early version of this entry.

See *capacity, effectiveness, efficiency, operations performance metrics, productivity, Total Productive Maintenance (TPM), utilization, value added ratio, yield.*

overhead – The cost of equipment, materials and services that is necessary to conduct business but is unrelated to the products or services the firm offers. ✪

Manufacturing overhead is often allocated to products based on direct labor hours.

See *Activity Based Costing (ABC), burden rate, direct labor cost, lean thinking, throughput accounting.*

overhead rate – See *burden rate.*

overproduction – Producing more than what is needed at the time.

See *7 Wastes, batch-and-queue.*

P

pacemaker – A lean manufacturing concept of using a single point to set the pace (speed) for the entire process; in the medical device context, a pacemaker is a medical device used to set the pace for a patient's heart.

In the lean manufacturing context, the pacemaker should be used to level-load the system over time and to set the pace for the other processes in the system. Processes before the pacemaker (upstream) should produce only to a pull signal from the next downstream process or directly from the pacemaker. This helps prevent overproduction and keeps the pacemaker from being starved. Processes after the pacemaker (downstream) should not block the pacemaker and should push materials in small order quantities, possibly using transfer batches, and should not be allowed to have inventories except in supermarkets or finished goods inventory.

The pacemaker is normally the assembly process in a Make to Stock system. In Make to Order system, the pacemaker is typically the process step where the product becomes unique.

Using a pacemaker simplifies scheduling, maintains a level output, focuses on the bottleneck, and prevents overproduction. The pacemaker concept is similar to the Drum-Buffer-Rope concept (Theory of Constraints) and to the CONWIP concept.

See *CONWIP, Drum-Buffer-Rope (DBR), lean thinking, supermarket, Theory of Constraints (TOC), transfer batch, upstream.*

Pack to Order – A customer-interface strategy that collects components and packs them into a box or some other shipping container in response to a customer order.

Pack to Order is similar to assemble to order because it is "assembling" the shipment (one or more parts, packaging, shipping information) in response to a customer order. Boston Scientific calls this "pack to demand." At Boston Scientific, they put a country and language specific label on the box and ship it to the distributor in the country.

See *Make to Order (MTO), mass customization, Respond to Order (RTO).*

Paired-cell Overlapping Loops of Cards with Authorization – See *POLCA.*

paradigm – A way of thinking or thought frame.

An old paradigm (way of thinking) can inhibit creative thinking about a new problem. A new paradigm might be a powerful new way of thinking about an old problem. For example, in the Soviet Union, the factory management paradigm (way of thinking) was that bigger and heavier machines were almost always better. This influenced reward systems and machine design in many ways.

Pareto analysis – See *Pareto Chart.*

Pareto Chart – A histogram (bar chart) that helps identify and prioritize the most common sources of errors or defects. ✪

A Pareto Chart displays the frequencies for each problem and is usually sorted from highest to lowest. The Pareto Chart, named for Vilfredo Pareto, was popularized as a quality management tool by Joseph M. Juran and Kaoru Ishikawa. The basic concept is based on Pareto's Law which teaches that each system has an "important few and a trivial many" (often called the 80-20 principle). The purpose of the Pareto Chart is to highlight the important few.

For example, an analysis of work stoppages on a production line captured the following data, presented here in order from highest to lowest frequency.

Cause of stoppage	Frequency	Relative Frequency	Cumulative Relative Frequency
Human error	12	41%	41%
Defective materials	8	28%	69%
Machine breakdown	4	14%	83%
Misplaced tooling	3	10%	93%
Other problems	2	7%	100%
Total	29	100%	

These data were graphed to create the following Pareto Chart. This Pareto Chart clearly highlights the need to focus on the causes of human errors. The line is the cumulative relative frequency and shows the total percent of the causes up to and including that cause. Fixing the first two causes (human error and defective materials) will remove 69% of the problems with stoppages, whereas fixing the last two will remove only 17%.

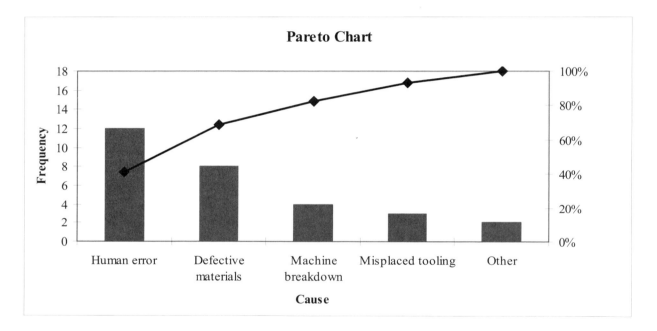

Contrary to the Wikipedia entry, Pareto Charts can easily be generated in Microsoft Excel. When you select the chart type, go to "custom types" and select "Line – Column on 2 Axes."

See *ABC classification, causal map, check sheet, Failure Mode and Effects Analysis (FMEA), histogram, Pareto's Law, Root Cause Analysis (RCA), seven tools of quality.*

Pareto's Law – The principle that most systems have a vital few and a trivial many; also called the 80-20 law. ✪

Pareto's Law is also known as the 80-20 principle, where 80% of the consequences come from only 20% of the causes. Some popular expressions of Pareto's Law include, "Don't sweat the small stuff" and "Major on the majors." Juran preferred to say "the vital few and the useful many" to indicate that the remaining causes should not be totally ignored. Pareto's Law can be 80-10 or 90-20 etc. where the two numbers do not add up to 100.

Pareto's Law can be observed in many situations such as the ABC inventory classification (most of the inventory value is in just a few items), supplier management (just a few suppliers provide account for most of our spend), customer sales distribution (few customers account for most of the sales), quality control (most of the defects can be attributed to just a few causes), human relations (most of the problems are caused by just a few people), medicine (most people die from a few causes), and international relations (most of the problems in the world are caused by just a few rogue countries). Several applications of Pareto's Law in this Encyclopedia include the ABC Classification (manage the high dollar volume items), FMEA (manage the high risk failure modes), Theory of Constraints (manage the bottleneck), dispatching rules (start the high priority jobs first), and critical path and critical chain analysis (manage the most important path in a project).

Alfredo Pareto was an Italian economist who lived in France in the early 1900s. In studying the distribution of wealth in Milan (Milano), he found that 20% of the people earned 80% of the wealth.

The implication of Pareto's Law for managers is that they need to find and focus on the important few issues, items, people, customers, etc. and not spend too much time on the many that do not matter as much. A Pareto Chart is a useful way to show a frequency count and to highlight the priority issues, etc.

Pareto's Law is unrelated to the economics concept of Pareto efficiency.

See *ABC classification, causal map, cycle counting, error proofing, Failure Mode and Effects Analysis (FMEA), Pareto Chart, Root Cause Analysis (RCA), Theory of Constraints (TOC)*.

Parkinson's Laws – Laws written by Professor C. Northcote Parkinson in the book *Parkinson's Law* (1958). ✪

Parkinson's most famous law is "Work expands to fill the time allotted to it." Parkinson's actual wording was "Work expands so as to fill the time available for its completion."

Here are a few other examples of Parkinson's main laws:

- Expenditure rises to meet income.
- Expansion means complexity, and complexity decay.
- Policies designed to increase production increase employment; policies designed to increase employment do everything but.
- Democracy equals inflation. (Professor Parkinson meant that where the working population, through control of the electoral process, ultimately determines its conditions of employment, there will be more demand for higher pay than for increased production.)
- When something goes wrong, do not "try, try again." Instead, pull back, pause, and carefully work out what organizational shortcomings produced the failure. Then, correct those deficiencies. Only after that return to the assault.
- Delay is the deadliest form of denial.
- The matters most debated in a deliberative body tend to be the minor ones where everybody understands the issues.
- Deliberative bodies become decreasingly effective after they pass five to eight members.

Much of the above was adapted from http://www.globalideasbank.org/socinv/SIC-117.HTML, October 18, 2003.

The British 20th Century author and professor of history, Cyril Northcote Parkinson (1909-1993) wrote some sixty books. These included historical fiction (often based on the Napoleonic period) and sea stories. He is even more famous for his satire of bureaucratic institutions, notably his "Parkinson's law and other studies." This is a collection of short studies explaining the inevitability of bureaucratic expansion, and why driving on the left side of the road is natural. As early as the 1930s Parkinson had successfully predicted that the British Navy would eventually have more admirals than ships. (Source: http://en2.wikipedia.org/wiki/C._Northcote_Parkinson, October 18, 2003.)

Professor Hill has written a few operations management corollaries to Parkinson's Laws. These include:

- Warehouse inventory expands to fill the space allotted to it.
- Factory equipment and inventory expand to fill the space allotted to them.
- The best way to improve on-time delivery is to reduce cycle time so that the product is on the customers' doorsteps before they have time to change their minds.
- Lying begets[5] lying. If a firm lies to customers about expected delivery dates, they will, in turn, lie to the firm about the actual need date.
- The later a project becomes, the more unlikely it is that the project manager will inform the customer of the project's lateness.
- The pi rule for project management: Poorly managed projects require approximately pi (3.1416) times more time than originally planned.

See *bullwhip effect, leadtime syndrome, Murphy's Law, project management*.

PARM (perishable asset resource management) – See *yield management*.

---

[5] *The word "begets" is an old English word that means to bring about, create, or father.*

parsimony – Adoption of the simplest assumption in the formulation of a theory or in the interpretation of data, especially in accordance with the rule of Ockham's razor.

See *Ockham's Razor*.

part number – See *check digit, Stock Keeping Unit (SKU)*.

partial expectation – See *safety stock*.

payback period – The time required to break even on an investment.

Payback ignores the time value of money and is regarded to be a crude and imprecise analysis. Much better methods include Net Present Value (NPV) and Economic Value Added (EVA). However, payback is still a commonly used approach for a "quick and dirty" investment analysis.

See *break-even analysis, financial performance metrics*.

p-chart – A quality control chart used to monitor the percent defective for a process.

To use a p-chart, a sample of *n* parts is collected from the process every so many lots, parts, or time periods. The percent defective in the sample is plotted on the control chart and a determination is made if the process is "under control" or not.

See *control chart, Statistical Process Control (SPC)*.

PDCA (Plan-Do-Check-Act) – A well-known four-step approach for process improvement. ✪

The PDCA cycle is made up of four steps for improvement or change. The following is a synthesis description of these four steps gathered from a number of sources:

- **PLAN** – Recognize an opportunity and plan the change. Plan to improve operations first by finding out what things are going wrong and come up with ideas for solving these problems. Decide what actions might reduce process variation.
- **DO** – Test the change. Try out the idea. Make changes designed to solve the problems on a small or experimental scale first. This minimizes disruptions while testing whether the changes will work or not.
- **CHECK** – Review the test, analyze the results, and identify learning. Use data to determine if the change was effective in reducing variation. Check whether the small-scale or experimental changes are achieving the desired result or not. Also, continuously check nominated key activities (regardless of any experimentation going on) to provide information on the quality of the output at all times and identify new problems that might appear.
- **ACT** – Take action based on what you learned in the check step. If the change was successful, incorporate the learning from the test into wider changes. If not, go through the cycle again with a different plan. Implement the idea permanently. Act to implement changes on a larger scale if the experiment is successful. This means making the changes a routine part of your activity. Also, act to involve other persons (other departments, suppliers, or customers) affected by the changes.

Upon conclusion of the cycle, another idea would be tried, and the cycle repeated. This variance reduction process would continue. The repeated application of the PDCA cycle to a process is known as continuous quality improvement.

The PDCA cycle is also known as the Shewhart cycle (1939). Walter A. Shewhart first discussed the concept of PDCA in his 1939 book, ***Statistical Method from the Viewpoint of Quality Control***. Shewhart said the cycle draws its structure from the notion that constant evaluation of management practices, as well as the willingness of management to adopt and disregard unsupported ideas, is the key to the evolution of a successful enterprise. W. Edwards Deming was the one who first coined the term "Shewhart cycle" for PDCA, naming it after his mentor and teacher at Bell Laboratories in New York. Deming promoted PDCA as a primary means of achieving continued process improvement. He also referred to the PDCA cycle as the PDSA cycle ("S" for study). Deming is credited with encouraging the Japanese in the 1950s to adopt PDCA. The Japanese eagerly embraced PDCA and other quality concepts, and to honor Deming for his instruction, they refer to the PDCA cycle as the Deming cycle.

The above information is synthesized from toledo-asq.org/PDCA.htm, sytsma.com/cism700/ CQI_TQM_BPR.html, and from hci.com.au/hcisite2/toolkit/pdcacycl.htm, January 14, 2005.

Most quality improvement projects today use a similar five-step approach called DMAIC, which comes from the Six Sigma movement. Most people find DMAIC more intuitive and easier to follow than the PDCA or PDSA approaches.

See *DMAIC, hoshin, Six Sigma, Total Quality Management (TQM)*.

PDM – See *product data management*.

PDSA (Plan-Do-Study-Act) – See *PDCA*.

pegging – The process of identifying the sources of the gross requirements in the MRP materials plan for an item.

Single-level pegging for a gross requirement goes up one level in the Bill of Material (BOM). Full-level pegging goes all of the way up to top level. Pegging is an important tool for helping production planners identify the impact that a late order might have on higher-level orders and customers.

See *Materials Requirements Planning (MRP)*.

perfect order fill rate – The percent of orders that are perfect in every way.

This could include the right delivery (on-time or filled from stock), right quality, right packaging, right information, right billing, etc. This concept was developed by the Grocery Management Association (GMA) and has been widely used in the food retailing industry.

See *fill rate, Make to Stock (MTS), service level*.

performance based contracting – A legal relationship that allows organizations (usually governmental organizations) to acquire services via contracts that define what is to be achieved rather than how it is done.

In many situations, performance based contracting provides good value products and services. In addition, performance based contracting gives firms the freedom to bring new approaches to their customers.

See *Service Level Agreement (SLA)*.

performance management system – A set of policies and procedures with a supporting information system used to help an organization achieve its goals through its workers.

A performance management system is intended to help the organization achieve its goals by helping workers set and achieve goals that are aligned with the organization's goals. A good performance management system is built on four main activities:

- **Planning** – The manager and direct report collaboratively establish goals, objectives, outcomes, and training requirements for the direct report.
- **Coaching** – The manager trains, observes, and provides feedback to workers to help improve performance.
- **Appraisal** – The manager provides performance feedback to an individual workers and then documents the results of this performance for both the pay and promotion decision processes.
- **Rewards** – The organization provides rewards in the form of recognition, pay raises, bonuses, and promotions.

While performance measurement focuses only on evaluating performance, performance management takes a broader view with more emphasis on intentional performance development. A good performance management system will align and coordinate individual behavior with the organization's strategic objectives.

See *financial performance metrics, work measurement*.

performance quality – The level of the product design standard (specifications) set for product and service attributes; Schroeder (2007) calls this quality of design. ✪

For example, the marketing and R&D people in a firm decide that a watch should be able to survive in 100 meters of water based on focus groups with customers, sales force feedback, etc. This watch is better (at least in its design) than a watch designed to only survive at 10 meters under water.

Performance quality is not the same as conformance quality. While the product design standards might be high, it is quite possible that the manufacturing process is flawed and that products often do not meet the standard. This kind of quality is called conformance quality.

See *conformance quality, product design quality, quality*.

performance rating – A subjective estimate of a worker's pace of work.

A 120% performance rating means that the observer estimated that the worker was working 20% faster than a normal worker. The performance rating is used to adjust the observed time to compute the normal time.

See *normal time, standard time, time study, work measurement*.

Period Order Quantity (POQ) – A simple lotsizing rule that defines the order quantity in terms of the periods supply; also known as the "Periodic Order Quantity."

The POQ is implemented in MRP systems simply by setting the lotsize to the sum of the next POQ periods of net requirements. The optimal POQ is the Economic Order Quantity (the EOQ) divided by the average demand per period. When defined in terms of years supply, the POQ is $\sqrt{2DS/(ic)}/D = \sqrt{2S/(icD)}$ periods, where D is the expected annual demand, S is the ordering (or setup) cost, i is the carrying charge, and c is the unit cost. When defined in terms of days supply, the average demand per day is $\bar{d} = D/365$ and the POQ is defined as $\sqrt{730S/(ic\bar{d})}$ periods.

See *Economic Order Quantity (EOQ), lotsizing methods, periods supply, time-varying demand lotsizing problem.*

periodic review system – An order-timing rule used for planning inventories; also known as a fixed-time period model, periodic system, fixed-order interval system, or *P*-model. ✪

A periodic review system evaluates the inventory position every P time periods and considers placing an order. The system is "time-triggered" rather than "event-triggered" as is the case of the reorder point system. In other words, a periodic review system only considers placing orders at the end of a predetermined time period. The graph below shows the periodic review system through two review periods.

Periodic review system graph

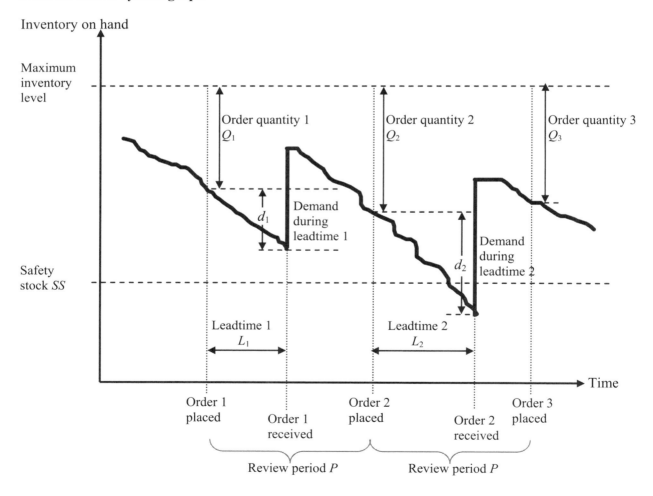

The periodic review system makes good economic sense when the firm has economies of scale in transportation cost. In other words, the periodic review system should be used when the firm can save money by shipping many items at the same time. The optimal review period is the POQ, which is EOQ / μ_D, where EOQ is the economic order quantity and μ_D is the average demand per period. However, in most situations, the review period is determined by other factors such as the transportation schedule.

The periodic review system can be implemented with either a fixed order quantity such as the EOQ or with an order-up-to lotsizing rule. The order-up-to rule is also known as a "base stock" system. This rule orders a quantity that brings the inventory position up to a "target" inventory at the end of each review period. The target inventory level is also called the base stock level. The optimal target inventory is $T = \mu_D(L + P) + SS$, where μ_D is the average demand per period, L is the replenishment leadtime, and P is the review period. The safety stock inventory is $SS = z\sigma_D\sqrt{L + P}$, where σ_D is the standard deviation of demand per period and z is the safety factor. The average lotsize is $\overline{Q} = \mu_D P$ and the average inventory is $\overline{Q}/2 + SS$. Compared to the reorder point system, the periodic system requires more safety stock inventory because it must protect against stockouts during the review period plus the replenishment leadtime rather than just the replenishment leadtime.

Most retail chains use a periodic review system to replenish their stores. Each store has a target inventory level (base stock level) for each SKU (stock keeping unit). Every week the stores order enough to bring their inventory position up to this base stock level and trucks move the orders from regional warehouses to the stores.

The paper "Smart Pull System" and the Excel workbook "smartpull.xls" on the **OMWW CD** available from www.ClamshellBeachPress.com. The paper explains how to set the safety factor z to achieve a user-specified unit fill rate. ◉

See *continuous review system, reorder point, safety stock, slow moving demand, supermarket.*

periods supply – The "time quantity" for an inventory; also known as days on hand, days supply, days of inventory, inventory days, inventory period, coverage period, weeks supply, and months' supply. ✪

The periods supply[6] is an expression of inventory turnover in terms of the periods (days, weeks, month, years) of demand. In other words, it is the expected time until the current inventory goes to zero, assuming that the current average demand rate does not change. The periods supply metric is often preferable to the turnover metric because it is easier to understand and can also be related to risk issues more directly.

Periods supply is estimated by taking the current inventory and dividing by some estimate of the current (or future) average demand. The current average demand might be a simple moving average, an exponentially smoothed average, or an exponentially smoothed average with trend. For example, a professor has 100 pounds of candy in his office and is consuming 20 pounds per day. Therefore, the professor has a 5 days supply.

The periods supply metric and the inventory turnover metric measure the same type of inventory performance and one can be easily computed from the other. The relationships between inventory turnover (T) and days on hand are $T = 365/DOH$ and $DOH = 365/T$. Inventory Dollar Days (IDD) is the unit cost times DOH.

The days supply for work-in-process (WIP) inventory can also be used as an estimate of the cycle time. For example, a firm with 10 days supply of WIP inventory has a cycle time of about 10 days. This concept is based on Little's Law, which states that the average inventory is the demand rate times the cycle time. Written in queuing theory terms, this is $L = \lambda W$, where L is the number in system (the work-in-process), λ is the mean arrival rate (the demand rate), and W is the time in system (the cycle time). Note that when days supply is calculated from financial measures, this estimate of the average cycle time is a dollar-weighted average.

See *cycle time, Inventory Dollar Days (IDD), inventory management, inventory turnover, lot-for-lot, Little's Law, lotsize, Period Order Quantity (POQ).*

Perishable Asset Resource Management (PARM) – See *yield management.*

perpetual inventory system – An inventory control system where a "real-time" record is kept on the amount of inventory for each item.

In a perpetual inventory system, records are updated with every receipt, withdrawal, and inventory balance correction. These systems often provide real-time visibility of inventory position (inventory on-hand and

---

[6] *The copy editor for a major research journal insisted that the phrase "periods supply" is a plural possessive noun (e.g., periods' supply). However, most authors do not follow that rule.*

inventory on-order). If an inventory system is not a perpetual system, the organization either updates inventory records periodically or has no inventory records at all.

personal operations management – A term coined by Hill (2010) that describes a philosophy and set of practices for helping people "apply lean thinking to getting more good things done."

The book *Personal Operations Management* by Hill (2010) is available through Clamshell Beach Press.

See *Getting Things Done (GTD)*, *two minute rule*, *tyranny of the urgent*.

PERT – See *Project Evaluation and Review Technique*.

phantom bill of material – A bill of material coding and structuring technique used primarily for transient (non-stocked) sub-assemblies.

A phantom bill of material represents an item that is physically built but rarely stocked before being used in the next level in the bill of material.

See *Bill of Material (BOM)*, *Stock Keeping Unit (SKU)*.

phase review – A step in the new product development process where approval is required in order to proceed to the next step.

See *New Product Development (NPD)*, *stage-gate process*.

phase-in/phase-out planning – A planning process that seeks to coordinate the introduction of a new product with the discontinuation of an existing product.

New products typically offer updated features and benefits that make the current product obsolete. The phase-in of the new product and the phase-out of the current product is complicated by many factors such as forecasting the demand for both products, planning the consumption and disposal of the inventory of the current product, filling the distribution channel with the new product, giving proper incentives to the sales force for both the current and new products, coordinating end-of-life policies for all related products and consumables, carefully designing a pricing strategy that maximizes contribution to profit, and last, but not least, creating an effective market communication program.

With respect to market communications, some firms have found themselves in trouble when information about a new product becomes public and causes the market demand for the current product to quickly decline.

Hill and Sawaya (2004) provide a good example of the phase-in/phase-out problem in the context of the medical device industry.

Acknowledgments: CEMBA 09 students Brian Clark, Brent Niccum, Tushar Patel, Rebecca Savoie, and Kate Walker contributed to this entry.

See *product lifecycle management*.

pick face – The primary location in a warehouse for picking orders that make up less than a pallet load.

See *picking*.

pick list – An output from an inventory control system designating those items, by part number, description, and quantity, to be picked from stock to satisfy customer demand; also called a picking list.

See *picking*.

picking – The process of collecting items from storage locations to meet the requirements of an order.

See *batch picking*, *first pick ratio*, *pick face*, *pick list*, *Warehouse Management System (WMS)*, *wave picking*, *zone picking*.

picking list – See *pick list*.

pipeline inventory – The number of units (or dollars) of inventory currently being moved from one location to another.

See *Work-in-Process (WIP) inventory*.

pitch – The time allowed to make one container of a product.

Pitch is used to check if actual production is keeping up with takt time requirements. Pitch is a multiple of takt time based on the container size. For example, if the container size is 60 units and the takt time is 10 seconds, pitch is 60x10=600 seconds (or 10 minutes) for each container. Pitch can also be expressed as a rate. For example, if pitch (as a time) is 10 minutes per container, pitch (as a rate) is 6 containers per hour.

See *cycle time*, *lean thinking*, *takt time*.

Plan-Do-Check-Act – See *PDCA*.

Plan-Do-Study-Act – See *PDCA*.

planned leadtime – See *cycle time, leadtime*.

planned order – See *Materials Requirements Planning (MRP)*.

planning versus forecasting – See *forecasting demand*.

planogram – A diagram used to communicate a plan for retail space designed to maximize the return on investment for the space.

A good planogram allows inexperienced employees to properly maintain the retail shelf stock and appearance. A good planogram system will help the retailer (1) control inventory investment, (2) improve inventory turnover, (3) control labor cost, (4) satisfy customers, (5) increase sales, and (6) increase profit.

See *assortment, facility layout*.

plant stock – An SAP term for on-hand inventory in a particular plant location.

plant-within-a-plant – A relatively autonomous process ("a plant") located within a facility that allows for more focus and accountability; sometimes called a focused factory.

Each plant-within-a-plant (or focused factory) will likely have unique operations objectives (cost, quality, delivery, etc.) and unique workforce policies, production control methods, accounting systems, etc. This concept was promoted by Professor Wickham Skinner at Harvard Business School in a famous article on the focused factory (Skinner 1974). See the *focused factory* entry for more details.

See *facility layout, focused factory, operations strategy*.

platform strategy – A new product development strategy that plans new products around a small number of basic product designs called platforms that allow for a many different final products with differing features, functions, and prices.

A platform strategy is well-known in the automotive industry where a platform is often a chassis/drive-train combination upon which many different models are built (e.g., Chevrolet, Buick, Cadillac, etc.). The same concept is used in many different industries such as personal computers (e.g., Dell), white goods (e.g., Whirlpool), and medical devices (e.g., Medtronic).

See *New Product Development (NPD)*.

PMI – See *Project Management Institute (PMI)*.

Point-of-Sale (POS) – A data collection device located where products are sold, usually a scanning and cash register device in a retail store.

POS data collection provides a rich source of data that can be used to provide real-time sales information for the entire supply chain.

See *Universal Product Code (UPC)*.

point-of-use – The lean manufacturing practice of storing parts, tools, and supplies close to where they are used instead of storing them in a separate storage area.

Point-of-use reduces non-value added time for moving items and also increases the visibility of the process.

Poisson distribution – A discrete distribution useful for modeling demand distributions when the average demand is low (say less than 9).

The mean of the Poisson distribution is λ (lambda). The probability mass function, $p(x)$, is the probability of x units and is only defined for integer values of x.

Probability mass and distribution functions:

$$p(x,\lambda) = \begin{cases} \dfrac{e^{-\lambda}\lambda^x}{x!} & \text{if } x \in \{0,1,...\} \\ 0 & \text{otherwise} \end{cases} \quad \text{and} \quad F(x,\lambda) = \sum_{i=0}^{\lfloor x \rfloor} p(x,\lambda) = \begin{cases} 0 & \text{if } x < 0 \\ e^{-\lambda}\sum_{i=0}^{\lfloor x \rfloor} \dfrac{\lambda^i}{i!} & \text{if } x \geq 0 \end{cases}$$

Statistics: Range non-negative integers $\{0, 1, ... \}$, mean λ (note that λ need not be an integer), variance λ, mode $\lambda - 1$ and λ if λ is an integer and $\lfloor \lambda \rfloor$ otherwise. Note that the operator $\lfloor x \rfloor$ rounds down to the nearest integer.

Excel: The Microsoft Excel function for the Poisson distribution is POISSON(x, λ, FALSE). This returns the probability that the random variable will be exactly x given that the mean of the Poisson distribution is λ. The Microsoft Excel function for the cumulative Poisson distribution is POISSON(x, λ, TRUE), which returns the probability that the random variable will be less than or equal to x given that the mean of the Poisson distribution is λ.

Excel simulation: In an Excel simulation, it is necessary to use a VBA function to generate Poisson distributed random variates because Excel does not have an inverse function for the Poisson distribution. Law and Kelton (2000) present a widely-used special-purpose method for generating Poisson distributed variates, but note that the inverse transform method with a search procedure can also perform well. Given that the Poisson distribution is typically used only for distributions with a low mean ($\lambda < 9$), a simple search procedure is quite fast computationally. The following is the VBA code that can be used to generate Poisson distributed variates. The formula in Excel is then POISSON_INVERSE(RAND(), λ).

```
Function poisson_inverse(p, lambda)
'  p          cumulative probability.
'  lambda   mean of the Poisson distribution.
'  This routine truncates the result at xmax.
Dim x As Integer
Const xmax = 60
    For x = 1 To xmax
        poisson_inverse = x
        If Application.WorksheetFunction.Poisson(x, lambda, True) >= p Then Exit Function
    Next x
    MsgBox "poisson_inverse(" & Format(p, "0.00%") & ") was truncated at " _
        & Val(xmax) & ".", vbExclamation
End Function
```

The following graph shows the Poisson probability mass function with mean $\lambda = 3$.

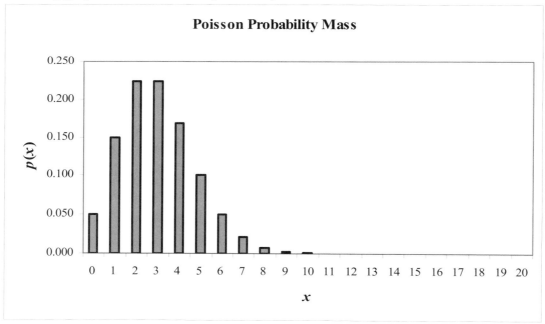

Relationships to other distributions: If X_1, X_2, ..., X_m are independent Poisson distributed random variables with mean λ_i, then $X_1 + X_2 + \ldots + X_m$ is also Poisson distributed with mean $\lambda_1 + \lambda_2 + \ldots + \lambda_m$. The Poisson and exponential distributions are unique in that they have only one parameter.

History: The French Mathematician Siméon Denis Poisson (1781-1840) discovered this distribution. Source: http://www-groups.dcs.st-and.ac.uk/~history/Mathematicians/Poisson.html.

See *bathtub curve, binomial distribution, dollar unit sampling, exponential distribution, hypergeometric distribution, newsvendor model, queuing theory, slow moving demand.*

poka-yoke – See *error proofing*.

POLCA (Paired-cell Overlapping Loops of Cards with Authorization) – A hybrid push/pull production control system for low-volume manufacturing developed by Professor Rajan Suri at the University of Wisconsin.

Professor Suri describes POLCA as follows: "POLCA is the most effective production-control system for low-volume or custom-engineered products. Lean concepts such as flow, takt time, and pull/Kanban systems often fail to meet the needs of custom-engineered product manufacturers. The hybrid push/pull system called POLCA (Paired-cell Overlapping Loops of Cards with Authorization) has proven successful in an environment that operates with the principles of Quick Response Manufacturing. POLCA combines the best features of card-based pull (Kanban) systems and push (MRP) systems and overcomes their drawbacks for low-volume production. Since 1998, POLCA has been implemented in numerous companies in the United States and Europe."

More information on Professor Suri and the Center for Quick Response Manufacturing at the University of Wisconsin can be found at http://www.engr.wisc.edu/centers/cqrm.

See *CONWIP, Drum-Buffer-Rope (DBR)*.

Pollaczek-Khintchine formula – A powerful, but simple, queuing formula that relates the standard deviation of the service time to the mean number of customers in queue for a single server queuing system.

The formula itself can be found in the *queuing theory* entry.

See *queuing theory*.

POMS – See *Production Operations Management Society*.

pooling – A practice of combining servers (or inventory) in order to reduce customer waiting time (or inventory).

Operations managers often have to decide if it is better to have separate systems (each with its own servers and queues) or combine them into one. This problem is called the pooling problem. A simple example with a queuing model will be used here to explore the benefits of pooling.

A firm has two technical experts -- one on the east coast and one on the west coast. Customers on the west coast are only allowed to call the west coast expert; and the same is true for the east coast. The average inter-arrival time[7] for customers calling the technical experts is $a = 0.4$ hours on both coasts. The average service time for the two identical experts was $p = 0.3$ hours. The utilization for each expert is $\rho = p / a = 0.3/0.4 = 75\%$. The coefficient of variation for the inter-arrival time is 1 and the coefficient of variation for the service time is also 1 (e.g., $cv_a = 1$ and $cv_s = 1$). Each expert is analyzed separately, which means that the number of servers is $s = 1$. Using the approximate G/G/s model, we find the average queue time is:

$$W_q = \left(\frac{p}{s}\right)\left(\frac{\rho^{\sqrt{2(s+1)}-1}}{1-\rho}\right)\left(\frac{cv_a^2 + cv_p^2}{2}\right) = \left(\frac{0.3}{1}\right)\left(\frac{0.75^{\sqrt{2(1+1)}-1}}{(1-0.75)}\right)\left(\frac{1^2+1^2}{2}\right) = 0.9 \text{ hours}$$

Therefore, customers will have to wait about 0.9 hours on average for each expert.

If the organization were to combine the two lines to form just one line for the experts it would "pool" the systems and would have only one line. In this case the inter-arrival time for combined system is half that of the separate systems (i.e., $a = 0.2$ hours), but the average service time remains the same ($p = 0.3$ hours). Again, using the approximate G/G/s model, we find the average queue time is:

$$W_q = \left(\frac{p}{s}\right)\left(\frac{\rho^{\sqrt{2(s+1)}-1}}{1-\rho}\right)\left(\frac{cv_a^2 + cv_p^2}{2}\right) = \left(\frac{0.3}{2}\right)\left(\frac{0.75^{\sqrt{2(2+1)}-1}}{(1-0.75)}\right)\left(\frac{1^2+1^2}{2}\right) = 0.395 \text{ hours}$$

Therefore, customers in the "pooled" system have to wait about 0.4 hours on average. In this case pooling reduced the average waiting time by about one-half (from 0.9 hours to 0.4 hours), a very significant difference.

---

[7] *This is the average time between arrivals for customers.*

Why is the pooled system so much better? The answer is that in the old system, it was quite possible that one expert was idle while the other had a long line. In other words, the pooled system makes better use of the technical experts.

The benefits of pooling are often very significant. The main teaching point here is not the queueing model, but rather the fact that many systems can be dramatically improved by pooling resources. Pooled systems make better use of the resources, reduce the waiting time for customers, and reduce the risk of long waiting times.

This pooling concept can be applied in many different contexts such as the following:

- The dean of a business school centralized all tech support people for the school into one office.
- Northwest Airlines shares parts with other airlines in Singapore. This reduces the risk of any airline not having a needed part and reduces the needed investment.
- Xcel Energy shares expensive parts for power generators with many other firms in the Midwestern part of the United States.
- A large service firm consolidated all of its call center operations into one center and was able to reduce waiting time substantially.

Of course, it should be noted that pooling has some disadvantages too. When the service firm consolidated it call centers, the local customers might not experience service that is culturally sensitive (especially if the call center is moved to another country). Also, very large call centers might experience diseconomies of scale. Finally, if the mean service times for the separate populations are very different from one another the coefficient of variation of the service time for the pooled model will increase and the average waiting time can increase.

See *addition principle*, *diseconomy of scale*, *queuing theory*.

POQ – See *Period Order Quantity*.

portal – See *corporate portal*.

POS – See *Point-of-Sale*.

post mortem review – The practice of reviewing a project after it has been completed to facilitate learning for (1) the members of the project team, (2) the sponsoring organization, and (3) the wider organization.

Organizations should seek to learn from both their successes and failures. Organizations that do not do this are doomed to repeat their mistakes over and over again. This is a critical activity for successful project management.

Mr. Gene Heupel of GMHeupel Associates recommends that project teams conduct three activities at the end of a project:

1. Create a project completion notice.
2. Conduct a post mortem review.
3. Create a project closing report.
   Each of these is discussed briefly below.

The project completion notice is a definitive project ending document that serves several purposes, including: (a) verifies that the deliverables in the project charter have been completed, (b) defines the plan to sustain the implementation, and (c) releases the team and establishes the end of project activities. He recommends that the project team have the project sponsor sign this document.

The post mortem review is comprehensive review conducted by the project team to make sure that the team and the organization has learned as much as they can from the project. Lessons learned from this review are documented in the project closing report.

The project closing report contains all of the significant documents related to the project as well as lessons learned. It becomes an important part of the knowledge base for the organization going forward.

See *project management*.

postponement – The principle of delaying differentiation (customization) for a product as long as possible in order to minimize complexity and inventory. ✪

Forecasting the demand for standard products is usually not difficult and the inventory carrying cost for these products is relatively low. However, forecasting the demand for products differentiated for a particular channel or customer is much harder and the carrying cost is often high due to obsolescence. The firm will likely have too much inventory for some differentiated products and too little for others. If the firm can delay the differentiation of the products until after the customer order has been received, then finished goods inventory is eliminated.

Postponement is a foundational principle for mass customization. It is sometimes called the "maximum delay" or "delayed differentiation" principle.

For example, HP was able to standardize all of its printers and put all of the country-specific power management technology in the cord. This allowed for lower inventory and better customer service.

See *mass customization, push-pull boundary*.

predictive maintenance – The practice of monitoring a machine with a measuring device that can anticipate and predict when it is likely to fail.

Predictive maintenance is often based on vibration. Maintenance is then scheduled based on information from the measuring device. Predictive maintenance should be targeted at equipment with high costs of failure and only makes sense when the precision of the predictive tools is high. For additional details see McKone and Weiss (2002).

See *bathtub curve, emergency maintenance, maintenance, preventive maintenance, Total Productive Maintenance (TPM)*.

preventive maintenance – The practice of checking and repairing a machine on a scheduled basis before it fails; also called preventative maintenance. ✪

The schedule is usually based on some historical information on the time between failures for the population of machines. The machine operators often perform it. The opposite of preventive maintenance is emergency maintenance, where the maintenance is done after the machine fails. In the practice of dentistry, preventive maintenance is the annual checkup and cleaning; emergency maintenance is the urgent trip to the dentist when the patient has a toothache.

See *bathtub curve, emergency maintenance, maintenance, predictive maintenance, Total Productive Maintenance (TPM)*.

price elasticity of demand – See *elasticity*.

price of non-conformance – See *cost of quality*.

primacy effect – A concept from psychology and sociology that suggests that people assign disproportionate importance to initial stimuli or observations.

For example, if a subject reads a sufficiently-long list of words, he or she is more likely to remember words read toward the beginning than words read in the middle. The phenomenon is due to the fact that the short term memory at the beginning of whatever sequence of events is, is far less "crowded" and since there are far fewer items being processed in the brain at the time when presented earlier rather than later, there is more time for rehearsal or pondering of the stimuli which can cause them to be "transferred" to the long-term memory for longer storage.

The recency effect is comparable to the primacy effect, but for the final stimuli or observations. In summary, the primacy effect and the recency effects predict that people will remember the items near the beginning and the end of the list. Lawyers scheduling the appearance of witnesses for court testimony, and managers scheduling a list of speakers at a conference, take advantage of these effects when they put speakers they wish to emphasize at the beginning or end. In measuring customer satisfaction, it is well-known that customers place undo emphasis on their first and most recent customer experiences.

See *service quality*.

Principal Components Analysis (PCA) – A mathematical procedure that transforms a number of possibly correlated variables into a smaller number of uncorrelated variables called principal components.

The first principal component accounts for as much of the variability in the data as possible, and each succeeding component accounts for as much of the remaining variability as possible.

Adapted from http://en.wikipedia.org/wiki/Principal_components_analysis.

See *cluster analysis*.

Print on Demand – See *Print to Order*.

Print to Order – A customer-interface strategy that prints books, manuals, and other materials in response to a customer order rather than creating an inventory of printed materials; also called print on demand.

Print to Order requires a printing process that can efficiently handle small printing batch sizes. Print to Order is made possible by new computer-based printing technologies.

See *mass customization, Respond to Order (RTO)*.

Prisoners' Dilemma – A conflict situation (a game) in which two players can decide to either cooperate or cheat.

The game received its name from the following hypothetical situation. Imagine two criminals, A and B, arrested under suspicion of having committed a crime together. However, the police do not have sufficient proof to convict them. The police separate the prisoners and offer each of them the same deal. If one testifies for the prosecution against the other and the other remains silent, the betrayer goes free and the silent accomplice receives the full 10-year sentence. If both stay silent, both prisoners are sentenced to only six months in jail for a minor charge due to lack of evidence. If each betrays the other, each receives a two-year sentence. Each prisoner must make the choice of whether to betray the other or to remain silent. However, neither prisoner knows what choice the other prisoner will make. The game can be summarized in the table below.

		Prisoner B	
		Prisoner B stays silent	Prisoner B betrays
Prisoner A	Prisoner A stays silent	Both serve six months	Prisoner A serves 10 years Prisoner B goes free
	Prisoner A betrays	Prisoner A goes free Prisoner B serves 10 years	Both serve two years

The gain for mutual cooperation in the prisoners' dilemma is kept smaller than the gain for one-sided betrayal so that players are always tempted to betray. This assumption is not generally valid. For example, it is easy to imagine that two wolves together would be able to kill an animal that is more than twice as large as the largest one that each of them might have killed on his own.

The prisoners' dilemma is meant to study short-term decision-making where the actors do not have any specific expectations about future interactions or collaborations (as is the case in the original situation of the jailed criminals). Synergy usually only gets its full power after a long-term process of mutual cooperation (hunting a deer is a very time-consuming and complicated business). If two entities repeatedly face a prisoners' dilemma's with each other, a fairly good strategy for each one is sometimes called "tit for tat," which means that if you cheated on the previous move, I'll cheat on this move; if you cooperated on the previous move, I'll cooperate on this move.

Adapted from pespmc1.vub.ac.be/PRISDIL.html and en.wikipedia.org/wiki/Prisoner's_dilemma. Axelrod (1984) is one of the primary references on this subject.

See *game theory*, *zero sum game*.

private carrier – A shipper that transports its goods in truck fleets that it owns or leases.

See *common carrier*, *logistics*.

pro bono – To work for the public good without charging a fee; short for the Latin *pro bono publico*, which means "for the public good."

When lawyers, consultants, and other professionals work "pro bono," they work without charging a fee.

Probit Analysis – See *logistic regression*.

process – A set of steps designed to achieve a particular goal. ✪

All processes have inputs and outputs. Ideally, processes will also have a feedback mechanism that measures the output and adjusts the inputs and the process to better achieve the desired goal.

Professor Hill uses the following framework to discuss process improvement:

- Better – How can we improve the process to deliver better quality?
- Faster – How can we improve the process so that it is faster and requires less time?
- Cheaper – How can we improve the process so that it is more efficient and has less cost?
- Stronger – How can we improve the process so that it is more robust and more aligned with our strategy?

The paper "Process Is Everything" is on the *OMWW CD* available from www.ClamshellBeachPress.com. ◉

See *systems thinking*.

process capability and performance – A Six Sigma methodology that measures the ability of a process to consistently meet quality specifications. ✪

Process capability and performance can be measured in many different ways. The simplest approach is to measure the Defects Per Million Opportunities (DPMO), where a defect is anything that does not meet the customer (or specification) requirements. A DPMO value can be translated into a sigma level, where the lower the DPMO, the higher the sigma level. (See the *Sigma level* entry.)

Another approach for measuring process capability is with the statistical measures C_p and C_{pk}. Similarly, process performance can be measured with the statistical measures P_p and P_{pk}. Process capability compares the process output for an "in-control" process with the customer's specification (tolerance limits) to determine if the common-cause variation is small enough to satisfy customer requirements. The figure below shows a process that is has a process mean in the middle of the lower and upper tolerance limit (e.g., the process is "centered"). This figure also shows that the process limits for the common-cause variation ($\pm 3\sigma$) are well within the specification (tolerance) limits. This process, therefore, is said to be both capable and centered.

One slightly humorous way to communicate this is to compare the specification limits to the width of a garage and the common-cause variation as the size of the SUV that must fit into the garage. If the garage is large and the SUV is small (and the driver is careful) the SUV will fit into the garage with no problem.

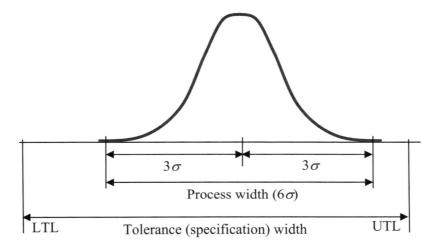

Several of the main process capability concepts are defined in more detail below.

Process Capability (C_p) – Process capability is defined as the difference between the tolerance (specification) limits divided by the process width. In mathematical terms, this is $C_p = (UTL - LTL)/(6\sigma)$, where *UTL* is the Upper Tolerance Limit and *LTL* is the Lower Tolerance Limit. C_p should be at least 1.33 for the process to be considered capable. (This is a defect rate of 0.0063%.) The standard deviation for C_p can be estimated with Moving Range, Range, or Sigma control charts. The inverse of process capability is called the process capability ratio (C_r), and should be no greater than 75% in order for the process to be considered capable.

Process Capability Index (C_{pk}) – The process capability index (C_{pk}) measures the ability of a process to create product within specification limits. C_{pk} is the difference between the process mean and the closest specification limit over the standard deviation times three. The C_{pk} adjusts C_p for a non-centered distribution and therefore is preferred over C_p. For example, in target shooting, if your shots hit the bottom right corner of the target and form a tight group you have a high C_p but a low C_{pk}. When you adjust your sight so this tight group is centered on the bull's-eye, you also have a high C_{pk}. C_{pk} is the smaller of the capability of the upper half and the lower half of the process. In mathematical terms, $C_{pu} = (UTL - \mu)/(3\sigma)$, $C_{pl} = (\mu - LTL)/(3\sigma)$, and $C_{pk} = \min(C_{pl}, C_{pu})$. When the C_{pk} is less than one, the process is said to be incapable. When the C_{pk} is greater than or equal to one, the process is considered capable of producing a product within specification limits. The C_{pk} for a Six Sigma process is 2. The process capability index (C_{pk}) can never be greater than the process capability (C_p). They will be equal when the process average is exactly in the middle of the specification limits.

Process Performance (P_p) – Similar to C_p except based on the sample standard deviation. The inverse of process performance is called the process performance ratio (P_r).

Process Performance Index (P_{pk}) – Similar to C_{pk} except based on the sample standard deviation. Process performance measures are based on the sample standard deviation, whereas process capability measures are based on the long-term "common-cause" standard deviation determined from the moving range, range, or sigma control charts. Process performance measures, therefore, measure the actual short-term performance of a system, whereas process capability measures the system's long-term potential to perform when under control. The difference between the two is the potential for improvement. The table below compares these two metrics.

	Process Capability	Process Performance
Interpretation	A measure of the long term potential or aptitude of the process.	A measure of recent short term actual performance for a sample.
Measures	C_p, C_{pk}, C_r	P_p, P_{pk}, P_r
Time horizon	Long term	Short term
How to estimate the standard deviation	Estimated over a longer period of time using Moving Range, Range, or Sigma control charts.	Estimated from a sample standard deviation.

Source: Professor Arthur V. Hill

See *business capability, control chart, cost of quality, Design for Six Sigma (DFSS), functional build, operations performance metrics, process validation, sigma level, Six Sigma, specification limits, Statistical Process Control (SPC)*.

process control – See *Statistical Process Control (SPC)*.

process design – The activities required to create a new manufacturing or service process. ✪

Process design includes many different activities such as facility location, facility layout, process planning, capacity planning, ergonomics, and work design. Process design should be simultaneous with product design and guided by the organization's strategy. One key component of process design is to error proof the process.

See *capacity, ergonomics, error proofing, facility layout, facility location, New Product Development (NPD), service blueprinting*.

process flow chart – See *process map*.

process improvement program – A systematic approach for improving organizational performance that consists of specific practices, tools, techniques, and terminology and implemented as a set of process improvement projects. ✪

Many process improvement program concepts are presented in this book. The best known programs are Six Sigma, Lean Sigma, and Lean.

See *benchmarking, Business Process Management (BPM), Business Process Re-engineering (BPR), error proofing, lean thinking, program management office, project hopper, project management, Six Sigma, standardized work, Theory of Constraints (TOC), Voice of the Customer (VOC)*.

process layout – An approach for organizing the physical configuration of a facility so that workcenters are grouped by process, rather than organized to match the requirements of a particular product.

A process layout will have all of the grinding machines together, all of the lathes together, etc. A process layout is appropriate for a "job shop" where the routing sequence for products is almost completely unpredictable.

See *facility layout, job order costing, product layout*.

process map – A diagram showing the logical flow of steps required for a task; also called a flowchart or process flowchart. ✪

The "as-is" process map shows how the process map currently actually operates. Note that this may differ substantially from the current process documentation. The "should-be" process map shows the team's recommendations for how the process should operate in the future.

The following is a list of process mapping best practices developed by this author:

Engage the "Gemba" to create the process map – Get the people who are closest to the process to brainstorm to create the process map. They are the only people who really know how it works. (Note: Gemba is the Japanese term for the "actual" or "real" place where work takes place (Hill, 2007).)

Use Post-it Notes[8] to brainstorm the steps in the process – Get those who are closest to the process to brainstorm using Post-it Notes to create the process map. Start on the far left with the event that starts the process and work to the right. Put Post-it Notes in a holding area on the far right until they are needed. Tape a

---

[8] *Post-it Notes is a registered trademark of the 3M Corporation.*

large roll of printer or butcher paper on the wall to hold the process map. When the process is done, this can be taken down and handed to someone to transcribe into Visio or Excel.

Use rectangles for process steps – This is standard practice throughout the world. Some people make the boxes very simple and include just the name of the process. Others add information such as the required inputs, the outputs, average processing time, average setup time, average batchsize, etc. During the brainstorming process, just use a regular Post-it Note for a process step.

Use a diamond for decision steps – This too is standard practice. Decision steps normally have two paths going out; one when the answer to the question is true and the other when the answer is false. Note that a decision step can have three or more outcomes when a numerical comparison is being made (e.g., $x < y$, $x = y$, or $x > y$) or when a question has multiple potential answers. During the brainstorming process, just use a square Post-it Note turned 45° to indicate a decision step. Many people seem to miss many decisions made in a process. When a process map is thought to be complete, ask the process owner, "How many decisions do you have in this process?" and then match that number with the process map. It is a common error for the process map to show only a few decisions when the process actually requires many decisions.

Use an oval to start and end the process – This too is fairly standard practice. This shape should ideally identify the trigger action that starts the process in action. Many process mapping activities are too limited in scope and as a result miss upstream and downstream opportunities for process improvement.

Do not bother with more sophisticated shapes – Many texts and consultants use many other shapes that represent stored data, merge, sort, inventory, etc. The website www.breezetree.com/article-excel-flowchart-shapes.htm, for example, provides about thirty different shapes that can be used. Most process improvement projects do not need any other symbols than those listed above.

Draw the map from left to right – While some people use a top down approach, the left to right approach has become the standard, particularly for larger process maps. It is generally best to have time going from left to right and having all steps organized from left to right in time order as much as possible.

Be careful to have the right scope – The scope of the process is defined by the starting and ending points. In some cases, the process mapping activity fails to achieve significant improvement because the scope does not include important upstream and/or downstream steps. The acronym SIPOC stands for Supplier, Inventory, Process, Output, and Customer. A good process map includes all five of these elements.

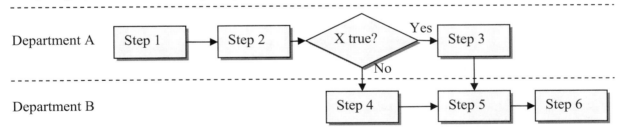

Clearly show the handoffs – Handoffs usually create queues (waiting lines) and almost always result in lost information. Also, organizational units often have different objectives that cause problems when these objectives lead to long cycle times, lost information, and poor customer service. Handoffs are often indicated with "swim lanes," which are horizontal lines that indicate organizational units. The example above shows swim lanes with handoffs between Department A and Department B. It is also possible (and sometimes much easier) to use dotted lines or color-coded boxes to indicate the handoffs between organizational units.

Include the average wait times in the process map – The waits and delays make up 80-95% of the total cycle time for most processes. If a process map does not include the wait time, it is capturing only a small portion of the total time for the process. Few organizations follow this practice so it might not be readily accepted at first. Some organizations use the "D" symbol for a wait or delay. However, most organizations just use a rectangle for this.

Show the numbers – Process maps can borrow a number of important ideas from value stream maps. Specifically, a process map should document process steps and decision points with important numerical information. For example, an inspection step (a diamond on the process map) might send 90% of the work on to the next step and 10% back to the previous step as a result of an inspection. Important numbers to show include:

- Average number of units arriving per hour or per day (the average demand or arrival rate).
- Machine capacity in hours.
- Labor capacity (or full-time equivalent headcount).
- Average cycle time (average time in system for this process step).
- Average setup time.
- Average run time per unit. (More sophisticated analysis might also include the standard deviation.)
- Average inventory in units and in dollars.
- Scrap rate as a percentage (or first pass yield).

Ideally, a process map will include the Key Process Input Variables (KPIVs) and the Key Process Output Variables (KPOVs), which are also called CTQs (Critical to Quality) metrics.

Start with the "as-is" before creating the "should-be" process map – The "as-is" process map is the way that the process actually works now. This is not what someone wants it to be, but rather what is actually in place now. Some experts recommend that the project team separate the "as-is" activity from the "should-be" activity in order to minimize "anchoring." Anchoring is defined as "… the difficulty of changing behavior that is heavily influenced by old habits."

Identify the bottleneck – According to the theory of constraints (Goldratt & Cox, 1990), all systems have one and only bottleneck.[9] It is important to identify the bottleneck for the overall process in order to prioritize process improvement efforts. The bottleneck is the process step that has the longest average cycle time. The bottleneck should be the focus for improving setup time, yield, processing time, etc. Inspection should be done before the bottleneck to make sure that the bottleneck capacity is not wasted. The bottleneck should not be allowed to run out of work (starved) and should not be stopped (blocked) by inventory in the output buffer.

Identify the risk points (fail points) – These are the process steps that are perceived by those who work the process to be the greatest sources of risk. Good process improvement will prioritize these risk points and strive to mitigate these risks. These are sometimes called "fail points." These may be points that have historically failed (possibly identified through Pareto Analysis) or points we believe might fail (possibly identified through Failure Modes Effects Analysis).

Identify the pain points – These are the process steps that are perceived by those who work the process to cause them the most pain (trouble, time, hardship, anxiety, discomfort, or attention). A simple way to find pain points is to have the people who work the process use a "multi-voting" process where each person gets to place two to four votes. For example, each person might be able to cast three votes.

Identify the non-value added steps – Those who work the process and their suppliers and customers should study each step in the process and ask the hard question, "Does my customer really care about this step?" If the answer is no, that step should be considered to be a non-value added step and should be eliminated if possible. However, many steps add no immediate value to the customer, but are still necessary for other steps that do add value. Non-value activities can be highlighted by showing the waits, moves, and inventories on the process map. The first two can be done easily by creating separate steps for waits and moves. Inventory information can be added to the appropriate steps in the process map. This information can be highlighted by using larger lines on the rectangles and/or bold colors.

Identify the rework loops – When work is not done right the first time, it is either scrapped or sent back to a previous step for rework. It is important that process maps identify the inspection point and the rework loops. These are often good opportunities for improvement. Use a diamond shape for the decision step that evaluates if something needs to be sent back for rework.

Identify the moments of truth – These are the points in the process where the process "touches" the customers. Moments of truth are points in the process where an organization (and its representatives) has the opportunity to show its "authenticity" or, alternatively, to show that it is deceptive, does not really care about

---

[9] *The argument here is that one an only one process has the longest average cycle time over the long run. While many processes might have almost the longest cycle time, only one will have the longest cycle time.*

customers, and is not worth their trust. Pine and Gilmore's book *Authenticity* provides many examples of how organizations can either create "authentic" or "inauthentic" experiences for customers (Pine and Gilmore 2007).

Identify the line of visibility – The line of visibility separates a service operation into front office customer-facing operations and back office operations that have no customer contact. Some consultants use a special type of process map called a service blueprint that emphasizes the pain points and the line of visibility. See Hill (2007) for more information about service blueprinting.

Use a hierarchical approach and normal-sized paper – Many process improvement experts are proud of their huge process maps that cover an entire wall. However, it is much easier if the process map is created in a hierarchical way and constrained to have each element of the hierarchy on a single normal-sized sheet of paper. The top level (for executives) might only have five to ten high-level steps on one piece of paper. These are the major sub-processes that make up the process. Each of these five to ten steps can then be broken down further into additional steps, with one or more sheets of paper for each of these. This approach allows process maps to be printed by anyone in the organization on normal-sized paper without having to resort to expensive large printers. This approach also makes it much easier for executives to understand the entire process without having to understand all of the details. (Note: This author has only rarely seen this approach used in practice.)

Identify and prioritize opportunities for improvement – The above analysis should help us identify and prioritize our opportunities for improvement. The goal of a process map is not to create a pretty drawing, but to get to improvement. One simple way to do this is to have the people who work the process[10] use "multi-voting" to identify priorities. With multi-voting, each person gets to place two to four "votes" for the process steps they believe should be the focus for process improvement going forward. Professor Hill's paper "The Process Improvement Checklist" offers a large number of potential opportunities for improvement collected from many organizations.

Many software tools are available for process mapping. However, the most popular tool appears to be Microsoft Visio. Simple process maps can be created in Microsoft Word, PowerPoint, and Excel.

While a value stream map is more visual than a process map, a process map is better than a value stream map from the standpoint of information value. A process map allows for decision points, but a value stream map does not. Also, a value stream map requires a diagram of the physical system, which works well in a factory, but is very difficult for a knowledge work process. This is particularly important for transactional processes in banks and other information intensive organizations where the processes have many decision points. Therefore, nearly all of the information in a value stream map can be included in a process map. To make the process map more visual, it is possible to add photos to make it more visual.

The paper "Process Mapping" is available from www.ClamshellBeachPress.com. ◉

See *facility layout, flowchart, service blueprint, seven tools of quality, SIPOC Diagram, value stream map.*

process performance qualification – See *process validation.*

process validation – A term used by the Food and Drug Administration (FDA) in the USA for establishing documented evidence that a process will consistently produce a product meeting specifications.

Process validation is a requirement of the Current Good Manufacturing Practices Regulations for Finished Pharmaceuticals and the Good Manufacturing Practice Regulations for Medical Devices. The following terms are important elements of process validation (source: www.fda.gov/CDER/GUIDANCE/pv.htm, June 30, 2008):

Installation Qualification (IQ) – Establishing confidence that process equipment and ancillary systems are capable of consistently operating within established limits and tolerances.

Process performance qualification – Establishing confidence that the process is effective and reproducible.

Product performance qualification – Establishing confidence through appropriate testing that the finished product produced by a specified process meets all release requirements for functionality and safety.

Prospective validation – Validation conducted prior to the distribution of either a new product, or product made under a revised manufacturing process, where the revisions may affect the product's characteristics.

Retrospective validation – Validation of a process for a product already in distribution based upon accumulated production, testing and control data.

---

[10] *Lean thinking uses the term "gemba" to describe the people who actually work the process. Lean process improvement leaders show respect for the people "in the gemba." This multi-voting process is one effective way to do that.*

Validation – Establishing documented evidence which provides a high degree of assurance that a specific process will consistently produce a product meeting its pre-determined specifications and quality attributes.

Validation protocol – A written plan stating how validation will be conducted, including test parameters, product characteristics, production equipment, and decision points on what constitutes acceptable test results.

Worst case – A set of conditions encompassing upper and lower processing limits and circumstances, including those within standard operating procedures, which pose the greatest chance of process or product failure when compared to ideal conditions. Such conditions do not necessarily induce product or process failure.

See *process capability and performance, quality assurance, Statistical Process Control (SPC)*.

procurement – See *purchasing*.

producer's risk – The probability of rejecting a lot that has a defect rate equal to the AQL for a given sampling plan.

The producer suffers when this occurs because a lot with an acceptable quality was rejected. This is called a Type I error. The Greek letter α (alpha) is used for Type I risk with typical values in range (0.2, 0.01).

See *Acceptable Quality Level (AQL), acceptance sampling, consumer's risk, operating characteristic curve, Type I and II errors*.

Product Data Management (PDM) – Software for managing product development information.

The best PDM systems are web-based collaborative applications for product development that allow enterprises to integrate business processes and product data with dispersed divisions, partners, and customers. The challenge is to maximize the time-to-market benefits of concurrent engineering while maintaining control of the data and distributing it automatically to the people who need it and when they need it. PDM systems cope with this challenge by having master data held only once in a secure vault where its integrity can be assured and all changes to it monitored, controlled, and recorded. Duplicate reference copies of the master data, on the other hand, can be distributed freely to users in various departments for design, analysis, and approval. The new data is then released back into the vault. When a change is made to data, what actually happens is that a modified copy of the data, signed and dated, is stored in the vault alongside the old data, which remains in its original form as permanent record. This is the simple principle behind more advanced PDM systems. (Adapted from www.windchill.com, www.pdmic.com, and www.pdmic.com/ undrstnd.html#brief.)

See *New Product Development (NPD)*.

product design quality – The degree to which the product design contributes to the creation of a high quality product.

Product design quality is the output of a team of knowledge workers typically residing in marketing, product design, development, quality assurance, and operations. The challenge is to integrate a quality philosophy and quality tools into the knowledge work process of creating a product design.

The knowledge workers' manager needs to have sufficient technical expertise to be seen as competent by the knowledge workers, but should manage the outcomes and the overall process rather than the details. In order to assure the quality of the creative process, the manager assures that the systems that communicate information to the design engineer are functioning properly. In summary, managers should audit the systems and results, not the knowledge or thought processes.

Acknowledgments: Rick Christensen, MOT Class of 2001, contributed to this entry.

Note that product design quality is not the same as either performance or conformance quality.

See *conformance quality, performance quality, warranty*.

product layout – An approach to organizing the physical configuration of a facility that is defined by the sequence of steps required to build a particular product.

See *assembly line, continuous flow, facility layout, process layout*.

product lifecycle management – Managing a product through its entire life, from concept to design, to development, to commercialization, to manufacturing, and finally to phase out.

Many firms struggle particularly with the early and late phases of the product lifecycle. During the start-up phase, the difficulties are in forecasting (see the entry on the *Bass Model*) and commercialization. In the later phases of the product lifecycle, many firms fail to clearly state their end-of-life policies regarding when they will stop selling a product and when they will stop supporting a product.

As products mature and reach technical obsolescence, and end-of-life policy delivers value to both the manufacturer and customer. The manufacturer cannot afford to indefinitely support obsolete products and technologies. The end-of-life policy sets boundaries and manages expectations about the supply and support guidelines for a product. Customers benefit from a policy that protects them from buying a product destined for obsolescence and/or with limited support. Many manufacturers provide support and replacement parts for up to five years after the date of sale, even if the product is removed from the market. For some critical products, the manufacturer takes the initiative to notify customers six months in advance of the product's scheduled end-of-life.

Some of the key events that need to be managed include:

End of Production – The date at which a product is no longer produced or shipped by a manufacturer.

End of Life – The date that a product is no longer marketed or sold.

End of Support – The last date that a product will be supported. Some customers might negotiate an extension for this date.

Many firms use a policy of having a "termination date" for products and components. A product and its unique components[11] are no longer sold or supported after the termination date. The advantages of having a termination date policy include:

- The termination date provides a clear plan for every functional area in the organization that deals with products (manufacturing, purchasing, inventory, service, engineering, and marketing). This facilitates an orderly, coordinated phase-out of the item.
- The termination date clearly communicates to the sales force and to the market that the product will no longer be supported (or at least no longer sold) after the termination date. This often provides incentive for customers to upgrade to a newer product.
- The termination date allows manufacturing and inventory planners to bring down the inventories for all unique components needed for the product in a coordinated way.

Good implementation practices of a termination date policy include the following policies:

- Plan ahead many years to give all stakeholders warning (this includes marketing, sales, product management, purchasing, and manufacturing).
- Make sure that all functions (and divisions) have "buy-in" to the termination date.
- Do not surprise customers by terminating a product without proper notice.

Acknowledgments: CEMBA 09 students Mark Anderson, Paul Beswetherick, Brian Clark, Tiffany Grunewald, Perry McGahan, Brent Niccum, Tushar Patel, Caitlyn Rosendahl, Sara Rottunda, Rebecca Savoie, Kate Walker, and Yarden Wolfe contributed to this entry.

The paper "Forecasting Lifetime Demand" and the Excel workbook "LIDA.xls" are on the *OMWW CD* available from www.ClamshellBeachPress.com. ◉

See *adoption curve, all-time demand, all-time order, Bass Model, bathtub curve, phase-in/phase-out planning, technology road map, termination date, time to market, value engineering.*

product mix problem – See *linear programming.*

product performance qualification – See *process validation.*

product simplification – See *value engineering.*

product structure – See *Bill of Material (BOM).*

product-process matrix – A descriptive model that relates the production volume requirements to the type of production process. ✪

The product-process matrix was introduced by Robert H. Hayes and Steven C. Wheelwright in two *Harvard Business Review* articles published in 1979 entitled "Link Manufacturing Process and Product Life Cycles" and "The Dynamics of Process-Product Life Cycles." The matrix consists of two dimensions, product structure/product life cycle and process structure/process life cycle. The process structure/process life cycle dimension describes the process choice (job shop, batch, assembly line, and continuous flow) and process structure (jumbled flow, disconnected line flow, connected line flow and continuous flow) while the product

---

[11] *The "unique" components are those that are needed only for the product being terminated. If a component is also needed in a product that is not being terminated, the component cannot be terminated.*

structure/product life cycle describes the four stages of the product life cycle (low volume to high volume) and product structure (low to high standardization). Later writers have added an additional stage in the upper-left corner for the project. The product-process matrix is shown below with some examples for the cells along the main diagonal.

Many authors argue that the ideal configuration is the main diagonal (the shaded boxes in the matrix) so that the product and process match with each other. Others point out that mass customization and flexible manufacturing systems are strategies to move down the matrix while still offering product variety. The matrix below is adapted from Hayes and Wheelwright and includes the project layout on the top row.

The product-process matrix

	Product structure/product life cycle					Flexibility & unit cost
Production volume	**Very low**	**Low**	**Medium**	**High**	**Very high**	
Standardization	None	Very low	Low	High	Very high	
Number of products	**Very high**	**Many**	**Many**	**Few**	**Very few**	
No flow (project layout)	Project Ex: building, ship building			**NOT FEASIBLE**	**NOT FEASIBLE**	High
Jumbled flow (job shop)		Job shop Ex: Printer, French restaurant			**NOT FEASIBLE**	
Disconnected line flow (batch)			Batch Ex: Heavy equipment			
Connected line flow (assembly line)	**NOT FEASIBLE**[12]			Assembly line Ex: Autos, Burger King		
Continuous flow (continuous)	**NOT FEASIBLE**[13]	**NOT FEASIBLE**			Continuous Ex: Refinery, consumer products	Low

Source: Professor Arthur V. Hill (adapted from many sources)

See *facility layout, Flexible Manufacturing System (FMS), mass customization.*

production function – A microeconomics concept that expresses the relationship between an organization's inputs and its outputs.

The production function is a mathematical model that indicates what outputs can be obtained from various amounts and combinations of factor inputs. In its most general mathematical form, a production function is expressed as $Q = f(x_1, x_2, ..., x_n)$, where Q is the quantity of output and $(x_1, x_2, ..., x_n)$ are the factor inputs, such as capital, labor, raw materials, land, technology, or management.

The production function can be specified in a number of ways, including an additive (linear) function $Q = a + b_1 x_1 + b_2 x_2 + ... + b_n x_n$ or a multiplicative (Cobb-Douglas) production function $Q = a x_1^{b_1} x_2^{b_2} ... x_n^{b_n}$. Other forms include the constant elasticity of substitution production function (CES), which is a generalized

---

[12] *In some cases, it is possible to still have an assembly line for low volume products by using mixed model assembly.*

[13] *It is possible to have continuous flow for low volume products by using automation and mass customization strategies.*

form of the Cobb-Douglas function, and the quadratic production function which is a specific type of additive function. The best form of the equation to use and the values of the parameters vary from company to company and industry to industry.

Adapted from http://dictionary.laborlawtalk.com/ Production_function, October 1, 2006.

See *Data Envelopment Analysis (DEA), economics.*

Production Operations Management Society (POMS) – An international professional society representing the interests of production and operations management professionals from around the world.

The purposes of the Society are (1) to extend and integrate knowledge that contributes to the improved understanding and practice of production and operations management (POM), (2) to disseminate information on POM to managers, scientists, educators, students, public and private organizations, national and local governments, and the general public, and (3) to promote the improvement of POM and its teaching in public and private manufacturing and service organizations throughout the world.

Professor Kalyan Singhal founded POMS on June 30, 1989 in collaboration with about three hundred professors and executives. The society held its first international meeting in Washington, D.C. in October 1990. The inaugural issue of the POMS journal, *Production and Operations Management*, was published in March 1992.

The POMS website is www.poms.org.

See *Operations Management (OM).*

production planning – See *aggregate production planning.*

productivity – A measure of the value produced by a system for a given level of inputs. ✪

Productivity is normally defined and measured as the ratio of an output measure divided by an input measure (e.g., hamburgers created per hour). It is a relative measure of how well a country, industry, business unit, person, or machine is using its resources. Productivity for a firm can be compared to another firm or to itself over time.

Total factor productivity is measured in monetary units. Partial factor productivity is measured in individual inputs or monetary units, with labor being the most common. Partial factor productivity can be misleading because a decline in the productivity of one input may be due to an increase in productivity of another input. For example, a firm might improve labor productivity by outsourcing production, but find that the overall cost per unit is up due to the high cost of managing the outsourcing partner.

Total factor productivity = output/input (goods and services produced/resources used)

Partial factor productivity: output/labor hour, output/capital, output/materials, output/energy, etc.

Multi-factory productivity: output/(labor + capital + energy), output/(labor + materials), etc.

Many firms define and report productivity in terms of cost/unit. This is not output divided by input, but rather input (cost) divided by output (units).

Example: A firm consumed 2400 hours of labor to process 560 insurance forms. What is the labor productivity? Answer: 2400/560 = 4.29 forms/hour. However, the firm prefers to express this in terms of hours per form (e.g., 0.23 hours/form) and dollars/form (e.g., $4.67/form).

See *Data Envelopment Analysis (DEA), efficiency, High Performance Work Systems (HPWS), Overall Equipment Effectiveness (OEE), utilization.*

program – A set of projects that need to be coordinated to achieve certain objectives of the organization.

A program in an on-going activity with a long-term goal, usually implemented with a series of many interrelated projects. Unlike a project, a program is often an on-going activity with no set end-date. Programs are often managed by a "program office" with a dedicated leadership team. An example of a program might be a quality program such as Six Sigma or might be very large scale construction project such as a nuclear reactor that requires years to complete.

See *program management office, project charter.*

program management office – An individual or group of people who are charged with overseeing a set of projects intended to achieve some overarching objective. ✪

One of the keys to success of process improvement programs such as Six Sigma is managing the "hopper" of potential projects so that the firm is carefully selecting the projects from a strategic point of view and matching them to resources (Black Belts and Green Belts) to develop the leadership "muscle" of the firm. According to

Englund, Graham, & Dinsmore (2003), "The project office adds value to the organization by ensuring that projects are performed within procedures, are in line with organizational strategies, and are completed in a way that adds economic value to the organization."

A research project by Zhang, Hill, Schroeder, and Linderman (2006) found two keys to success for any process improvement program – Strategic Project Selection (SPS) and Discipline Project Management (DPM). The research found a causal linkage from DPM to SPS to operating performance. The SPS and DPM activities are both outcomes of a well-managed program management office.

Other related terms include project management office and project control (Englund, Graham, and Dinsmore 2003). Still other firms use the name of the program to name the office (e.g., Six Sigma Champion, Lean Promotion Office, Director of Management Information Systems, etc.). These programs could be related to new product development projects, building projects, process improvement projects, marketing research projects, etc.

See *champion, lean promotion office, lean thinking, process improvement program, program, project charter, project management, Six Sigma*.

project – See *project management*.

project charter – A document that clearly defines the key attributes of a project such as the purpose, scope, deliverables, and timeline. ✪

The charter is essentially a contract between the project sponsor and the project leader and team. Like a good product design or a good building blueprint, a well-designed project charter is a strong foundation for a successful project.

Recommended project charter template

The following project charter format has been developed over the course of several years by Gene Heupel and Professor Arthur Hill. Mr. Heupel was the Director of Project Control at Xcel Energy for many years and is now the President of GMHeupel Associates, a consultancy that provides process improvement and project management services. This framework draws from his experience, a large number of company examples, and the Project Management Institute's recommended format.

- **Project name:** Usually a short descriptive name.
- **Project number:** Often a budget number or project designator in the "portfolio" of projects.
- **Problem:** A clear and concise business case for the project. This statement should include enough background to motivate the project. (See the *business case* entry for detailed suggestions on how to write a business case.)
- **Objectives:** The targeted benefits (improvement) in cost, sales, errors, etc. This requires both selection of the metrics to be used and the target values for these metrics. In some cases, the benefits may be hard to quantify (e.g., customer satisfaction); however, in general, it is best to define quantifiable objectives. Some firms require separate sections for "financial impact" and "customer impact."
- **Deliverables:** A list of products to be delivered, for example, improved procedures, an NPV analysis, training, implementation plan, and how these will be delivered to the project sponsor (e.g., workshop, PowerPoint presentation, Excel workbook, or training).
- **Scope:** A clear statement of the project boundaries, including clear and deliberate identification of what is out-of-scope.
- **Assumptions:** Key beliefs about the problem. For example, a key assumption for one project was that the process improvement efforts did not require fundamental changes to the information systems.
- **Schedule:** A short list of the most important planned completion dates (milestones) for each of the main activities and deliverables in the project.
- **Budget:** The estimated labor hours and cost. Identify expenses and hours for key resources.
- **Risk mitigation:** The barriers that might keep the project from being completely successful, including a statement about how these should be addressed. For example, a project might be at risk if one user group fails to embrace a new process. The mitigation for this might be to assign a key representative of this user group to the process design team and provide training for all the users before the new process is implemented.

- **Team:** A list of the team members' names and titles along with their roles (e.g., team leader, team member, team support person). Some organizations add their planned utilization, start date, and end date. Subject matter experts (SMEs) should also be listed with an explanation of their roles, such as providing advising or reviewing. SMEs are not formal team members and therefore can be included without increasing the size of the team.
- **Sponsor:** The name of the project sponsor or sponsors. Sponsors should be included from every organization that is significantly impacted by the project.
- **Approvals:** Signatures from all of the project sponsors before the project is started. It is important to revise the charter and get new approvals whenever the scope is changed. In some situations, such as new product development, signoffs are required at the end of each phase of the project.

Lean Sigma project charter template

The book ***What is Lean Six Sigma?*** (George, Rowlands, and Kastle, 2003) recommends the following project charter template for Lean Sigma projects:
- **Description**
- **Background**
- **Scope** (defining both in-scope and out of scope).
- **Key Process Output Variable** (KPOV)
- **Goals**
- **Assumptions**
- **Other benefits**
- **Team** (role, name, utilization, start date, end date)

A3 Report (lean manufacturing) project charter template

In lean manufacturing, the project charter is called an "A3 Report" and is required to fit onto one page. The following outline is adapted and shortened from "A3 Standards for Lean Projects" by David Mann of the Office Lean Consulting Team at Steeelcase (February 22, 2006):

Problem statement
- State specifically what we have that we do not want and/or what we want that we do not have.
- State the implications and result of the problem for performance of the department and of the business.
- State the causes of the problem if known.

Objectives
- Clearly state desired outcomes of a successful project.
- Define measures of success that should be directly derivable from the objectives.
- State the actions to deliver specific improvements using action verbs such as: improve, reduce, develop, create, and revise.
- If the improvement is quantitative, then state how much improvement.
- If the improvement is not quantitative, then state the desired change.
- State how much is attainable in 90 days or list longer-term goals with intermediate milestones.

Measures
- Specific, verifiable, objective, reflecting end-to-end process performance, directly derived from objectives.
- If applicable, stated the planned increments of improvement per period of time.

Implementation plan
- Summarize project/loop plan on single A3, e.g., "ABC Project Summary A3"
- List kaizen events/tasks within kaizens in logical sequence.
- Document each kaizen on its own A3.
- Name person responsible for each line item.
- The paper "Project Charters" is on the ***OMWW CD*** available from www.ClamshellBeachPress.com. ●

See *A3 Report, business case, champion, lean thinking, New Product Development (NPD), program, program management office, project management, scope creep, scoping, Six Sigma, SME (Subject Matter Expert), stage-gate process, stakeholder analysis.*

Project Evaluation and Review Technique (PERT) – An approach for project planning developed by the U.S. Navy for the Polaris submarine project.

In its original form, PERT required that each task have three task time estimates, the optimistic task time (a), the most likely task time (m), and the pessimistic task time (b). PERT estimates the mean task time using the equation $(a+4m+b)/6$ and the variance of the task time as $(b-a)^2/36$. These equations were supposedly based on the beta distribution, but Sasieni (1986) noted that these equations have little or no scientific basis. However, Littlefield and Randolph (1987) attempted to refute Sasieni's assertions. Sasieni was probably closer to the truth on this issue.

The mean of the critical path time is estimated by adding the means of the tasks along the critical path; similarly, the variance of the critical path time is estimated by adding the variances along the critical path. The confidence interval for the project completion time is then estimated as the mean plus or minus z standard deviations, where the standard deviation of the project time is the square root of the variance of the project time.

This approach assumes that (1) the distribution of the project completion time is determined only by the critical path time (*i.e.*, that no other path could become critical), (2) the project completion time is normally distributed, and (3) the equations for the mean and variance are correct. In reality, none of these assumptions is correct. Few organizations find that the three-task time approach is worth the time, confusion, and cost.

See *beta distribution, critical chain, Critical Path Method (CPM), project management, slack time, work breakdown structure (WBS).*

project hopper – A simple tool that helps the champion for a process improvement program manage the set of current and potential projects.

The project hopper is a tool used to help store and prioritize potential process improvement projects. This is usually done with an Excel workbook. Ecolab and other firms prioritize potential projects based on two dimensions (1) benefits (sales growth, cost reduction, improved service) and (2) effort (cost, resources, time to achieve benefits). Ecolab graphs each project on the two dimensions and uses that information as a visual tool to help managers prioritize potential projects. Preliminary project charters are then written for the most promising projects and then the benefit and cost assessment is performed one more time to finally select which projects to officially charter, resource, and initiate.

See *process improvement program, Six Sigma.*

project management – The planning, organizing, scheduling, directing, and controlling of a one-time activity to meet or exceed stakeholder-defined constraints on scope, schedule, and cost. ✪

According to the Project Management Institute's Project Management Book of Knowledge (PMBOK), "A project is a temporary endeavor undertaken to create a unique product or service."

Key success factors for project management include a strong project charter, avoiding scope creep, and a good post mortem review so that the organization learns from its projects management mistakes and successes. This encyclopedia includes entries on each of these subjects.

The following is a list of project management "laws" written with a little humor. Many of these have been adapted from long lost sources. Of course, well-managed organizations resist the downward pull of these laws.

- **Murphy's Law:** If it can go wrong, it will.
- **Second Law of Thermodynamics (Law of Entropy):** All systems tend towards their highest state of disorder. (Murphy's Law is really just an application of this law.)
- **Parkinson's Law:** Work expands to fill the time allotted to it. (Parkinson's exact wording was "Work expands so as to fill the time available for its completion.") This is only one of many laws found in his book (Parkinson, 1958).
- **The Pi Rule:** All poorly managed projects take π times longer than originally predicted. (Note $\pi \approx 3.1416$.) People think the completion path is a straight line (the diameter of the circle), when it is really the circumference of the circle.
- **The optimistic time estimate law:** Projects rarely do what was promised and are rarely completed on time, within budget, and with the same staff that started them. **Corollary a:** It is highly unlikely that your project

will be the first. **Corollary b:** A carelessly planned project will take $\pi \approx 3.1416$ times longer to complete than expected – a carefully planned project will take only $e \approx 2.7183$ times as long. **Corollary c:** When the project is going well, something will go wrong. **Corollary d:** When things cannot get any worse, they will. **Corollary e:** When things appear to be going better, you have overlooked something.

- **The last 10 percent law:** Projects progress rapidly until they are 90 percent complete. The last 10 percent then takes 50 percent of the time.
- **Brooke's Law:** Adding people to a late project generally makes it later.
- **The project employment law:** Projects requiring more than 18 months tend to lose their identity as a "project" and become a permanent part of the organization. **Corollary:** If the project objectives are allowed to change freely, the team might unintentionally turn the project into guaranteed long-term employment.
- **The project charter law:** A project without a clearly written charter will be subject to scope creep – and will help you discover many of your organization's worst political problems.
- **The project correction law:** The effort required to correct a project that is off course increases every day it is allowed to continue off course.
- **The matrix organization law:** Matrix organizations tend to be dysfunctional. All employees really have only one boss – the person making their next salary decision. However, matrix organizations are essential in the modern firm.
- **The project leader law:** A great way to sabotage an important project is to assign whoever is currently completely idle as the project leader.
- **The technical leadership law:** The greater the project's scope and organizational complexity, the less likely a technician is needed to manage it. **Corollary:** Get the best project manager that can be found. A good project manager will find the right technical people for the project.
- **The belief in the system law:** If the user does not believe in the system, a parallel informal system will be developed – and neither system will work very well.
- **The post mortem project law:** Organizations that do not do a complete post-project review are doomed to repeat their mistakes over and over again.

Again, well-managed organizations will resist the downward pull of these laws!

Project Management Institute's Project Management Book of Knowledge (PMBOK) is the accepted standard for project management practices. The condensed version of the book can be found at the following website pmi.org/prod/groups/public/documents/info/pp_pmbokguide2000excerpts.pdf. Another source of project management knowledge is the Automotive Project Management Guide published by AIAG (Automotive Industry Action Group, website: www.aiag.org). AIAG publishes a set of books used by Ford, GM, and Daimler Chrysler for managing automotive projects and suppliers.

The Excel workbook entitled "Project schedule template.xls" is available on the *OMWW CD* available from www.ClamshellBeachPress.com. This is a simple project scheduling tool. ◉

See *critical chain, critical path, Critical Path Method (CPM), Design Structure Matrix (DSM), Earned Value Management (EVM), facility layout, finite scheduling, Gantt Chart, infinite loading, load leveling, Murphy's Law, New Product Development (NPD), Parkinson's Laws, post mortem review, process improvement program, program management office, project charter, Project Evaluation and Review Technique (PERT), Project Management Institute (PMI), scope creep, scoping, slack time, stage-gate process, waterfall scheduling, work breakdown structure (WBS).*

Project Management Institute (PMI) – The leading membership association for the project management profession.

PMI is actively engaged in advocacy for the profession, setting professional standards, conducting research and providing access to a wealth of information and resources. PMI also promotes career and professional development and offers certification, networking, and community involvement opportunities.

PMI was founded in 1969 and had its first official meeting at the Georgia Institute of Technology in Atlanta, Georgia. Since then, the Institute has grown to become the global advocate for the project management profession with more than 240,000 members in over 160 countries. With nearly 242,000 credential holders worldwide, PMI's Project Management Professional (PMP®) certification is the most widely recognized in the profession.

The website for PMI is www.PMI.org.

See *Operations Management (OM), project management.*

project management office – See *program management office.*

prospective validation – See *process validation.*

prototype – In the product development context, an example built for evaluation purposes.

A prototype is usually a trial model that is often used for evaluation purposes. Prototypes are also built as a standard for subsequent units produced. Prototypes are often built quickly to help users evaluate certain features and/or capabilities.

In the software development context, prototyping is particularly important for getting user input before the final design is implemented. Prototyping is closely related to the software development concept of agile design. A beta test is the test of new software by a user under actual work conditions and is the final test before release to the public. In contrast, an alpha test is the first test conducted by the developer done under test conditions.

See *beta test, breadboard, New Product Development (NPD).*

public-private partnership – A form of cooperation between government and private enterprise with the goal of provide service for society through both private for-profit and not-for-profit organizations.

For example, PPL is public private partnership in the City of Minneapolis, Minnesota that has served Hennepin Country for more than thirty years. The mission of PPL is to assist lower income people and families working toward self-sufficiency by providing housing, jobs, and training. One of PPL's main divisions is called "PPL Industries Disassembly and Reclamation" which employs hundreds of ex-convicts to disassemble tens of thousands of electronic products such as televisions, stereos, telephones, VCRs, and computers collected by Hennepin Country (Minneapolis) each year. This service provides value to society by giving jobs and job training to just released convicts -- and also helps protects the environment.

Acknowledgments: CEMBA 09 students Brian Clark, Brent Niccum, Tushar Patel, Rebecca Savoie, and Kate Walker contributed to this entry.

See *triple bottom line.*

Pugh Matrix – A decision tool that facilitates a disciplined, team-based process for concept generation, evaluation, and selection.

The Pugh Matrix is a scoring matrix that defines the important criteria for a decision, defines the weights for each criterion, defines the alternatives, and then scores each alternative. The selection is made based on the consolidated scores. The Pugh matrix allows an organization to compare different concepts, create strong alternative concepts from weaker concepts, and arrive at the best concept that may be a hybrid or variant of the best of other concepts.

Several concepts are evaluated according to their strengths and weaknesses against a reference concept called the datum (base concept). The datum is the best current concept at each iteration of the matrix. The Pugh matrix encourages comparison of several different concepts against a base concept, creating stronger concepts and eliminating weaker ones until an optimal concept is finally reached.

This tool is very similar to Kepner-Tregoe Model.

See *Analytical Hierarchy Process (AHP), decision tree, Design for Six Sigma (DFSS), force-field diagram, Kano Analysis, Kepner-Tregoe Model, New Product Development (NPD), Quality Function Deployment (QFD), Six Sigma, Triz, Voice of the Customer (VOC).*

pull systems – A system that determines how much to order and when to order in response to a customer demand, where the customer may be either an internal or external customer. ✪

All production and inventory control systems deal with only two fundamental decision variables: (1) when to order and (2) how much to order. It is easiest to understand "push" and "pull" systems for managing these two variables in a logistics context. Suppose, for example, a factory supplies two warehouses. With a push system, the people at the factory decide when and how much to ship to each of the two warehouses based on forecasted demand and inventory position information. With a pull system, the problem is disaggregated so that the people at each warehouse decide when and how much to order from the factory based on their need. Of course, the factory might not have the inventory, so some of these orders might not be filled.

The following table compares push and pull systems.

A comparison of push and pull systems

Dimension	Push	Pull
Signal to produce more	Schedule or plan	Customer signal
Timing of signal	Advance of the need	At the time of the need
Typical signal	Paper or computer	Container, square, cart, or paper
Information scope	Global	Local only
Planning horizon	Fairly long	Very short
Level demand needed	No	Generally yes
Standard parts/products	Not necessary	Generally necessary
Large queues possible	Yes	No
Negatives	Too much inventory Not visual Requires more information Long planned leadtimes	Does not plan ahead. Misses customer demand at the beginning of the product lifecycle and too much inventory at the end
Best for	Non-repetitive, batch, seasonal demand, short product lifecycles. Long leadtime purchasing.	Repetitive, high-volume manufacturing, with stable demand.
Visibility	Not visible	Visible
Stress to improve	Little	Much
Problems found from	Computer reports	Shop floor/visible signals

Source: Professor Arthur V. Hill

Hopp and Spearman (2004) provide a different perspective in their comparison of push and pull systems. They define a pull system as one that limits the amount of work in process that can be in the system and a push system as one that has no limit on the amount of work in process that can be in the system. They argue further that the definition of push and pull is largely independent of the make to order/make to stock decision.

See *CONWIP*, *lean thinking*, *two-bin system*.

purchasing – The business function responsible for (1) selecting suppliers, (2) negotiating contracts, and (3) ensuring the reliable supply of materials for the firm. ✪

The goals of a purchasing organization are usually defined in terms of on-time delivery, quality, and cost. Some purchasing organizations, particularly in the larger firms, also get involved in helping their suppliers improve their performance.

Purchasing organizations are also known as procurement, supply management, supplier management, supplier development, strategic sourcing, and buying. The *sourcing* and *supplier scorecard* entries have more information on this subject.

See *blanket purchase order*, *Business Process Outsourcing*, *commodity*, *e-procurement*, *leverage the spend*, *logistics*, *Materials Requirements Planning (MRP)*, *MRO (Maintenance-Repair-Operations)*, *outsourcing*, *purchasing leadtime*, *reverse auction*, *single source*, *sourcing*, *supplier qualification and certification*, *supplier scorecard*, *supply chain management*.

purchasing leadtime – The time between the release and receipt of a purchase order from a supplier; also known as purchase leadtime and replenishment leadtime.

The parameter in the ERP (or MRP) system should be the planned purchasing leadtime, which is often set to the average actual value. The safety stock is then used to handle variability in the demand and the leadtime.

See *cycle time*, *leadtime*, *purchasing*.

push system – See *pull systems*.

push-pull boundary – The point at which a supply chain (or firm) switches from building to forecast (push) and filling an actual customer order (pull); Hopp (2007) calls this the inventory/order (or I/O) interface; Schroeder (2008) calls this the customization point; others call it the order penetration point; still other sources call this the "decoupling point" or the "customization process decoupling point." ✪

The push-pull boundary is the point at which the customer order is started in the system. For example, with an Assemble-to-Order (ATO) system, the point of entry is just before the final assembly. ATO systems, therefore, generally inventory all major components, fasteners, etc. so that the product can be assembled very quickly to the customer's requirements.

Moving the push-pull boundary to a point earlier in the process allows firms to be more responsive to customer demand and avoid mismatches in supply and demand. However, the customer leadtime will usually get longer. One of the best examples is Dell Computer that assembles computers in response to a customer order. The push-pull boundary is closely related to the concept of postponement (postponed differentiation). See the *postponement* and *Respond-to-Order* entries for more detailed information.

See *cumulative leadtime, customer leadtime, leadtime, Make to Order (MTO), Make to Stock (MTS), mass customization, postponement, Respond to Order (RTO).*

Q

QFD – See *Quality Function Deployment.*

QR – See *Quick Response.*

QRM – See *Quick Response Manufacturing.*

QS 9000 – A supplier development program developed by a Chrysler/Ford/General Motors supplier requirement task force.

The purpose of QS 9000 is to provide a common standard and a set of procedures for the suppliers of the three companies.

quadratic formula – A basic algebraic approach for finding the roots of a second order polynomial of the form $y = ax^2 + bx + c = 0$.

The quadratic formula is $x = (-b \pm \sqrt{b^2 - 4ac})/(2a)$. For example, the roots (solution) of the equation $y = x^2 + 3x - 4 = 0$ are $x = -4$ and 1, which means that the graph of the equation crosses the x-axis (e.g., $y = 0$) at both $x = -4$ and $x = 0$.

qualification – See *supplier qualification and certification.*

quality – Fitness for use; conformance to customer requirements. ✪

See *conformance quality, cost of quality, performance quality, quality at the source, quality circles, Quality Function Deployment (QFD), service quality, Statistical Process Control (SPC), Statistical Quality Control (SQC), Total Quality Management (TQM), Voice of the Customer (VOC).*

quality assurance – The process of ensuring that the products and service produced meet the required standards for their customers.

The basic principles of quality assurance include: (1) quality, safety, and effectiveness must be designed and built into the product; (2) quality cannot be inspected or tested into the finished product; and (3) each step of the manufacturing process must be controlled to maximize the probability that the finished product meets all specifications. Process validation is a key element in assuring that these quality assurance goals are met. (Adapted from: www.fda.gov/CDER/GUIDANCE/pv.htm, July 1, 2008.)

See *process validation, Statistical Process Control (SPC).*

quality at the source – The philosophy that organizations should not try to inspect quality into a system, but rather ensure that perfect conformance quality happens at every step of the process.

The person who does the work should be responsible for ensuring their own quality. Checking quality in a later step is a waste of time and tends to encourage workers to be a lazy when they know that someone else will be checking their work. For example, data entry personnel should ensure that every number is entered properly and this work should not have to be inspected by someone else.

See *quality.*

quality circles – A small group of volunteers who meet together to identify, analyze, and improve their processes and workplace environment.

Typical discussion topics include safety, product design, and process improvement. Unlike many process improvement teams, quality circles remain intact over time. According to Wikipedia, quality circles were started in Japan in 1962 by Kaoru Ishikawa as a method for improving quality. Quality circles were popular in the 1980s and early 1990s in North America, but then fell out of favor.

See *brainstorming, quality*.

Quality Function Deployment (QFD) – A method for ensuring that the customer has a voice in the design specification of a product; also known as house of quality. ✪

QFD uses cross functional teams from manufacturing, engineering, and marketing. The process begins with market research to define customer needs and then break these needs down into categories called customer requirements. Requirements are then weighted based on their importance to the customer. Customers are asked to rate the firm's products against competitors' products. This process assists the firm in determining what the customer values and how the customer rates the product compared to a competitor's product. QFD results in a better focus on customers' needs and product characteristics in need of improvement.

Quality Function Deployment (QFD) is the only comprehensive quality system aimed specifically at satisfying the customer. It concentrates on maximizing customer satisfaction (positive quality) and is measured by metrics, such as repeat business and market share. QFD focuses on delivering value by seeking out both spoken and unspoken needs, translating these into design targets, and communicating this throughout the organization.

See *affinity diagram, concurrent engineering, cross functional team, New Product Development (NPD), Pugh Matrix, quality, Voice of the Customer (VOC)*.

quality management – See *Total Quality Management (TQM)*.

quality trilogy – A concept promoted by Joseph Juran and the Juran Institute stating that quality consists of three basic quality-oriented processes: quality planning, quality control, and quality improvement.

Joseph Juran (1986) expanded on these three processes using the following bullet points:

Quality Planning
- Identify both internal and external customers.
- Determine customer needs.
- Develop product features that respond to customer needs. (Products include both goods and services.)
- Establish quality goals that meet the needs of customers and suppliers alike, and do so at a minimum combined cost.
- Develop a process that can produce the needed product features.
- Prove process capability - prove that the process can meet the quality goals under operating conditions.

Quality Control
- Choose control subjects - what to control.
- Choose units of measurement.
- Establish measurement.
- Establish standards of performance.
- Measure actual performance.
- Interpret the difference (actual versus standard).
- Take action on the difference.

Quality Improvement
- Prove the need for improvement.
- Identify specific projects for improvement.
- Organize to guide the projects.
- Organize for diagnosis—for discovery of causes.
- Diagnose to find the causes.
- Provide remedies.
- Prove that the remedies are effective under operating conditions.
- Provide for control to hold the gains.

See *Six Sigma, Total Quality Management (TQM)*.

quantity discount – A pricing mechanism that offers customers a lower price per unit when they buy more units.

Sellers often offer a lower price to customers when they order in larger quantities. The difference between the normal price and the reduced price is called a discount.

Two policies are common in practice – the incremental units discount and the all-units discount. The incremental units discount gives the customer a lower price on the units ordered above a breakpoint. For example, if a customer orders more than 100 units, the price for the units over 100 is lowered from $10 to $9.

The all-units discount policy offers a lower price on all units ordered. For example, if a customer orders more than 100 units, the price for all units ordered will be lowered from $10 to $9. The optimal (minimum total increment cost) order quantity will always be at a breakpoint where the price changes or at a feasible EOQ.

See *Economic Order Quantity (EOQ)*.

queue time – See *wait time*.

queuing theory – A branch of mathematics that deals with understanding systems with customers (orders, calls, etc.) arriving and being served by one or more servers; also known as queueing theory; also spelled queueing. ✪

Managers often need to make important decisions about how much capacity to have, how many lines to have, and where to invest in process improvement. Intuition around these decisions is often wrong and computer simulation models are often too expensive and too complicated to be of practical value. Queuing theory can provide value to managers in three ways:

- A powerful language for describing systems with waiting lines (queues). Terms such as utilization, average waiting time, and probability of delay are standard queuing theory concepts.
- Practical intuition that is helpful for understanding all queuing systems.
- Computationally fast analytical tools that can be implemented in Excel and used to help answer a variety of "what-if" questions such as, "How much will our average waiting time go down if we add a server?"

Nearly all queuing theory models assume that the mean service rate and the mean arrival rate do not change over time. These models then evaluate the steady state (long-term) system performance with statistics such as utilization, mean time in queue, mean time in system, mean number in queue, and mean number in system. Unfortunately, queuing models are often limited by the required assumptions that the mean arrival rate and mean service rate do not change over time; therefore, most queuing analyses are approximations of the real world.

Definitions of a few terms are necessary before going further. Customers arriving to the system can be people, orders, phone calls, ambulances, etc. The server (or servers) in the system can be machines, people, buildings, etc. Customers often spend time waiting in queue (in line) before they begin service. The customer's time in system is the sum of their waiting time in queue and their service time. Utilization is the percentage of the time that the server(s) are busy. The mean service time is the inverse of the mean service rate ($\tau = 1/\mu$ and $\mu = 1/\tau$) and the mean time between arrivals is the inverse of the mean arrival rate ($\delta = 1/\lambda$ and $\lambda = 1/\delta$).

One of the fundamental managerial insights from queuing theory is that the relationship between utilization and the mean time in the system is highly non-linear. The graph below shows this relationship under typical assumptions. This particular graph has a mean arrival rate of 100 customers per hour and eight servers. However, the shape of the graph is very similar no matter what parameters are used. The practical implication of this insight is that managers who seek to maximize utilization might find themselves dramatically increasing the mean time in system, which might mean very long customer waiting times, high inventories, etc.

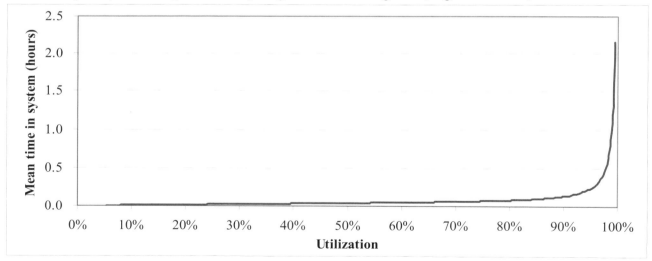

The most basic queuing model has a single server ($s = 1$) and requires three assumptions: (1) the time between arrivals follows the negative exponential distribution, (2) service times also follow the negative exponential distribution, and (3) the service discipline is first-come-first-served. (Note: The negative exponential distribution is often called the exponential distribution.) The model also assumes that all parameters are stationary, which means that the mean arrival rate and mean service rate do not change over time and are not affected by the state of the system (i.e., a long waiting line will not affect the arrival rate). This model is known as the M/M/1 queue. The first "M" notation indicates that the arrival process is Markovian. The second "M" indicates that the service process is Markovian. The "1" indicates that the system has one server. A Markovian arrival process has inter-arrival times that follow the exponential distribution. A Markovian service process has service times that follow the exponential distribution. A Markovian process is also called a Poisson process.

Define μ (mu) as the mean service rate (customers/period) and λ (lambda) as the mean arrival rate (customers/period). The steady state results for the M/M/1 queue are then:

Average utilization:	$\rho = \lambda / \mu$ (Note: ρ is the Greek letter "rho.")
Average time in system:	$W_s = 1/(\mu - \lambda)$
Average time in queue:	$W_q = \rho W_s = \rho /(\mu - \lambda)$
Average number in system:	$L_s = \lambda /(\mu - \lambda)$
Average number in queue:	$L_q = \lambda^2 /[\mu(\mu - \lambda)]$
Probability of n customers in system:	$P(n) = (1 - \rho)\rho^n$
Probability that $TIS > t$:	$P(TIS > t) = e^{-\mu(1-\rho)t}$ (Note: TIS is the time in system.)
Probability that $TIQ > t$:	$P(TIQ > t) = \rho e^{-\mu(1-\rho)t}$ (Note: TIQ is the time in queue.)
Little's Law:	$L_s = \lambda W_s$ and $L_q = \lambda W_q$

More detail and examples on Little's Law can be found in the entry for Little's Law.

The Pollaczek-Khintchine (sometimes called the PK formula) can be used for the M/G/1 queue, which is a Markovian (Poisson) arrival process for a single server with a general (G) service time distribution. The service time distribution is defined by the mean service time τ, which is the inverse of the mean service rate (e.g., $\tau = 1/\mu$), and the standard deviation of the service time (σ). The PK formula shows that the mean number in queue is given by $L_q = \dfrac{\lambda^2\sigma^2 + \rho^2}{2(1-\rho)}$, where $\rho = \lambda / \mu$ is utilization. Applying Little's Law shows that $W_q = L_q / \lambda$ and applying basic queuing theory shows that $W_s = W_q + 1/\mu$. This important formula shows how the average time in system increases with the variance of the service time.

Similar (but much more complex) equations are also available for multiple servers (M/M/s) and for situations where the arrival and/or service processes may not be Markovian (M/G/s).

When the number of servers is greater than one, the arrival process is not Markovian, or the service process is not Markovian, the following "heavy-traffic" approximation can be used:

$$W_q = \frac{1}{s\mu}\left(\frac{\rho^{\sqrt{2s+2}-1}}{1-\rho}\right)\left(\frac{cv_A^2 + cv_S^2}{2}\right)$$

where cv_A is the coefficient of variation of the time between arrival distribution and cv_S is the coefficient of variation of the service time distribution. Again, applying Little's Law shows that $L_q = \lambda W_q$ and applying basic queuing theory shows that $W_s = W_q + 1/\mu$, and applying Little's Law once more shows that $L_s = \lambda W_s$.

Finite population queuing models are used when the size of the calling population is small. For example, a finite queuing model should be used when the "customers" in the system are a limited number of machines in a factory. State-dependent queuing models are applied when the mean arrival rate or the mean service rate are dependent upon the state of the system. For example, when customers arrive to the system and see a long waiting line, they may become discouraged and exit the system.

The Excel workbooks "Queue.xls" and "Staffit.xls" and the paper entitled "Queuing Theory" are available on the **OMWW CD** available from www.ClamshellBeachPress.com. ●

See *balking, call center, capacity, exponential distribution, Little's Law, operations performance metrics, Poisson distribution, Pollaczek-Khintchine formula, pooling, utilization, value added ratio, wait time.*

Quick Response (QR) – See *Quick Response Manufacturing.*

Quick Response Manufacturing – An approach for reducing leadtimes developed by Professor Rajan Suri, Director of the Center of Quick Response Manufacturing, University of Wisconsin - Madison.

See *agile manufacturing, Efficient Consumer Response, lean thinking, time-based competition.*

R

RACI Matrix – A matrix that identifies the roles and responsibilities for all stakeholders involved in any process; the activity of creating a before and after RACI Matrix is called responsibility charting.

When an organizational is going through any type of change, it is important to identify the people involved in the process (the stakeholders) and understand how their roles and responsibilities change from the current process to the new process. The RACI matrix can be used to ensure that all team members, managers, sponsors, and others know what their role is for each step in the new process. The benefits of using the RACI Matrix include fewer misunderstandings and less time wasted in meetings and turf battles, increased productivity and capacity, and better ownership of the final roles and responsibilities.

The matrix identifies the process steps down the left side and the individuals and/or functional roles on the columns across the top. For each step in the process, the matrix indicates the following roles ("decision rights") for each individual or function:

- **R = Responsible** – The person responsible for the actions and implementation of the change. Ideally, only one person assigned to each task and each row will have only one R cell.
- **A = Accountable** – The person ultimately responsible and accountable for making sure that the task is completed. This person is ultimately answerable for the decision or activity. "The buck stops here." This person has the decision rights ("yes/no" authority) with respect the important decisions. Only one person should be accountable for each task, which means that each row should have one and only one A cell.
- **C = Consulted** – This person should be consulted before and during the task with two-way communication. This person should be "in the loop" for the entire project and consulted prior to any final decisions.
- **I = Informed** – This person should be informed when the task occurs or is completed. This is usually one-way communication. This person should be "kept in the picture."

The project team has its own project RACI Matrix and the process has both a before ("as is") and after ("should-be") RACI Matrix. Begin with the A for each task. The RACI matrix can also be used as the basis of a communication plan before the project and the control plan at the end of the project. Colors can be assigned based on the letter in the cell. Each row should have exactly one A, very few Rs, and only a few Cs and Is. Be careful that each column does not have too much work for any one individual. The *stakeholder analysis* entry discusses these issues further. The following a simple hypothetical example RACI Matrix.

Example RACI Matrix

Task	Product Manager	Design Engineer 1	Design Engineer 2	Marketer 1	Marketer 2	Manufacturing Manager	Plant Engineer 1	Plant Engineer 2
Create product specifications	A	R	C	R	C	C	I	
Validate technical specifications	C	R	C	A		I	I	
Run the pilot test	C	I	I	C	C	R	A	C
Product launch	A	I		C	I	R	C	I

See *control plan*, *Six Sigma*, *stakeholder analysis*.

Radio Frequency Identification (RFID) – The attachment of transponders (which may be read only or read/write) to products, as an alternative to linear barcodes, to enable product identification from some distance away from the scanner or when out of line of sight. ✪

Although these technologies are generally used inside a plant, some interesting new options are now available to use the Internet and even satellite technologies to help with this.

See *barcode*, *EPC (Electronic Product Code)*, *Universal Product Code (UPC)*.

random number – A uniformly distributed value in the range (0, 1]; often used in a computer simulation.

Random numbers can be generated on a computer using a pseudo-random number generator. These generators typically generate a recursive sequence of long integer values, where the next value in the sequence is computed from the previous value. These integers are then translated into the range (0, 1] by dividing by the largest possible integer. This is called a "pseudo" random number generator because the values appear to be random from a statistical point of view, but are not truly random.

For example, Von Neumann developed the simple, mid-square pseudo-random number generator in 1946. With a given seed integer, the next random integer is found by squaring the previous value and finding the middle integer value. For example, the table below shows the sequence for the mid-square random number generator with a seed integer of 1111. The random number is the random integer divided by 10,000. The last column shows the random integer squared and uses square brackets [ ] to highlight the middle integer. The random integer 1111 squared is 1234321, which has a middle integer 2343, which becomes the second random integer. The third random integer is the middle integer of 2343^2, which is 4896.

	Random Integer I	Random Number $r = I/10000$	I^2	Eight character text for I^2
Seed	1111	0.1111	1234321	01[2343]21
1	2343	0.2343	5489649	05[4896]49
2	4896	0.4896	23970816	23[9708]16
3	9708	0.9709	94245264	94[2452]64
4	2452	0.2452	6012304	06[0123]04
5	0123	0.0123	15129	00[0151]29

Source: Professor Arthur V. Hill

The random number seed uniquely identifies the entire sequence (stream) of random integers and random numbers. In other words, entire sequence can be repeated exactly for multiple simulation experiments by using the same random number seed each time.

While the mid-square random number generator is a good way to teach the concept of a random number generator, it has poor cycle length (it repeats itself fairly quickly) and has poor statistical properties. In fact, the mid-square method in the example above begins to repeat every fifth value starting with the 54-th random number. In other words, the mid-square random number generator should never be used for any simulation.

The linear congruential random number generator (and others) can generate streams of millions of random numbers without repeating and also have good statistical properties vis-à-vis the runs test, serial correlation, and other tests.

In Excel, random numbers can be generated with the formula RAND(). Note that the RAND() function can return a value of zero, which can occasionally cause a problem. The Excel function RANDBETWEEN(A, B) can be used to generate equally probable (uniformly distributed) random integers between A and B. The Excel formula =A+RAND()*(B-A) can be used to generate continuous uniform values between A and B.

In VBA for Excel, random numbers can be generated with the Rnd() function. To generate a stream of random numbers with a user-defined random number seed, use Rnd(-1) immediately before using Randomize[stream_number] statement.

A good presentation of the details for random number generators can be found in Law and Kelton (2000).

See *inverse transform method, simulation*.

random number generator – See *random number*.

random storage location – An efficient warehouse storage location system that allows any product to be stored in any shelf location and in multiple locations, and therefore requires an information system to keep track of all storage locations.

Storage locations in a warehouse can be either fixed or random. Fixed storage locations do not work well over time because (1) new items are added to inventory, (2) old items are removed from inventory, (3) the demand rate for some items decrease, and (4) the demand for other products increase. All four of these issues create problems because the firm needs to reallocate space to the "fixed" storage locations with each change.

A random storage location allocates inventories to the first available location that has enough (but not too much) space. This approach will end up with most items stored in more than one location. Random storage makes much better use of the space and does not require that the fixed storage locations be changed; however, random storage systems require much more information to keep track of where items are stored. With random storage, it is almost impossible for people to remember where an item is stored. Most firms use a combination of fixed and random storage systems.

See *fixed storage location, Warehouse Management System (WMS), zone storage location*.

range – The difference between the maximum and the minimum of a set of observed values.

The range is a measure of the dispersion (or variability) of a random variable. The range will be roughly 6σ.

See *r-chart, standard deviation*.

Rapid Process Improvement Workshop (RPIW) – See *kaizen event*.

raw materials – Items that a manufacturer uses as input to a process.

Raw materials are usually basic commodities such as chemicals and metals. Some firms make a distinction between raw materials and components, where components are typically assemblies or manufactured parts.

r-chart – A quality control chart that monitors the range (variability) of the process.

A sample of n parts is collected from the process every so many parts or time periods. The range (maximum minus minimum) of the sample is plotted on the control chart and a determination is made if the process is "under control" or not.

See *control chart, range, Statistical Process Control (SPC)*.

recency effect – See *primacy effect*.

red tag – A lean manufacturing practice used in the "sort" step of 5S to label parts, tools, furniture, measurement instruments, office materials, books, magazines, scrap, etc. that are no longer needed so they can be removed and used in another location, stored, recycled, sold, or discarded; red tags are also used to signal the need to dispose of defective materials.

The sort step in the 5S process often finds many items in a work area that are not necessary for the job. These items might have some value, but make the work area less visible. If an item might have some value, it is "red tagged" to signal that it should be moved to the red tag area. If an item obviously has no value, it should be discarded, with special care for hazardous materials. The items in the red tag area should be reviewed regularly (say every two weeks) by a cross functional team of supervisors and engineers. Organizations often invite employees to peruse the red tag area for items they could use in their own areas or buy for their personal use. The result of a good red tag process is a more visible workplace, which is one of the main lean objectives.

Note that "red tag" can be either a noun or a verb.

See *5S, lean thinking*.

re-engineering – See *Business Process Re-engineering (BPR)*.

refurb – See *refurbished*.

refurbished – Products that have been returned by the customer, disassembled, repaired, tested, and repackaged for sale; sometimes called "refurb" or "refurbed" products.

The refurbishing (remanufacturing) process often involves disassembly, replacement of some parts, and reassembly. In some cases, these products are marked as "refurb" products and sold at a discount with a shorter warranty. However, in some industries, refurb products are used interchangeably with new ones. While this might appear to be an unethical to many, but these firms are typically using components that have a very long MTBF (Mean Time Between Failure) and find that this practice rarely affects the performance of the product.

See *remanufacturing.*

regional sourcing – See *sourcing.*

regression – See *linear regression.*

Relative Absolute Error (RAE) – A forecasting performance metric that compares the forecast error to a very simple forecasting model; defined mathematically as the mean of the absolute value of the forecast errors divided by absolute error from some naïve (simplistic) forecasting model.

The *RAE* is the forecast error expressed as a percent of the error from a very simple forecasting model. When this ratio is close to zero, the forecasting model is good; when this ratio is greater than one, the forecasting model is worse than the naïve forecasting model.

Armstrong and Collopy (1992) proposed the simplest Relative Absolute Error metric. This metric compares the forecast errors against the absolute error of a random walk forecast. A random walk uses the actual demand from the previous period as the forecast for this period. In other words, for a random walk, the one-period ahead forecast is the actual demand from the previous period. The equation for the Relative Absolute Error with the random walk forecast as the basis of comparison is:

$$RAE_{rw} = \frac{1}{T} \sum_{t=1}^{T} \frac{|E_t|}{|D_t - D_{t-1}|}$$

Where, E_t is the forecast error in period t, D_t is the actual demand (sales) in period t, and T values have been collected so far. The difference $D_t - D_{t-1}$ is the change in the demand from last period to this period.

One problem with this approach is that when the demand is constant for two successive periods (e.g., $|D_t - D_{t-1}| = 0$), the RAE_{rw} will have a divide-by-zero problem; and when this difference is small, the ratio can be very large. Collopy and Armstrong (2006) suggest "Winsorizing" (bounding) the *RAE* in each period so the ratio does not exceed some maximum value. Many authors suggest a bound of 1. For example, if the demand is zero and the forecast error is 20 units, $|E_t|/D_t$ should be set to 1. This means that *MAPE* is defined in the range (0, 100%).

A slightly more sophisticated approach is to generate the naïve forecast with a simple exponential smoothing model with $\alpha = 0.1$. Mathematically, this is expressed as $SA_{t-1} = 0.1D_{t-1} + 0.9SA_{t-2}$, where SA_{t-1} is the smoothed average demand at the end of period $t-1$ and is used as the naïve forecast for period t. One advantage of this method is that the smoothed average will almost never be zero and therefore the value of $|D_t - SA_{t-1}|$ will also almost never be zero.

All *RAE* metrics can have a divide-by-zero problem similar to the *MAPE*. When the naïve forecast is equal to the demand, the denominator of the ratio will be zero. This problem can be avoided by bounding the value in any period at 100%. In other words, the metric should never be allowed to have a value greater than 100%. For example, if the forecast error in a period was 20 units and the naïve forecast had a zero error, the maximum value added in the summation should be 1.

In the opinion of this author (and many others as well), the Mean Absolute Scaled Error (*MASE*) is a much better metric. Thiel's U, a metric closely related to the *RAE* metrics, is not recommended.

The paper "Forecast Error Metrics" is on the **OMWW CD** available from www.ClamshellBeachPress.com. ●

See *bias, exponential smoothing, forecast error metrics, Mean Absolute Deviation (MAD), Mean Absolute Percent Error (MAPE), Thiel's U, Winsorizing.*

reliability – See *maintenance, Mean Time Between Failure (MTBF).*

reliability engineering – See *maintenance, Total Productive Maintenance (TPM).*

remanufacturing – The process of repairing, refurbishing, and/or disassembling products into reusable components.

Remanufacturing is being driven by both economic and environmental rationale. In some countries, remanufacturing is required by law. Examples include aircraft engines, diesel engines, and other expensive equipment.

See *Design for Disassembly, green manufacturing, refurbished (refurb), reverse logistics.*

reorder point – A method for managing independent demand items that releases an order when the inventory position hits a certain level called the reorder point; also called an order point system. ✪

The graph below shows the reorder point system through two order cycles. Whenever the inventory position (on-hand plus on-order minus allocated) goes below the reorder point, a new order is placed.

An order point system is a continuous review system, which means that it compares the inventory position with the reorder point after every transaction. The standard equation for the reorder point is $R = L\mu_D + SS$, where L is the constant planned leadtime, μ_D is the average demand per period, and SS is the safety stock in units. The safety stock is normally set to $SS = z\sqrt{L}\sigma_D$, where z is the safety factor and σ_D is the standard deviation of the demand per period. The entry on safety stocks explains how to select the safety factor z and the planned leadtime L to achieve a user-specified service level.

Reorder point system graph

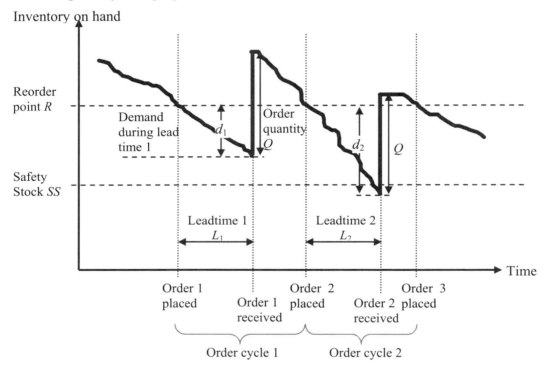

The first term of the reorder point ($L\mu_D$) is the expected (or forecasted) demand during leadtime, which could be a moving average, a simple exponentially smoothed average, or a more sophisticated forecast that also includes trend and seasonal factors. In contrast, a time-phased order point system (e.g., MRP) uses the planned requirements (consumption) from higher-level assemblies to forecast (or plan) the demand during leadtime. The second term of the reorder point is the safety stock. See the *safety stock* entry for more information on how this can be calculated.

The paper "Inventory Management" and the Excel workbooks "safety stock.xls" and "Order cycle service level tutorial.xls" are on the *OMWW CD* available from www.ClamshellBeachPress.com. ⬤

See *continuous review system, demand during leadtime, fill rate, inventory management, leadtime, periodic review system, safety stock, service level, time-phased order point, two-bin system.*

replenishment leadtime – See *purchasing leadtime, leadtime.*

Request for Proposal (RFP) – A request for a vendor to submit a proposal supported by cost breakdown.

An RFP provides a description of the items to be procured. This proposal may include specifications, quantities, time and place of delivery, method of shipment, packaging and instruction manual requirements, materials to be furnished, and data requirements, both support and administrative.

Not only do buyers submit an RFP, many buyers often submit an RFI (Request for Information) or an RFQ (Request for Quotation). Both an RFQ and RFI are frequently used in the realm of operations. In general, an RFI is a screening process to determine which suppliers can meet the specifications. An RFI is commonly used when a buyer is interested in discovering if a supplier has the capabilities to supply products and/or services but the buyer does not want to reveal actual volume or service requirements. (This approach is commonly used in procuring chemicals because giving away volume information can ultimately lower the buyer's leverage in negotiating a price.) An RFP takes an RFI one step further by requesting that the supplier bid on specific items defined by specification, quantities, delivery locations, packaging, method of shipment, etc. An RFQ is used when a supplier is already familiar with the buyer's requirements and the main concern is price.

Resource Requirements Planning (RRP) – A process used to check the production plan (or the business plan or the Sales and Operations Plan) to make sure sufficient resources are available.

This is done at the product family/aggregate unit level and is done before the master schedule is created. In other words, this is a high-level resource/capacity check. The acronym "RRP" is rarely used.

See *Business Requirements Planning (BRP), capacity, Capacity Requirements Planning (CRP), Master Production Schedule (MPS), Rough Cut Capacity Planning (RCCP), Sales & Operations Planning (S&OP)*.

Respond to Order (RTO) – A customer-interface strategy that postpones one or more value-adding activities in the supply chain until after the customer order has been received. ✪

The term "Respond to Order" was coined by Professor Arthur Hill to include many related concepts such as Assemble to Order, Make to Order, Engineer to Order and other customer-interface systems that support customization. The following table contrasts the Make to Stock (MTS) strategy with the three main RTO strategies – Assemble to Order (ATO), Make to Order (MTO), and Engineer to Order (ETO).

RTO strategy	Concept	Inventory	Customer leadtime	Examples
Make to Stock (MTS)	Standard products stored in inventory in anticipation of demand. MTS will build to a forecast, which might be the average demand.	Large finished goods inventory. Usually also has WIP and raw materials.	Only the delivery time from the finished goods to the customer.	Medical devices, many consumer products.
Assemble to Order (ATO)	Standard modules and assembled in response to a customer order.	Inventory of modules. Usually also WIP and raw materials.	Only the assembly and delivery time.	Dell computer assembling the components of a computer based on a customer order. Pack to order is a special case.
Make to Order (MTO)	Raw materials are transformed into a final product in response to a customer order.	Usually inventories of raw materials. It is possible to implement with almost no inventory.	Fabrication, assembly, delivery, and possibly purchased raw material leadtime.	Customized clothing, injection-molded parts. Print to Order is a special case.
Engineer to Order (ETO)	A design is developed and produced in response to a customer order.	Potentially no inventory. Could inventory standard components and/or raw materials.	Design, fabrication, assembly, and delivery time.	Custom home construction, customer circuit boards.

Source: Professor Arthur V. Hill

Similar RTO customer interface strategies include:

- Build to Order (BTO) – Another name for Make to Order (MTO) or Assemble to Order (ATO). See Gunasekaran and Ngai (2005) for an article on BTO.
- Configure to Order (CTO) – A customer interface strategy that adjusts parameters or adds modules to a product in response to a customer order.
- Pack to Order – A customer-interface strategy that collects components and packs them in a box or some other shipping container in response to a customer order.
- Print to Order – A customer-interface strategy that prints books, manuals, and other materials in response to a customer order rather than creating an inventory of printed materials. This is commonly called Print-on-Demand in the publishing industry.

The *service level* entry presents metrics for all types of RTO strategies.

See *Assemble to Order (ATO), Build to Order (BTO), Configure to Order (CTO), Engineer to Order (ETO), flexibility, Make to Order (MTO), Make to Stock (MTS), mass customization, order-to-cash, Pack to Order, Print to Order, push-pull boundary, service level.*

response time – The time between a request for service and the time that the service actually begins.

In a field service context, response time is usually defined as the time from initial customer request for service until the technician appears at the customer site. In some cases, the technician might not actually get to the machine to be repaired for some time after arriving at the site due to building security and walking time. Some field service organizations offer a response time guarantee.

See *service guarantee.*

resource based view – A strategic point of view that holds that firms can gain competitive advantage if and only if they have superior resources and those resources are protected by barriers to entry.

See *core competence, operations strategy.*

responsibility charting – See *RACI Matrix.*

Results-Only Work Environment (ROWE) – An employment policy innovated by Best Buy, Inc. that allows workers to choose when and where they work as long as they achieve their required goals.

ROWE is a radical experiment designed to provide unparalleled freedom for employees to decide when and where they work. With ROWE, the job is not defined in terms of showing up for work but rather in terms of doing the work that needs to be done. Workers are often not even required to attend meetings in person.

While this program began only for white-collar (salaried) employees, it has been extended to hourly (blue-collar) workers as well. Salaried employees are only required to work as much time as it takes to complete their goals. Hourly employees, however, have to work a set number of hours to comply with federal labor regulations, but they can still choose when they work.

Advantages reported for ROWE	Disadvantages reported for ROWE
• Greater loyalty to the company • Lower employee turnover and less hiring expense • Better work/life balance • Better relationships with family and friends • More focused and energized work	• Blurred distinction between work and personal time • Concern that some people might be lazy • Some people might work long hours to the detriment of their health • Potential for stress and conflict

Sources: money.cnn.com/magazines/business2/business2_archive/2007/03/01/8401022/index.htm, June 20, 2008 and www.workforce.com/section/09/feature/24/54/28/, June 20, 2008.

See *socio-technical design.*

retrospective validation – See *process validation.*

return logistics – See *reverse logistics.*

Return on Assets (ROA) – A financial measure of a company's after tax profitability relative to its total assets.

ROA is calculated as (net income)/(total assets).

See *financial performance metrics.*

Return on Capital Employed (ROCE) – A measure of how effectively a firm is using its capital.

ROCE is calculated as EBIT/(capital employed), where EBIT is earnings before interest and taxes and capital employed is total assets less current liabilities.

See *financial performance metrics.*

Return on Investment (ROI) – The rate of return of an investment over some time period.

ROI is calculated as (net income)/(total assets).

See *financial performance metrics*.

Return on Net Assets (RONA) – A measure of the productivity of a company's invested capital regardless of the amount of financial leverage employed.

RONA is calculated as (profit after tax)/(fixed assets + working capital), where working capital is defined as current assets minus current liabilities.

See *DuPont Analysis, financial performance metrics*.

revenue management – See *yield management*.

reverse auction – An auction in which a buyer submits requests for quotations from suppliers for goods or services.

The buyer calls for bids for something that it needs to buy and the suppliers quote the price and volume at which they are willing to supply the good or service. For example, General Electric will notify a group of qualified suppliers that they are invited to participate in an electronic auction. General Electric defines the date and product specifications. At the time of the auction, participating bidders assemble at a common Internet site and bid for the General Electric contract.

See *Dutch auction, e-auction, e-business, e-procurement, purchasing, sniping*.

reverse engineering – The process of dismantling a competitor's products to understand the strengths and weaknesses of the designs.

reverse logistics – The management of the return flow for products, salvage, and/or waste from the customer for either safe disposal or reuse, often via the manufacturer or distributor; also called return logistics.

The materials could be either hazardous or non-hazardous. For example, 3M has its field service technicians manage the return hazardous circuit boards for refurbishing or proper disposal. Volkswagen takes back old cars to recycle and reuse some seat materials. Interest in reverse logistics is driven by both environmental concerns and cost saving opportunities.

Reverse logistics involves managing movement of goods and related information from the points of consumption towards upstream facilities in a manufacturing or service system. These reverse flows are common in a variety of industries, such as consumer goods, reusable components, and packaging material. Returned items can be directly reused, repaired, recycled, re-manufactured or disposed. Recently, integration of the forward and reverse logistics activities attracted considerable attention, resulting in a growing body of literature on closed-loop supply chains.

Many order management systems have reverse logistic modules that allow service reps to create RMAs (Return Merchandise Authorizations) to send to customers so that items can be brought back into the retailer's supply chain and tracked appropriately.

Acknowledgments: CSOM MBA students Jeremy Green, Tanya Raso, and Amy Schmidt contributed to this entry.

See *distribution, green manufacturing, logistics, remanufacturing, upstream*.

RFID – See *Radio Frequency Identification (RFID)*.

RFP – See *Request for Proposal*.

Richards Curve – See *logistic curve*.

risk – A source of danger.

In everyday usage, "risk" is often used synonymously with "probability," but in professional risk assessments, risk combines the probability of a negative event with how harmful that event might be. Risk is not a probability and not a measure of the financial impact of the unexpected event, but rather the combination of the two. An event is said to be of high risk only if the probability and the impact are high. See http://en.wikipedia.org/wiki/Risk for a good summary on this topic.

See *Failure Mode and Effects Analysis (FMEA), risk assessment, risk mitigation*.

risk assessment – The identification and evaluation of nearly all possible causes (modes) of failure.

For each possible failure mode, a thorough risk assessment considers (1) what can go wrong, (2) how likely it is to occur, and (3) what are the consequences of the failure. The *Failure Model and Effects Analysis (FMEA)* entry describes this process in more detail.

See *decision tree, Failure Mode and Effects Analysis (FMEA), fault tree analysis, risk, risk mitigation*.

risk management – The assessment and mitigation of risk.

See *risk assessment, risk mitigation*.

risk mitigation – Actions taken to (1) reduce the probability of an adverse event and (2) lower the impact of an adverse event.

Of course, the best risk mitigation will take steps to complete prevent the event. It is important to also lower the impact of the event if it does occur. This includes planning the means by which recovery should be implemented.

See *error proofing, Failure Mode and Effects Analysis (FMEA), fault tree analysis, FMEA, risk, risk assessment*.

Robinson-Patman Act – A law passed by the U.S. Congress in 1936 to supplement the Clayton Antitrust Act.

The act, advanced by Congressman Wright Patman, forbade any person or firm engaged in interstate commerce to discriminate in price to different purchasers of the same commodity when the effect would be to lessen competition or to create a monopoly. Sometimes called the Anti-Chain-Store Act, this act was directed at protecting the independent retailer from chain-store competition, but it was also strongly supported by wholesalers eager to prevent large chain stores from buying directly from the manufacturers for lower prices.

robotics – The science, development, and application of self-contained, programmable, multifunctional electronic, electric, and/or mechanical devices called robots that can function without human intervention and can augment humans in activities such as manufacturing.

Robots combine artificial intelligence software, mechanical manipulators, sensors, controllers and computers to provide programmable automation. Czech writer Karel Capek introduced the word "robot" in his play "R.U.R" (Rossuum's Universal Robots) in 1921. The Czech word "Robot" comes from the Czech word "robota," which means "compulsory labor." The word was brought into popular Western use by famous science fiction writer Isaac Asimov.

See *artificial intelligence (AI), Automated Guided Vehicle (AGV), automation*.

robust – Hard to break; useful in a wide variety of situations.

If a component can be used in a wide variety of products, it is said to be "robust." If a part is sturdy and almost never breaks, it too is said to be robust. A process is also said to be "robust" if it can withstand a wide variety of stresses. Robust design is designing such that an increase in variability will not result in defective products.

See *commonality, Failure Mode and Effects Analysis (FMEA)*.

rolled throughput yield – See *yield*.

Root Cause Analysis (RCA) – A tool to identify the contributors to an adverse event (or events) after the fact.

Unlike FMEA, root cause analysis is conducted after an adverse event (or events) or situation rather than beforehand. The purpose of RCA is to identify what caused the event and then improve the system so that the problem does not reoccur. As the name implies, the goal is to track down and fix the root cause (the first cause) of the problem, and not simply deal with the symptoms of the problem.

Many tools can be useful in root cause analysis. The "5 Whys" and Pareto analysis are both particularly useful starting points. C&E Diagrams, causal maps and fishbone diagrams can take the 5 Whys approach one step further and can be facilitated with a Nominal Group Technique (NGT) and affinity diagrams. If some data is available, linear regression analysis and graphical tools such as scatter diagrams can often help identify the potential problem "drivers." Of course, the end result of a root cause analysis should be an action plan for fixing the causes of the problem. Root Cause Analysis is fundamental to all process improvement programs such as Lean, Lean Sigma, and Six Sigma. The *causal map* entry argues that the term "root cause" is misleading because most problems have more than one cause.

See *5 Whys, affinity diagram, causal map, error proofing, Failure Mode and Effects Analysis (FMEA), FMEA, impact wheel, issue tree, Nominal Group Technique (NGT), Pareto Chart, scatter diagram, sentinel event*.

Root Cause Tree (RCT) – A causal map that begins with the undesired effect and tracks back to root causes.

A root cause tree is very closely related to the C&E Diagram and has the same purpose. The only real difference is that the RCT is easier to draw and makes it easier to identify the causes of the causes. The RCT usually puts the undesired effect (the problem) at the top of the page, identifies the main causes of the problem below it, and then identifies the causes for each cause below that.

See *causal map*.

Root Mean Squared Error (RMSE) – See *Mean Squared Error (MSE)*.

Rough Cut Capacity Planning (RCCP) – A process that checks if enough capacity is available to achieve a given master schedule.

The rough cut capacity planning process converts the master schedule into requirements through a "bill of resources" for a few key resources. The process then compares the resources required by the plan and the resources available.

Some consultants (including Thomas Wallace of S&OP fame) use the term "rough cut capacity planning" to describe the process of checking the capacity for the highest level production plan. However, according to the APICS dictionary, this should be called the "resource requirements plan."

See *Bill of Resources, Business Requirements Planning (BRP), capacity, Capacity Requirements Planning (CRP), Master Production Schedule (MPS), Resource Requirements Planning (RRP), Sales & Operations Planning (S&OP)*.

routing – The sequence of manufacturing operations (steps) required to build an item.

All manufactured items have a routing. The routing includes the item identification (sometimes called the material, part number, item number, or SKU) and a series of operations (steps). Each operation is identified by sequence number, a workcenter, and operation effectivity date. Each operation could also include a setup time and a run time.

See *alternate routing, Bill of Material (BOM), run time, shop floor control, workcenter*.

RTO – See *Respond to Order (RTO)*.

run time – The time required to produce a single part or product.

The total time for an operation is the setup time plus the batch size (lotsize) times the run time. The total time for an order is the sum of the operation times for all operations in the routing. The planned leadtime for an order should also include queue time.

See *Economic Lot Scheduling Problem (ELSP), leadtime, routing, setup time, touch time*.

running setup – Another name for an off-line (or external) setup.

See *setup reduction methods*.

S

S&OP – See *Sales & Operations Planning (S&OP)*.

SaaS (Software as a Service) – A software application delivery model where a software vendor develops a web-native software application and hosts and operates (either independently or through a third party) the application for use by its customers over the Internet.

Customers do not pay for owning the software itself but rather for using it (Wikipedia, 2008). The SaaS model is well suited for smaller vendors interested in a scalable technical solution so they can participate in certain trading relationships including Vendor Managed Inventory.

Acknowledgments: CSOM MBA students Jeremy Green, Tanya Raso, and Amy Schmidt contributed to this entry.

safety capacity – Capacity that is available in case of an emergency.

Examples include a medical doctor "on call," a supervisor who can help in time of need, or capacity for overtime. Safety capacity is not just having too much capacity; it is capacity that is not actually working, but can be called to work in case of emergency. Note that safety capacity is different from safety stock.

See *capacity, safety leadtime, safety stock*.

safety factor – See *safety stock*.

safety leadtime – The planned or average actual time that an order is received earlier than needed. ✪

Safety leadtime is the "extra" planned leadtime used in production planning and in purchasing. The same concept can be used in project scheduling.

For example, if it takes a student an average of 30 minutes to get to school, and the student plans to leave 35 minutes before a class begins, the student will arrive 5 minutes early on average. This means that the student will have a safety leadtime of 5 minutes. Safety leadtime should absorb the variability in the actual leadtimes. Safety stock should be used to absorb the variability in the demand or yield, whereas safety leadtime should be used to protect against uncertainty in leadtimes or task times.

See *safety capacity*, *safety stock*, *sequence-dependent setup time*, *slack time*.

safety stock – The planned or actual average inventory on-hand just before a replenishment order is received from the source of supply (either internal or external); sometimes called buffer stock. ✪

The figure below shows the safety stock as the lowest point on each of the five order cycles. The actual safety stock over this time period is the average of these five values.

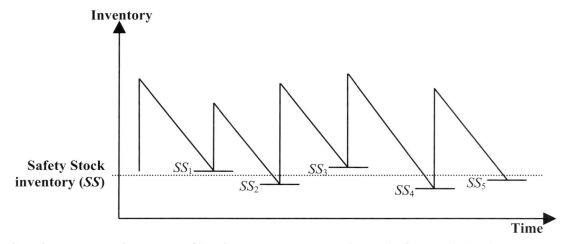

If an item has a current inventory of I units, a recent average demand of μ_D units/period, an average lotsize of $\overline{Q}$ units, and is t time periods into the current order cycle, an estimate of the current actual safety stock is $SS \approx I - \overline{Q} + t\mu_D$ units. Given that the average lotsize inventory is just one-half the average lotsize, the average inventory is then $\overline{I} = SS + \overline{Q}/2$ units.

Background

Nearly all stocked items throughout a supply chain need some safety stock to protect against uncertainty in the demand during the replenishment leadtime. This is necessary because of uncertain demands, uncertain replenishment leadtimes, and uncertain yields that affect the demand and/or supply while the organization waits for an order to replenish the inventory. Safety stock is management's primary control variable for balancing carrying cost and service levels. If the safety stock is set too high, the inventory carrying cost will be too high. If safety stock is set too low, the shortage cost will be too high. Safety stock should be used to absorb the variability in the demand or yield and safety leadtime should be used to protect against uncertainty in leadtimes.

Managers often confuse safety stock with related concepts such as an order-up-to level (for determining the lotsize), a reorder point (a "minimum" inventory for triggering a new order), or the average inventory. Safety stock is the average on-hand inventory when a new order is received. It is not the minimum, maximum, or average inventory.

It is common practice in industry to define safety stocks in terms of a constant days supply. While it is fine to communicate safety stocks in terms of days supply, it is a bad idea to use a constant days supply for all items, unless, of course, all items have the same variability of demand during leadtime (i.e., same standard deviation of demand per period, same replenishment leadtime, and same yield).

The reorder point system, the time-phased order point (MRP) system, and other types of inventory planning systems, manage inventory with a planned demand during the replenishment leadtime. The purpose of safety stock inventory is to protect the organization from demand during the leadtime (*DDLT*) that is greater than planned. Therefore, safety stock should be based on the standard deviation of the demand during leadtime (σ_{DDLT}) and not the average demand during leadtime (μ_{DDLT}).

Safety stock equations

The standard equation for safety stock is $SS = z\sigma_{DDLT}$, where z is called the safety factor (usually between 1 and 3) and σ_{DDLT} is the standard deviation of the demand during the leadtime. Assuming that the demands are serially independent (i.e., independent from time period to time period), the standard deviation of demand during the leadtime is $\sigma_{DDLT} = \sqrt{L}\sigma_D$, where L is the planned replenishment leadtime and σ_D is the standard deviation of the demand per period. In other words, the standard safety stock model is $SS = z\sqrt{L}\sigma_D$. The following sections discuss the leadtime (L), safety factor (z), and standard deviation of demand during leadtime parameters needed for this model.

The leadtime parameter (*L*) for the safety stock model

The basic safety stock model assumes that the L is a constant. However, the leadtime is almost never constant (e.g., the leadtime is a random variable). When L is not constant, safety stock can be computed in two different ways: the maximum leadtime approach and the variance of leadtime approach.

The maximum leadtime approach – Replace L in the safety stock equation (and only in the safety stock equation) with an estimate of the maximum leadtime (e.g., L for the 95-th percentile of the distribution of historical leadtimes). However, this approach requires that the organization manage two leadtime parameters – the average leadtime and the maximum leadtime. With this approach, the average leadtime is the planned leadtime used in the planning system (used for MRP/time-phased order point and reorder point systems), whereas the maximum leadtime parameter is only used in the safety stock equation.

The variance of the leadtime approach – When the leadtime is highly variable and an estimate of the standard deviation of the leadtime is available, the following equation can be used:

$$SS = z\sqrt{\mu_L \sigma_D^2 + \mu_D^2 \sigma_L^2}$$

where z is the safety factor, μ_L is the average leadtime per order, σ_L is the standard deviation of the leadtime per order, μ_D is the average demand per period, and σ_D is the standard deviation of the demand per period. However, most organizations find it difficult to estimate σ_L because of limited availability of recent (relevant) observations on the leadtime. Note that this equation reduces to the simpler SS equation when the standard deviation of the leadtime is zero (e.g., when $\sigma_L = 0$, $SS = z\sqrt{\mu_L \sigma_D^2 + \mu_D^2 \sigma_L^2} = z\sqrt{\mu_L \sigma_D^2} = z\sqrt{\mu_L}\sigma_D = z\sqrt{L}\sigma_D$, assuming that $L = \mu_L$).

The safety factor (*z*) for the safety stock model

The safety factor z determines the service level, with the service level increasing in a non-linear way with z. Many academic textbooks are often imprecise on this subject. The following paragraphs present three approaches for defining the service level (*SL*) and calculating the safety factor (*z*) for that service level.

Order cycle service level approach for setting the safety factor z – This approach defines the service level as the probability of a shortage event on one order cycle. This is sometimes called the cycle service level. An order cycle is defined as the time between placing orders, and the average number of order cycles per year is A/Q, where A is the annual demand in units and Q is the average order quantity. The safety factor for this approach is based on the standard normal distribution (i.e., $z = F^{-1}(SL)$). This z value can be found in any standard normal table or can be found in Excel using NORMSINV(SL).

However, this approach does not consider issues such as how many order cycles are expected per year or how many units might be short in a stockout event. While many firms, texts, and software vendors (including SAP) use the order cycle service level approach, most experts agree that this is an inferior approach. The main problem is that different items will have a different number of order cycles. For example, item A has a target service level of 90% and has only one order cycle per year, which means that it has a probability of having no stockout events during the year of 90%. Item B has the same 90% target service level, but it has 12 order cycles per year, which means it has a 28.2% probability ($0.9^{12} = 0.282$) of having no stockout events during the year. The Excel workbook "Order cycle service level tutorial.xls" (available on the **OMWW CD**) exposes the folly of using an order cycle service level and argues for using the unit fill rate service level.

The unit fill rate service level approach for setting the safety factor z – This approach defines the service level as the expected percentage of units demanded that are immediately available from stock. While this approach is more complicated than the order cycle service level approach, it is a better approach for most applications.

When demand during leadtime is discrete (taking on only integer values), the expected number of units short on any one order cycle is:

$$EUS = \sum_{DDLT=R}^{\infty} (DDLT - R)p(DDLT)$$

where $DDLT$ is the demand during leadtime (a random variable), R is the reorder point, and $p(DDLT)$ is the probability mass function for $DDLT$. (For a time-phased order system, R can be replaced with the planned demand during the leadtime.) Typically, the demand during leadtime is treated as a continuous variable:

$$EUS = \int_{DDLT=R}^{\infty} (DDLT - R)f(DDLT)dDDLT$$

where $f(DDLT)$ is the density function for $DDLT$. Replacing the reorder point (R) with $\mu_{DDLT} + z_0 \sigma_{DDLT}$ and replacing the random variable $(DDLT - \mu_{DDLT})/\sigma_{DDLT}$ with z yields:

$$EUS = \sigma_{DDLT} \int_{z=z_0}^{\infty} (z - z_0)f(z)dz = \sigma_{DDLT} G(z)$$

where $G(z) = \int_{z=z_0}^{\infty} (z - z_0)f(z)dz$. This function is called the partial expectation function by Brown (1967) and Silver, Pyke, and Peterson (1998). (Other authors such as Nahmias (2004) call this the standard loss or unit normal lost function.) For normally distributed demand, $G(z) = f(z) - z(1 - F(z))$, where $F(z)$ is the distribution function for the standardized demand during leadtime. Assuming that the demand during leadtime is normally distributed (a common assumption), the partial expectation is easy to compute in Excel with the formula NORMDIST(z, 0, 1, FALSE) - z*(1-NORMDIST(z, 0, 1, TRUE)).

For a given service level (SL), the expected number of units short on one order cycle is $EUS = Q(1 - SL)$, where the lotsize Q is the average demand per order cycle. Putting together the two equations for EUS above ($EUS = \sigma_{DDLT}G(z)$ and $EUS = Q(1 - SL)$), results in the equation $Q(1 - SL) = \sigma_{DDLT}G(z)$, which means that $G(z) = Q(1 - SL)/\sigma_{DDLT}$. Finding z, therefore, requires the inverse function for $G(z)$ (e.g., $z = G^{-1}(Q(1 - SL)/\sigma_{DDLT})$).

No exact closed-form G^{-1} exists, but the following approximate model is reasonably accurate for normally distributed demand: $g_z = Q(1 - SL)/\sigma_{DDLT}$, $g = \sqrt{\ln(25/g_z^2)}$, $z_{top} = a_0 + a_1 g + a_2 g^2 + a_3 g^3$, $z_{bot} = b_0 + b_1 g + b_2 g^2 + b_3 g^3 + b_4 g^4$, $z = z_{top}/z_{bot}$, with parameters (a_0, a_1, a_2, a_3) = (−5.3925569, 5.6211054, −3.8836830, 1.0897299) and $(b_0, b_1, b_2, b_3, b_4)$ = (1.0, −0.72496485, 0.507326622, 0.0669136868, −0.00329129114). Source: Silver, Pyke, and Peterson (1998), page 735-736.

Professor Hill tested this approximation for G^{-1} in the range $0 < z < 5$ and found that the maximum absolute percent error was less than 1.89%.

The following is a graph of the partial expectation function that shows $G(z)$ decreasing with z.

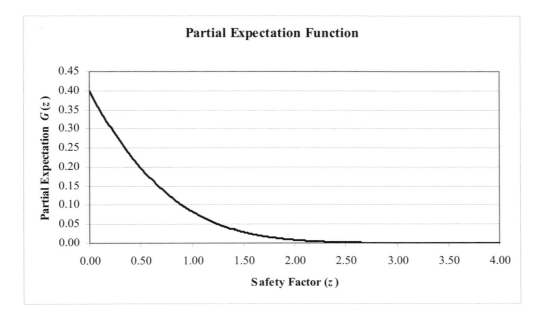

For example, if an item has a safety factor of $z = 1$, then $G(z) = 0.0833$. Given that $\sigma_{DDLT} = 500$ for this item, the expected number of units stocked per order cycle is $EUS = \sigma_{DDLT}G(z) = 500 \cdot 0.0833 \approx 42$ units. If $Q = 1000$ units, the item will have a unit fill rate of about $(1 - 42/1000) \approx 95.8\%$. In contrast, achieving a 95.8% order cycle service level requires a safety factor of $z = 1.73$, which is about 73% more safety stock inventory.

Stockout cost approach for setting the safety factor z – The above approaches require the target service level as an input. However, without a good estimate of the cost of a shortage, it is not clear how to select the right service level (*SL*) parameter. Most organizations, therefore, make subjective estimates based on experience and intuition.

Ideally, safety stocks should be set based on economic logic that balances the cost of a shortage with the cost of carrying inventory. If management is willing and able to estimate of the cost for a shortage of one unit, it is not hard to use the newsvendor model to determine the safety factor (z) that will minimize the total incremental cost (carrying cost plus shortage cost). This model balances the cost of having to carry a unit in safety stock inventory and the cost of having a unit shortage. The model requires the following variable definitions:

S Ordering cost per order.
c_s Cost of a shortage per unit short (assuming that the sale is lost forever and not backordered).
h Cost of carrying one unit for one period. This is the annual carrying charge (i) times the unit cost (c). Be sure to use the same time periods for both h and A.
A Annual demand rate in units.
Q Average order quantity in units.

$F(z)$ Cumulative density function for the distribution of the demand during leadtime evaluated at z standard deviations above the mean.

The total annual incremental cost (TIC) is the sum of the annual ordering cost, the annual carrying (holding) cost, and the annual shortage cost, which can be stated mathematically as $TIC = SA/Q + (Q/2 + z\sigma_{DDLT})h + c_s\sigma_{DDLT}G(z)A/Q$. For the shortage cost term, $\sigma_{DDLT}G(z)$ is the number of units short per order cycle, A/Q is the number of order cycles per year, and c_s is the cost per unit short. Taking the derivative of the TIC with respect to the safety factor z, and setting this to zero, shows that the optimal z is $z = F^{-1}(1 - hQ/(c_sA))$. See Silver, Pyke, Peterson (1998) page 722 for more details.

For a given safety factor z, the implied shortage cost per unit can be estimated as $c_s = Qh/(A(1 - F(z)))$. This is a useful sanity check on the safety factor and corresponding target service level. The Excel formula (assuming normality) is Q*h/A/(1-NORMSDIST(z)).

Similarly, for a given safety factor z, the implied service level is $SL = 1 - \sigma_{DDLT}G(z)/Q$, where $G(z) = f(z) - z(1 - F(z))$. In Excel, $G(z)$ can be computed as NORMDIST(z, 0, 1, FALSE)-z(1-NORMSDIST(z)).

Unfortunately, this model is difficult to implement because it is difficult to estimate the cost of a shortage for one unit even at the retail level. It is even more difficult to translate a shortage into a cost at a distribution center, factory warehouse, or finished goods inventory.

Standard deviation of demand during leadtime parameter for the safety stock model

For a periodic review system with a time between reviews of P time periods, L should be replaced with $L + P$ in all of the above equations. In other words, when ordering only every P time periods, the safety stock is $SS = z\sqrt{L + P}\,\sigma_{DDLT}$. Note that P equals zero for a continuous review system.

If a firm places replenishment orders based on a time-phased order point system (based on forecasts), the safety stock should be defined in terms of the standard deviation of the forecast error rather than the standard deviation of demand. In other words, the above equations should replace s_d with s_e, the standard deviation of the forecast error per period. Unfortunately, many managers, systems designers, professors, students, and textbooks do not understand this important concept.

The standard safety stock equation $SS = z\sqrt{L}\,\sigma_{DDLT}$ is based on the assumption that the demands are independent from period to period (i.e., demand is not serially correlated). This is usually not true. Brown (1967) suggests the following simple model to inflate the safety stock to account for serial correlation: $SS = zL^{0.7}\sigma_{DDLT}$. However, Professor Hill has conducted extensive experiments and has found that this model is not a good approach in many situations. A better approach is to adjust the safety stock for serial correlation with the equation $SS = z\sqrt{L + U}\,\sigma_{DDLT}$ where $U = 2\rho\left(L - (1 - \rho^L)/(1 - \rho)\right)/(1 - \rho)$ and where ρ is an estimate of the first order correlation coefficient (e.g., $\rho = \text{cor}(D_t, D_{t-1})$).

Conclusions about safety stocks

Safety stock optimization (or at least improvement) is often a major opportunity for organizations to simultaneously improve service levels and reduce inventory. Unlike most lotsizing decisions, subjective safety stocks are often far from optimal. Most organizations can use the concepts presented here to replace inventory and poor service with information and analysis.

The papers "Safety Stock" and "Safety Stock with Serial Correlation" and the Excel workbooks "Safety stock.xls" and "Order cycle service level tutorial.xls" can be found on the *OMWW CD* available from www.ClamshellBeachPress.com. ◉

See *aggregate inventory management, cycle stock, demand during leadtime, Economic Order Quantity (EOQ), fill rate, lotsizing methods, newsvendor model, periodic review system, reorder point, safety capacity, safety leadtime, square root law for safety stocks, stockout, time-phased order point.*

Sales & Operations Planning (S&OP) – A business process used to create the Sales & Operations Plan, which is a consensus plan involving Marketing/Sales, Operations/Logistics, and Finance that balances market demand and resource capability; sometimes called Sales, Inventory & Operations Planning (SI&OP or Si&OP). ✪

S&OP by function

The S&OP process is an important process in virtually all firms, but it is particularly critical in manufacturing firms. Fundamentally, S&OP is about finding the right balance between demand and supply. If the demand is higher than supply, customers will be disappointed and customer satisfaction will be low; if the supply is greater than the demand, the cost will be too high.

S&OP involves many different business functions. The following table compares the differing needs for each of the major functional areas involved in a typical S&OP process in a manufacturing firm. S&OP is inherently a political process where conflicting departmental plans and reward systems need to come together to develop a common plan.

Demand ⟷ Supply

S&OP by function

	Marketing	Sales	Finance and Accounting	Production and Purchasing	Logistics and Distribution
Long term needs	Set annual plans for new and existing products, promotional efforts, channel placement, and pricing.	Set goals for the sales force and define incentives to motivate sales people and set sales force size.	Plan revenues, costs, profits, and margins by product and by strategic business unit. Allocate capital. Communicate to Wall Street and owners.	Plan new plant, equipment, and workforce, including capital requests. Product/plant assignments. Hiring and firing.	Plan new warehouse facilities, transportation equipment, transportation contracts, target inventory levels.
Short term needs	Adjust short pricing and promotions.	Adjust sales force size and define incentive plans.	Make short-term capital reallocations, update Wall Street and owners, update standard costs.	Create production plan and master schedule to drive production. Plan hiring/firing and tooling.	Update inventory targets by product by location.
Level	Product or product line	Product by territory and/or region	Corporate, division, product line	Products and materials in each location	Product by location

Source: Arthur V. Hill

The S&OP process

The diagram below presents an example of an S&OP process. (This diagram is based on concepts found in Wallace (2004) and in Ling and Goddard (1995).) However, it should be noted that each firm will implement S&OP in a different way. Most experts recommend that the S&OP process be repeated each month. Step 1 of the process usually begins with statistical forecasts at either a product or product family level. These forecasts are then modified with market intelligence from sales management, usually for each region. However, some experts argue that providing the statistical forecasts to sales management gives them an easy way out of doing the hard work of creating the forecast. Statistical forecasts are useful for the majority of products, and most experts consider it is a waste of time to not use the statistical forecasts as a starting point.

An example S&OP process

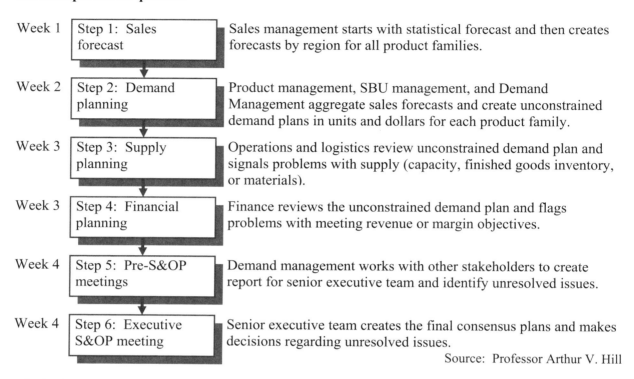

Week 1	**Step 1:** Sales forecast	Sales management starts with statistical forecast and then creates forecasts by region for all product families.
Week 2	**Step 2:** Demand planning	Product management, SBU management, and Demand Management aggregate sales forecasts and create unconstrained demand plans in units and dollars for each product family.
Week 3	**Step 3:** Supply planning	Operations and logistics review unconstrained demand plan and signals problems with supply (capacity, finished goods inventory, or materials).
Week 3	**Step 4:** Financial planning	Finance reviews the unconstrained demand plan and flags problems with meeting revenue or margin objectives.
Week 4	**Step 5:** Pre-S&OP meetings	Demand management works with other stakeholders to create report for senior executive team and identify unresolved issues.
Week 4	**Step 6:** Executive S&OP meeting	Senior executive team creates the final consensus plans and makes decisions regarding unresolved issues.

Source: Professor Arthur V. Hill

In step 2, the forecasts product management, and SBU (Strategic Business Unit) management works with the demand management organization to convert the sales forecasts into an unconstrained demand plan, which factors in higher level issues such as industry trends, pricing, and promotion strategy. The demand plan is expressed in both units and dollars.

In step 3, operations and logistics have the opportunity to check that the supply (either new production or inventory) is sufficient to meet the proposed demand plan. If major changes need to be made, they can be made in steps 4 or 5.

In step 4 (parallel to step 3), finance reviews the demand plan to make sure that it meets the firm's financial objectives (revenues, margins, profits) and creates a financial plan in dollars. In step 5, the demand management organization coordinates with the other organizations to put together a proposed Sales & Operations Plan that is a consensus plan from the demand plan, supply plan, and financial plan. Finally, in step 6, the executive team meets to finalize the S&OP plan.

At every step in the process, assumptions and issues are identified, prioritized, and passed along to the next step. These assumptions and issues play an important part in steps 5 and 6.

S&OP challenges

Most firms have serious problems creating and executing a high-level Sales & Operations plan. Some of these challenges include:

- **Creating conflicting and disjointed plans** – This is the most commonly mentioned problem with planning processes in most manufacturing firms. The right hand and the left hand do not talk to one another and therefore are working off of different plans. The phrase "consensus plan" is often used in the S&OP planning process.
- **Tolerating conflicting reward systems and cultures** – For example, sales might want to have more inventory so they can sell more, but manufacturing and logistics want less inventory because they are held accountable for inventory levels.

- **Confusing the distinctions between forecasts, plans, and goals** – The president of a large firm increased the sales forecast by 10% across all products because he wanted to provide a stretch goal for his firm. The problem with this, of course, is that if the stretch goals are not achieved, the firm is left with high inventories and high costs.

- **Not measuring or holding people accountable for forecasting and planning** – It is common that firms have almost no accountability for the people making the forecasts (typically sales, marketing, and product management). Therefore, they tend to create biased forecasts, which often tend to be higher than the actual demand. Similarly, firms have little accountability for operations and logistics to follow the plan. For example, one manufacturing director boasted that manufacturing had wisely chosen to disregard the S&OP because the manufacturing managers knew better. The challenge for that manufacturing director is to embrace the S&OP process and make their voices heard earlier in the process. When manufacturing (or any other functional area of the business) ignores the S&OP process, the entire process becomes a waste of time. To use an old metaphor, top management turned the wheel of the ship only to find that the rudder was not connected to the wheel.

- **Trying to create high-level plans for too many items** – It is "easier" to forecast for specific products because that is how salespeople usually think about their business and that is how the ERP system collects and organizes the sales data. However, if the firm has hundreds or even thousands of products, this becomes an impossible task. The best practice is to create product families that are used for forecasting and accountability purposes. Unfortunately, it is often not easy to create these product families. Most experts agree that the product families should be defined in terms of market segments rather than shared capacities or shared materials, but it is still a non-trivial task.

- **Not properly connecting the planning and execution processes** – Many firms have an S&OP process, but find that it has little relevance to the real planning process. For example, in the short term, manufacturing orders are based on sales orders rather than on the S&OP plan.

- **Not integrating new product introductions into the planning process** – Clearly, new product introductions should be included so that the firm captures the associated revenues, costs, and factory load.

- **Not understanding the timing issues** – Nearly all consultants recommend a monthly process to help the firm develop a regular pattern. However, for manufacturing, the monthly update is generally not short enough. The trend in manufacturing is to be able to respond immediately to changes in demand. However, the sales people find it difficult to update their forecasts more than once per month. In some sense, the ideal would be real-time, event-driven updates for both sales and manufacturing, but this is nearly impossible for most firms.

- **Not taking S&OP to the supply chain** – Ideally, the S&OP process should extend beyond the boundaries of the firm to the suppliers of the suppliers and the customers of the customers.

See *aggregate production planning, Business Requirements Planning (BRP), Capacity Requirements Planning (CRP), chase strategy, closed-loop MRP, demand management, forecasting, Master Production Schedule (MPS), Resource Requirements Planning (RRP), Rough Cut Capacity Planning (RCCP), time fence.*

Sales Inventory & Operations Planning (SI&OP) – See *Sales & Operations Planning (S&OP).*

salvage value – The value of an item when it is scrapped instead of sold.

Both retailers and manufacturers can usually find a salvage firm or discounter to buy obsolete inventory. 3M uses a salvage firm to buy unsold electronic parts. The salvage firm pays a low price to 3M (such as $0.01 per pound) and keeps the parts in inventory for years. In the rare case of a demand, the salvage firm sells the parts back to 3M at the original book value (say $250).

sample size calculation – A statistical method for estimating the number of observations that need to be collected to create a confidence interval that meets the user's requirements.

It is often necessary to estimate values such as the average time or cost. However, with only a few observations, the estimate might not be accurate. Therefore, it is necessary to know not only the estimated mean but also a measure of the accuracy of the estimate. A confidence interval can help with this problem.

A confidence interval is a statement about the reliability of an estimate. For example, a confidence interval on the time required for a task might be expressed as "25 hours plus or minus 2 hours with a 95% confidence level" or more concisely "25 ± 2 hours." The first number (the 25) is called the "sample mean." The second number (the 2 above) is called the "half-width" of the confidence interval. The "95% confidence" suggests that we if were to make this estimate many times, the true mean would be included ("covered") in the confidence interval about 95% of the time. It is sometimes stated as, "We are 95% sure that the confidence interval contains the mean."

Sometimes some observations have already been collected and the goal is to develop a confidence interval from these observations. At other times, the required half-width is known, and it is necessary to find the number of observations needed to compute this half-width with a certain degree of confidence. It is also possible to express the half-width as a percentage. The five most common problems related to confidence intervals are:
- Problem 1: Create a confidence interval given that n observations are available.
- Problem 2: Find the sample size needed to create the desired confidence interval with a pre-specified half-width.
- Problem 3: Find the sample size needed to create the desired confidence interval with a pre-specified half-width expressed as a decimal percentage.
- Problem 4: Find the sample size needed to create the desired confidence interval on a proportion with a pre-specified half-width percentage.
- Problem 5: Develop a confidence interval for a stratified random sample.

The entry in the encyclopedia on confidence intervals addresses Problem 1. Problem 2 is presented here. For Problem 2, the goal is to find the smallest sample size n necessary to achieve a two-tailed $100(1 - \alpha)\%$ confidence interval with a pre-specified half-width of h units.

Step 0. **Define parameters.** Specify the desired half-width h (in units), the estimated size of the population N, and the confidence level parameter α. If the size of N is large but unknown, use an extremely large number (e.g., $N = 10^{10}$). Compute $z_{\alpha/2} = \text{NORMSINV}(1 - \alpha/2)$.

Step 1. **Take a preliminary sample to estimate the sample mean and standard deviation.** Take a preliminary sample of n_0 observations, where n_0 is at least 9 observations, and estimate the sample mean and standard deviation ($\overline{x}$ and s) from this sample.

Step 2. **Estimate the required sample size.** Compute $n^* = (z_{\alpha/2} s / h)^2$. Round up to be conservative. If the sample size n is large relative to the total population N (e.g., $n^*/N > 0.05$), use $n^* = (z_{\alpha/2} s)^2 / [h^2 + (z_{\alpha/2} s)^2 / N]$ instead. (This assumes that n^* will be greater than 30 so that it is appropriate to use a z value.)

Step 3. **Take additional observations.** If $n^* > n_0$, take $n^* - n_0$ additional observations.

Step 4. **Re-compute the sample mean and sample standard deviation.** Re-compute $\overline{x}$ and s from the entire n observations.

Step 5. **Compute the half-width and create the confidence interval.** Compute the half-width $h' = z_{\alpha/2} s / \sqrt{n}$. If the sample size n is large relative to the total population N (e.g., $n/N > 0.05$), use $h' = \left(z_{\alpha/2} s / \sqrt{n} \right) \sqrt{1 - n/N}$ instead. The confidence interval is then $\overline{x} \pm h'$.

Step 6. **Check results.** Make sure that $h \geq h'$; if not then repeat steps 2 to 6.

The larger the number of observations (n), the smaller the confidence interval. The goal is to find the lowest value of n that will create the desired confidence interval. If n observations are selected randomly many times from the population of all possible observations, the confidence interval ($\overline{x} \pm h'$) will contain the true mean about $100(1 - \alpha)\%$ of the time.

Three papers (Confidence Intervals, Audit Sampling, and Dollar Unit Sampling) and three companion Excel workbooks (confidence intervals.xls, audit sampling.xls, and DUS.xls) related to this topic are on the **OMWW CD** available from www.ClamshellBeachPress.com. ⊙

See *central limit theorem, confidence interval, dollar unit sampling, sampling, standard deviation*.

sampling – The selection of items from a population to help a decision maker make inferences about the population.

Sampling is frequently used when the population is very large and/or it is impossible, impractical, or too costly to evaluate every item in the population. Sampling allows decision makers to make inferences about the population from which the sample is drawn. A random sample provides characteristics identical to those of the population. ReVelle (2004) suggests that decision makers should be aware of three categories of sampling error: bias (lack of accuracy), dispersion (lack of precision), and non-reproducibility (lack of consistency).

See *acceptance sampling, ANOVA (Analysis of Variance), central limit theorem, confidence interval, dollar unit sampling, normal distribution, sample size calculation, standard deviation, t-test, work sampling.*

SAP – A leading Enterprise Resources Planning (ERP) software vendor headquartered in Germany.

The firm was founded in Germany in 1972 by five ex-IBM engineers. SAP is the German acronym for Systeme, Andwendungen, Produkte in der Datenverarbeitung, which translated to English means Systems, Applications, Products in Data Processing.

Being incorporated in Germany, the full name of the parent company is SAP AG. Headquartered in Walldorf Germany, SAP has subsidiaries in over 50 countries in the world. SAP America, which has responsibility for North America, South America and Australia, is headquartered just outside of Philadelphia.

Source: http://www.thespot4sap.com/Articles/TheBasics_1.asp.

See *ABAP (Advanced Business Application Programming), Advanced Planning and Scheduling (APS), Enterprise Resources Planning (ERP).*

satisficing – The effort needed to obtain an outcome that is good enough, but is not exceptional.

Satisficing action can be contrasted with maximizing action, which seeks the biggest, or with optimizing action, which seeks the best. In recent decades, doubts have arisen about the view that in all rational decision-making the agent seeks the best result. Instead, some argue it is often rational to seek to satisfice (i.e., to get a good result that is good enough although not necessarily the best). The term was introduced by Herbert A. Simon in his book Models of Man (Simon 1957).

Adapted from The Penguin Dictionary of Philosophy ed. Thomas Mautner, ISBN 0-14-051250-0, http://www.utilitarianism.com/satisfice.htm.

See *bounded rationality, learning curve, learning organization.*

SBU – See *Strategic Business Unit.*

scalability – The ability to increase capacity without adding significant cost or the ability to grow with the organization.

For example, software is said to be "scalable" if it can handle a significant increase in transaction volume.

See *flexibility.*

scatter diagram – **A** graphical display of data showing the relationship between two variables; also called scatterplot.

The scatter diagram is usually drawn as a set of points on the graph. When the points appear to fall along a line (say from bottom left to top right), the user might hypothesize a linear relationship.

The scatter diagram is one of the seven tools of quality.

See *linear regression, seven tools of quality.*

scientific management – An approach to management and industrial organizational, developed by Frederick Winslow Taylor (1856-1915) in his 1911 monograph *The Principles of Scientific Management* (Taylor, 1911).

Taylor believed that every process had "one best way" and developed important industrial engineering and operations management approaches such as the time and motion study to find that one best way. For example, in one of Taylor's most famous studies, he noticed that workers used the same shovel for all materials. His research found that the most effective load was 21½ pounds, and proceeded to design shovels for each material for that weight.

Taylor made many important contributions to the field of operations management, emphasizing time motion studies, division of labor, standardized work, planning, incentives, management of knowledge work, and selection and training. Taylor also influenced many important thought leaders including Carl Barth, H.L. Gantt, Harrington Emerson, Morris Cooke, Hugo Münsterberg (who created industrial psychology), Frank and Lillian Gilbreth, Harlow S. Person, James O. McKinsey and many influential organizations such as Harvard University's Business School, Dartmouth's Amos Tuck School, University of Chicago, Purdue University, McKinsey (the consulting firm), and the American Society of Mechanical Engineers. His work also influenced industrial development in many other nations including France, Switzerland, and the Soviet Union.

One criticism of scientific management is that it separated managerial work (e.g., planning) and direct labor. This led to jobs where workers were not allowed to think. In contrast, many successful Japanese firm stress worker suggestions and require managers to begin their careers on the shop floor.

See *best practices, division of labor, standardized work, time study, work measurement.*

scope creep – The tendency for project boundaries and requirements to expand over time, often resulting in large, unmanageable, and never-finished projects.

Scope creep is reflected in subtle changes in project requirements over time. For example, a software project might start out as a simple table that needs to be accessed by just a single type of user. However, as the user group becomes engaged in the project, the "scope" increases to include a larger and more complicated database with multiple tables and multiple types of users.

One of the main keys to successful project management is avoiding scope creep. If the users want to increase the scope of a project, they should be required to either go back and change the charter (and get the appropriate signed approvals) or defer the changes to a new project. If management does not manage scope creep, the project will likely not be completed on time or within budget.

In a consulting context, scope creep is additional work outside of the project charter that the client wants for no additional charge. If the client is willing to change the charter and pay for the work, it is an "add-on sale" and is not considered scope creep.

See *focused factory, project charter, project management, scoping.*

scoping – The process of defining the limits (boundaries) for a project.

Defining the project scope is a critical determinant of the success of a project. When scoping a project, it is just as important to define what is not in scope as it is to define what is in scope.

See *project charter, project management, scope creep.*

SCOR model – A process reference model that has been developed and endorsed by the Supply-Chain Council as the cross-industry, standard, diagnostic tool for supply-chain management, spanning from the supplier's supplier to the customer's customer. ✪

Known as the Supply-Chain Operations Reference-model (SCOR), SCOR enables users to address, improve, and communicate supply-chain management practices within and between all interested parties. The SCOR framework attempts to combine elements of business process design, best practices, and benchmarking. The basic model can be found below. Some of the benefits of the SCOR model include: (1) standardized terminology and process descriptions, (2) pre-defined performance measures, (3) best practices, and (4) basis for benchmarking a wide variety of supply chain practices.

The SCOR model

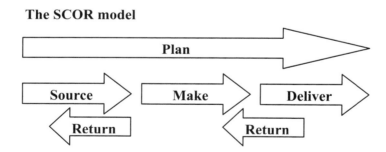

The SCOR model was developed to describe the business activities associated with all phases of satisfying a customer's demand. The SCORE model can be used to describe supply chains that are very simple or very complex using a common set of definitions.

An overview can be found on the home page of the Supply Chain Council www.supply-chain.org/public/scor.asp.

See *benchmarking, bullwhip effect, Supply Chain Council, supply chain management, value chain.*

scrap – The number of units that are judged to be defective and cannot be sold or reworked to produce saleable product.

Scrap is any material that is outside of specifications and cannot be reworked. Scrap should be disposed of properly according to environmental laws.

See *yield*.

search cost – The cost of finding a supplier that can provide a satisfactory product at an acceptable price.

See *switching cost, total cost of ownership, transaction cost*.

seasonal factor – A parameter used in forecasting to adjust the forecast for seasonal effects.

Most forecasting models apply a multiplicative seasonal factor. The forecast, therefore, is equal to the underlying average times the seasonal factor. For example, a retailer might have a seasonal factor for the month of December (Christmas season) that is 4, whereas the January factor might be 0.6. While not recommended, it is also possible to have an additive seasonal factor.

See *exponential smoothing, forecasting, seasonality*.

seasonality – The demand for a product is said to have seasonality if it is affected by the time of the year or the time of the day.

For example, the retail sales at Best Buy are significantly affected by the Christmas season.

See *exponential smoothing, forecasting, seasonal factor*.

sensei – A reverent Japanese term for a teacher or master.

In the lean manufacturing context, a sensei is a master of lean knowledge with many years of experience. In traditional lean environments, it is important for the sensei to be a respected and inspirational figure. Toyota uses a Japanese-trained sensei to provide technical assistance and change management advice when it is trying something for the first time or to help facilitate transformational activities.

sensitivity analysis – The process of estimating how much the results of a model will change if one or more of the inputs to the model are changed slightly.

While the concept of sensitivity analysis can be used with any model, it is a particularly powerful part of linear programming analysis. For example, in linear programming, it is possible to change a capacity constraint to find out how much additional profit the firm will make. The economic benefit of changing the constraint by one unit is called the "shadow price" of the constraint.

See *Linear Programming (LP)*.

sentinel event – A healthcare term used to describe any unintended and undesirable occurrence that results in death or serious injury not related to the natural course of a patient's illness; sometimes called a "never event."

A sentinel is a guard or a lookout. Serious adverse healthcare events are called "sentinel" events because they signal the need for immediate "guard" (error prevention) attention. Examples of sentinel healthcare events include death resulting from a medication error, suicide of a patient in a setting where they receive around-the-clock care, surgery on the wrong patient or body part, and infection-related death or permanent disability.

Following a sentinel event (or potential sentinel event), nearly all healthcare organizations conduct a root cause analysis to identify the hazards that caused the event and then develop an action plan to mitigate the risk of the event reoccurring. The Joint Commission (JCAHO) tracks statistics on sentinel events and reports these statistics on the website www.jointcommission.org/SentinelEvents.

See *adverse event, causal map, Joint Commission (JCAHO), Root Cause Analysis (RCA)*.

sequence-dependent setup cost – See *sequence-dependent setup time*.

sequence-dependent setup time – A machine changeover time that changes with the order jobs are run.

For example, a paint manufacturing process might be easy to change over from making white to yellow, but much more difficult to change over from black to white. The optimal sequence to the sequence-dependent setup problem can be found by solving the famous "Traveling Salesperson Problem." The changeover time (or cost) can be represented with a matrix of from-to times (or costs), similar to the travel time matrix on the back of a roadmap. This is called a combinatorial optimization problem.

See *major setup cost, safety leadtime, setup, setup cost, setup time, Traveling Salesperson Problem (TSP)*.

serial correlation – See *autocorrelation*.

service – A product that is simultaneously produced and consumed. ✪

Services are said to be "intangible," which means that the service is not a physical "thing." However, many (if not most) services have facilitating goods. For example, a dinner at a nice restaurant will have comfortable chairs, nice plates, and good food. However, the chairs, plates, and food are not the service; they are only the facilitating goods for the service.

Services cannot be inventoried, which means that they cannot be stored. For example, a flight from London to Paris at 12 noon on July 4, cannot be "stored" in inventory until July 5. Once the aircraft leaves the ground, that capacity is gone forever.

While most services are labor intensive (e.g., hair cuts, surgery, and teaching), some are capital intensive (e.g., power generation). Many services require that the customer have intensive contact in the process throughout the production of the service (e.g., surgery), but others require only limited contact with the customer at the beginning and end of the process (e.g., car repair).

See *experience engineering, service failure, service guarantee, service profit chain, service quality, service recovery.*

service blueprinting – A process map for a service that includes moments of truth, line of visibility, fail points, and additional information needed to create the right customer experience.

During the process design stage, business process managers, architects, interior designers, marketing managers, operations managers, and IT professionals use the blueprint to guide the design process. After the design is completed and implemented, the blueprint defines the required features and quality of the service for the service managers. Some recommended steps for service blueprinting include:

1. Clearly identify the targeted customer segment.
2. Develop a process map from the customer's point of view – This should include the choices the customers need to make when they buy, use, and assess the service. It should also include all activities, flows, materials, information, failure points, and customer waiting points (queues).
3. Map employee actions, both onstage and backstage – This involves drawing the lines of interaction and visibility, then identifying the interactions between the customer and employee, and all the visible and invisible employee actions.
4. Link customer and contact person activities to needed support functions – This involves drawing the line of internal interaction and linking the employee actions to the support processes.
5. Add evidence of service at each customer action step – This involves showing evidence of the service that the customer sees and receives at each point of the service experience.

The service blueprint should show all points of interaction between the customer and service providers (known as "moments of truth"), identify "fail points" and the "line of visibility," and should include fairly precise estimates of the times required for each step, including the queue times. The line of visibility separates a service operation into back office operations that take place without the customer's presence and front office operations in direct contact with the customer. Some people argue that the only difference between a process map and a service blueprint is the identification of the fail points and the demarcation of the line of visibility.

A service blueprint is better than a verbal description because it is more formal, structured, and detailed, and shows the interactions between processes. The blueprint provides a conceptual model that facilitates studying the service experience prior to implementing it and makes the implementation easier.

See *experience engineering, line of visibility, moment of truth, process design, process map, service failure, service guarantee.*

service failure – A situation when a service provider does not provide satisfactory service. ✪

The best service organizations pay a great deal of attention to these situations and try to recover dissatisfied customers before they become "terrorists" and give a bad report to a large number of potential customers. (Note: The word "terrorists" has been used in this context by service quality experts for many years; however, in light of recent events many experts are now shying away from using such a strong and emotionally-charged word.)

For example, when traveling through the Logan airport in Boston on the way to Europe, a certain restaurant served some very bad clam chowder that caused a number of travelers to get sick. The restaurant offered a free coupon for more food to the travelers. This service failure was not followed up with an adequate service recovery, and the traveler became a terrorist who reported the service failure to thousands of people. (Note: This restaurant, the Port of Boston, is no longer in business in the Logan Airport.)

See *service, service blueprinting, service guarantee, service recovery.*

service guarantee – A set of two promises offered to customers before they buy a service. The first promise is the level of service provided and the second promise is what the provider will do if the first promise is not kept. ✪

Hays and Hill (2001) found empirically that a service guarantee often has more value for operations improvement than it does for advertising. A carefully defined service guarantee can have the following benefits:

- Defines the value proposition for both customers and employees.
- Supports marketing communications (e.g., advertising) in attracting new customers, particularly those who are risk-adverse.
- Helps the service firm retain "at risk" customers.
- Lowers the probability that dissatisfied customers will share negative word-of-mouth reports with others.
- Motivates customers to provide useful process improvement ideas.
- Motivates service firm employees to learn from mistakes and to improve the service process over time.
- Clearly predefines the service recovery process for both the customer and the employee.
- Ensures that the service recovery process does not surprise the customer.

A service guarantee is usually applied to organizations serving external customers, but it can also be applied to internal customers as well.

Service guarantees are not without risk. Offering a service guarantee before the organization is ready can lead to serious problems. Announcing the withdrawal of a service guarantee is tantamount to announcing that the organization is no longer committed to quality.

A service guarantee is a promise related to the intangible attributes of the service (e.g., timeliness, results, satisfaction, etc.), whereas a product warranty is a promise related to the physical attributes of the product (durability, physical performance, etc.). Product warranties are similar to service guarantees from a legal perspective and have many of the same benefits and risks.

Hays and Hill (1999) developed the figure below to shows that increasing the percent satisfied, the percent who complain, and the percent recovered will all have a significantly positive impact on the firm's market share. Organizations never want to increase the percentage of dissatisfied customers, but they do want to increase the percentage of dissatisfied customers who complain so that they hear all customer complaints.

Service guarantees and customer satisfaction

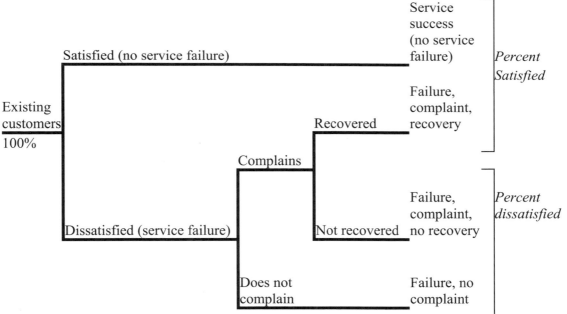

Source: Professor Arthur V. Hill

The story of the Domino's Pizza guarantee is an interesting one. For many years, Domino's offered a "30-minutes or it's free" guarantee. Unfortunately, Domino's settled major lawsuits for dangerous driving in 1992 and again in 1993, which led the firm to abandon its "on-time delivery" guarantee and replace it with an unconditional satisfaction guarantee. The story about a Domino's driver killing a small child walking along side the street is evidently not true. (Source www.snopes.com/business/consumer/dominos.asp, October 5, 2007.)

The Excel workbook "SG.xls" for analyzing a service guarantee is on the ***OMWW CD*** available from www.ClamshellBeachPress.com. ⦿

See *brand, response time, service, service blueprinting, service failure, Service Level Agreement (SLA), service quality, service recovery, value proposition, warranty.*

service level – A measure of the degree to which a firm meets customer requirements. ✪

Make to Stock products – For Make to Stock (MTS) products, the service level is usually measured as the percent of the demand immediately filled from stock. More specifically, service level is measured in terms of the unit fill rate, the line fill rate, or the order fill rate. The order fill rate is sometimes called the "percentage of orders shipped complete" or more simply "shipped complete."

Many members of the Grocery Manufacturing Association in North America use a metric called the "perfect order fill rate," which is the percent of orders that are perfect in every way. Many retailers use a measure of the time that the inventory is in-stock (or out of stock) called "in-stocks."

Many textbooks and ERP systems define the service level for MTS products as the order cycle service level, which is defined as the probability of not having a stockout event on an order cycle. However, most experts agree that this is a poor service metric compared to the unit fill rate metric because the order cycle service level does not take into account the number of order cycles per year or the severity of a stockout event.

See the *safety stock* entry for more detail on these metrics.

Respond to Order products – Respond to Order (RTO) products are assembled, built, fabricated, cut, mixed, configured, packaged, picked, customized, printed, or engineered in response to a customer's request (order). The service for these products is usually measured as the percent of orders that are filled on time, otherwise known as On-Time Delivery (OTD). OTD is the percent of orders shipped (or received) complete within the promise date (or request date).

Ideally, firms should compute OTD based on the customer request date because the promise date may or may not satisfy the customer's requirements. However, most firms find this difficult to implement and therefore use only the promise date. This is complicated by the fact that the promise date can be "updated" as the situation changes. In other words, it is possible that the promise date is updated (e.g., revised, manipulated) so that orders are rarely late.

Firms should compute OTD from the customer's perspective. Therefore, firms should measure OTD based on the customer receipt date rather than the manufacturer's ship date. However, most firms do not have access to the customer receipt date information, and therefore measure OTD against their shipping dates, and then hold their distribution/transportation partners responsible for their portion of the customer leadtime.

OTD can be improved by either (1) make safer promises (e.g., promise three weeks instead of two weeks) or (2) reducing the mean and/or variance of the manufacturing leadtime. The first alternative can have a negative impact on the demand. The second alternative requires Six Sigma thinking to reduce the mean and variability of the customer leadtime. Hill and Khosla (1992) and Hill, Hays, and Naveh (2000) address issues such as the leadtime elasticity of demand and finding the "optimal" customer leadtime to offer to the market.

The customer leadtime for a Respond to Order product is the actual time between the order receipt and the delivery to the customer. Customer leadtime, therefore, is a random variable that has a mean, mode, standard deviation, etc. The planned leadtime (or planned customer leadtime) is usually a fixed quantity, which may be conditioned on some attribute of the order (quantity, complexity, routing, materials, size, etc.). For example, a firm might offer a two-week leadtime for standard products, and a three-week leadtime for non-standard products.

Some academics define additional measures for Respond to Order products such as the mean and standard deviation of lateness, earliness, and tardiness. Defining A as the actual delivery date (or time) and D as the due date (or time) for a particular order, lateness is defined as $D - A$, earliness is defined as $\max(D-A, 0)$, and tardiness is defined as $\max(A-D, 0)$. Using more sophisticated mathematical notation, earliness = $(D-A)^+$ and tardiness = $(A-D)^+$, where $(x)^+ = \max(x, 0)$. Note that lateness can be either positive or negative. Negative lateness means that the delivery was early.

The paper "Service Level Metrics" is on the ***OMWW CD*** available from www.ClamshellBeachPress.com. ⦿

See *delivery time, fill rate, in-stocks, job shop scheduling, Make to Stock (MTS), operations performance metrics, perfect order fill rate, reorder point, Respond to Order (RTO), Service Level Agreement (SLA), stockout.*

Service Level Agreement (SLA) − A contract between a service provider and a customer that specifies in measurable terms the type and quality of services that will be provided.

The SLA is an effective means for the customer and supplier to engage in a serious discussion at the beginning of a relationship to determine what is important to the customer and to clearly specify expectations. The service provider is usually obliged to pay the customer a penalty if any condition of the SLA is not satisfied. SLAs are then used to measure and monitor a supplier's performance and to force the supplier to take corrective action when the conditions of the agreement are not met.

For example, a number of capital equipment firms offer a menu of field service SLAs to their customers that allow customers to make tradeoffs between the price and service quality as measured by equipment downtime, technician response time, etc.

See *Business Process Outsourcing*, *outsourcing*, *performance based contracting*, *service guarantee*, *service level*, *service quality*, *warranty*.

service parts − Components, parts, or supplies used to maintain or repair machinery or equipment.

Service parts are sometimes called "spare parts." The term "spare" implies that they are not needed, which is often not the case (Hill 1992).

The entry *slow moving demand* presents an inventory model based on the Poisson distribution that is often appropriate for managing service parts.

The paper "Managing Slow-Moving Inventory" and the Excel workbook "slowmove.xls" are on the ***OMWW CD*** available from www.ClamshellBeachPress.com. These are both oriented towards managing service parts. ●

See *slow moving demand*.

Service Profit Chain − A conceptual model that relates employee satisfaction to customer satisfaction, revenue, cost, and profit.

The Service Profit Chain model was developed by Heskett, Jones, Loveman, Sasser, and Schlesinger (1994) in an article in the ***Harvard Business Review*** and put forward in the book ***The Service Profit Chain*** by Heskett, Sasser, and Schlesinger (1997). The model begins with "internal service quality," which involves workplace design and job design for employees. The central concept is that if employees are satisfied, they will have lower turnover (higher employee retention) and better productivity. Higher employee satisfaction, retention, and productivity will then translate into better "external service value" and satisfaction for the customer. This higher customer satisfaction then translates into higher customer loyalty, revenue, and ultimately profitability for the firm. This model is promoted by several consulting firms including Heskett's firm the Service Profit Chain Institute (http://www.serviceprofitchain.com). The model is below.

The Service Profit Chain

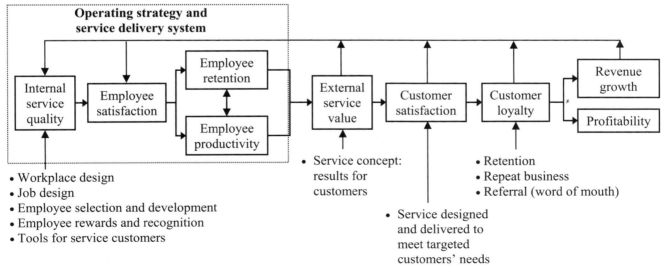

Adapted slightly from Heskett, Jones, Loveman, Sasser, and Schlesinger (1994)

See *service*, *service quality*.

service quality – A customer's long-term overall evaluation of a service provider. ✪

Hays and Hill (2001) defined service quality as a customer's long-term overall evaluation of a service provider and customer satisfaction as the customer's evaluation of a specific service episode (a service event). However, some authors reverse these definitions.

A common slogan for service leaders is that "we need to delight our customers!" However, great care should be taken in applying this slogan. When I traveling to Europe several years ago, an airline agent allowed me to use a domestic upgrade coupon to upgrade from coach to business class. A couple of weeks later I flew the same route and was denied the same upgrade. The first time I was delighted, but the second time I was very disappointed. The principle here is that "today delight becomes tomorrow's expectation." Service providers should not delight customers unless they can do so consistently. When service provides perform a "one-off" special service, they should manage the customer's expectations for the future.

Service quality is perceived differently based on three types of product attributes – search qualities, experience qualities, and credence qualities:

Search qualities – Product attributes that can be fully evaluated prior to purchase are called search qualities. For example, the color of a dress purchased in a store can easily be evaluated before purchase. Color, style, price, fit, and smell are generally considered to be search qualities.

Experience qualities – Product attributes that cannot be evaluated without the product being purchased and consumed (experienced) by the customer are called experience qualities. For example, the flavor of a food product cannot be evaluated until it is consumed. Given that the customer cannot fully evaluate the quality of the product until it is purchased, customers often have to rely more on personal recommendations for products that have experience qualities.

Credence qualities – Product attributes that cannot easily be evaluated even after purchase and consumption have credence qualities. For example, the quality of the advice from lawyers, doctors, and consultants is often hard to evaluate even after the advice has been given because it is often quite subjective.

Many authors define the service quality "gap" as the difference between the expectations and the delivery for a particular service episode. However, this model suggests that service quality (or customer satisfaction) is high when customers expect and receive bad service. In response to this problem, Professor Hill created the simple "FED up" model, which states that F equals E minus D, where F = Frustration, E = Expectation, and D = Delivery. When $F = 0$, the customer is not necessarily satisfied; the customer is just not frustrated.

The critical incidents method is a good approach for identifying potential service quality dimensions. (See the *critical incidents method* entry.) The gap model is a good structure for measuring these dimensions on a survey. The gap model measures both importance and performance for each dimension of service quality, and then defines Gap = Importance − Performance. The concept here is that if a service quality dimension has high importance but has low performance it has a large gap and should be given high priority.

Many hotels use three questions to measure customer satisfaction and service quality:
- Willingness to return – Do you intend to return to our hotel in the next year?
- Willingness to recommend – Would you recommend our hotel to your friends and family?
- Overall satisfaction – Overall, were you satisfied with your experience at our hotel?

More recently, many hotels have simplified the measurement process and now use primarily the Net Promoter Scale developed by Reichheld (2003), which is a modification of the "Willingness to recommend" question above. See the *Net Promoter Scale (NPS)* entry for more details on this subject.

Pine and Gillmore's book (2007) on "Authenticity" argues that in a world increasingly filled with deliberately staged experiences and manipulative business practices (frequent flyer miles comes to mind here), consumers choose to buy based on how real and how honest they perceive a service provider. This is related to moments of truth concept.

See *critical incidents method, experience engineering, Kano Analysis, line of visibility, moment of truth, Net Promoter Score (NPS), primacy effect, quality, service, service guarantee, Service Level Agreement (SLA), Service Profit Chain, SERVQUAL, single point of contact, triage.*

service recovery – Restoring customers to a strong positive relationship with the firm after they have been experienced a service failure. ✪

The six steps to service recovery are (1) listen, (2) apologize and show empathy, (3) ask the service recovery question "What can we do to completely satisfy you?" (4) fix the problem quickly (prioritize customers and escalate if needed), (5) offer symbolic atonement (something tangible that the customer will appreciation), (6) follow up to make sure that the relationship is fixed. The slogan here is that, "It is much easier to keep an existing customer than it is to find a new one."

The "three fixes of service quality" are (1) make sure that the customer's problem is fixed, (2) make sure that the customer relationship is fixed so they will come back next time, and (3) make sure that the system problem is fixed so that this customer (and all future customers) does not have the same problem ever again.

See *service, service failure, service guarantee*.

SERVQUAL – A service quality instrument (survey) created by Parasuraman, Zeithaml, and Berry (1988) that measures the gap between customer expectations and perceptions after a service encounter.

The SERVQUAL instrument has been used in numerous service industries. The SERVQUAL instrument is organized around five dimensions of customer service:

Tangibles - Physical facilities, equipment, and appearance of personnel
Reliability - Ability to perform the promised service dependably and accurately
Responsiveness - Willingness to help customers and provide prompt service
Assurance - Competence, courtesy, credibility, and security
Empathy - Access, communication, and understanding

The instrument has been criticized in a number of different research papers for a number of different reasons, but continues to be popular in many industries. One of the main criticisms is that service quality may not be a function of the gap between expectation and service, but rather a function of the value that is delivered to the customer. For example, if someone hates White Castle hamburgers and goes to White Castle and buys a White Castle hamburger, they get what they expect. However, the customer does not perceive this as good quality.

See *service quality*.

setup – The process of preparing a process (usually a machine) to produce a product. ✪

A setup is a common term in a factory where the tooling on a machine has to be changed to start a new order. However, setups are an important part of all human activity. For example, a surgical operation has a setup time and setup cost in preparing the room for the surgery.

See *sequence-dependent setup time, setup cost, setup reduction methods, setup time*.

setup cost – In a manufacturing context, the cost to prepare a process (e.g., a machine) to start a new product; in a purchasing context, the cost to place a purchase order; also known as the changeover cost or order cost. ✪

Background

The ordering cost (or setup cost) is an important parameter for managerial decision making for manufacturers, distributors, and retailers. This cost is particularly important when making order sizing (lotsizing or batchsize) decisions. If the ordering cost is zero, the firm can justify small lotsizes (order sizes) and approach the ideal of "just-in-time" ("one-piece flow"). In a purchasing context, the ordering cost is the cost of placing and receiving an order. In a manufacturing context, the order cost is the cost of setting up (changing over) the process (the machine) to begin a batch of parts. This cost is usually called the "setup" or "changeover" cost.

In both the purchasing and manufacturing contexts, the ordering cost should reflect only those costs that vary with the number of orders. For example, most overhead costs (such as the electricity for the building) are not relevant to lotsizing decisions and therefore should be ignored. The ordering cost is said to be "lotsize independent" because it is not dependent on the number of units ordered. The total annual ordering cost is dependent only on the number of orders placed during the year.

Standard costing approach

The typical standard costing approach used in many firms includes allocated overhead in the order cost. In a manufacturing context, the number of standard labor hours for the machine setup is multiplied by the "burden" (overhead) rate. For many firms, the burden rate is over $200. Many accountants make the argument that "all costs are variable in the long run" and therefore the overhead should be included in the ordering cost. While this argument is probably true for product costing, it is not true for estimating the ordering cost for determining lotsizes. Inventory theorists argue that the ordering cost (setup cost) should be treated as a marginal cost, which means that overhead costs should be ignored.

Purchasing context

In the purchasing context, the cost components include the following:
- Order preparation component – Computer processing, clerical processing.
- Order communication component – The marginal cost of mailing, faxing, or electronic communication of the order to the supplier.
- Supply order charge – Any order processing charge from the supplier.
- Shipping cost component – The fixed portion of the shipping cost. (Note that the per unit shipping cost should be considered part of the unit cost and not part of the ordering cost.)
- Receiving cost – Cost of handling the receipt of an order. This cost includes the accounting costs, the per order (not per unit) inspection costs, and the cost of moving the order to storage. Again, costs that vary with the number of units should not be included here.

Manufacturing context

In the manufacturing context, the cost components included in the setup cost include the following:
- Order preparation component – Computer processing and clerical processing.
- Order communication component – Sending the order paperwork or electronic information to the shop floor.
- Setup labor cost component – The incremental labor cost of setting up the machine. This cost should include their hourly wage and fringes, but should not be assigned any other factory overhead (burden).
- Opportunity cost of the machine time lost to setup – At a bottleneck machine, time lost to a setup has tremendous value. In fact, for every hour that the bottleneck is sitting idle, the entire plant is also idle. Therefore, the opportunity cost of the capacity at the bottleneck is the opportunity cost of lost capacity for the entire plant. For example, if a plant is generating $10,000 in gross margin per hour, one hour lost to a setup at the bottleneck has an opportunity cost of $10,000. The opportunity cost for time lost to a setup at a non-bottleneck machine is zero. Goldratt and Cox (1992) and Raturi and Hill (1988) expand on these ideas.
- Shop floor control cost component – The cost of handling data entry activities associated with the order. Again, this is the cost per order that is handled.

Many plants have large setups between families of parts and small setups between parts within a family. The setups between families are sometimes called "major setups" and the setups between parts within a family are called "minor setups." A sequence-dependent setup is a changeover time dependent on the order in which jobs are run. For example, it might be easy to change a paint-making machine from white to gray, but difficult to change from black to white. Sometimes, setups are not sequence-dependent between items within a product family, but are sequence-dependent between families of products. When setup costs are sequence-dependent, we need to create a "from-to" table of costs, much like a "from-to" travel time table on the back of a map. This type of problem is called a combinatorial optimization problem.

The papers "Estimating Ordering and Setup Costs" and "How to Reduce Setup Cost and Time" are on the *OMWW CD* available from www.ClamshellBeachPress.com. ⊚

See *batch process, burden rate, carrying charge, carrying cost, continuous process, major setup cost, opportunity cost, sequence-dependent setup time, setup, setup time, Single Minute Exchange of Dies (SMED), standard cost, Theory of Constraints (TOC)*.

setup reduction methods – Procedures used to reduce the cost and time to prepare a machine to run a batch of parts. ✪

For many processes, the key to process improvement is to reduce the setup time and cost. Setup reduction enables small lotsizes, which in turn reduces the variability of the processing time, reduces queue time, reduces cycle time, and ultimately improves quality through early detection of defects.

The best method for doing this is generally to move the setup time "off-line," which is a setup that is done while the machine is still running. Another name for this is an "external" setup. Professor Hill has coined the term a "running setup" because the next job is being set up while the machine is still running.

For example, at the Indianapolis 500 race, the crew will prepare the tires, fuel, and water for the race car while the car is still going around the track. When the racecar arrives in the pit area, the crew changes all four tires, adds fuel, and gives the driver water. All of this is done in about 18 seconds. Another example is a surgery in a hospital where the nurses prepare the patient while another patient is still in surgery in the operating room.

Setup teams can also reduce setup times. When a setup is needed, a signal (such a light) indicates that all members of the setup team should converge on the machine. The setup team then quickly does its job. Some people who do not understand managerial accounting might challenge the economics of using a team. However, for a bottleneck process, the labor cost for the setup team is often far less than the cost of the capacity lost to a long setup. In other words, the increased capacity for the bottleneck and the plant is often worth more than the cost of the setup team.

Managers and engineers have only a limited time available for setup reduction. Therefore, it is important that setup reduction efforts be prioritized. Goldratt emphasizes that the priority should be on the bottleneck capacity. Professor John Leschke at the University of Virginia has several written articles on this subject that emphasize that some setups are shared by many items and therefore deserve higher priority in a setup reduction program.

See *external setup, mixed model assembly, one-piece flow, running setup, setup, setup time, Single Minute Exchange of Dies (SMED), Theory of Constraints (TOC).*

setup time – The time required to prepare a machine for the next order; also called changeover time. ✪

See *batch process, continuous process, Economic Lot Scheduling Problem (ELSP), run time, sequence-dependent setup time, setup, setup cost, setup reduction methods, Single Minute Exchange of Dies (SMED).*

seven tools of quality – Quality improvement tools that include the histogram, Pareto Chart, check sheet, control chart, cause and effect diagram (C&E Diagram), flowchart (process map), and scatter diagram.

The ASQ website (www.asq.org/learn-about-quality/seven-basic-quality-tools/overview/overview.html) uses the above list, but Professor Thomas Foster's website and Schroeder (2007) replace the check sheet with the run chart (cf., www.freequality.org/sites/www_freequality_org/Documents/knowledge/basicseventools.pdf).

See *causal map, check sheet, control chart, flowchart, histogram, Pareto Chart, process map, scatter diagram, Statistical Process Control (SPC).*

seven wastes – See *7 Wastes.*

shadow board – A holder for tools with outlines of tools to show where they should be stored.

Shadow boards are a standard practice used in the Set-in-order phase of 5S to organize tools and materials. The purpose of a shadow board is to call immediate attention to a failure to follow the discipline of "a place for everything and everything in its place" which is fundamental to 5S and to lean thinking.

Acknowledgement: CEMBA students '10 Ben Irby, Ryan Foss, Shyam Pakala, Julie Woessner, Tonja Bivins, and Sanjay Patel contributed to this entry.

See *5S, error proofing, lean thinking, visual control.*

shadow price – See *sensitivity analysis.*

Shingo Prize – A recognition given to a number of organizations each year by the Shingo Prize Board of Governors based on how well they have implemented lean thinking; an organization headquartered at Utah State University that manages the Shingo Prize evaluation process, conferences, and training events.

According to the webpage for the Shingo Prize, "The Shingo Prize is regarded as the premier manufacturing award recognition program for North America. As part of the Shingo Prize mission and model, the Prize highlights the value of using lean/world-class manufacturing practices to attain world-class status." The Shingo Prize evaluation process and conferences are sponsored by Utah State University. Similar to the Malcolm Baldrige Award, the Shingo Prize has developed a model (framework) that can used prescriptively to evaluate the performance of an organization.

The prize is named after the Japanese industrial engineer Shigeo Shingo who distinguished himself as one of the world's leading experts in improving manufacturing processes. According to the Shingo Prize webpage, Dr.

Shingo "has been described as an engineering genius who helped create and write about many aspects of the revolutionary manufacturing practices which comprise the renowned Toyota Production System."

The webpage for the Shingo Prize is http://bigblue.usu.edu/shingoprize.

See *lean thinking*, *Malcolm Baldrige National Quality Award (MBNQA)*.

shipping container – A large metal shipping box of a standard size that is used to securely and efficiently transport goods by road, ship, or rail, without having to be repacked.

In 2006, 20 million shipping containers were in use. Although containers are essential for international trade and commerce, no single system governs the international movement of containers, which makes it difficult to effectively track a container through the supply chain.

There are many different sizes and varieties of containers. The International Organization for Standardization (ISO) regulates container sizes to ensure some consistency throughout the world. The standard width for containers is 8 feet, but the lengths can vary. Below are the more common types of containers:

General purpose (dry cargo) container – This is the most commonly used shipping container, as it can carry the widest varieties of cargo. It is fully enclosed, weatherproof, and is equipped with doors either on the end wall (for end loading) or the side wall (for side loading.) The most common lengths of general purpose containers are 20 feet and 40 feet. Containers are measured in 20-foot equivalent units (TEU), meaning that a 20-foot container is 1 TEU and a 40-foot container is 2 TEU. Other general purpose container sizes include a 10-foot length (mostly used in Europe and by the military) and the high-cube container, which is for oversized freight.

Thermal container (reefer) – This container has insulated walls, doors, roof, and floor, which helps limit the amount of temperature gained or lost. The thermal container generally is used for perishable goods such as meat, fruits, and vegetables. In addition to the insulation, this type of container often has a heating or cooling device inside it.

Flat rack (platform) – This is not an actual container, but rather a means for securing oversize cargo that will not fit into a regular container. The flat rack is equipped with top and bottom corner fittings that hold the cargo in place on the top deck of the vessel. The flat rack generally is used for machinery, lumber, and other heavy or large objects.

Tank container – This type of container is used for bulk gases and liquids.

Dry bulk container – This container is used to ship dry solids in bulk without packaging, such as grains and dry chemicals. It is similar to the general purpose container, except that it is usually loaded from the top instead from the side or the end. Each container has its own code that is used for identification. Each code consists of four letters that identify which ocean carrier owns the containers (such as CSCL for China Shipping Container Lines) plus several numbers. After a container is loaded and sealed, the seal is assigned a number that is valid only for that shipment.

Container ships can vary greatly in size and capacity. A small container vessel might carry as few as 20 TEU, but most modern vessels carry approximately 1,000 TEU or more. Currently, the largest container vessel in the world has a capacity of 8,063 TEU. On a typical vessel, containers are loaded into tall slots that extend from three to six containers below deck to three to six containers above deck. The containers are then connected at the corners with locking devices.

Much of this content was contributed by Katherine McIntosh as a part of a course project, May 7, 2005.

See *Less than Container Load (LCL)*, *Less than Truck Load (LTL)*, *multi-modal shipments*.

shipping terms – See *terms*.

shop floor control – The management of all of the activities required to monitor the process of moving an order through a factory, from order release to order completion. ✪

Shop Floor Control, also known as production activity control, involves information systems to communicate the status of shop orders and workcenters. Major functions of shop-floor control include:
- Assigning priorities for each shop order.
- Maintaining work-in-process inventory information.
- Conveying shop-order status information.
- Providing historical output data for capacity control purposes.
- Providing shop order status data for both WIP inventory and accounting purposes.
- Measuring efficiency, utilization, and productivity of manpower and machines.

See *Manufacturing Execution System (MES)*, *routing*.

shortage – See *stockout*.

shrinkage – Inventory lost due to scrap, deterioration, shoplifting (theft from "customers"), breakage, employee theft, and counting discrepancies.

Shrinkage is usually discovered during a cycle count.

See *carrying charge, cycle counting, obsolescence*.

SIOP – See *Sales & Operations Planning (S&OP)*.

sigma level – A metric that measures the defect rate for a process in terms of the standard normal distribution with an assumed shift in the mean of 1.5 standard deviations.

The sigma metric is commonly used in Six Sigma programs as a measure of effectiveness for a process. The estimation process assumes that the control limit is set based on a standard normal random variable with mean zero and standard deviation 1, but the true process has a standard deviation of 1 and mean of 1.5 (instead of 0). The sigma level metric uses this model to estimate the number of defects that will occur in one million opportunities.

The table below shows the DPMO (defects per million opportunities) for a range of sigma level and mean shift values. The table is from the Sigma level.xls workbook.

Sigma level versus Defects Per Million Opportunities (DPMO)

Sigma level (*SL*)	Assumed shift in the mean (*MS*)			
	0.0	0.5	1.0	1.5
6.0	0.0	0.0	0.3	3.4
5.6	0.0	0.2	2.1	20.7
5.2	0.2	1.3	13.3	108
4.8	1.6	8.6	72.4	483
4.4	10.8	48.6	337	1,866
4.0	63.3	236	1,350	6,210
3.6	318	988	4,663	17,865
3.2	1,374	3,575	13,917	44,567
2.8	5,110	11,208	36,003	96,809
2.4	16,395	30,582	81,094	184,108
2.0	45,500	73,017	160,005	308,770
1.6	109,599	153,530	278,914	461,140
1.2	230,139	286,529	434,644	621,378
0.8	423,711	478,889	615,190	768,760
0.4	689,157	723,888	806,504	893,050

Notice that the famous "3.4 defects per million opportunities" can be found in the top right cell of the table. For a sigma level of $SL = 6$ and mean shift $MS = 1.5$, the probability of a defect in the right tail is 0.000003398, the probability of a defect in the left tail is practically zero, and the overall probability of a defect is 0.000003398. The total expected number of defects is, therefore, $3.3977 \approx 3.4$ defects per million opportunities.

The Excel formula for converting a "sigma level" (*SL*) with a mean shift (*MS*) into a defect rate (per million opportunities) is = (1 - (NORMDIST(*SL*, *MS*, 1, TRUE) - NORMDIST(-*SL*, *MS*, 1, TRUE)))*1000000. As noted above, it is commonly assumed that the mean is off by $MS = 1.5$ sigma.

It is important to understand that the Six Sigma standard may not be the ideal. The optimal sigma level may be lower or higher than six sigma based on the cost of a defect relative to the cost of preventing a defect. Contrary to the hyperbole found in many popular practitioner publications, the optimal sigma level is almost never zero and in fact is almost always more than six sigma.

The Excel workbook "sigma level.xls" is on the *OMWW CD* available from www.ClamshellBeachPress.com. This Excel workbook was used to generate the above table. ◉

See *Defects Per Million Opportunities (DPMO), DMAIC, operations performance metrics, process capability and performance, Six Sigma, specification limits.*

simulated annealing – A heuristic search method used for combinatorial (discrete) optimization problems.

Simulated annealing is analogous to how the molecular structure of metals is disordered at high temperatures but ordered (crystalline) at low temperatures. In simulated annealing, the "temperature" starts out high and the search for a better solution has a high probability of accepting an inferior solution. This allows the procedure to jump out of locally optimal solutions and potentially find a better solution. As the temperature is lowered, this probability decreases and the best solution found becomes frozen.

See *Operations Research (OR).*

simulation – A representation of reality used for experimentation purposes. ✪

In operations management, a computer simulation is often used to study systems such as factories or service processes. The computer simulation model allows the analyst to experiment with the model to find problems and opportunities without having to actually build or change the real system.

Simulation models can be categorized as either deterministic or stochastic. Deterministic simulations have no random components and therefore will always produce exactly the same results. Deterministic simulations, therefore, only need to be "run" once. On the other hand, stochastic simulations generate random variables and allow the user to explore the variability of the system. For example, a financial planning model might specify the mean and standard deviation of the demand and the mean and standard deviation of the unit cost. The simulation model might be run for many replications in order to compute the net present value of a number of different strategies. Stochastic simulations are also known as Monte Carlo simulations. Note that Monte Carlo simulations usually do not require a time dimension. For example, a Monte Carlo simulation could be used to cast two die several million times to get a distribution of the product of the two values.

Computer simulations can be further classified as either being discrete, continuous, or combined discrete and continuous. A discrete simulation processes distinct events, which means that the computer logic moves to a point in time (i.e., an event time) and changes one or more of the system state variables, and then schedules the next event. In other words, the simulation model skips from one time point to the next and the system status changes only at these points in time. In contrast, a continuous simulation model represents the movement of continuous variables changing over time (e.g., the course of a rocket in flight).

The inverse transform method can be used to generate a random variable from any distribution with a known distribution function. More computationally efficient special-purpose generators are available for several probability distributions such as the normal. See the entry on *random numbers* for more detail.

Many analysts new to simulation make several common errors in their simulation modeling efforts. Some of these errors include:

Not conducting a proper statistical analysis – Many new simulation users are tempted to let the simulation run for a few thousand observations and then compare the mean performance for the different alternatives considered in the experiment. The problem with this is that the means might not be statistically different due to the variability of the system.

Improper start up conditions – Simulation models often need user-defined start-up conditions, particularly for queuing systems. Starting a system "empty and idle" will often cause serious bias in the average results.

Creating improper confidence intervals – Simulation statistics such as the average number of customers (or units) in the system are highly correlated over time. In other words, the number in system at time t is highly correlated with the number in system at time $t + 1$. As a result, many simulation analyses underestimate the variability of the mean and create confidence intervals on the mean that are far too small (narrow). The proper approach is to use batch means (the means over long time intervals) and then treat each batch mean as a single observation for computing a confidence interval. This often has significant implications for the number of observations that are needed.

Not considering all of the sources of variability – A research study done at the University of Michigan many years ago found that the biggest shortfall of most simulation models was the missing variables. For example, an inventory simulation might do a good job of handling the normal variability of the demand during the leadtime. However, this same simulation might ignore catastrophic events such as fire in a supplier's plant which might shut down the entire firm for a month.

Not taking advantage of common random number streams – Most simulation languages such as Arena allow the user to run multiple simulations on the "same track" with respect to the sequence of random values. This is done by dedicating a random number seed to each random process (e.g., the demand quantity, time between arrivals, etc.). This approach allows the analyst to have far more comparable results.

Simulation modeling has come a long way in the last 20 years. Commercial simulation software such as Arena makes simulation modeling easy. Unfortunately, it is just as easy today as it was 20 years ago to make serious errors in modeling and analysis. As an old saying goes, "Simulation should be a method of last resort." In other words, simpler models such as queuing theory an optimization should be used before simulation.

See *confidence interval, inverse transform method, Operations Research (OR), random number, systems thinking.*

simultaneous engineering – A systematic approach to the integrated concurrent design of products and their related processes including manufacturing and support.

Benefits of simultaneous engineering include reduced time to market, increased product quality, and lower product cost. Simultaneous engineering is closely related to Design for Manufacturing (DFM). Simultaneous engineering appears to be synonymous with concurrent engineering and integrated product development.

See *concurrent engineering, Integrated Product Development (IPD), New Product Development.*

Single Minute Exchange of Dies (SMED) – A lean manufacturing methodology for reducing setup time to less than a single digit (e.g., less than 10 minutes).

This term was coined by Shigeo Shingo in the 1950s and 1960s. The term is used almost synonymously with quick changeovers. The setup time is the time from the last good part for one order to the first good part of the next order. A single minute is not required, but is used as a target value.

See *lean thinking, one-piece flow, setup cost, setup reduction methods, setup time.*

single piece flow – See *one-piece flow.*

single point of contact – A service quality principle that suggests that a customer should have to talk to only one person for the delivery of a service.

The single point of contact is summarized nicely with the slogan "one customer, one call, one relationship." This slogan emphasizes that each customer should only have to make one phone call and should only have to establish a relationship with one service provider. Unfortunately, the opposite of this occurs in many service organizations when a customer waits a long time in queue only to be told by the unfriendly service worker (or the phone system) that they have to go see someone else. The customer never builds a relationship with any service worker, and no service worker ever takes any "ownership" of the customer's needs.

Advantages of the single point of contact principle include (1) the firm builds a closer relationship with the customer, (2) the customer does not have to wait in multiple queues, (3) much less information is lost in the "hand-offs" between multiple service workers, (4) the job design is more satisfying for the service worker because they get to "own" the entire set of the customer's needs, and (5) the company may benefit from a reduced cost of service delivery in a "once and done" environment.

However, the single point of contact model is not without cost. In many cases the single point of contact increases the cost of service because (1) workers require more training and (2) one worker might have a long queue while another sits idle. In other words, from a queuing theory standpoint, the single point of contact dedicates each server to a particular set of customers. If not managed carefully, this can increase average waiting time and overall system performance.

See *service quality.*

single sampling plan – See *acceptance sampling.*

single source – The practice of using only one supplier (vendor) to supply a commodity or service even though other supplier could also be used as a source of supply.

With a single source supplier, a firm still has other qualified sources of supply that it can use in case of emergency. In contrast, with a sole source supplier, the firm has one and only one source capable of supplying the commodity or service. A sole source supply is basically a monopoly situation and can be risky for the customer. However, in some situations a sole source relationship is unavoidable. An example of a sole source is a music CD, where the artist has one and only one distribution company. Best Buy has no choice but to have a sole source of supply if it wants to carry music from that artist.

See *purchasing, sourcing.*

SIOP – See *Sales & Operations Planning (S&OP).*

SIPOC Diagram – An acronym for Suppliers, Inputs, Process, Outputs, and Customers, which is a tool used to identify all relevant elements of a process for the purposes of process improvement.

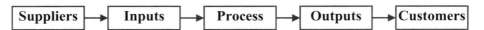

All process improvement projects should consider all five of these elements. Note that this is a useful tool for all process improvement projects, not just supply chain projects.

See *process map, supply chain management.*

Six Sigma – A process improvement program developed at Motorola, expanded by General Electric, and now promoted by many consultants throughout the world; also called Lean Sigma and Lean Six Sigma. ✪

Five views of Six Sigma

GE defined Six Sigma as "the disciplined methodology of defining, measuring, analyzing, improving and controlling the quality in every one of the Company's products, processes and transactions-with the ultimate goal of virtually eliminating all defects." However, this broad definition has been implemented and promoted from at least five different points of view. From the metric point of view, Six Sigma is about maximizing the "sigma level" (minimizing the defect rate) for processes, often with the target of 6 sigma (or 3.4 defects per million opportunities). From the tool point of view, Six Sigma is about applying managerial tools (e.g., brainstorming) and statistical tools (e.g., design of experiments) to problem solving. From the project point of view, Six Sigma is about defining and executing Six Sigma projects with Black Belts or Green Belts project leaders using the DMAIC five-step problem solving methodology. From the program point of view, Six Sigma is about a program management office that finds and prioritizes problems that need to be addressed and then charters and resources projects to address those problems. From the philosophy point of view, Six Sigma is about building a sustainable culture of leaders who are relentless about continuous improvement.

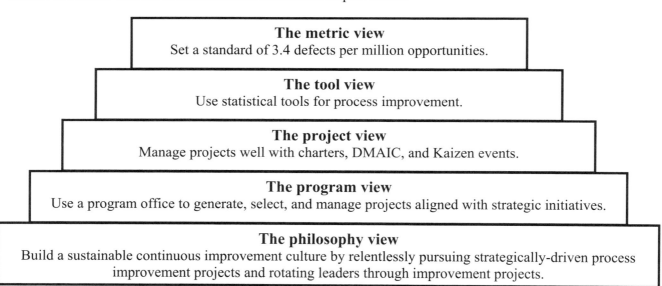

Source: Professor Arthur V. Hill

The DMAIC process

Six Sigma projects are managed with a five-step process called DMAIC – Define, Measure, Analyze, Improve, and Control. These five steps are described in more detail in the *DMAIC* entry. Six Sigma projects are often driven by an understanding of the "entitlement" (i.e., the best possible performance) for a process. However, the target may be different from the entitlement. See *entitlement*. Six Sigma training includes a large number of standard quantity management tools and techniques which are listed below.

Key roles and responsibilities

Six Sigma identifies five key roles for its successful implementation (Harry & Schroeder, 2000). Certification programs for most of these roles are available from many sources. Some of the content below is the ASQ.org site. The Executive leadership and Champions work at the program level, whereas Master Black Belts, Black Belts, Green Belts, Yellow Belts, and White Belts work at the project level.

- **Executive Leadership:** Provide overall leadership for the program office by aligning Six Sigma projects with corporate and business unit strategies. They also make sure that proper resources are allocated to the program. The leadership should include the CEO and other key top executives. They are responsible for setting the vision for the Six Sigma program. They also empower the other role holders with the freedom and resources to explore new ideas for breakthrough improvements.
- **Champions:** Lead the Six Sigma Program. The Champion is selected by the Executive Leadership and is usually a member of the executive team. The Champion must translates the company's strategies and goals into projects. They also identify resources and remove barriers to program and project success. Champions also act as mentors to the Master Black Belts and Black Belts. At GE, this level of certification is now called "Quality Leader." The Champions manage the project selection process, which includes managing the project hopper (i.e., the set of potential projects) and selecting people to become Black Belts.
- **Master Black Belts:** Assist Champions in program management and train and coach Black Belts and Green Belts in project management. Identified by Champions, they act as in-house expert coaches and trainers. They usually devote 100% of their time to Six Sigma. Apart from the usual rigor of statistics, their time is spent on ensuring integrated deployment of Six Sigma across various functions and departments. Master Black Belts should be experienced Black Belts.
- **Black Belt:** Lead problem-solving projects and trains and coaches their team members, while operating under Master Black Belts. Black Belts are usually assigned full time to Six Sigma. They usually have between four to eight weeks of training and are normally assigned to manage Six Sigma projects full-time for a limited period (normally 2-3 years). They focus primarily on Six Sigma project execution, whereas Champions and Master Black Belts focus on identifying projects/functions for Six Sigma.
- **Green Belt:** Assist Black Belts on Black Belt projects. May also lead Green Belt projects. They maintain their full-time job responsibilities. Green belts usually have between two and four weeks of training.
- **Yellow Belt:** Participate as a project team member. Reviews process improvements that support the project.
- **White Belt:** Work on local problem-solving teams that support overall projects, but may not be part of a Six Sigma project team. Understands basic Six Sigma concepts from an awareness perspective.

The Sigma metric

Four-sigma represents an average performance level across many industry sectors. If the entire world was operated on a four-sigma standard, the world would have some serious problems:

- 20,000 lost articles of mail per hour
- Unsafe drinking water almost 15 minutes per day
- 5,000 incorrect surgical operations per week
- Two short or long landings at major airports each day
- 200,000 wrong prescriptions each year
- No electricity for almost 7 hours each month

See the entry *sigma level* for the statistics behind the sigma level metric.

A comparison of Six Sigma programs and traditional TQM programs

The following table compares TQM and Six Sigma programs. Thanks to Professors Weiyong Zhang (VCU) and Kevin Linderman (University of Minnesota) for help on an earlier version of this comparison. The definitions of TQM and Six Sigma are not precise and tend to change over time. This comparison is based on a particular point of view that is not shared by all experts.

	TQM	Six Sigma
Alignment with strategy	Little alignment. Often initiated by people who run the process and not aligned with strategy.	Usually driven by strategy. Project selection usually driven by strategic objectives.
Goal orientation	Sometimes goal oriented, but not consistently.	Clearly defined goals. Projects nearly always have a charter.
Financial accountability	Sometimes roll-up results; rarely audited.	Nearly always audited. Tracks and audits the financial impact of projects and reports total impact for program.
Integration with human resources	Little integration. Most projects run by the quality organization and are not considered to be part of a leadership development program. Little impact on careers.	Much integration. Often viewed as the firm's primary leadership development program with black belt certification required for promotion to executive ranks.
Training content	Quality improvement.	Quality & process improvement, project management, and organizational change.
Training level	Managers, engineers, and direct labor.	Everyone, including senior executives.
Organizational structure	Almost no organizational structure. Employees often initiate and lead improvement projects on own processes.	Much structure. Prescribed organizational structure with well-defined roles for Champion, Black Belts, and Green Belts.
Integrated set of concepts	Little integration. Generally taught as a philosophy and a set of tools.	Much integration. Integrated approach to implementation, project management, and tools.
Specific project management tools	PDCA often presented as an abstract concept and not always implemented.	DMAIC used nearly universally for process improvement. Each DMAIC step has tools to accomplish specific objectives.
Project management discipline	Little discipline. No standard project management disciplines except for PDCA.	Much discipline. Champions often conduct reviews at the end of each DMAIC step. Fact-based decision-making is emphasized all the time.
Common language	Good technical training.	Leadership development program, common language for firm.
Statistics tools	Standard set of tools (Cause and effect diagrams, Pareto analysis, FMEA, process mapping, multivariate statistics, control charts, histograms, etc.)	

Source: Professor Arthur V. Hill

Lean Sigma training program content

The following is a list of topics that are often included in Lean Sigma and Six Sigma training programs. Almost all of these topics can be found in this encyclopedia.

Program management skills

• Role of the executive leadership • Role of the Lean Sigma Champion • Program infrastructure (organizational structure, roles for master blackbelts, blackbelts, greenbelts, project sponsors, and process owners) • Project generation (finding potential projects for the	• Project hopper (portfolio) management (project prioritization and selection) • Human resource development (selecting and training Black Belts and other key resources with the leadership development view) • Project staffing (assigning people to projects)

| project hopper) | • Program communication plan |
| | • Program performance measurement |

Project management tools

• Brainstorming methods (affinity diagrams, nominal group technique)	• Work breakdown structure (WBS)
• Project charters	• Project scheduling and reporting
• Project team selection	• Project reviews
• Leading effective meetings (agenda, schedules, frequency, notes, task assignments)	• DMAIC
	• Kaizen events
• Managing for change (conflict management, stakeholder analysis, RACI matrix)	• Project closing (project completion notice, post-project review, project closing report)
• Project communication plan	• Microsoft Project or Excel (for project management)
• Issue trees	• Microsoft PowerPoint (for project presentations)

Use of process metrics

• Balanced scorecard concepts (Better, Faster, Cheaper)	• Waiting time measurement (mean time in system and in queue, utilization, Little's Law)
• Cost of quality (prevention cost, detection cost, internal failure, external failure)	• Customer satisfaction measurement
	• Forecast error measurement tools
• Defect measurement (DPMO, sigma level, yield, first-pass yield)	• Measurement system analysis
	• Gage R&R
• Process capability and performance metrics (Cp, Cpk, Pp, Ppk, Sigma level, DPMO)	• Overall Equipment Effectiveness (OEE)
• Cycle time measurement (cost of long cycle times, quality, time elasticity of demand)	• Labor efficiency and productivity (includes methods time measurement studies)
• Inventory turnover measurement	• Learning measurement (trend line, learning curve, half-life curve, Moore's Law)
• Marginal versus full cost	• Supplier scorecards
• Cost of carrying inventory	• Standard red/yellow/green scorecard dashboards

Process diagnostic tools

• Identify the 7 wastes	• Knowledge mapping (also called mind mapping)
• Process mapping	• Root cause analysis
• Value stream mapping	• Theory of Constraints (identifying and protecting the bottleneck, the bottleneck as the pacemaker)
• SIPOC analysis	
• Causal mapping	• Microsoft Visio and Excel (for process mapping)

Six Sigma and lean process improvement tools

• FMEA (Failure Mode and Effects Analysis)	• Pull versus push
• Error proofing (Mistake-proofing, Poke yoke)	• Lean scheduling tools focusing on the pacemaker workcenter
• 5S	
• Standardized work and writing standard operating instructions	• Queue management concepts
	• Cellular manufacturing (benefits of cells, Chaku Chaku, justification of cells, etc.)
• Setup and lotsize reduction tools (SMED)	

Statistical tools

• Descriptive statistics (mean, median, mode, range, standard deviation, etc.)	• Confidence intervals
	• Sampling plans (sample size calculations, stop and go rules, dollar-unit sampling)
• Exploratory data analysis	
• Pareto analysis	• Hypothesis testing
• Graphical analysis (histograms, scatter plots, box plots, etc.)	• Design of experiments (Taguchi methods, full factorial, factional factorial, ANOVA)
• Statistical process control (x-bar charts, r-charts, c-charts, p-charts, run charts)	• Non-parametric statistics
	• Microsoft Excel (for simple statistical analysis)
• Regression analysis	• Minitab, SAS, or SPSS (for statistical analysis)

Voice of the customer tools

• Customer satisfaction surveys • Marketing research surveys • Quality Function Deployment/House of Quality	• Kano analysis • Conjoint analysis • Pugh matrix

New product development tools

• Design for Six Sigma (DFSS) • Design for manufacturing (plus other DFx concepts such as Design for Assembly, Design for Disassembly, Design for Environment, Design for Reliability, etc.) • IDOV and DMADV • Triz	• Taguchi methods • New product development organization (e.g., heavyweight NPD teams) • Service blueprinting • Service guarantees • Experience engineering • Designing and managing a NPD stage-gate process

Source: Professor Arthur V. Hill

The Excel workbook "sigma level.xls" and the paper "The Process Improvement Checklist" are on the **OMWW CD** available from www.ClamshellBeachPress.com. The checklist includes a large number of the best process improvement ideas used in many Six Sigma and process improvement projects. ◉

See *benchmarking, C&E Diagram, C&E Matrix, Capability Maturity Model (CMM), causal map, champion, control chart, control plan, Critical To Quality (CTQ), Deming's 14 points, deployment leader, Design for Six Sigma (DFSS), Design of Experiments (DOE), DMAIC, entitlement, Failure Mode and Effects Analysis (FMEA), Gauge R&R, impact wheel, Key Process Output Variable (KPOV), lean sigma, lean thinking, linear regression, Metrology, PDCA (Plan-Do-Check-Act), process capability and performance, process improvement program, program management office, project charter, project hopper, Pugh Matrix, quality trilogy, RACI Matrix, sigma level, stage-gate process, stakeholder analysis, Statistical Process Control (SPC), statistical quality control (SQC), strategy map, Total Quality Management (TQM), transactional process improvement, Zero Defects.*

SKU – See *Stock Keeping Unit (SKU)*.

slack time – The free time in a schedule relative to the due date. ✪

In the project scheduling context, the slack time is the time that a task can be delayed without delaying the overall project completion time. In a job shop scheduling context, the slack time is the due date less the sum of the remaining processing time. The slack time rule is a good dispatching rule for many job shops.

For example, a student has a report due in 14 days but believes that it will take only three days to write the report and one day to get copies printed. Therefore, the student has a slack time of ten days.

See *critical chain, Critical Path Method (CPM), job shop scheduling, Project Evaluation and Review Technique (PERT), project management, safety leadtime.*

slow moving demand – A product with a low average demand, where low is usually defined to be less than five to nine units per period. ✪

Background

Many products have a low average demand. In fact, for many firms, most products tend to be slow moving, with a demand less than nine units per period. Some slow moving items are high-price (or high-cost) items such as medical devices, service parts, and capital goods (e.g., jet engines) and often have a high shortage (or stockout) cost. (A distinction between shortage and stockout cost is described in other places in this book.) Clearly, these items need to be carefully managed to find the right balance between having too much and too little inventory. Many other slow moving items are low-price (or low-cost) items and make up a small part of the firm's total revenue (or investment). Most inventory management texts appropriately urge managers to focus on the "important few" and not worry too much about the "trivial many." However, managers still need inventory systems to manage the "trivial many" or they will be overwhelmed by transactions, stockouts, inventory carrying cost, and errors. As a group, these items still require significant investment and still have a major impact on customer service.

It is often possible to make significant improvements in both service levels and inventory levels for slow moving items by developing a "one-for-one" (use one-order one) system that applies the following principles:

- **Use a perpetual inventory system with a one-for-one replenishment policy** – This approach can achieve high service levels with little inventory. This is particularly helpful when inventory is in short supply and must be "allocated" to the multiple stocking locations.
- **Set the "target inventory level" that finds the optimal balance between the carrying and shortage costs** – If the target is set too low, the system will have too many angry customers and too much shortage cost. If the target is set too high, the system will have too much inventory and too much carrying cost. Given that the order quantity is fixed at one, the target inventory is the only decision parameter for this model.

Advantages of the one-for-one model

- **It can improve both service levels and inventory investment** – The model can help find a consistent policy across all stocking points and across all items. The inventory targets can be used to help with the "phase-in" of new products and "phase-out" of old products in a rational and consistent manner. When an organization has some items on "allocation," the model can help ration these items to stocking points in an objective manner.
- **It can keep the safety stock in the finished goods inventory or central warehouse so the company can "pool" the risk** – The safety stock should be "pooled" in a central location as much as possible so it is available when and where needed.
- **It rewards people in the field for communicating the actual demand as quickly as possible** – End-of-month or end-of-quarter "hockey stick" reporting and ordering cause variability in the demand and create a need for substantially more safety stock than is really needed.

The inventory model

This model seeks to find the optimal value of the target inventory level, S, to minimize the sum of the carrying and shortage cost for one item at a particular inventory stocking point (vehicle, warehouse, retail store, etc.). If S is set too high, organizations incur too much carrying cost. If S is set too low, they experience too much shortage cost. The definitions of terms for this model are as follows:

S The target inventory level. The inventory decision rule is to order one unit whenever the on-hand inventory is below S.

D Average demand (in units) per day.

C_H Carrying cost (holding cost) per unit per period.

C_S Shortage cost per unit not filled immediately from inventory.

To find the optimal value of the target inventory S, it is necessary to conduct a search with $S = 0, 1, 2$, etc. for the value of S that satisfies the relationship $R(S) = C_H /(DC_S)$. For every trial value of S, find the ratio $R(S) = p(S)/F(S)$, where $p(S)$ is the probability that the demand during leadtime is S units and $F(S)$ is the cumulative probability that the demand during leadtime is less than or equal to S. In other words, find the lowest value of S such that $p(S)/F(S) \leq C_H /(DC_S)$.

Example

A hospital uses a pacemaker that has a unit cost of $1000. The demand for this item for the next year is expected to be 50 units. It takes about 2 days for the hospital to order and receive a replacement pacemaker. In other words, the replenishment leadtime is two days. The shortage cost was set to only 20% of the unit cost (0.2 x $1000 = $200) because the hospital could almost always find a backup unit at another hospital or from their sales rep – but it still cost them some trouble – about $200 worth. The carrying charge was set at 24% per year and was based on the hospital's cost of capital (about 10%) plus an additional charge for risk of obsolescence and storage. Other input parameters are displayed below:

Inventory stocking point	Jones Hospital
Model	ABC-123
Expected unit sales per year	50 units per year
Number of workdays per year	246 days
Replenishment leadtime	2 days
Unit cost	$1,000
Annual carrying charge (carrying cost as a percent of unit cost)	24.0%
Shortage cost as a percent of unit cost	20.0%

The model calculates several variables and then finds that the optimal (minimum cost) target inventory for the hospital is 7 pacemakers.

Average sales per workday	1.000 units per workday
Average demand during replenishment leadtime	2.000 units
Carrying cost per year	$240 per unit per year
Carrying cost per day	$0.66 per unit per day
Shortage cost	$200 per unit short
Optimal target inventory	7 units

The following graph shows the carrying cost, shortage cost, and total cost functions.

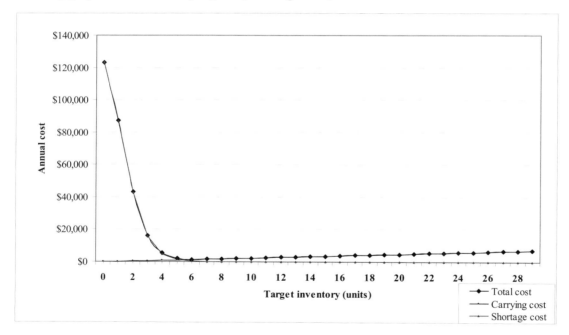

The paper "Managing Slow-Moving Inventory" and the Excel workbook "slowmove.xls" are on the *OMWW CD* available from www.ClamshellBeachPress.com. ◉

See *all-time demand, newsvendor model, periodic review system, Poisson distribution, service parts.*

SMART – A useful and easy-to-remember acronym for a simple approach for setting goals; also called SMARTS, SMARTER, and SMARTIE.

The SMART acronym is a popular and useful goal setting tool at both the organizational level and also for an individual. While many websites attribute this acronym to Drucker (1954), according to the website www.rapidbi.com/created/WriteSMARTobjectives.html (May 26, 2008), "there is no direct reference to SMART by Drucker … While it is clear that Drucker was the first to write about management by objectives, the SMART acronym is harder to trace."

The most common SMART acronym

Many different variants of this popular acronym can be found on the web. In fact, only the first two letters seem to be universally accepted. The following list includes what appears to be the most popular variant for SMART goals. This is the list that is recommended by this author:

(S) Specific – Goals should be stated in plain, simple, unambiguous, specific language and written down so that they are easy to remember, easy to communicate to others, and easy to know when the goal has been accomplished. A goal of losing weight is not specific; a goal of losing 20 pounds by Christmas is specific.

(M) Measurable – Goals should be quantifiable to that it is possible to measure progress towards them. The slogan "you cannot management what you cannot measure" has been popular for many decades. For example, progress towards a measurable weight loss goal is measurable, while progress towards being healthier is not.

(A) Achievable – Goals should be realistic and also under control of the person who defines them. According to goal theory, a goal set too high will be discouraging and a goal set too low is not motivating. Collins and Porras (1996) suggest that organizations need a "Big Hairy Audacious Goal" or "BHAG" to serve as a clear and compelling vision and catalyst for improvement. It is also imperative that goals be under the control of the organization or individual who defines them. If a goal is outside of a person's control, it is just a wish or a dream. For example, a manager wants the firm's profit to increase by 10%, but profit is affected by many actions (e.g., competitor's pricing) outside of the firm's control.

(R) Results oriented – Goals should be a statement of an outcome and should not be a task or activity. In the words of David Allen (2001), this is the "desired outcome."

(T) Time specific – Goals should have a realistic time limit for accomplishing the outcome. Someone once defined a goal as "a wish with a time limit." It is not enough to set a goal of losing 20 pounds; it is also important to set a time frame (e.g., lose 20 pounds by Christmas).

Other variants for the SMART acronym

The following list includes many of the variants for each letter in the SMART acronym. Note that many of these variants lead to redundancy and many substitute ideas that are not synonyms, and therefore change the entire concept.

(S) Specific – Strategic, simple, stimulating. These alternatives do not appear to be very popular.

(M) Measurable – Motivational. This alternative does not appear to be very popular.

(A) Achievable – Attainable, appropriate, accepted, agreed, agreed-to, aligned, actionable, action-based, and action-oriented. The alternative "attainable" appears to be quite popular, but it is a synonym so it really does not matter. Accepted, agreed, greed-to, and aligned all present an important point for the implementation of goals. If the organization goals conflict with other organizational goals or with the goals of individuals, it is unlikely that the goals will be realized. Actionable, action-based, and action-oriented are already included in "measurable" and "results-oriented."

(R) Results oriented – Realistic, recorded, relevant, rewarding, and risky. Realistic is redundant with achievable. Recorded can easily be included in specific. Relevant emphasizes that the outcomes should be under the control of the person or organization that has set the goal, but that idea can be included under "achievable." Rewarding emphasizes that it is important to identify the benefits for achieving the goal. Steve Flagg, President of Quality Bicycle Products in Eden Prairie Minnesota, uses "risky" here to suggest that the goals should stretch people to drive innovation and transformation. He asserts that "(the term) realistic supports maintenance of the *status quo* instead of innovative goal setting."

(T) Time specific – Timely, time-limited, time-related, timed, timescaled, time-bound, time-oriented, and trackable. All of these are communicate the same idea that a well-defined goal should define the deadline for completion.

Other variants of the acronym

SMARTS: This includes the "S" at the end for "shared," "stretch," or "sub-goaled." Having goals that are shared by all of the stakeholders is always a good idea. This is consistent with the ideas of "aligned," "agreed-to" and "agreed." However, using both "stretch" and "achievable" in the same list is somewhat contradictory. The term "sub-goaled" is a good idea, but is quite awkward.

C-SMART: This variant puts the word "Challenging" in front. Again, suggesting that goals be both achievable and challenging is somewhat contradictory. The balance issue can and probably should be included in the "achievable" item.

SMARTER: This variant adds the "ER," where E = enthusiasm, extending, exciting, or evaluated and R = rewarding or recorded.

SMARTIE: This variant adds the "IE," where the I and E stand for "interesting" or "inspiring" and "exciting."

Conclusions

The SMART acronym has been around a long time, but no one variant seems to be universally accepted. Many leaders have embraced SMART to help their organizations develop specific and measurable goals. However, the goal theory debate continues between the extremes of risky and challenging versus attainable and realistic. Combining all of the variants into one long list suggests that SMART goals should be specific, strategic, simple, stimulating, measurable, motivational, achievable, attainable, appropriate, accepted, agreed, agreed-to, aligned, actionable, action-based, action-oriented, results oriented, realistic, recorded, relevant, rewarding, risky, time specific, timely, time-limited, time-related, timed, timescaled, time-bound, time-oriented, trackable, shared, stretch, sub-goaled, challenging, enthusiastic, extending, exciting, evaluated, rewarding, recorded, interesting, inspiring, and exciting.

Steve Flagg, President of Quality Bicycle Products in Eden Prairie Minnesota, wisely asserts that every goal should have a corresponding "purpose statement that precedes it." "The purpose is just as important as the goal." For example, if your goal is to lose ten pounds before the end of the year, this aligns with purposes such as to be healthy, to honor God in your body, to love your spouse by taking care of yourself, and to model healthy living for your children.

The source for some of the above terms is rapidbi.com/created/WriteSMARTobjectives.html, May 26, 2008.

See Professor Hill's papers entitled "How to Create a Mission Statement" and "Strategy Mapping" available from Clamshell Beach Press.

See *mission statement*.

SME – See *Society of Manufacturing Engineers (SME)*.

SME (Subject Matter Expert) – Someone who is knowledgeable about a particular topic and therefore is designated to serve as a resource for a consulting project or process improvement project team.

SMEs are normally considered to be advisors to the project team rather than full team members. Consulting firms use the term SME for consulting experts who provide deep information on a particular topic. Some consulting firms are now moving away from this term and are now calling these people "subject area specialists."

See *project charter*.

SMED – See *Single Minute Exchange of Dies*.

smoothing – See *exponential smoothing*.

sniping – The practice of waiting until the last minute to bid in an auction.

Sniping is a common practice in on-line auctions such as eBay and is often an effective strategy for helping bidders avoid price wars and get what they want at a lower final price (Roth & Ockenfels, 2002). Some on-line auctions allow the deadlines to be extended to foil the sniping strategy. For example, Amazon auctions have a scheduled end time, but the auction is extended if bids are received near the scheduled end. The rule at Amazon is that the auction cannot end until at least ten minutes have passed without a bid.

See *Dutch auction, e-auction, e-business, e-commerce, reverse auction*.

Society of Manufacturing Engineers (SME) – A professional society dedicated to bringing people and information together to advance manufacturing knowledge.

For 75 years, SME has served manufacturing practitioners, companies, and other organizations as their source for information, education, and networking. SME supports manufacturers from all industries and job functions through events and technical and professional development resources.

SME produces several publications including the practitioner-oriented *Manufacturing Engineering Magazine* and two scholarly journals, the *Journal of Manufacturing Systems (JMS)* and the *Journal of Manufacturing Processes (JMP)*. The *JMS* focuses on applying new manufacturing knowledge to design and integration problems, speeding up systems development, improving operations and containing product and processing costs. The *JMP* presents the essential aspects of fundamental and emerging manufacturing processes such as material removal, deformation, injection molding, precision engineering, surface treatment and rapid prototyping.

SME's website is www.sme.org.

See *Operations Management (OM)*.

socio-technical design – The interaction between people and the processes in which they work; a methodology for creating jobs that have a carefully considered interaction between the people and the process. ✪

Socio-technical design considers how people and processes interact. Organizations can often benefit by designing a work environment that motivates workers to achieve their full potential in ways that also benefit the organization. A deep understanding of socio-technical design requires an understanding of behavioral science, organizational behavior, organizational design, psychology, human resources management, economics, and engineering.

Socio-technical design is important in almost every operations management topic. For example, visual management, a key lean manufacturing concept, is a good socio-technical design because when processes are made more visual, workers can understand them better and be more productive. Socio-technical design concepts are considered in many entries in this encyclopedia.

Socio-technical design is closed related to ergonomics.

See *cross-training, ergonomics, gainsharing, Hawthorne Effect, High Performance Work Systems (HPWS), job enlargement, job rotation, lean thinking, New Product Development (NPD), Results-Only Work Environment (ROWE), standardized work, work measurement, work simplification*.

sole source – See *single source*.

SOP – Standard operating procedures. See *standardized work*.

sourcing – Identifying, qualifying, and developing agreements with suppliers; also known as purchasing. ✪

Sourcing is usually used in the context of a purchasing organization finding, evaluating, and selecting suppliers for direct and indirect materials. The term is only rarely used for sourcing technology, labor, intellectual property, or capital.

"In-sourcing" is the practice of vertical integration so that the organization provides its own source of supply. "Outsourcing" is the practice of having another legal entity serve as the source of supply. While outsourcing is often on another continent, it can be on the same continent. In other words, outsourcing and offshoring are not synonyms. Global sourcing is the practice of searching the entire world for the best source of supply. Regional sourcing is the practice of finding local suppliers to assure low replenishment leadtimes and low freight costs. Regional sourcing often has political benefits as well; some countries have local content laws that require that a certain percentage of the product cost be from local suppliers.

The decision to sole, single, or multiple source a commodity is an important strategic decision. The paper "Sole Versus Single Versus Multiple Source of Supply" is available on the www.ClamshellBeachPress.com website. ◉

See *business process outsourcing, outsourcing, purchasing, single source, supply chain management*.

spaghetti chart – A diagram that shows the travel paths for one or more products (or people) that travel through a facility.

The numerous colored lines make it look like a plate of spaghetti. This tool helps identify opportunities for reducing the travel and move times in a process.

See *facility layout*.

spare parts – See *service parts*.

SPC – See *Statistical Process Control (SPC)*.

special cause variation – The causes of variation in a process that have an identifiable source and can eventually be eliminated; also known as assignable cause.

Causes of variation in a process that are not inherent in the process itself but originate from circumstances that are out of the ordinary. Special causes are indicated by points that fall outside the limits of a control chart.

See *common cause variation, control chart, Statistical Process Control (SPC), tampering*.

specification – See *specification limits*.

specification limits – The required features and performance characteristics of a product, as defined at different levels of detail.

Specifications are defined in terms of an upper and/or lower specification limit. Specification limits may be two-sided, with upper and lower limits, or one-sided, with either an upper or a lower limit. Unlike control limits, specification limits are not dependent on the process in any way. Specification limits are the boundary points that define the acceptable values for an output variable of a particular product characteristic. Specification limits are determined by customers, product designers, and management.

See *control chart, process capability and performance, sigma level, Statistical Process Control (SPC)*.

speed to market – See *time to market*.

SQC – See *statistical quality control*.

square root law for safety stocks – When the replenishment leadtime increases by a factor of f, the safety stock will increase approximately by the factor $\sqrt{f}$.

This relationship is based on the safety stock equation. This relationship becomes particularly helpful when considering offshoring production to another continent. As the manufacturing and delivery time increase, the safety stock will also increase.

See *safety stock*.

square root law for warehouses – A simple mathematical model stating that the total inventory in a system is proportional to the square root of the number of stocking locations.

The practical application of this "law" is that the inventory in stocking locations (such as warehouses) will increase with the square root of the number of stocking locations that serve the market. For example, doubling the number of stocking locations will increase inventory by a factor of the square root of two (e.g., 1.414) or about 41%. This law warns managers against the naïve assumption that adding stocking locations will require no additional inventory.

Mathematically, the law can be stated as $I = a\sqrt{n}$, where I is the total inventory, n is the number of stocking locations (typically warehouses), and a is a constant. A more useful version of this model is $I_{new} = I_{old}\sqrt{n_{new}/n_{old}}$, where I_{old} and I_{new} are the old and new inventory levels and n_{old} and n_{new} are the old and new number of stocking locations.

As mentioned above, this law states that if a firm doubles the number of warehouses, it should expect to increase inventory by a factor of $I_{new}/I_{old} = \sqrt{n_{new}/n_{old}} = \sqrt{2/1} \approx 1.414$. In other words, doubling the number of stocking locations should increase inventory by about 41%. Similarly, if the firm cuts the number of stocking locations in half, it should expect to see inventory go down by a factor of $1/\sqrt{2} \approx 0.707$. In other words, cutting the number of stocking locations in half should reduce inventory by about 30%. The table below shows the multiplicative percentage increase or decrease in inventory as the number of stocking points changes.

		Number of future stocking points							
		1	2	3	4	5	10	15	20
Number of current stocking points	1	100%	141%	173%	200%	224%	316%	387%	447%
	2	71%	100%	122%	141%	158%	224%	274%	316%
	3	58%	82%	100%	115%	129%	183%	224%	258%
	4	50%	71%	87%	100%	112%	158%	194%	224%
	5	45%	63%	77%	89%	100%	141%	173%	200%
	10	32%	45%	55%	63%	71%	100%	122%	141%
	15	26%	37%	45%	52%	58%	82%	100%	115%
	20	22%	32%	39%	45%	50%	71%	87%	100%

Source: Professor Arthur V. Hill

The square root law has been discussed as far back as 1962 (Starr & Miller, 1962) and was proven mathematically by Maister (1976) based on a reasonable set of assumptions. Evers (1995) found that the square root law can be applied to both safety stock and cycle stock, and therefore can be applied to total inventory. Coyle, Bardi, and Langley (2002) provide an example showing that this model can fits reality very nicely.

Zinn, Levi and Bowersox (1989) found that the square root law is most accurate when the markets have demands that are negatively correlated. They found little or no benefit from consolidating stock when the demands faced by the various stocking points were positively correlated. They also found that the accuracy of the model increased with the demand uncertainty at each location (measured by the coefficient of variation).

Acknowledgments: Mr. Randall Thorson (Carlson School MBA 08) contributed to this entry.

The paper "Square Root Law of Warehouses" is available on the www.ClamshellBeachPress.com website. ◉

See *supply chain management*.

stage-gate process – A project management and control practice commonly used for new product development that uses formal reviews at predetermined steps in the project to decide if the project will be allowed to proceed; also called phrase review, toll gate, or gated process.

The term "stage-gate" was coined by Cooper (1993, 2001) to help firms improve their new product development process. Many have argued that compared to a traditional process, the stage-gate process brings products to market in less time, with better quality, greater discipline, and overall better performance (Cooper 1993).

A gate is a decision point (milestone or step) where the project status is reviewed and a decision is made to go forward, redirect, hold, or terminate the project. A formal stage-gate process will have a standardized set of deliverables for each gate. This standardization allows the management team to compare the relative value of NPD projects in the new product portfolio, and to make trade-off decisions. A gate scorecard can be used to evaluate the deliverables against the standard. For example, demonstrating robust design may be a requirement in an early stage. The scorecard status may be yellow (caution) if the C_{pk} of a critical quality parameter is only 1.

Cooper (2001) outlines the following typical stage-gate phases:

1. **Discovery:** Pre-work designed to discover and uncover opportunities and generate ideas. (Gate = Idea screen)
2. **Scoping:** A quick, preliminary investigation of the project –largely desk research. (Gate = Second screen)
3. **Building the business case:** A detailed investigation involving primary research, both technical and marketing, leading to a business case. This business case includes the product definition, project justification, and a project plan.
4. **Development:** The detailed design and development of the new product, and the design of the production process.
5. **Testing and validation:** Trials in the marketplace, lab, and plant to verify and validate the proposed new product and its marketing and production.
6. **Launch:** Commercialization (beginning of full production, marketing, and selling).

The stages from the Advanced Product Quality Planning (APQP) process of the Automotive Industry Action Group (AIAG) are **Concept approval**, **Program approval**, **Prototype**, **Pilot**, and **Launch**.

A typical stage-gate process is as follows:

1. **Market analysis:** Various product concepts that address a market need are identified.

2. **Commitment:** The technical feasibility a particular product concept is determined and design requirements are defined.

3. **Development**: All activities necessary to design, document, build, and qualify the product and its associated manufacturing processes are included.

4. **Evaluation**: Final design validation of the product is conducted per evaluation plans during this phase. Clinical and/or field studies are conducted and regulatory approval to market and distribute the product is also obtained.

5. **Release**: The product is commercially distributed in markets where regulatory approval has been obtained.

The table below summarizes the three frameworks above. Note that all three of these are quite similar.

Cooper	AIAG	Typical
Discovery		
Scoping	Concept approval	Market analysis
Building the business case	Program approval	Commitment
Development	Prototype	Development
Testing and validation	Pilot	Evaluation
Launch	Launch	Release

Many Six Sigma programs use a similar "gated" process at the end of each of the steps in the DMAIC framework to provide accountability and keep the project on track. However, some experts argue that stage-gates create too much overhead and slow a project down and therefore should only be used for large projects. Some project management experts argue that stage-gates should be based on the nature of the specific project rather than on the DMAIC framework.

Acknowledgments: CEMBA 06 students Michael Kargel, Sharon Rozzi, Suzanne Naimon, Mohammed Mahmood, William Kellogg, Elda Macias, and James Meier contributed to this entry. CEMBA 10 students Chas Anderson, Grant Bistram, Robert Doty, Oscar Hernandez, Yevette Jaszczak, Vasanti Mudkanna, and Jeff Thaler also contributed to this entry.

See *Design for Six Sigma (DFSS)*, *New Product Development (NPD)*, *phase review*, *project charter*, *project management*, *Six Sigma*, *waterfall scheduling*.

stakeholder analysis – A technique for identifying, evaluating, and mitigating political risks that might affect the outcomes of an initiative such as a process improvement project.

The goal of stakeholder analysis is to win the most effective support possible for the initiative and to minimize potential obstacles to successful implementation. Stakeholder analysis is particularly important in major quality management, process improvement, and Business Process Re-engineering programs.

The three steps in stakeholder analysis are:

- **Identify the stakeholders** – Identify people, groups, and institutions that might influence the activity (either positively or negatively). The RACI Matrix is a good tool for helping with this process. See *RACI Matrix*.
- **Evaluate "what is in it for me"** – Anticipate the kind of influence, positive or negative, these groups will have on your initiative.
- **Develop communication and involvement strategies** – Decide how all of the stakeholders should be involved in the initiative and how the team will communicate with all of the stakeholders on a regular basis.

The following table is a good approach for conducting a formal stakeholder analysis. This can easily be implemented in Excel or Word. Define each stakeholder's goals and then identify how the project might help or hinder those goals. The involvement strategy seeks to (1) define the right level of involvement for each key stakeholder group, (2) get them involved early in the project, and (3) recruit them to help refine the communication strategy. The communication strategy is built around explaining the positives and mitigating negatives for each stakeholder group.

	Stakeholder		
	Randy (Sister unit)	**Steve (MIS)**	**Sally (Support unit)**
Goals	Maintaining revenue for the firm and for his unit. Concerned about losing head count.	Concerned about keeping the application backlog from growing.	Concerned about the quality of our deliverables.
Positives	Could help add new business opportunities.	The system will be more complex, but we can mitigate this.	We will get her department involved from the beginning.
Negatives	Concerned about losing business for his unit.	Concerned about systems becoming more complex.	Concerned about her department not being involved.
Involvement strategy	Ask to sit on our advisory council. Keep informed of all major decisions.	Ask him to appoint someone to be on the project team.	Ask her to join team.
Communication strategy	Have several formal and informal meetings with him early in the process.	Have team member send regular communications to MIS.	Have her send regular communications her unit.

The following is a list of potential benefits for employees: remove frustration, remove bottlenecks, reduce bureaucracy, make things simpler, improve morale, improve teamwork, improve communication, accelerate learning, help them serve customers better, free time for more important work.

Some consultants talk about "co-opting" a potential opponent by inviting them to participate on the project team or by inviting them to be a Subject Matter Expert (SME) to advise the team. The idea is to get your potential opponents on your side early in the process and use their energy to move the project forward rather than to get in the way.

Part of this was adapted from website http://erc.msh.org/quality/ittools/itstkan.cfm, January 10, 2005.

The paper "Stakeholder Analysis" is available on the **OMWW CD** available from www.ClamshellBeachPress.com. ◉

See *Business Process Re-engineering (BPR)*, *lean sigma*, *lean thinking*, *project charter*, *RACI Matrix*, *Six Sigma*, *Total Quality Management (TQM)*.

standard cost – A system of determining the cost for a product based on direct labor, direct materials, and allocated overhead. ✪

The standard costing system in most manufacturing firms defines the standard cost as (standard time for direct labor) x (standard labor rate) + direct materials + overhead. Overhead is typically allocated on the basis of the direct labor cost. More sophisticated firms allocate overhead using Activity Based Costing methods.

When firms allocate overhead to products based on direct labor as the only cost driver, they are often allocating the largest component of cost (i.e., overhead) based on the smallest component (i.e., direct labor). Because of product variety and complexity, a constant burden rate (overhead rate) based on direct labor is no longer appropriate for many firms. This approach has several problems, including:

- Undo focus on direct labor – Because overhead is allocated on the basis of direct labor, many managers assume that they can reduce overhead by reducing direct labor, which is clearly wrong and misguided.
- Poorly informed outsourcing decisions – When managers assume that the overhead will go away when direct labor goes away, they sometimes make poorly informed outsourcing decisions and only later discover that the overhead does not disappear.
- Death spiral overhead costs – When decisions are made to outsource a product and the overhead does not go away, overhead then has to be reallocated to other products and the firm enters into a "death spiral" with the same overhead being allocated to fewer and fewer products.
- Poor understanding of product costs – Allocation of overhead on direct labor hides the true product costs, especially when direct labor is a small portion of the total cost.

See *absorption costing*, *Activity Based Costing (ABC)*, *burden rate*, *setup cost*, *standard time*, *variable costing*.

standard deviation – A measure of the variability of a variable; the square root of the variance. ✪

Given a set of n observations on a random variable labeled $(x_1, x_2, \ldots, x_n)$, the sample standard deviation is the square root of the sample variance and is defined by:

$$\hat{\sigma} = \sqrt{\sum_{i=1}^{n}(x_i - \overline{x})^2 / (n-1)} = \frac{1}{\sqrt{n-1}} \sqrt{\sum_{i=1}^{n} x_i^2 - \frac{1}{n}\left(\sum_{i=1}^{n} x_i\right)^2}$$

The first expression is known as the definitional form; the second expression is known as the computational form because it is easier for computing purposes. The computational form requires only "one pass" on the data. The population standard deviation has a denominator of n instead of $n-1$. Most authors use either the symbol $\hat{\sigma}$ (sigma hat) or s for the standard deviation of a sample, whereas the symbol σ (sigma) is used for the standard deviation of the population. The variance is the standard deviation squared. The unit of measure for the standard deviation is the same as that of the raw data and the mean. An estimate of the standard deviation for a normally distributed random variable is $1.25MAD$, where MAD is the Mean Absolute Deviation.

See *coefficient of variation, confidence interval, forecast error metrics, Mean Absolute Deviation (MAD), Mean Squared Error (MSE), range, sample size calculation, sampling.*

Standard Operating Procedures (SOP) – See *standardized work.*

standard time – The planned processing time per part. ✪

Standard times are used for planning machine and labor load, machine and labor capacity, and for assigning costs to products as they pass through a process. Standard time is calculated as the normal time adjusted for allowances, which include time for bathroom breaks, rest, etc. Allowance is typically around 15%. Standard times can be set for both setup time and for run time. Creating standard times is one of the traditional roles for the industrial engineering function.

See *normal time, performance rating, standard cost, time study, work measurement, work sampling.*

standardization – See *standardized work.*

standardized loss function – See *safety stock.*

standardized work – The discipline of creating and following a single set of formal, written work instructions for each process. ✪

Frederick Taylor, the father of scientific management, emphasized standardized work and the "one best way" for a job design (Taylor, 1911). Traditionally, organizations in North America have called these work instructions "Standard Operating Procedures" or SOPs. More recently, the Lean Enterprise Institute and other leaders of the lean manufacturing movement have called these Standardized Work Instructions (SWIs). Standardized work is a key element of the Toyota Production System (TPS).

Standardized work is particularly important when a process is performed by different people, in different workcenters, in different locations, and/or on different shifts. While normally applied primarily to repetitive factory and service work, it can also be applied to less repetitive knowledge work done by professionals and salaried workers. For example, a doctor should have an SOP for a surgical procedure. Supervisors and managers should also have some standardized work as well.

In lean manufacturing, SWIs use simple text and photos so are clear for workers from a wide variety of educational, cultural, and language backgrounds. They are required to be located next to the process so the operators can see them often and so they are readily available for training purposes.

In some firms, language can be an issue due to a multi-lingual workforce. In these situations, it is important to provide SOPs in multiple languages. Again, photos and diagrams can be very helpful.

Some firms have implemented SOPs on computer systems. These systems allow for multiple languages and can also provide photos, videos, animations, and games for training. They can also administer tests for an internal training certification program.

Purpose – The purpose of an SOP is as follows:
- Document the correct process
- Control the organization
- Control work processes
- Provide training content
- Help implement change
- Produce consistent outcomes (reduce variability)

Benefits – The benefits of standardized work include:
- Less variation in how work is performed
- Improved quality
- Fewer defects
- Reduced cycle time
- Faster training
- Help the organization find new work methods

Requirements – Standard procedures should meet the following requirements:

- Be clear, complete, and concise
- Be realistic
- Written for the user
- Revised promptly
- Define limits of authority

- Cover emergency situations
- Define the process for where to go to get help
- Define the minimum performance standards
- Define training requirements
- Be routinely used for training

Suggested format – A suggested format for an SOP follows.

ADMINISTRATION
- Author
- Approval authority
- Title with revision control
- Effective date
- File name and page numbering
- Approval steps/sign off

CONTENT
- Purpose
- Overview
- Affected departments
- Scope
- Definitions
- Responsibilities and organization
- Instructions with photos, process maps, steps, narrative, etc.
- Regulatory responsibilities

ATTACHMENTS/REFERENCES

According the ***Lean Lexicon*** (Marchwinski & Shook 2006), standardized work in a production process is based on three elements:
1. Takt time, which is the rate at which products must be made in a process to meet customer demand.
2. The precise work sequence in which an operator performs tasks within takt time.
3. The standard inventory, including units in machines, required to keep the process operating smoothly.

Acknowledgements: The above bulleted points are from Gene Heupel, President of GMHeupel Associates.

See *5S, Business Process Re-engineering (BPR), division of labor, ISO 9000, job enlargement, lean thinking, process improvement program, scientific management, socio-technical design, Total Productive Maintenance (TPM), work simplification.*

starving – Forcing a process to stop because of lack of input materials. ✪

Starving is bad for the bottleneck process because it will reduce the output of the entire system. Starving a non-bottleneck process generally has few consequences for the overall output of the system. Starving a non-bottleneck process might signal that the worker should be moved to somewhere else in the process. Given that the bottleneck resource defines the capacity for the entire plant, starving a bottleneck resource results in the loss of capacity for the entire plant. Starving at a bottleneck resource might signal the need to improve the planning system and/or to increase some buffers to avoid the situation going forward. Starving and blocking are often discussed in the same context and are important concepts in the Theory of Constraints literature.

See *blocking, kanban, Theory of Constraints (TOC).*

station time – The "touch time" at each workstation.

See *cycle time.*

Statistical Process Control (SPC) – A set of statistical tools that can be used to monitor the performance of a process. ✪

SPC is usually implemented using graphical methods called control charts to check if the process performance is within the upper and lower control limits. Ideally, a control chart will signal a problem with all special (unusual) causes of variation and ignore normal variation.

Sometimes, people confuse control limits with product specification limits. Control limits are a function of the natural variability of the process. Assuming we use 3-sigma limits, the position of the control limits is a function of the process standard deviation (sigma). Unlike control limits, specification limits are not dependent on the process in any way. Specification limits are the boundary points that define the acceptable values for an output variable of a particular product characteristic. Specification limits are determined by customers, product designers, and management. Specification limits may be two-sided, with upper and lower limits, or one-sided, with either an upper or a lower limit.

Inspection can be performed by variables or by attributes. Inspection by variables is usually done for process control and is performed with an x-bar chart (to control the mean) or an r-chart (to control the range or variance). Inspection by attributes is usually done for lot control (acceptance sampling) and is performed with a p-chart (to control the percent defective) or a c-chart (to control the number of defects).

See *acceptance sampling, Attribute, c-chart, common cause variation, control chart, operating characteristic curve, p-chart, process capability and performance, process validation, quality, quality assurance, r-chart, seven tools of quality, Six Sigma, special cause variation, specification limits, statistical quality control (SQC), tampering, Total Quality Management (TQM), x-bar chart, Zero Defects.*

Statistical Quality Control (SQC) – A set of statistical tools for analyzing and controlling quality with a focus more on the product than the process.

See *hypergeometric distribution, quality, Six Sigma, Statistical Process Control (SPC).*

stickiness – The ability of a website to hold the attention of the visitor.

Stickiness is generally accomplished through intriguing, useful, and/entertaining content.

Stock Keeping Unit (SKU) – A unique identification number (or alphanumeric string) that defines an item for inventory management purposes. ✪

A SKU is sometimes called a part number or an item number. SAP uses the term "material."

In retail applications, a SKU may designate style, size, and color. A more detailed identifier for a specific item is called a serial number or unique identifier.

In manufacturing, some items might exist for a short period of time in the assembly process; however, if these items are not inventoried, they should usually not be given a SKU identifier. Sometimes, a part number is used to identify the "generic" item, but the SKU is used for recording the inventory count for that part number at a specific location.

Some consultants used to promote the concept that part numbers should use only numerical values (0-9) and not mix alpha (letters A-Z) and numeric (0-9) characters. The rationale for this is that many numbers and letters appear the same. For example, the number 1 and the letter l, the number 5 and the letter S, and the number 0 and the letter O. In addition, many letters sound the same. For example, K and A, M and N, and Y and I all sound alike. If SKUs are restricted to only numeric values (e.g., 0 to 9), the probability of a data entry error is reduced significantly. It is also considered good practice to use short numbers, say seven digits or less. Longer part numbers have more meaning for the users (location, commodity type, etc.), but may require more work for data entry and can be more error prone. If letters are used, they should not be case-sensitive. The widespread use of bar coding, RFID, and EDI has made these issues less important.

Check digits are often added to the base part number in order to make it possible to conduct a quick validity check. See the entry on check digits for more information.

See *active item, barcode, check digit, item number, phantom Bill of Material (BOM), Radio Frequency Identification (RFID), Universal Product Code (UPC).*

stockout – A situation in which a customer demand cannot be immediately satisfied from current inventory. ✪

Stockouts can often be attributed to either incorrect safety stock parameters (e.g., bad numbers in the computer) or poor ordering disciplines (planners not following the numbers in the computer).

The cost of a stockout may be nothing if the organization has a monopoly and customers are willing to wait. However, in most situations, the stockout cost includes the lost margin. In some severe situations, the stockout cost includes the total lifetime value of the customer or even the total lifetime value of that customer and many others who are influenced by that customer.

The word "stockout" is often used to imply that the sale is lost, whereas a "shortage" implies that the customer is inconvenienced, but the sale is not lost. If the customer is willing to wait, the demand is said to be "backordered," and we have a shortage, but not a stockout.

Statistical models can be used to infer (impute) the implied stockout cost for a given reorder point or target inventory value. In other words, for a given reorder point (or target inventory level), we can use some math to estimate the implied stockout cost.

See *backlog, backorder, newsvendor model, opportunity cost, safety stock, service level.*

stockout cost – See *stockout.*

story board – Large, visual communications of important information and key points.

Consultants often talk about their "story board" for a PowerPoint presentation. This is just a high-level overview of the main points that they want to make in their presentation.

See *MECE, Minto Pyramid Principle.*

Straight Through Processing (STP) – An initiative used by financial trading firms to eliminate (or at least drastically reduce) the time to process financial transactions.

Straight through processing is enabled by computer-based information and communication systems that allow transactions to be transferred in the settlement process without manual intervention. While presently only a concept, STP represents a major shift from present-day three-day trading to same-day settlement. One of the benefits of STP is a decrease in settlement risk because the shortening of transaction-related processing time increases the probability that a contract or an agreement is settled on time.

Adapted from http://www.investopedia.com/terms/s/straightthroughprocessing.asp, December 10, 2007.

Strategic Business Unit (SBU) – A business unit that has either value propositions, core competences, or markets that are different from the other business units in the firm, and therefore must have its own unique strategy.

strategic sourcing – See *sourcing.*

strategy map – A causal map that shows the relationships between the critical elements of the organization's business system. ✪

Kaplan and Norton (2000) proposed strategy maps as a tool for communicating the critical relationships and metrics needed to understand and implement the organization's strategy. According to Larry Bossidy, former Chairman of Honeywell, many companies fail to execute their strategy and therefore fail in the marketplace because they do not clearly communicate their strategy to those responsible for executing it (Bossidy, Charan, & Burck, 2002). Many so-called "leaders" give only a vague description to their "troops" of what they should do and why each task is important. As a result, they ultimately "lead" their firms to failure. With mixed messages and unclear direction from the top, managers will do what they think is in the best interests of the firm, their own departments, and their own careers.

In the information age, businesses must create and manage complex business systems in order to offer distinctive value. These business systems are defined by highly interdependent relationships between customers, distributors, suppliers, employees, buildings, machines, product technologies, process technologies, information technologies, knowledge, and culture. These relationships must be made clear if the strategy is going to be understood and implemented in these complex business systems.

Strategy maps can show cause and effect relationships for business system relationships such as the following:

- The firm's value proposition, target markets, and business performance.
- The firm's value proposition and investments in people, systems, R&D, capacity, and process technology.
- Employee recognition programs, employee reward systems, employee motivation, service quality, customer satisfaction, and customer loyalty.
- Sales force size, incentives, and sales.
- Advertising investment, message, and media selection.

Strategy maps can also highlight the key metrics that will be used to motivate and monitor the execution of the strategy. Kaplan and Norton (1996) argue that the strategy map should focus on the few "balanced scorecard" metrics that drive the strategy to success. These metrics should be reported at a high level in the firm. Goldratt (1984) emphasizes that most organizations have only one constraint (bottleneck) that constrains performance and that this constraint should be the focus for the strategy and the metrics.

Kaplan and Norton's strategy maps show the causal relationships going

Financial
Customer
Internal
Learning and growth

from the bottom up to the top and require four perspectives (levels) for the strategy map -- financial, customer, internal, and learning and growth (see the figure to the right). They require that the causal linkages always go in the order from learning and growth at the bottom to financial at the top.

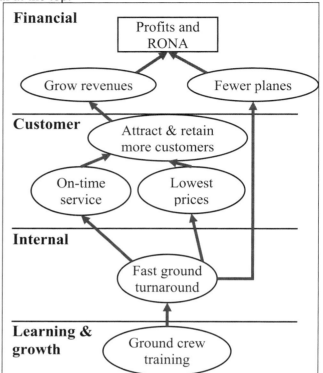

The figure to the right is a simplified example of a strategy map from the Kaplan and Norton **Strategy Maps** book (Kaplan & Norton 2004). This example shows how the four perspectives cascade up the causal map to create the airline's strategy.

The strategic analysis begins at the top with the question of "how do we improve RONA." The answer in this analysis was to grow the business without adding more aircraft. As the analysis moves down the causal linkages, the key strategic initiative must be ground crew training to improve the ground turnaround. (Note: Spear (2008) asserts that this fast turnaround is the main competitive advantage of Southwest Airlines.)

Each link in the strategy map states a "hypothesis" or a belief about the causal relationship. For example, in this strategy map, we see that manage believes that "ground crew training" will improve the turnaround time. Now that this link is explicitly communicated as a part of the strategy, it can be openly discussed and even tested.

In the causal mapping work by Scavarda, Bouzdine-Chameeva, Goldstein, Hays, and Hill (2006) and others, strategy maps can be drawn in any direction and do not require Kaplan and Norton's four perspectives. They argue that BSC imposes too much structure on the causal mapping process. See the entry on *causal maps* for a strategy map presented in a causal mapping format. See the *Balanced Scorecard* entry for a complete list of references.

The papers "Strategy Mapping," "Causal Mapping," and "Learning Models" are on the **OMWW CD** available from www.ClamshellBeachPress.com. ◉

See *balanced scorecard, causal map, DuPont Analysis, hypothesis, mindmap, operations performance metrics, operations strategy, Six Sigma, value proposition, Y-tree.*

suboptimization – The problem of finding the "optimal" (best) solution to only one part of a problem, resulting in a solution that is not globally optimal.

For example, a sales organization might "optimize" the commissions for the sales organization, but at the expense of having too much inventory. Good leaders practice systems thinking, which leads them to seek to understand the entire system and seek to find global rather than suboptimal solutions.

See *systems thinking.*

sunk cost – A powerful managerial economics principle that once a cost has been incurred, it becomes irrelevant to all future decision making.

For example, a firm has invested $10 million in developing a new product. The firm needs to decide what it should do with respect to the new product. A careful analysis of the situation should consider the opportunities for the firm going forward without regard to the amount of money already invested.

See *financial performance metrics.*

supermarket – A lean manufacturing concept of using a buffer inventory on the shop floor to store components for downstream operations.

In the context of lean manufacturing, a supermarket is typically a fixed storage location and is designed to provide highly visual current status information. A withdrawal of a unit from a supermarket will usually signal the need for more production.

See *fixed storage location, lean thinking, pacemaker, periodic review system.*

supplier managed inventory – See *Vendor Managed Inventory (VMI).*

supplier qualification and certification − A supplier is said to be qualified by a customer when it has been determined that the supplier is capable of producing a part; the supplier is said to be certified when it has delivered parts with perfect quality over a specified time period.

When a supplier becomes certified, the customer usually stops inspection. Ideally, the two firms then share in the cost savings.

See *dock-to-stock, inspection, purchasing, supply chain management*.

supplier scorecard − A tool for customers to give evaluative feedback to their suppliers about their performance, particularly with respect to delivery and quality.

Introduction to supplier scorecards

A supplier scorecard is a powerful tool for customers to give feedback to their suppliers about their performance and to help them improve over time. In addition, many leading firms such as Best Buy also use supplier scorecards as a mechanism for inviting suppliers to give them feedback so they work together to improve supplier coordination and communication. Each firm has different needs and therefore should have a unique scorecard format. Ideally, supplier scorecards should be as simple as possible, measure only the vital few metrics, and be updated regularly.

Standardizing the supplier scorecard for an entire firm has many advantages with respect to systems, communications, and training. Multi-divisional firms need to standardize their scorecards so suppliers that supply to more than one division will see only one supply scorecard − or at least only one supplier scorecard format. However, many firms have found this to be a difficult challenge.

Benefits of supplier scorecards

Supplier scorecards have many benefits for both the customer and the customer's supply network. These include:

- **Creation benefits** − The process of setting up a supplier scorecard program forces the customer to align competitive priorities and the supply management strategy by deciding which supplier metrics are most important to the business. For example, if a customer competes primarily on product innovation, a responsive supply chain is important and the metrics should focus on new product development collaboration and leadtimes and de-emphasize price (or cost). Similarly, if the customer competes on price, an efficient supply chain is important and the metrics should focus on price (Fisher, 1997). It is common for customers to constantly "beat up" suppliers, telling them that they need to improve everything or they will lose business. However, the reality is that many metrics conflict with each other and a supplier can really only successfully focus on improving a few metrics at a time. If too many metrics are chosen, the supplier will spread limited resources too thin, and no metrics will improve.
- **Communication and prioritization benefits** − An effective supplier scorecard helps customers and suppliers communicate on a higher level. When a scorecard is published, the leadership of the supplier's organization receives a clear message about what is important to the customer.
- **Process improvement program benefits** − An effective supplier scorecard system helps the supplier prioritize process improvement projects in light of the customer's requirements.
- **Rapid correction benefits** − If the measurement period is properly established, a good scorecard program can help point out easily correctable problems. For instance, if the metrics are measured every week, and it is noted that there is a pattern of higher lot rejects every fourth week, it could indicate that problems are arising at the end of each month because the supplier rushes to get inventory out the door to make monthly shipping goals.
- **Supplier selection benefits** − The scorecard program will also serve as an objective tool for making data-driven supplier selection (sourcing) decisions. It is easy for customers to focus only on the most recent disappointment (e.g., the most recent late shipment or rejected lot) and to make judgments based on perception and emotion. Once a scorecard program has been implemented, it becomes easier to analyze the data in order to reach sound conclusions about which course of action should be taken. The supplier with the highest scorecard rating will likely retain the business and be awarded a larger share of any new business.

- **Commitment benefits** – A properly developed scorecard program can help create a climate of cooperation that can benefit both the customer and the supplier.

In order to be sustainable, a scorecard program must be credible, effective, and timely (Stork, 1998).
- **Credible** – The data being measured should be objective rather than subjective. Subjective data is often viewed as unfair in the eyes of the organization being measured.
- **Effective** – Only a few important metrics should be measured. Most operations executives agree that delivery and quality are the two most important metrics to measure.

Timely – The data should be presented soon after the measurement period ends (Stork, 1998). Depending on the industry, scorecards could be published weekly or even daily. Most agree that scorecards should be published at least monthly.

Supplier scorecard metrics

The typical measurement for Make to Stock items is the percentage of orders that are filled from stock. In addition, average days-late information may also be recorded. For Make to Order and Assemble to Order items, the metrics relate to on-time delivery. This metric must define the "on-time" standard, which could be defined as the requested delivery date, the original promised delivery date, or a revised promised delivery date. Most firms use the original promised delivery date.

In addition to being delivered on time, a product must also meet customer's quality requirements. The parts should meet the agreed-to level of quality for construction and tolerances based on the specifications that the parts are ordered to. Quality can either be measured in percentages of lots accepted (first pass yield), defects per million opportunities (DPMO), or other similar measures.

Delivery and quality are the foundation for nearly all supplier scorecard programs, but many customers also use one or two additional metrics such as:

- Customer service
- Delivery flexibility (particularly volume flexibility)
- Leadtime – standard versus actual
- Pricing
- R&D metrics
- Financial metrics

- Cost savings ideas
- Supply base development
- Improvement in process capabilities/SPC
- Technical Support
- Innovation

However, many of these metrics are difficult and costly to measure, making it important for the supplier and customer to define these jointly and to agree on the measurement method. An example of a typical supplier scorecard is shown below.

Supplier scorecard example

Quality Profile Rating		Late Delivery (last 6 months) (PO Date > 7 days)		Customer Satisfaction	Process Health/ Lean/Six Sigma
Actual	Points	Actual	Points		
100	50	0%	30	10	10
90	45	1%	27	9	9
80	40	2%	24	8	8
77	39	3%	21	7	7
70	35	4%	18	6	6
67	34	5%	15	5	5
57	29	6%	12	4	4
54	27	7%	9	3	3
47	24	8%	6	2	2

Supplier Scorecard Rating: Blue (91-100), Green (75-90), Yellow (51-74), Red (0-50)

Adapted from oasis.northgrum.com/misc/SupplierScorecardGuidelines.pdf

Benchmarking

Suppliers and buyers should work together to create realistic benchmarks for each metric based on industry standards and on historical performance. These benchmarks can be used to motivate ongoing improvement in supplier performance and help the suppliers prioritize their process improvement projects.

One typical performance goal is to go half the distance from the baseline to entitlement. Entitlement is defined as the best value that can be expected. For example, the best on-time delivery percentage is 100%. Therefore, 100% is the entitlement for on-time delivery. If a company's current on-time delivery is 80%, the goal might be to improve to 90%, which is half the distance to the entitlement.

Creating incentives in a supplier scorecard program

Proper incentives need to be put into place for a scorecard program to be effective. The customer should make it clear that it will reward suppliers that achieve the greatest improvements and penalize suppliers that fail to meet expectations.

One of the keys to taking advantage of a scorecard program is to implement a regular, formal review process between the supplier and customer (Dasai, 1995). This meeting should be attended by the decision makers from both organizations who have the authority to make agreements and to drive actions based on the outcome of the reviews. This shows the level of commitment from both organizations, and can help to foster a stronger partnership or a severance of the relationship where appropriate.

It can also be beneficial to provide suppliers with a standard measurement matrix which anonymously ranks all suppliers (Dasai, 1995). This information can be critical to help suppliers understand how and why certain decisions are made. This data lets the supplier know where they need to be in order to continue to be competitive, or what they will need to do in order to gain an advantage. In the end, the customer, and the entire supply chain will benefit from this type of competition.

Most importantly, the suppliers must begin to see rewards for their improvement efforts. These rewards can be delivered in a number of ways. One of the easiest and most effective rewards is a supplier of the year award delivered at some sort of supplier summit. This gives the customer the opportunity to bring all of their suppliers together, and to publicly acknowledge great improvement efforts. In addition, when the award is displayed at the supplier's site, all employees have the opportunity to see what their contribution has done for the company. This is an effective way to improve performance in the supply chain. As suppliers are recognized for their efforts, other suppliers will strive to win the award the next year. Of course, the most important reward is the additional business that is given to the best suppliers.

Implementation challenges

The biggest challenge of implementing a scorecard program is creating the structure to implement and sustain the program internally (Dasai, 1995). The resources must be made available to collect the data and disseminate it to the supply base. It is also critical that the data be accurate and that the process be simple and easy. If the supplier and customer are not able to correlate their data for the metrics the measurement system will quickly become meaningless and no real gains will be made through the program.

Once the program is implemented, it can be difficult for buyers to accept what the data tells them. In the absence of data, decisions are made based on relationships and emotion. Seasoned buyers may find it difficult to change the way that they make decisions and ultimately do business. The first time a scorecard is published, it can come as a shock to many managers in the supply chain. It is not uncommon for the first few scorecards to show extremely poor delivery performance. This issue needs to be discussed with both parties up front so the first reactions are not overly negative. All parties must understand that the point of implementing a scorecard program is to drive improvements in the supply chain.

It is recommended that one person (or job function) be responsible for owning the process of managing the scorecard program. To achieve its full potential, it is also critical that the program have a project champion at a higher level within the organization to break down any internal barriers that could cause the program to fail to achieve its full potential.

Supplier scorecard conclusions

Many companies could benefit from the implementation of a supplier scorecard program. Scorecards have the potential to significantly improve supplier performance without large capital investments. A properly structured program will give the buying organization the necessary tool for making important sourcing decisions. A good supplier scorecard program can also help the purchasing organization prioritize its supplier development/supplier process improvement efforts as well.

In some cases the customer will see supplier improvement that is due to superficial improvement, such as increased sorting of defective parts. Ideally, a good scorecard program should drive improvements backward through the supply chain so the customer has transparency into the capabilities of the suppliers' processes.

Many leading firms such as Best Buy also use supplier scorecards as a mechanism for inviting suppliers to give them feedback so they can work together to improve supplier coordination and communication.

Acknowledgments: The entry was adapted from a student paper by John Mullin (CSOM MBA 07) and Heren Berry (CSOM MBA 07).

See *balanced scorecard, benchmarking, buyer/planner, dashboard, operations performance metrics, purchasing, supply chain management.*

Supply Chain Council – A non-profit professional society dedicated to meeting the needs of supply chain management professionals; most famous for its development and use of the SCOR model.

The Supply Chain Council was founded in 1996 by the consulting firm Pittiglio Rabin Todd & McGrath (PRTM) and AMR Research and initially included 69 voluntary member companies.

The Supply Chain Council now has about 1,000 corporate members worldwide and has established international chapters in North America, Europe, Greater China, Japan, Australia/New Zealand, South East Asia, Brazil and Southern Africa. Development of additional chapters in India and South America are underway. The Supply Chain Council's membership consists primarily of practitioners representing a broad cross section of industries, including manufacturers, services, distributors, and retailers.

The Supply Chain Council is closely associated with the SCOR model. The website for the Supply Chain Council is www.supply-chain.org.

See *Operations Management (OM), SCOR model, supply chain management.*

supply chain management – The activities required to manage the flow of materials, information, people, and money from the suppliers' suppliers to the customers' customers. ✪

Supply chain management is the integration of and coordination between a number of traditional business functions, including purchasing, operations, transportation/distribution/logistics, marketing/sales, and information systems. The table below lists the responsibilities, entities, and decisions for each of the primary functions involved in supply chain management. All of these functions must be involved in coordinating with the others in order for the organization and the supply chain to be successful.

Function	Main responsibility	Main entities	Decisions
Purchasing/ procurement	Acquiring products and materials	Suppliers, materials, purchase orders, commodities, technologies.	Suppliers, orders, support for new product development.
Operations	Making products	Facilities, equipment, workforce, materials, products, purchase orders, customer orders, manufacturing orders, customers.	Processes, locations, product assignments, workforce, systems, inventories.
Transportation/ logistics/ distribution	Moving and storing products and materials	Carriers, facilities, warehouses, customers, products, transport orders.	Modes of transport, carriers, warehouses, inventories, schedules, service levels, contracts.

| Marketing/sales | Managing the channel to the customer | Customers, channels, channel partners, sales force, customer orders, products. | Channel strategy, channel partners, sales force, prices, sales force incentives, forecasting. |
| Information systems | Providing information | Systems, databases, technology suppliers. | Systems for the firm (e.g., ERP) and for the supply chain (e-procurement, e-auctions, EDI). |

The Supply Chain View figure below was developed in an extensive survey of over 300 supply chain experts. The figure emphasizes that supply chain management begins with the fundamental premise that coordination and collaboration and a sense of "co-destiny" can be beneficial to all of the members in the supply chain. In the words Professor K.K. Sinha, "Competition is no longer firm against firm, but supply chain against supply chain." Starting with this supply chain view, the members of the supply chain need to design the supply chain to ensure a fit between the members and a common strategy. These activities require collaboration and trust. Based on this strategy, the supply chain "partners" then need to coordinate their efforts for both new and existing products. This requires some shared metrics, scorecards to communicate these metrics, and information systems to help with the coordination and scorecards. In parallel to the coordination, it is critical that the supply chain "partners" seek to develop a deep understanding of the customers for the supply chain (not just their immediate customers), how they are linked together (information systems, transportation, etc.), and the cost structure for the entire supply chain.

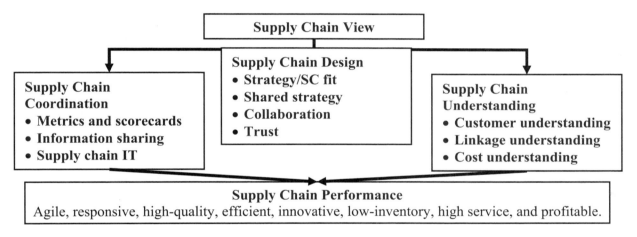

Source: "Ten Commandments of Supply Chain Management" project by Professor Hill and colleagues, 2003.

The result of good supply chain management should be lower total system cost (lower inventory, higher quality), higher service levels, increased revenues, and increased profits for the supply chain. However, the key issue is how the supply chain will share the benefits of improvements between the players in the supply chain.

Supply chain management is a major theme of this book. The reader can find more information on supply chain management principles by going to the links listed below.

See *bullwhip effect, Business Process Outsourcing, channel integration, channel partner, contract manufacturer, demand chain management, disintermediation, forecasting, inventory management, logistics, make versus buy decision, Maquiladora, materials management, offshoring, operations strategy, outsourcing, purchasing, SCOR model, SIPOC Diagram, sourcing, square root law for warehouses, supplier qualification and certification, supplier scorecard, Supply Chain Council, systems thinking, value chain, Vendor Managed Inventory (VMI), vertical integration.*

sustainability – The characteristic of a process that can be indefinitely maintained at a satisfactory level; often equated with green manufacturing and environmental stewardship and/or social responsibility. ✪

In the environmental context, sustainability usually refers to the longevity of systems such as the climate, agriculture, manufacturing, forestry, fisheries, energy, etc. Ideally, all of these systems will be "sustainable" for a very long time to the benefit of society.

For example, Bristol-Myers Squibb has defined specific goals for 2010 on the following dimensions (Source: bms.com/static/ehs/vision/data/sustai.html, October 11, 2008):

- Environmental, health, and safety
- Safety performance
- Environmental performance
- Sustainable products
- Supply chain
- Sustainability awards
- Biotechnology
- Community
- Social
- Endangered species
- Land preservation

Acknowledgments: CEMBA 09 students Steve Arsenault, Nick Ehrman, Nancy Fenocketti, Sonja O'Brien, and Connie Scheer contributed to this entry.

See *green manufacturing*, *triple bottom line*.

swim lanes – See *process map*.

switching cost – The customer's cost of switching from one supplier to another. ✪

For example, the switching cost for a medical doctor to change from implanting one type of pacemaker to another is quite significant because the doctor will have to learn to implant a new type of pacemaker and learn to use a new type of programmer to set the parameters for the pacemaker.

It is often in the supplier's best interest to increase the customer's switching costs so the customer does not defect to the competition the first time the competition offers a slightly lower price. Some suppliers have been successful in increasing switching costs through frequent-purchase reward programs. For example, large airlines offer frequent flyer miles to encourage flyers to be "loyal" to their airline. Others have increased switching costs by helping customers reduce transaction costs through information systems. For example, a hospital supply firm provided free computer hardware to hospitals to use to order their supplies. This lowered the hospital's transaction cost, but also made it harder for the hospitals to change (switch) to another supplier.

An interesting study by Oberholzer-Gee and Calanog (2007) found that trust increased the perceived switching cost and created barriers to entry. Customers were reluctant to change suppliers when they had a supplier that they could trust, even when a competitor's product appeared to offer superior benefits.

See *search cost*, *total cost of ownership*, *transaction cost*.

synchronous manufacturing – The Theory of Constraints ideal of the entire production process working in harmony to achieve the profit goal of the firm.

When manufacturing is truly synchronized, its emphasis is on total system performance, not on localized measures such as labor or machine utilization.

See *Theory of Constraints (TOC)*.

system – Any set of interdependent parts that interact over time. ✪

A system is a set of interdependent elements (often including people, machines, tools, technologies, buildings, information, and policies) that are joined together to accomplish a mission. A good example of a system is a supply chain.

See *systems thinking*.

systems thinking – A worldview that encourages a holistic understanding of how a collection of related entities interact with each other and the environment over time to fulfill its mission.

Systems thinking is a holistic way of understanding the world. It not only considers the system at a point in time, but also considers how the system changes over time in response to changes in its environment. Contrary to Descartes' reductionist view, systems thinking argues that a system cannot be understood just by studying its parts. Systems thinking acknowledges that a change in one area of a system can adversely affect other areas of the system.

For example, the reductionist approach to improving the braking system in a car would study each component separately (brake pads, brake pedal, brake lights, etc.). In contrast, systems thinking studies all of the components related to the braking system of the car, including the braking system, the car display, the driver, the road, and the weather, and how these components interact with each other over time.

A good example of how systems thinking can inform a problem area is the emergence of the supply chain management discipline. The application of systems thinking to the supply chain has created what many consider to be a new business discipline with multiple professional societies, journals, and job titles that did not exist until the mid-1980s.

See *process, simulation, suboptimization, supply chain management, system.*

T

Taguchi methods – An approach to the design of experiments developed by Genichi Taguchi.

Dr. Genichi Taguchi developed a practical approach for designing quality into products and processes. His methodology recognized that quality should not be defined as simply within or not within specifications and created a simple quadratic "loss function" to measure quality. The two figures below contrast the typical 0-1 loss function used in quality with the Taguchi quadratic loss function.

Traditional "loss" function

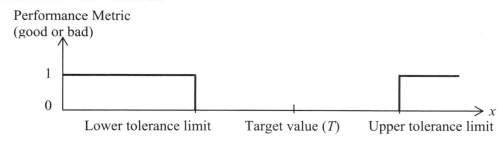

Taguchi loss function

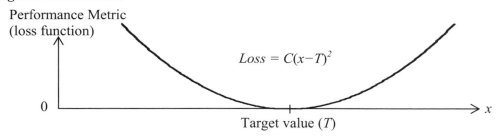

$$Loss = C(x-T)^2$$

Taguchi methods are often applied on the Japanese manufacturing floor by the technicians to improve products and processes. The goal is not just to optimize an arbitrary objective function, as they are often used in North America, but to reduce the sensitivity of engineering designs to uncontrollable factors or noise by maximizing the signal to noise ratio. This moves design targets toward the middle of the design space so that external variation affects the behavior of the design as little as possible. This approach permits large reductions in both part and assembly tolerances, which are major drivers of manufacturing cost. Taguchi methods are also called robust design in the USA.

See *ANOVA (Analysis of Variance), Design of Experiments (DOE), functional build.*

takt time – The desired time between completions of a product, synchronized to the customer demand rate.

According to the German-English dictionary (http://dict.leo.org), takt is the German word for "beat" or "musical time." (Note: Several sources define takt as the baton that an orchestra conductor uses to regulate the beat for the orchestra. This is not correct. The German word for baton is "taktstock.")

The Japanese picked up the German word and use it to mean the "beat time" or "heart beat" of a factory. Lean production uses takt time to set the production rate to match the market demand rate. The takt time, therefore, can be defined as:

$$\text{takt time} = \frac{\text{Available production time}}{\text{Forecasted demand rate}}$$

Be sure to use the same time unit for both the numerator and denominator (e.g., use minutes, hours, days, weeks, or months for both the available production time and the demand rate per unit time).

Takt time, therefore, should be set by the customer demand rate, and should be adjusted when the market demand rate changes. If the takt time and the customer demand rate do not match, the firm (and the supply chain) will have either not enough inventory or too much inventory.

For example, a factory has a forecasted market demand of 100 units per day and the factory operates for 10 hours per day. The target production rate should be the same as the market demand rate (100 units per day or 10 units per hour). The takt time for this factory should be (10 hours/day)/(100 units/day) = 0.1 hours per unit or 6 minutes per unit. The factory should complete one unit about every six minutes, on average.

Many lean manufacturing consultants do not seem to understand that difference between a rate and a time and use the term takt time to mean the target production rate. However, a rate is measured in units per hour rather than as a time measured in hours (or minutes) per unit. For example, a 10 unit per hour "takt time" should be expressed as a takt time of six minutes per unit.

Takt time is nearly identical to the traditional industrial engineering definition of cycle time, which is the target time between completions. The only difference between takt time and this type of cycle time is that takt time is defined by the market demand rate, whereas cycle time is not necessarily driven by the market demand.

Some people confuse takt time and throughput time. It is possible to have a long throughput time (say six weeks), but still have a takt time of six seconds. Takt time is the time between completions and can be thought of as time between units "falling off of the end of the line." The entry on *cycle time* compares cycle time and throughput time.

See *cycle time, heijunka, leadtime, lean thinking, pitch.*

tampering – The practice of taking a special action in response to common cause variation, which introduces more variation into the system.

See *common cause variation, control chart, special cause variation, Statistical Process Control (SPC).*

tardiness – The amount of time that an order is past the due date (or due time).

Tardiness is zero when an order is on-time or early. Average tardiness is a commonly used measure, but should be used with caution because it only considers orders that are tardy. For example, a firm has hundreds of orders every month, with an average tardiness of two days. The firm re-engineers the process and dramatically improves on-time performance for nearly all orders. However, the next month it has only two orders that are tardy, but the average tardiness increases to four days. Cleary, overall tardiness improved, but in this example, the average tardiness was worse.

See *dispatching rules.*

target cost – The desired final cost for a new product development effort.

Many firms design a product, estimate the actual cost, and then add the margin to set the price. In contrast to this practice, with a target costing strategy, the firm determines the price based on the market strategy and then determines the target cost by subtracting the desired margin from this margin. The resulting "target cost" becomes the requirement for the product design team. The four major steps of target costing are:

1. Determine the price. The amount customers are willing to pay for a product or service with specified features and functions.
2. Set the target cost per unit and in total. The target cost per unit is the market price less the required margin. The total target cost is the per unit target cost multiplied by the expected number of units sold over its life.
3. Compare the total target cost to the currently feasible total cost to create the cost reduction target. The currently feasible total cost is the cost to make the product, given current design and process capabilities. The difference between the total target cost and currently feasible cost is the cost reduction target.
4. Design (or redesign) products and processes to achieve the cost reduction target. This can be an iterative process until both the product or service and its cost meet marketing and financial objectives.

See *job order costing, target price.*

target inventory – See *periodic review system.*

target price – The practice of establishing a sales price based on market penetration or price points rather than building from standard cost.

Target price is the price at which the firm believes a seller will buy a product, based on market research. The easiest approach for determining a target price is to study similar products sold by competitors.

The target price may be used to calculate the target cost, which is the maximum cost that the seller is willing to pay to have the product manufactured. When the actual cost of manufacturing increases beyond the target cost, it may no longer be profitable for the seller to sell the product.

In an investment context, the target price is the price at which a stockholder is willing to sell his/her stock.

See *Customer Relationship Management (CRM), target cost.*

technological forecasting – The process of predicting the future characteristics and timing of technology.

The prediction usually estimates the future capabilities of a technology. The two major methods for technological forecasting include time series and judgmental methods. Time series forecasting methods for technological forecasting fit a mathematical model to historical data to extrapolate some variable of interest into the future. For example, the number of millions of instructions per second (MIPS) for a computer is fairly predictable using time series methods. (However, the underlying technology to achieve that performance will change at discrete points in time.) Judgmental forecasting may also be based on projections of the past, but information sources in such models rely on the subjective judgments of experts.

The growth pattern of a technological capability is similar to the growth of biological life. Technologies go through an invention phase, an introduction and innovation phase, a diffusion and growth phase, and a maturity phase. This is similar to the S-shaped growth of biological life. Technological forecasting helps to estimate the timing of these phases. This growth curve forecasting method is particularly useful in determining the upper limit of performance for a specific technology.

Adapted from wiley.com/college/dec/meredith298298/resources/addtopics/addtopic_s_02a.html, February 5, 2005.

See *Delphi forecasting, forecasting, technology road map.*

technology road map – A technique used by many business and research organizations to plan the future of a particular process or product technology.

The goal of a technology roadmap is to anticipate externally-driven technological innovations by mapping them on a time line. The technology roadmap can then be linked with the research, product development, marketing, and sourcing. Some of the benefits of technology roadmapping include:

- Support the organization's strategic planning processes with respect to new technologies.
- Plan for the integration of new technologies into current products.
- Identify business opportunities for leveraging new technologies in new products.
- Identify needs for technical knowledge.
- Inform sourcing decisions, resource allocation, and risk management decisions.

One approach for structuring the technology roadmapping process is to use a large matrix on a wall to capture the ideas. The top row should be labeled Past → Now → Plans → Future → Vision. The left column have the row labels markets, products, technologies, and resources. The markets row is used to explore markets, customers, competitors, environment, industry, business trends, threats, objectives, milestones, and strategies. PRODUCTS is used to explore products, services, applications, performance capabilities, features, components, families, processes, systems, platforms, opportunities, requirements, and risks. The technologies row is used to map new technologies, competencies, and knowledge. The resources row is used for skills, partnerships, suppliers, facilities, infrastructure, science, and R&D projects. Post-it™ notes are then used to "map" and link each of these dimensions over time.

The Centre for Technology Management at the University of Cambridge has a number of publications on this topic. www.ifm.eng.cam.ac.uk/ctm/publications/tplan. Their standard "T-Plan" process includes four major steps that focus on (1) the market (performance dimensions, business drivers, SWOT, gaps), (2) the product (features, strategy, gaps), (3) technology (solutions, gaps), and (4) roadmapping (linking technology resources to future market requirements). Technology roadmapping software is offered by www.roadmappingtechnology.com. The University of Minnesota Center for the Development of Technological Leadership (CDTL) (www.cdtl.umn.edu) makes technology roadmapping a key topic in many of its programs.

See *disruptive technology, New Product Development (NPD), product lifecycle management, technological forecasting.*

termination date – A calendar date by which a product will no longer be sold and/or supported.

Many manufacturing and distribution companies use a policy of having a "termination date" for products and components. A product (and its associated unique components) is no longer sold or supported after the termination date. The advantages of having a termination date policy include:

- The termination date provides a clear plan for every functional area in the organization that deals with products (manufacturing, purchasing, inventory, service, engineering, and marketing). This facilitates an orderly, coordinated phase-out of the item.
- The termination date clearly communicates to the sales force and to the market that the product will no longer be supported (or at least no longer be sold) after the termination date. This often provides incentive for customers to upgrade to a newer product.
- The termination date allows manufacturing and inventory planners to bring down the inventories for all unique components needed for the product in a coordinated way.

Best practices for a termination date policy include the following policies: (1) plan ahead many years to give all stakeholders warning (this includes marketing, sales, product management, purchasing, and manufacturing), (2) make sure that all functions (and divisions) have "buy-in" to the termination date, and (3) do not surprise customers by terminating a product without proper notice.

The paper "Forecasting Lifetime Demand" and the Excel workbook "LIDA.xls" are on the *OMWW CD* available from www.ClamshellBeachPress.com. ◉

See *all-time demand, obsolescence, product lifecycle management.*

terms – A statement of a seller's payment requirements.

Terms generally include discounts for prompt payment, if any, and the maximum time allowed for payment. The shipping terms (also called International Commercial Terms or Incoterms) determine who is responsible for the freight throughout the shipment. Therefore, a shipper will only be concerned about tracking the container to the point where another party takes ownership. This causes problems with container tracking because information may not be shared throughout all links in the supply chain.

Incoterms can be found at www.iccwbo.org/incoterms/understanding.asp. This site includes a useful wall chart.

See *Accounts Payable (A/P), Cash on Delivery (COD), demurrage, FOB, waybill.*

Theory of Constraints (TOC) – A management philosophy developed by Dr. Eliyahu M. Goldratt that focuses on the bottleneck resources to improve overall system performance. ✪

TOC recognizes that organizations usually have just one resource that defines its capacity. Goldratt argues that all systems are constrained by one and only one resource. As Goldratt states, "a chain is only as strong as its weakest link." This is really an application of Pareto's Law to process management and process improvement. TOC concepts are consistent with managerial economics that teach that the setup cost for a bottleneck resource is the opportunity cost of the lost gross margin and that the opportunity cost for a non-bottleneck resource is nearly zero.

The "constraint" is the bottleneck, which is any resource that has capacity less than the market demand. Alternatively, the constraint can be defined as the process that has the lowest average processing rate for producing end products. The constraint (the bottleneck) is normally defined in terms of a resource such as a machine, process, or person. However, in TOC, the definition of a constraint can also be broadened to include tools, people, facilities, policies, culture, beliefs, strategies, etc. For example, the binding constraint in a business school in Moscow in 1989 was the mindset of the dean (the rector), who could not think beyond the limits of Soviet Communism and could not imagine that it might be possible to make photocopies of anything.

Goldratt's first book, *The Goal* (Goldratt, 1992) became popular and was followed by a movie of the same name. One of the characters in both the book and movie was a Boy Scout named Herbie who slowed down the troop of Boy Scouts going for a long hike though the woods. In other words, Herbie was the "bottleneck." The teaching points of this story were (1) we need to allow Herbie to pace the operation – the troop could walk no faster than Herbie; (2) we need to help Herbie with his load – all of the other Boy Scouts took some of Herbie's things (bedding, food, etc.) so that Herbie could walk faster. In the end, the troop was able to go much faster as a team because it had done a good job of managing the bottleneck (e.g., Herbie).

According to TOC, if performance is to be improved, an organization must identify its constraints, exploit the constraints in the short run, and in the longer term, find ways to overcome the constraints (limited resources). The theory of constraints promotes the following five-step methodology:

1. **Identify the system constraint** – No improvement is possible unless the constraint or weakest link is found. The constraint can often by discovered by finding the largest queue.

2. **Exploit the system constraints** – Manage the constraint to protect it from being starved, blocked, or wasted capacity. Reduce setup times, increase lotsizes, and inspect products before the constraint.

3. **Subordinate everything else to the system constraint** – Make sure that all other resources (the unconstrained resources) support the system constraint, even if this reduces the efficiency of these resources. For example, the other processes can produce in smaller lotsizes so that the constrained resource is never starved. The unconstrained resources should never be allowed to overproduce.

4. **Elevate the system constraints** – If this resource is still a constraint, find more capacity. More capacity can be found by working additional hours, using alternative routings, purchasing capital equipment, or subcontracting.

5. **Go back to Step 1** – After this constraint problem is solved, go back to the beginning and start over. This is a continuous process of improvement.

Underlying Goldratt's work is the notion of synchronous manufacturing, which refers to the entire production process working in harmony to achieve the goals of the firm. When manufacturing is truly synchronized, its emphasis is on total system performance, not on localized measures such as labor or machine utilization.

The three primary TOC metrics are throughput (T), inventory (I), and operating expenses (OE), often called T, I, and OE. Throughput is defined as sales revenue minus direct materials per time period. Inventory is defined as direct materials at materials cost. Operating expenses include both labor and overhead. Better bottleneck management will generally result in increased throughput, reduced inventory, and the same or better operating expense.

The paper "Theory of Constraints" is on the **OMWW CD** available from www.ClamshellBeachPress.com. ◉

See *alternate routing, Bill of Resources, blocking, bottleneck, buffer management, CONWIP, critical chain, Drum-Buffer-Rope (DBR), facility layout, gold parts, Herbie, Inventory Dollar Days (IDD), lean thinking, opportunity cost, pacemaker, Pareto's Law, process improvement program, setup cost, setup reduction methods, starving, synchronous manufacturing, throughput accounting, Throughput Dollar Days (TDD), transfer batch, utilization, variable costing, VAT analysis.*

Theta Model – A forecasting model developed by Assimakopoulos and Nikolopoulos (2000) that combines a long-term and short-term forecast to create a new forecast; sometimes called the Theta Method.

The M3 Competition runs a "race" every few years to compare the top time series forecasting methods on hundreds of real times series (Ord, Hibon, & Makridakis, 2000). The winner in the last competition was a relatively new forecasting method called the Theta Model developed by Assimakopoulos and Nikolopoulos (2000). This model was quite difficult to understand until the Hyndman and Billah (2001) simplified the mathematics. More recently Assimakopoulos and Nikolopoulos (2005) wrote their own simplified version of the model. While the two simplified versions are very similar in intent, they are not mathematically equivalent.

The basic concept of Theta is that it makes forecasts that are the average of a long-term forecast and a short-term forecast. In the simplified models, the longer term forecast is a linear regression fit to the historical demand points and the shorter term forecast is a forecast produced with simple exponential smoothing. (The Theta Model assumes that all seasonality has already been removed from the data using classical decomposition methods such as the centered moving average.) The apparent success of this simple time series forecasting method is that the exponential smoothing component captures the "random walk" part of the time series and the least squares regression trend line captures the longer-term trend.

The paper "Forecasting with the Theta Model" is available on the **OMWW CD** available from www.ClamshellBeachPress.com. ◉

See *forecasting, linear regression.*

Thiel's U – An early Relative Absolute Error (*RAE*) measure of forecast errors developed by Henri Thiel (1966).

Thiel's *U* statistic (or Thiel's inequality coefficient) is a metric that compares forecasts to an upper bound on the naïve forecast from a random walk, which uses the actual value from the previous period as the forecast for this period (Thiel 1966). Thiel proposed two measures for forecast error that Armstrong calls U_1 and U_2. SAP uses still another variant of Thiel's coefficient labeled U_3 below:

$$U_1 = \frac{\sqrt{\sum_{t=1}^{T} E_t^2}}{\sqrt{\sum_{t=1}^{T} D_t^2} + \sqrt{\sum_{t=1}^{T} F_t^2}} \; ; \; U_2 = \frac{\sqrt{\sum_{t=1}^{T} E_t^2}}{\sqrt{\sum_{t=1}^{T} D_t^2}} \; ; \; U_3 = \frac{\sqrt{\sum_{t=1}^{T} E_t^2}}{\sqrt{\sum_{t=1}^{T} (D_t - D_{t-1})^2}}$$

According to Armstrong and Collopy (1992), the U_2 metric has better statistical properties than U_1 or U_3. Although Thiel's U metrics are included in many forecasting tools and texts, Armstrong and Collopy do not recommended them because other *RAE*-type metrics are easier to understand and have better statistical properties.

See *forecast error metrics*, *Mean Absolute Percent Error (MAPE)*, *Relative Absolute Error (RAE)*.

Third Party Logistics (3PL) provider – A firm that provides outsourced logistics and distribution services to its customers but does not take title to the product.

The parties in a supply chain relationship include the following:

First party	The supplier
Second party	The customer
Third party	A company that offers multiple logistics services to customers such as transportation, distribution, inbound freight, outbound freight, freight forwarding, warehousing, cross-docking, customs, order fulfillment, inventory management, and packaging. In the United States, the legal definition of a 3PL in HR4040 is "a person who solely receives, holds, or otherwise transports a consumer product in the ordinary course of business but who does not take title to the product." (Source: www.scdigest.com, January 1, 2009.)
Fourth party	A Fourth Party Logistics (4PL) provider is an organization that manages the logistics and supply chain activities of multiple service providers (such as 3PLs) to deliver a comprehensive supply chain solution to the client firm. The official definition from Accenture is "A 4PL is an integrator that assembles the resources, capabilities, and technology of its own organization and other organizations to design, build and run comprehensive supply chain solutions."

3PLs are becoming more popular as companies seek to improve their customer service capabilities without making significant investments in logistics assets, networks, and warehouses. The supplier firm outsources its logistics to two or more specialist firms (third party logistics firms) and then hires another firm (the fourth party) to coordinate the activities of the third parties. Fourth Party Logistics differs from third party logistics in the following ways (Source: www.scdigest.com, January 1, 2009):

- The 4PL organization is often a separate entity established as a joint venture or long-term contract between a primary client and one or more partners.
- The 4PL organization acts as a single interface between the client and multiple logistics service providers.
- All aspects of the client's supply chain are managed by the 4PL organization.
- It is possible for a third party logistics provider to form a 4PL organization within its existing structure.

Acknowledgments: CSOM MBA students Jeremy Green, Tanya Raso, and Amy Schmidt contributed to this entry.

See *bullwhip effect*, *Logistics*.

throughput accounting – Accounting principles based on the Theory of Constraints developed by Goldratt.

Throughput is the rate at which an organization generates money through sales. Goldratt defines throughput as the difference between sales revenue and unit-level variable costs such as materials and power. Cost is the most important driver for our operations decisions, yet costs are unreliable due to arbitrary allocation of overhead, even with Activity Based Costing. Since the goal of the firm is to make money, operations can contribute to this goal by managing three variables:

- Throughput (T) = Revenue less materials cost less out-of-pocket selling costs. Note that this is a rate and is not the same as the throughput time.
- Inventory (I) = Direct materials cost and other truly variable costs with no overhead.
- Operating expenses (OE) = Overhead and labor cost (the things that turn "I" into "T")

Throughput accounting is a form of contribution accounting, where all labor and overhead costs are ignored. The only cost that is considered is the direct materials cost.

When we apply throughput accounting to the bottleneck (constraint), we must look at key performance measurements: output, setup time (average setup time by product and total setup time per period), downtime (planned and emergency), and yield rate. We focus on the constraint because it can have the biggest impact on our throughput accounting measures (I, T, OE), which in turn affect the goal, which is making money for the firm. The book by Noreen, Smith, and Mackey (1995) is a good reference on this subject.

The paper "Throughput Accounting" is on the **OMWW CD** available from www.ClamshellBeachPress.com.

   See *absorption costing, Activity Based Costing (ABC), overhead, Inventory Dollar Days (IDD), Theory of Constraints (TOC), variable costing, Work-in-Process (WIP) inventory*.

Throughput Dollar Days (TDD) – A Theory of Constraints (TOC) measure of the reliability of a supply chain defined in terms of the dollar-days of late orders.

The entry *Inventory Dollar Days (IDD)* has much more detail on this measure.

See *Inventory Dollar Days (IDD), operations performance metrics, Theory of Constraints (TOC)*.

throughput time – See *cycle time*.

throughput ratio – See *value added ratio*.

time burglar – A personal time management term that refers to anything (including a person) that steals time from someone else; someone who wastes the time of another person.

It is a "crime" for someone to steal precious time from another and that it should be looked at as a crime. Time burglars are people who often stop by and ask, "Got a minute?" and then proceed to launch into twenty minutes of low value discussion. Some situations such as a friend stopping by to say "hello" are just minor misdemeanors. However, disruptions that arrive during a critical work situation could be considered a felony.

The key time management principle for managers to learn is to explain the situation and then offer to schedule another time for a visit. A reasonable script is, "I can see this is going to take some more time to discuss. Let's schedule some time to talk about this further. When is a good time for you?"

The term "time burglar" can also be applied to junk email, unnecessary meetings, too much TV, and other time wasting activities. Time burglars are everywhere. Watch out for them and stop them before they strike.

The book *Personal Operations Management – Lean Principles for Getting Good Things Done* (Hill 2010) is available from www.ClamshellBeachPress.com. ☻

Acknowledgments: CEMBA 09 students Mark Anderson, Paul Beswetherick, Tiffany Grunewald, Perry McGahan, Caitlyn Rosendahl, Sara Rottunda, and Yarden Wolfe contributed to this entry.

time fence – A policy of freezing a schedule to reduce system nervousness; sometimes called a planning time fence.

The time fence separates the planning horizon into two segments – a firmed time segment and a tentative time segment. The firmed time segment usually stretches several weeks into the future. During this time period, the production plan and master production schedule cannot be altered and it is said to be "frozen." The tentative time segment is the remainder of the planning horizon after the time fence.

See *Materials Requirements Planning (MRP), Sales & Operations Planning (S&OP)*.

time in system – See *cycle time, queuing theory, wait time*.

time study – A work measurement practice of collecting data on work time by observation, typically using a stop watch or some other timing device. ✪

The average actual time for each worker in the study is adjusted by their performance rating to determine the normal time for a task. The standard time is then defined as the normal time with an allowance for breaks.

See *normal time, performance rating, scientific management, standard time, work measurement, work sampling*.

time to market – The time it takes to develop a new product from an initial idea to initial market sales; sometimes called speed to market.

In many industries, a short time to market can provide a competitive advantage by allowing the firm that is first to market with a new product to command a higher margin, capture a larger market share, and establish its brand as the strongest brand in the market. Precise definitions of the starting and ending points vary from one firm to another, and may even vary between products within a single firm. The time to market includes both product design and commercialization. Time to volume is a closely related concept.

See *clockspeed, New Product Development (NPD), product lifecycle management, time to volume, time-based competition*.

time to volume – The time from the start of production to the start of large-scale production.

See *New Product Development (NPD), time to market*.

time-based competition – A business strategy to shorten leadtimes in order to (1) segment the demand in order to target the time-sensitive (and price-insensitive) customers, (2) reduce finished goods inventory cost, (3) drive out non-value activities (e.g., JIT and lean manufacturing concepts), and (4) bring products to market faster. ✪

George Stalk's article (1988) and the Stalk and Hout's book on time-based competition (Stalk & Hout, 1990) make some strong claims about the profitability of such a strategy. The *strategy map* entry presents a causal map that summarizes the time-based competition strategy.

See *agile manufacturing, flow, operations strategy, Quick Response Manufacturing, time to market, value added ratio*.

time-phased order point – An extension of the reorder point system that uses a demand forecast to plan when the inventory position will hit the safety stock level.

An order is then planned to arrive at that time. The start date for the order is planned to be "L" time units earlier, where "L" is the planned leadtime.

See *Materials Requirements Planning (MRP), reorder point, safety stock*.

time-series forecasting – A forecasting method that identifies patterns in historical data in order to make forecasts for the future. ✪

An historical record of values listed in time order (such as a sales history) is called a time series. A time series can normally be broken into a level (or mean), trend, and seasonal pattern. If the level, trend, and seasonal patterns are removed from a time series, all that remains is what appears to be random error. Box-Jenkins methods attempt to identify and model the serial correlation structure in this random error.

Univariate time-series methods simply extrapolate a single time series into the future. Multivariate time series methods consider historical data for several related variables to make forecasts.

A moving average is the simplest time series forecast method, but it is not very accurate because it does not include either trend or seasonal patterns. The Box-Jenkins method is probably the most accurate, but is more complicated than most managers can handle. The exponential smoothing model with trend and seasonal factors is a good compromise for most firms.

See *Box-Jenkins forecasting, Durbin-Watson statistic, exponential smoothing, forecasting, linear regression, moving average, trend*.

time-varying demand lotsizing problem – The problem of finding the set of lotsizes that will "cover" the demand over the time horizon and will minimize the sum of the ordering and carrying costs.

Common approaches for solving this problem include the Wagner-Whitin lotsizing algorithm, the Period Order Quantity (POQ), the Least Total Cost method, the Least Unit Cost method, and the Economic Order Quantity. Only the Wagner-Whitin algorithm is guaranteed to consistently find the optimal solution. All of the other lotsizing methods are heuristics; however, the cost penalty in using these heuristics is generally very small.

The paper "Lotsizing" and the Excel workbooks "lotsizing.xls" and "EOQ.xls" are on the *OMWW CD* available from www.ClamshellBeachPress.com. The Excel workbook lotisizing.xls implements all of the major lotsizing methods for time-varying demand. ⬤

See *Economic Order Quantity (EOQ), lotsizing methods, Period Order Quantity (POQ), Wagner-Whitin lotsizing algorithm*.

TOC – See *Theory of Constraints*.

ton-mile – A measure of freight traffic equal to moving one ton of freight one mile. See *logistics*.

total cost of ownership – The total cost that a customer incurs from before the purchase until the final and complete disposal of the product.

These costs include the acquisition, purchasing administration, shipping, expediting, inspection, rework, scrap, maintenance and repair, service, downtime, and disposal.

See *financial performance metrics, search cost, switching cost, transaction cost.*

Total Productive Maintenance (TPM) – A systematic approach to ensure uninterrupted and efficient use of equipment; also called Total Productive Manufacturing. ✪

TPM is a manufacturing-led collaboration between operations and maintenance that combines preventive maintenance concepts with the kaizen philosophy of continuous improvement. With TPM, maintenance takes on its proper meaning to "maintain" rather than just repair.

Some leading practices related to TPM include:

- Implement a 5S program with a standardized work philosophy.
- Apply predictive maintenance tools where appropriate.
- Use an information system to create work orders for regularly scheduled preventive maintenance.
- Use an information system to maintain a repair history for each piece of equipment.
- Apply autonomous maintenance, which is the concept of using operators to inspect and clean equipment without heavy reliance of mechanics, engineers, or maintenance people. (This is in contrast to the old thinking which required operators to wait for mechanics to maintain and fix their machines.)
- Clearly define cross functional duties.
- Train operators to handle equipment related issues.
- Measure performance with Overall Equipment Effectiveness (OEE).

Some indications that a TPM program might be needed include frequent emergency maintenance events, long downtimes, high repair costs, reduced machine speeds, high defects and rework, long changeovers, high startup losses, high Mean Time to Repair (MTTR), and low Mean Time Between Failure (MTBF). Some of the benefits claimed for TPM include reduced cycle time, improved operational efficiency, improved OEE, improved quality, and reduced maintenance cost.

(Some of the above content was adapted from www.mfgeng.com/TPM.htm, April 14, 2004 and http://wcm.nu/tpm.html, November 13, 2007)

See *5S, autonomous maintenance, bathtub curve, emergency maintenance, maintenance, Manufacturing Execution System (MES), Mean Time Between Failure (MTBF), Mean Time To Repair (MTTR), MRO (Maintenance-Repair-Operations), Overall Equipment Effectiveness (OEE), predictive maintenance, preventive maintenance, standardized work, Weibull distribution.*

Total Productive Manufacturing (TPM) – See *Total Productive Maintenance (TPM).*

Total Quality Management (TQM) – An approach for improving quality that involves all areas of the organization, including sales, engineering, manufacturing, purchasing, etc. with a focus on employee participation and customer satisfaction. ✪

TQM can involve a wide variety of quality control and improvement tools. TQM pioneers such as Juran (1986), Deming, and Crosby emphasized a combination of managerial principles and statistical tools.

See the entry on the quality trilogy developed by Juran (1986).

See *causal map, Deming's 14 points, inspection, Malcolm Baldrige National Quality Award (MBNQA), PDCA (Plan-Do-Check-Act), quality, quality trilogy, Six Sigma, stakeholder analysis, Statistical Process Control (SPC), Zero Defects.*

touch time – The direct value-added processing time.

See *cycle time, run time, value added ratio.*

Toyota Production System (TPS) – An approach to manufacturing developed by Eiji Toyoda and Taiichi Ohno at Toyota Motor Company in Japan; also called the Toyota Manufacturing System.

The *lean thinking* entry describes the Toyota Manufacturing System.

See *autonomation, jidoka, Just-in-Time (TPS), lean thinking, muda.*

T-plant – See *VAT analysis.*

TPM – See *Total Productive Maintenance (TPM).*

TPS – See *Toyota Production System (TPS).*

TQM – See *Total Quality Management (TQM).*

traceability – The identification of items and products that enables firms to track the batch number and the source of supply for every item.

> Lot traceability and serial number traceability are required for nearly all medical products.
> See *EPC (Electronic Product Code)*.

tracking signal – An exception report given when the forecast error has a consistent bias, e.g., the forecast error is positive or negative over many time periods.

> The exception report signals the manager or analyst to intervene in the forecasting process. The intervention might involve manually changing the forecast, the trend, underlying average, and seasonal factors, or changing the parameters for the forecasting model. The intervention also might require canceling orders and managing both customer and supplier expectations.

> **Tracking signal measurement** – The tracking signal is measured as the forecast bias divided by a measure of the average size of the forecast error.

> **Measures of forecast bias** – The simplest measure of the forecast bias is to accumulate the forecast error over time (the cumulative sum) with the recursive equation $R_t = R_{t-1} + E_t$, where R_t is the running sum of the errors and E_t is the forecast error in period t. The running sum of the errors is a measure of the bias and an exception report is generated when R_t gets "large." Another variant is to use the smoothed average error instead of the running sum of the error. The smoothed error is defined as $SE_t = (1-\alpha)SE_{t-1} + \alpha E_t$.

> **Measures of the average size of the forecast error** – One measure of the size of the average forecast error is the Mean Absolute Deviation (*MAD*). With T periods of history, the *MAD* is defined as $MAD = (1/T)\sum_{t=1}^{T}|E_t|$.

> A more computationally efficient approach to measure the *MAD* is with the smoothed mean absolute error, which is defined as $SMAD_t = (1-\alpha)SMAD_{t-1} + \alpha|E_t|$, where alpha ($\alpha$) is the smoothing constant ($0 < \alpha < 1$). Still another approach is to replace the smoothed mean absolute deviation ($SMAD_t$) with the square root of the smoothed mean squared error, where the smoothed mean squared error is defined as $SMSE_t = (1-\alpha)SMSE_t + \alpha E_t^2$. In other words, the average size of the forecast error can be measured as $\sqrt{SMSE_t}$. The smoothed *MAD* is the most practical approach for most firms.

> In summary, the tracking signal is a measure of the forecast bias relative to the average size of the forecast error and is defined by $TS = bias/size$. The forecast bias can be measured as the running sum of the error (R_t) or the smoothed error (SE_t) and the size of the forecast error can be measured with the *MAD*, the smoothed mean absolute error ($SMAD_t$) or the square root of the mean squared error ($SMAD_t$). It is not clear which method is best.

> See *demand filter, exponential smoothing, forecast bias, forecast error metrics, forecasting, Mean Absolute Deviation (MAD), Mean Absolute Percent Error (MAPE)*.

transaction cost – The cost of processing one transaction such as a purchase order.

> In a supply chain management context, this is the cost of processing one purchase order.
> See *search cost, switching cost, total cost of ownership*.

transactional process improvement – Improving non-manufacturing activities.

> The term "transactional process improvement" is used by many Lean Sigma consultants to describe efforts to improve non-manufacturing processes in manufacturing firms and also improve processes in service organizations. Examples include back-office operations (e.g., accounting, human resources) and front-office operations (order-entry, customer registration, teller services).

> These processes are different from manufacturing processes because they do not handle a tangible product. The entity that flows through these processes may be customers, patients, paper, lab specimens, or information and may travel across several departments. Lean Sigma programs can often improve transactional processes by reducing non-value added steps, reducing queue time, reducing cycle time, reducing travel, improving quality, reducing cost, and improving customer satisfaction.

> See *lean thinking, Six Sigma, waterfall scheduling*.

transfer batch – A set of parts that is moved in quantities less than the production batch size.

When a large batch is started on a machine, smaller batches can be moved (transferred) to the following machines while the large batch is still being produced. The smaller batch sizes are called "transfer batches," whereas the larger batch produced on the first machine is called a "production batch." This concept has been promoted in the "Theory of Constraints" literature to reduce total throughput time and total work in process inventory. When possible, transfer batches should be used at the bottleneck to allow for large production batch sizes, without requiring large batch sizes after the bottleneck. It is important to have large batch sizes at the bottleneck to avoid wasting valuable bottleneck capacity on setups.

See *lotsizing methods*, *pacemaker*, *Theory of Constraints (TOC)*.

Transportation Management Systems (TMS) – An information system that supports transportation and logistics management; also called fleet management systems and transportation systems.

Transportation Management Systems are information systems that manage transportation operations of all types, including shippers, ocean, airlines, bus, rail, taxi, moving companies, transportation rental agencies and all types of activities including shipment scheduling through inbound, outbound, intermodal, and intra-company shipments. TMSs can track and manage every aspect of a transportation system including: fleet management, vehicle maintenance, fuel costing, routing and mapping, warehousing, communications, EDI, traveler and cargo handling, carrier selection and management, accounting, audit and payment claims, appointment scheduling, and yard management. Most TMSs provide information on rates, bills of lading, load planning, carrier selection, posting and tendering, freight bill auditing and payment, loss and damage claims processing, labor planning and assignment, and documentation management.

Many TMSs also provide GPS satellite navigation and terrestrial communications technologies to enable government authorities and fleet operators to better track, manage, and dispatch vehicles. With this technology, dispatchers can locate vehicles and respond to emergencies, send a repair crew, and notify passengers of delay.

The main benefits of a TMS include lower freight costs (through better mode selection, route planning, and route consolidation) and better customer service (better shipment tracking, increased management visibility, and better on-time delivery). A TMS can provide improved visibility of containers and products, aid in continuous movements of products, and reduce empty miles.

See *Advanced Shipping Notification (ASN)*, *cross-docking*, *Electronic Data Interchange (EDI)*, *Over/Short/Damaged Report (OSD Report)*, *Warehouse Management System (WMS)*.

transportation problem – A mathematical programming problem of finding the optimal number of units to send from location i to location j in order to minimize the total transportation cost.

The transportation problem is usually shown as a table or a matrix. The problem requires that we determine how many units should be shipped from each "factory" (row) to each "market" (column). Each factory has limited capacity (the sum of the values along each row) and each market has limited demand (the sum of the values in each column).

The mathematical statement for the problem with N factories and M markets is:

$$\text{Minimize} \sum_{i=1}^{N} \sum_{j=1}^{M} c_{ij} x_{ij}$$

$$\text{Subject to} \sum_{i=1}^{N} x_{ij} \geq D_j, \text{ for } j = 1, 2, ..., M \quad \text{and} \quad \sum_{j=1}^{M} x_{ij} \leq C_i, \text{ for } i = 1, 2, ..., N$$

where c_{ij} is the cost per unit of shipping from factory i to market j, D_j is the market demand in units for market j, and C_i is the capacity (in units) for factory i. The goal is to minimize total transportation cost. The first constraint ensures that all demand is met. The second constraint ensures that the product does not exceed the capacity.

The transportation model is often formulated with equality constraints. This often requires either a "dummy" plant to handle market demand in excess of capacity or a "dummy" market to handle capacity in excess of market demand. The cost per unit for shipping from the dummy plant is the cost of a lost sale; the cost of shipping to the dummy market is the cost of excess capacity.

The transshipment problem is an extension of the transportation model to handle shipping across more than two echelons (e.g., from plant to warehouse and then from warehouse to market).

The transportation and transshipment problems can be easily extended to handle multiple periods where the product is "shipped" from one period to the next with an associated carrying cost. The size of these problems can become quite large, but network algorithms can handle large networks efficiently. However, one major problem with network algorithms is that they assume the system has only a single commodity. In other words, the standard formulation only allows for one product to be shipped. More general linear programming approaches can be used when the firm has multiple products. Unfortunately, the solution algorithms for linear programming problems are far less efficient.

The transportation and transshipment problems can be solved with special-purpose algorithms, network optimization algorithms, or with general purpose linear programming algorithms. Even though they are both integer programming problems, they can be solved with any general linear programming package and can be still guaranteed to produce integer solutions because the problems are unimodular.

See *assignment problem*, *Linear Programming (LP)*, *logistics*, *network optimization*, *Traveling Salesperson Problem (TSP)*.

transshipment problem – See *transportation problem*.

Traveling Salesperson Problem (TSP) – The problem of finding the minimum cost (distance or travel time) sequence for a single vehicle to visit a set of cities (nodes, locations), visiting each city exactly once, and returning to the starting city; also spelled travelling salesperson problem.

The problem used to be called the "Traveling Salesman Problem." This is one of the most studied problems in all of operations research and many methods are available for solving the problem. The methods can be divided into optimal ("exact") methods and heuristics. Optimal methods are guaranteed to find the best (lowest cost or lowest travel time) solution, but the computing time can be extremely long. The computing time required for finding the proven mathematically optimal solution for this problem increases dramatically as N increases. (The problem is said to be "NP-hard.") On the other hand, heuristic methods are computationally fast, but may find solutions that are far from optimal.

Extensions of the problem include the multiple-vehicle TSP and the Vehicle Scheduling Problem (VSP). The VSP can involve multiple vehicles, time window constraints on visiting each node, capacity constraints on each vehicle, total distance and time constraints for each vehicle, and demand requirements for each node. Both the TSP and the VSP are important problems in logistics and transportation. Similar combinatorial problems are found in many problem contexts. For example, the problem of finding the optimal sequence of jobs for a machine with sequence-dependent setups is essentially a TSP. Some printed circuit board design problems can also be formulated as a TSP.

The mathematical programming formulation of the problem is:

$$\text{Minimize} \sum_{i=1}^{N}\sum_{j=1}^{N} c_{ij}x_{ij}$$

$$\text{Subject to} \sum_{i=1}^{N} x_{ij} = 1, \text{ for } j = 1, 2, ..., N$$

$$\sum_{j=1}^{n} x_{ij} = 1, \text{ for } i = 1, 2, ..., N.$$

$$y_i - y_j + (n-1)x_{ij} \leq n-2, \text{ for all } (i, j), j \notin \text{depot}.$$

where, $x_{i,j} \in (0,1)$ for all (i, j), c_{ij} is the cost (time or distance) to travel from city i to city j, and $x_{ij}=1$ if node i immediately follows node j in the tour and $x_{ij}=0$ otherwise.

The objective is to minimize the total transportation cost (or distance or time). The first two constraints require that all nodes have exactly one incoming and one outgoing arc. The third constraint requires that the solution has no "sub-tours," where a sub-tour is defined as a circuit that does not connect to the "depot." (Alternative formulations for this constraint can also be found in the literature.) The final constraint requires that all of the x_{ij} decision variables be constrained to be either a zero or a one.

The paper "The Traveling Salesperson Problem" is on the **OMWW CD** available from www.ClamshellBeachPress.com. ⊙

See *algorithm, assignment problem, Linear Programming (LP), logistics, sequence-dependent setup time, transportation problem.*

trend – The average rate of increase for the demand. ✪

The trend is the slope of the demand versus time graph. One simple way to estimate this rate is with a simple linear regression using time as the "x" variable. In exponential smoothing, the trend can be smoothed with its own smoothing constant.

See *exponential smoothing, forecasting, time-series forecasting.*

trend line – See *linear regression.*

triage – The process of directing (or sorting) customers into different streams based on their needs.

Triage is used to allocate a scarce commodity to the most deriving of it. The word comes from *trier*, which is old French and means to sort.

In a healthcare context, a triage step can be used to sort injured people into groups based on their need for or likely benefit from immediate medical treatment. In a battlefield context, triage means to select a route or treatment path for the wounded. In a service quality context, adding a triage step means to place a resource (a person, computer, or phone system) at the beginning of the process. This resource "triages" incoming customers and directs them to the right resource and process.

The advantages of triage include (1) it protects valuable resources from being wasted on less important tasks, and (2) it assigns customers to the most appropriate service for their needs. For example, a clinic should usually not have a highly-paid Ear-Nose-Throat (ENT) specialist seeing a patient with a minor sore throat. The clinic should have a "triage nurse" directing patients to the right medical professional. Patients with minor problems should see a nurse or physician's assistant; patients with major non-urgent problems should be scheduled to see a doctor at a later date; patients with major urgent problems should see a doctor right away. With a good triage system, a patient will be quickly directed to the proper level for the proper medical help and the system will be able to deliver the maximum benefit to society for any given budget constraint.

See *service quality.*

triangular distribution – A continuous distribution that is useful when little or no historical data is available and/or the distribution is not symmetrical.

Parameters: Minimum (a), mode (b), and maximum (c).

Density and distribution functions:

$$f(x) = \begin{cases} \dfrac{2(x-a)}{(c-a)(b-a)} & \text{if } a \leq x \leq b \\[2mm] \dfrac{2(c-x)}{(c-a)(c-b)} & \text{if } b < x \leq c \\[2mm] 0 & \text{otherwise} \end{cases}$$

$$F(x) = \begin{cases} 0 & \text{if } x < a \\[2mm] \dfrac{(x-a)^2}{(c-a)(b-a)} & \text{if } a \leq x \leq b \\[2mm] 1 - \dfrac{(c-x)^2}{(c-a)(c-b)} & \text{if } b < x \leq c \\[2mm] 1 & \text{if } c < x \end{cases}$$

Statistics: Range $[a, b]$, mean $(a+b+c)/3$, mode a, and variance $(a^2 + b^2 + c^2 - ab - ac - bc)/18$.

Inverse: The following is the inverse of the triangular distribution function with probability of p:

$$x = F^{-1}(p) = \begin{cases} a & \text{for } p \leq 0 \\[2mm] a + \sqrt{p(c-a)(b-a)} & \text{for } 0 < p \leq (b-a)/(c-a) \\[2mm] c - \sqrt{(1-p)(c-a)(c-b)} & \text{for } (b-a)/(c-a) < p < 1 \\[2mm] c & \text{for } 1 \leq p \end{cases}$$

In other words, when $p = F(x)$ then $x = F^{-1}(p)$. Using the inverse of the triangular distribution is often a practical approach for implementing the newsvendor model when little is known about the demand distribution. When the probability p is set to the critical ratio, the inverse function returns the optimal value. A simulation in Excel can generate triangularly distributed variates with $x = F^{-1}(\text{RAND}())$.

Excel: Excel does not have any formulas for the triangular distribution, but they are fairly easy to create in Excel with the above equations. VBA functions for the triangular density, distribution, and inverse distribution functions can be found in the Excel workbook "Distributions.xls" on the **OMWW CD** available from www.ClamshellBeachPress.com. ☉

Excel simulation: The inverse transform method can be used with $x = $ TRIANGULAR_INVERSE(RAND()), a, b, c), using the function in the Excel workbook distributions.xls.

Graph: The following is a graph of the triangular density function with parameters (1, 2, 10).

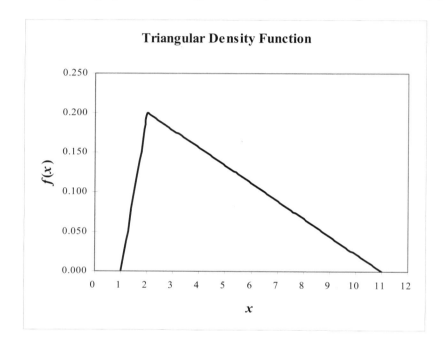

Triangular Density Function

Parameter estimation: An expert (or team) estimates three parameters: minimum (a), mode (b), and maximum (c). When collecting subjective probability estimates, it is a good idea to ask the respondent for the maximum and minimum values first so they do not "anchor" (bias) their subjective estimates with their own estimate of the mode.

It is imprecise to talk about the "maximum" and the "minimum" for distributions that are not bounded. For example, with a little imagination, the "maximum" demand could be extremely large. In this situation, it would be more precise to ask the expert for the values at the 95-th percentile and the 5-th percentile of the distribution. However, this mathematical fact does not seem to bother most practitioners who use this distribution in a wide variety of situations.

The Excel workbook "Distributions.xls" is on the **OMWW CD** available from www.ClamshellBeachPress.com. ☉

See *newsvendor model*.

tribal knowledge – Any unwritten information that is not commonly known by others within an organization.

Tribal knowledge is a term used to describe undocumented and informal information that is closely held by a few individuals. This information is often critical to the organization's product or process design and will be lost when these individuals depart the organization.

See *knowledge management*.

trim – A statistical procedure that eliminates (removes) outliers (i.e., exceptional values) from a sample; also known as trimming; in Visual Basic Assistant (VBA), the Trim(S) function removes leading and trailing blanks from a text string.

See *trimmed mean*, *Winsorizing*.

trimmed mean – A measure of central tendency that eliminates (removes) outliers (i.e., exceptional values) from the sample that is used to compute the mean (average) value.

When data is highly skewed, the trimmed mean is often a better measure of the central tendency than the simple average. The trimmed mean is computed by removing a certain percentage of values from the bottom and top of a data set that is sorted in rank order. When the bottom and top α percent are removed from the sample, a trimmed mean of $\alpha = 0$ is the simple mean, and a trimmed mean of $\alpha = 50\%$ is the median (assuming that only the middle value remains after the trimming process). The trimmed mean, therefore, can be considered as a measure of the central tendency somewhere between the simple average and the median.

Acknowledgments: CEMBA 09 students Leslie Bronk, Terry Collier, Rick Mann, and Adam Podbelski contributed to this entry.

See *median*, *trim*.

triple bottom line – An organizational performance evaluation that includes social and environmental performance indicators as well as the typical financial performance indicators.

The term "triple bottom line" was coined by Elkington (1994), who argued that an organization's responsibility is to its entire group of stakeholders rather than just to its shareholders. The stakeholders include everyone who is affected directly or indirectly by the actions of the organization.

The triple bottom line is also referred to as the "Three P's," which are People (human capital), Planet (natural capital), and Profits (economic benefit). Wikipedia makes an interesting distinction here between the profit for the triple bottom line and the profit that typically shows up on a firm's income statement. The triple bottom line profit is the economic benefit enjoyed by all of the stakeholders, rather than just the shareholders.

Acknowledgments: CEMBA 09 students Tushar Kshirsagar, Susan Knox, Rob Harveland, Nate O'Connor, Cheryl Huuki, and Carol Rodgers contributed to this entry.

See *green manufacturing*, *public-private partnership*, *sustainability*.

triple exponential smoothing – See *exponential smoothing*.

Triz – A methodology for generating creative ideas.

TRIZ is the Russian acronym for the phrase "Theory of Inventive Problem Solving" (Теория Решения Изобретательских Задач). Developed by Genrich Altshuller and his colleagues in the former USSR, TRIZ is practiced throughout the world. After reviewing over 400,000 patents, Altshuller devised 40 inventive principles that distinguished breakthrough products. TRIZ is a methodology that uses these inventive principles for innovative problem solving and design. Furthermore, these principles can be codified and taught, leading to a more predictable process of invention. TRIZ challenges the "Eureka" process of invention, by proposing that invention is not serendipitous, but can be anticipated through conscious system development. Although primarily associated with technical innovation, these principles can be applied in a variety of areas including service operations, business applications, education, and architecture.

The following is the TRIZ list of 40 inventive principles (http://www.triz-journal.com/archives/1997/07/b/index.html).

Principle 1. Segmentation
Principle 2. Taking out
Principle 3. Local quality
Principle 4. Asymmetry
Principle 5. Merging
Principle 6. Universality
Principle 7. "Nested doll"
Principle 8. Anti-weight
Principle 9. Preliminary anti-action
Principle 10. Preliminary action
Principle 11. Beforehand cushioning

Principle 22. "Blessing in disguise" or "Turn Lemons into Lemonade"
Principle 23. Feedback
Principle 24. "Intermediary"
Principle 25. Self-service
Principle 26. Copying
Principle 27. Cheap short-living objects
Principle 28. Mechanics substitution
Principle 29. Pneumatics and hydraulics
Principle 30. Flexible shells and thin films
Principle 31. Porous materials

Principle 12. Equipotentiality
Principle 13. "The other way round"
Principle 14. Spheroidality - Curvature
Principle 15. Dynamics
Principle 16. Partial or excessive actions
Principle 17. Another dimension
Principle 18. Mechanical vibration
Principle 19. Periodic action
Principle 20. Continuity of useful action
Principle 21. Skipping

Principle 32. Color changes
Principle 33. Homogeneity
Principle 34. Discarding and recovering
Principle 35. Parameter changes
Principle 36. Phase transitions
Principle 37. Thermal expansion
Principle 38. Strong oxidants
Principle 39. Inert atmosphere
Principle 40. Composite materials

Sources: The TRIZ Journal: http://www.triz-journal.com, http://www.content-village.org/incacontent/upload/TRIZ_130904.ppt#353,5,Background: TRIZ

See *Analytical Hierarchy Process (AHP), ideation, Kepner-Tregoe Model, New Product Development (NPD), Pugh Matrix*.

truck-load – Designation for motor carrier shipments exceeding 10,000 pounds.

A motor carrier may haul more than one truck-load (TL) shipment in a single vehicle.

See *Less than Container Load (LCL), Less than Truck Load (LTL), logistics*.

TS 16949 quality standard – A quality standard developed by the American automotive industry.

Beginning in 1994 with the successful launch of QS 9000 by DaimlerChrysler, Ford and GM, the automotive OEMs recognized the increased value that could be derived from an independent quality system registration scheme and the efficiencies that could be realized in the supply chain by "communizing" system requirements. In 1996, the success of these efforts led to a move towards the development of a globally accepted and harmonized quality management system requirements document. Out of this process, the International Automotive Task Force (IATF) was formed to lead the development effort. The result of the IATF's effort was the ISO/TS 16949 specification, which forms the requirements for automotive production and relevant service part organizations. ISO/TS 16949 used the ISO 9001 Standard as the basis for development and included the requirements from these standards with specific "adders" for the automotive supply chain. The 2002 revision of TS builds off the ISO9001:2000 document. Adapted from www.ul.com/services/ts16949.html.

See *ISO 9000*.

TSP – See *Traveling Salesperson Problem (TSP)*.

t-test – A statistical technique that uses the Student's t-test statistic to test if the means of two variables (populations) are significantly different from each other based on a sample of data on each variable.

The null hypothesis is that the true means of two variables (two populations) are equal. The alternative hypothesis is either that the means are different (e.g., $\mu_1 \neq \mu_2$), which is a two-tailed test or that one mean is greater than the other (e.g., $\mu_1 < \mu_2$ or $\mu_1 > \mu_2$), which is a one-tailed test. With n_1 and n_2 observations on variables 1 and 2, and sample means and standard deviations $(\overline{x}_1, s_1)$ and $(\overline{x}_2, s_2)$, the t-statistic is:

$$t = \frac{\overline{x}_1 - \overline{x}_1}{s_{\overline{x}_1 - \overline{x}_2}}, \text{ where } s_{\overline{x}_1 - \overline{x}_2} = \sqrt{\frac{(n_1 - 1)s_1^2 + (n_2 - 1)s_2^2}{n_1 + n_2 - 2}\left(\frac{1}{n_1} + \frac{1}{n_2}\right)}$$

The term $s_{\overline{x}_1 - \overline{x}_2}$ simplifies to $\sqrt{(s_1^2 + s_2^2)/n}$, when $n = n_1 = n_2$.

If each member in population 1 is related to a member in the other population (e.g., a person measured before and after a treatment effect), the observations will be positively correlated and the more powerful paired t-test (or matched pairs test) can be used. The paired t-test computes the difference variable $d_i = x_{1i} - x_{2i}$, then computes the sample mean ($\overline{d}$) and standard deviation (s_d), and then finally the t-statistic $t = \overline{d}/(s_d\sqrt{n})$.

For a two-tailed test, the t-test rejects the null hypothesis of equal means in favor of the alternative hypothesis of unequal means when this t-statistic is greater than the critical level $t_{\alpha/2, n_1 + n_2 - 2}$, which is the

Student's t value associated with probability $\alpha/2$ and n_1+n_2-2 degrees of freedom. For a one-tailed test, $\alpha/2$ should be replaced by α. For a paired t-test, use $n=n_1=n_2$ degrees of freedom. In Excel, use TINV(α, n_1+n_2-2) for a two-tailed test and TINV(2α, n_1+n_2-2) for a one-tailed test. The counter-intuitive p-values (α and 2α) are used because TINV assumes a two-tailed test.

The t-test assumes that the variables are normally distributed and have equal variances. If the variances of the two populations are not equal, then Welch's t-test should be used.

The t-test can be done in one Excel function. The TTEST(ARRAY1, ARRAY2, TAILS, TYPE) function returns the probability (the "p-value") that two samples are from two populations that have the same mean. ARRAY1 and ARRAY2 contain the ranges for sample data from the two populations (variables). TAILS specifies the number of tails for the test (one or two). Two tails should be used if the alternative hypothesis is that the two means are not equal. The TYPE parameter defines the type of t-test to use in the Excel TTEST function:

TYPE	Type of test
1	Paired t-test
2	Two-samples with equal variance test
3	Two-sample with unequal variance

The table below summarizes the parameters for the Excel functions assuming equal variances.

Test	Number of tails	Level of significance	Degrees of freedom	Excel with TINV	Excel with TTEST
Paired t-test	2	$1-\alpha/2$	n	TINV(α, n)	TTEST(A1, A2,2,1)
Paired t-test	1	$1-\alpha$	n	TINV(2α, n)	TTEST(A1, A2,1,1)
Two sample	2	$1-\alpha/2$	n_1+n_2-2	TINV(α, n_1+n_2-2)	TTEST(A1, A2,2,2)
Two sample	1	$1-\alpha$	n_1+n_2-2	TINV(2α, n_1+n_2-2)	TTEST(A1, A2,1,2)

The t-distribution was first published in 1908 by William Sealy Gosset, while working at a Guinness brewery in Dublin. He was not allowed to publish under his own name, so he used the pseudonym Student. The t-test became well-known through the work of R.A. Fisher, who called the distribution "Student's t-distribution." (This paragraph was adapted from en.wikipedia.org/wiki/Student_t.)

See *ANOVA (Analysis of Variance)*, *confidence interval*, *sampling*.

Turing Test – A face validity test proposed by (and named after) Alfred Turing (1950) in which an expert or expert panel compares the results of two processes, typically a computer program and an expert, and tries to determine which process is the computer process.

If the experts cannot tell the difference, the computer process is judged to have a high degree of expertise. For example, an expert system is presented with a series of medical cases and makes a diagnosis for each one. A medical expert is given the same series of cases and also asked to make a diagnosis for each one. A second expert is then asked to review the diagnoses from the two sources and discern which one was the computer. If the second medical expert cannot tell the difference, the computer system is judged to have face validity.

See *simulation*.

turnover – In the field of operations management, turnover is usually assumed to mean inventory turnover.

However, employee turnover is also an important concept. In most of the world outside of North America, the word "turnover" is used to mean revenue or sales.

See *employee turnover*, *inventory turnover*.

two-bin system – A simple inventory system that has two bins, where an empty bin is used to signal the need for a replenishment order.

A two-bin system is a popular lean manufacturing concept that uses two bins, normally of the same size. When a bin is emptied, it is sent back to the supplier to signal the need to fill up the bin. Meanwhile, the inventory in the other bin is used to satisfy the demand. In many cases, a card is associated with the bin so that the card (rather than the bin) can be sent back to the supplier to request replenishment.

From a simple inventory perspective, this is a reorder point system, where the bin size is the reorder point and the order quantity. In many firms, the empty bins (or cards) are only sent to suppliers once per week, which is a periodic review order-up-to system with a minimum order quantity (the size of a bin).

This author visited a plant that had implemented a two-bin system that had shut down the plant when first implemented. The problem was that they set all bin sizes to "three weeks supply." They should have used the reorder point equation $R = \overline{d}L + z\sqrt{L}\sigma_d$ to set bin sizes. Bin size should be a function of the leadtime, average demand, and standard deviation of the demand – and not just the average demand. In some cases, it is a good idea to put a lock on the reserve bin to ensure that the ordering discipline is enforced.

See *lean thinking*, *pull systems*, *reorder point*.

two minute rule – The time management principle that tasks requiring less than two minutes should be done immediately and should not put on a task list.

It requires about two minutes to record and review a task. Therefore, it is often better to do such tasks and not add them to a list. However, sometimes it is better to make a quick note and stay focused on the task at hand.

See *Getting Things Done (GTD)*, *personal operations management*, *tyranny of the urgent*.

Type I and II errors – In the field of statistics, the two types of errors that can be made in hypothesis testing.

A type I error is when we incorrectly reject a true null hypothesis. A type II error is when we fail to reject a false null hypothesis.

<table>
<tr><td></td><td></td><td colspan="2" align="center">**TRUTH**</td></tr>
<tr><td></td><td></td><td>H0 True</td><td>H0 False</td></tr>
<tr><td>**DECISION**</td><td>Reject H0</td><td>Type I error</td><td>Correct</td></tr>
<tr><td></td><td>Do not reject H0</td><td>Correct</td><td>Type II error</td></tr>
</table>

Some authors define a Type III error as working on the wrong problem.

See *consumer's risk*, *producer's risk*.

tyranny of the urgent – A time management concept popularized by Hummel (1967) that suggests that people are often so driven by urgent activities and never get around to the important ones and, as a result, do not accomplish their life goals.

See *Getting Things Done (GTD)*, *Personal Operations Management*, *two minute rule*.

U

uniform distribution – A continuous probability distribution that is useful for modeling a random variable in the range (a, b).

For example, it can be used to model the time for a random arrival during a time interval.

Density and distribution functions: The uniform distribution is defined in the range (a, b) and has density and distribution functions:

$$\text{Density function} \quad f(x) = \begin{cases} \dfrac{1}{b-a} & \text{for } a \le x \le b \\ 0 & \text{otherwise} \end{cases} \qquad \text{Distribution function} \quad F(x) = \begin{cases} 0 & \text{for } x < a \\ \dfrac{x-a}{b-a} & \text{for } a \le x \le b \\ 1 & \text{for } b < x \end{cases}$$

Statistics: The a parameter is the location parameter and $b-a$ is the scale parameter. The mean is $(a+b)/2$ and the variance is $(b-a)^2/12$.

Excel: Excel does not have a function for the uniform distribution, but it can be handled easily with the random number function RAND().

Excel simulation: A uniformly distributed random variable in the range can be generated in Excel with =A+RAND()*(B-A).

Discrete uniform distribution: The discrete uniform generates integer values in the range (a, b), where a and b are integers. This distribution is useful when selecting from a limited number of random options. In Excel, a discrete uniform random variable in the range (a, b) can be generated with = Int((B-A+1)*RAND()+A).

The mean and variance for the discrete uniform are $\mu = (a+b)/2$ and $\sigma^2 = ((b-a+1)^2 - 1)/12$ respectively. Note that the variances for the continuous and discrete uniform distributions are different.

unit fill rate – See *fill rate*.

unit of measure – The standard method for counting an item used for inventory records and order quantities.

This can be tricky when a box is inside a box, which is inside another box.

See *aggregate inventory management, aggregate production planning*.

Universal Product Code (UPC) – The standard barcode symbol for retail packaging in the United States.

A UPC is a product identification number that uniquely identifies a product and the manufacturer. It is a series of thick and thin vertical bars (lines) printed on consumer product packages. All UPC identifiers have an associated numeric 12-digit code. The UPC barcode can be scanned at the point-of-sale. The information allows retailers to record data at checkout to record the SKU, size, color, and other data items when an item is sold and to transmit this data to a computer monitoring unit sales, inventory levels, and other factors.

The EAN is the international version of the UPC and has 13 rather than 12 digits. EAN stands for European Article Number. When it was introduced, the idea was to expand the UPC across the world with this new code, while still being UPC compliant. To do this, a prefix number was added to the UPC, where the prefix 0 was reserved for existing UPCs. Many firms that import from around the world use both UPCs and EANs in their information systems.

Acknowledgments: CSOM MBA students Randall Thorson, Chaouki Khamis, and Mahesh Rege contributed to this entry.

See *barcode, EPC (Electronic Product Code), item number, Point-of-Sale (POS), Radio Frequency Identification (RFID)*.

upstream – A manufacturing and supply chain term referring to any process that comes before a given process.

This term makes an analogy between a stream or a river and a manufacturing or supply chain system. Just as water moves downstream, the product flows "downstream." A downstream process is any process that comes after a given process. So, if the painting process comes after the molding process, the painting process is said to be a "downstream" process.

Likewise, an "upstream" process is one that comes before. Therefore, the molding process is said to be "upstream" from the painting process.

See *bullwhip effect, Drum-Buffer-Rope (DBR), pacemaker*.

utilization – The percent of the available work time that a resource is working.

Understanding utilization is essential to understanding operations, especially to understanding capacity management. Utilization is a critical operations metric, essential queuing systems metric, and is also one of the three elements of the Overall Equipment Effectiveness (OEE) metric. Operations managers sometimes strive to maximize productivity by maximizing utilization in order to amortize fixed costs over more units. However, maximizing utilization can often be a foolish strategy because high utilization also means high inventory, high customer wait time, and poor customer service. For example, the ideal utilization for an emergency vehicle such as a fire engine is close to zero. The entry on queuing theory discusses utilization from a queuing theory point of view.

See *bottleneck, capacity, cellular manufacturing, efficiency, Overall Equipment Effectiveness (OEE), productivity, queuing theory, Theory of Constraints (TOC), wait time*.

V

validation – See *process validation*.

validation protocol – See *process validation*.

value added ratio – The ratio of the processing time (direct value adding time) to the total cycle time (total throughput time); also called Manufacturing Cycle Effectiveness (MCE), throughput ratio, and cycle time efficiency.

In a manufacturing context, the total cycle time (throughput time) is the total time in the system, which usually includes the queue time (wait time), run time, post-operation wait time, and move time. The value adding time is the "touch time" plus time spent in other value adding operations such as baking in an oven, curing, drying, etc. In labor intensive manufacturing operations, the value adding time is just the "touch time."

In a service context, the value added ratio is often defined as the percent of the time that the customer is receiving actual value-added service divided by the time that the customer is in the system.

When the value added ratio is close to zero, the process is considered to be an inefficient process; when the ratio approaches one, it is considered an efficient process. Many processes in practice have a value added ratio less than 20%.

See *batch-and-queue, cycle time, lean thinking, Overall Equipment Effectiveness (OEE), queuing theory, time-based competition, touch time, wait time.*

Value Added Reseller (VAR) – An organization that adds value to a system and resells it.

For example, a VAR could purchase computer components (e.g., CPU, mother board, case, and monitor) and graphics software from a number of different suppliers and package them together as a specialized CAD system. Although VARs typically only repackage and sell products, they might also include software and/or services they have developed themselves. Adapted from www.pcmag.com/ encyclopedia_term, October 25, 2006.

See *Original Equipment Manufacturer (OEM).*

value analysis – See *value engineering.*

value chain – A concept developed by Michael Porter to describe the activities that take place in a business and relate them to an analysis of the competitive strength of the business. ✪

Porter (1985) suggested that the activities of a business could be grouped under two headings:

Primary Activities are those that are directly concerned with creating and delivering a product (e.g., component assembly)

Support Activities are not directly involved in production but may increase effectiveness or efficiency (e.g., human resource management). It is rare for a business to undertake all primary and support activities. The concept was first communicated in Porter's text (1985).

According to Porter (1985), the primary value chain activities are:

- **Inbound Logistics** – All relationships with suppliers, including all activities required to receive, store, and disseminate inputs.
- **Operations** – All activities required to transform inputs into outputs (products and services).
- **Outbound Logistics** - All activities required to collect, store, and distribute the output.
- **Marketing and Sales** – All activities to inform buyers about products and services, induce buyers to purchase them, and facilitate their purchase.
- **Service** – All activities required to keep the product or service working effectively for the buyer after it is sold and delivered.

Porter lists secondary activities as:

- **Procurement** – Acquisition of inputs, or resources, for the firm.
- **Human Resource management** – All activities involved in recruiting, hiring, training, developing, compensating and (if necessary) dismissing or laying off personnel.
- **Technological Development** – Equipment, hardware, software, procedures, and technical knowledge brought to bear in the firm's transformation of inputs into outputs.
- **Infrastructure** – Serves the company's needs and ties the various parts together. Infrastructure consists of functions or departments such as accounting, legal, finance, planning, public affairs, government relations, quality assurance and general management.

Porter suggests that firms can gain competitive advantage through either cost leadership or differentiation. In a **cost leadership** strategy, a firm sets out to become the low-cost producer in its industry. The sources of cost advantage are varied and depend on the structure of the industry. They may include the pursuit of economies of scale, proprietary technology, preferential access to raw materials, and other factors. In a **differentiation** strategy, a firm seeks to be unique in its industry along some dimensions that are widely valued by buyers. It selects one or more attributes that many buyers in an industry perceive as important, and then uniquely positions itself to meet those needs. It is rewarded for its uniqueness with a premium price.

Value chain analysis can be broken down into three sequential steps:

- Break down a market/organization into its key activities under each of the major headings in the model.

- Assess the potential for adding value via cost advantage or differentiation, or identify current activities where a business appears to be at a competitive disadvantage.
- Determine strategies built around focusing on activities where competitive advantage can be sustained.

Many authors now use the terms "value chain" and "supply chain" almost interchangeably. However, most scholars make a distinction between the terms. The value chain takes a business strategy point of view, considers product design and after sales service, and emphasizes assignment of activities to firms based on core competencies. In contrast, supply chain management usually takes a materials and information flow point of view and emphasizes suppliers, inventories, information flow, and pricing.

See *bullwhip effect, SCOR model, supply chain management*.

value engineering – An approach for designing and redesigning products and services to achieve the same functionality at less cost or alternatively to achieve better functionality at the same cost; also known as value analysis.

Value engineering techniques (1) identify the functions of a product or service, (2) establish a worth for each function, (3) generate alternatives through the use of creative thinking, and (4) select alternatives to reliably fulfill the needed functions to achieve the lowest lifecycle cost without sacrificing safety, quality, or environmental attributes of the project. Value engineering is usually conducted by a multi-disciplined team and applies a well-developed methodology.

Value engineering is closely related to product simplification, which is the process of finding ways to reduce product complexity while not sacrificing important functionality. Value engineering is also closely related to commonality, which involves using common parts across many products.

See *commonality, product lifecycle management*.

value proposition – A statement of the benefits offered by a product or service to a market.

The value proposition is a statement of how a bundle of product and service offers value to a set of customers and how that value is differentiated from competitors' offerings. In an economic sense, the value proposition is the difference between the life-cycle benefits and the life-cycle cost.

See *service guarantee, strategy map*.

value stream manager – A lean manufacturing term for an individual who has been assigned the responsibility for a value stream.

The value stream may be on the product or the business level.

value stream map – A lean manufacturing process mapping methodology based on the material and information flow maps developed at Toyota and later adapted by the Lean Enterprise Institute in the book ***Learning to See*** by Rother, Shook, Womack, and Jones (2003). ✪

Value Stream Mapping is a visual tool that graphically identifies every process in a product's flow from "door-to-door," giving visibility to both the value-adding steps as well as the non-value-adding steps. The processes that create value are thoroughly detailed for complete process flow of a particular product or product family. The current state is drawn from observation and data gathering of the actual processes. This exercise exposes the waste and redundancy. The future state map is based on lean principles and world-class benchmarks.

Value stream analysis activities include:
- Review demand profile (Pareto Chart, histogram)
- Conduct flow analysis (Parts process matrix, Spaghetti diagram)
- Calculate takt time (peak demand, average demand)
- Value Stream Mapping (Material & Information Flow diagram using Learning to See format, Current State and Future State Gap Analysis)
- Deliverables (Current State Map, Future State Map, Change loops and kaizen breakthroughs, Vision for the Lean Transformation, Implementation plan)

The following diagram is a simple example of a value stream map, where C/T is the average cycle time, B/N is the bottleneck utilization, V/A is the value-added time, and FTE is the full-time equivalent workforce.

The data associated with each step usually includes:
- C-T (or C/T) = Cycle time.
- V-T (or V/T) = Value added time or the percentage of total time that is value added time.
- C-0 (or C/O) = Changeover time from one product to another.

- U-T (or U/T) = The time that the process is available for work or the percentage of the total time that the process is available for work.
- FPY = First pass yield, which is the percentage of the time that the quality standards are met the first time that a product goes through the process.
- FTE = Number of full-time equivalent workers required for this process.
  The benefits claimed for Value Stream Mapping include:
- Helps users identify and eliminate waste.
- Creates a vision of the future by uncovering wastes and opportunities to create flow.
- Enables broad participation.

- Improves understanding of product cost.
- Helps reduce work in process.
- Helps reduce cycle time.
- Focuses on customer pull signals.

Value Stream Map

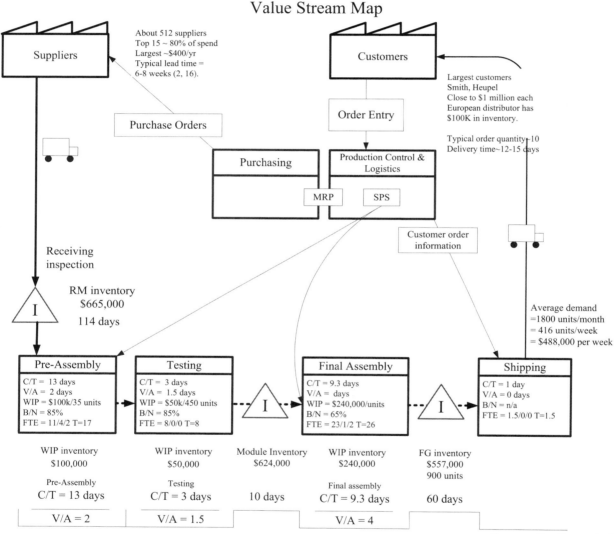

Source: Professor Arthur V. Hill

The standard reference on value stream maps is the book ***Learning to See Version*** by Rother, Shook, Womack, and Jones (2003).

See *lean thinking, process map*.

values statement – See *mission statement*.

variable costing – An accounting method that adds all traceable costs of resources used to unit-level costs and ignores all fixed overhead costs.

The contribution margin (under variable costing) is sales revenue minus all variable costs.

See *absorption costing*, *Activity Based Costing (ABC)*, *standard cost*, *Theory of Constraints (TOC)*, *throughput accounting*.

variance – See *standard deviation*.

VAT analysis – A classification system used in the Theory of Constraints to describe different types of general materials flows and their related Bill of Materials structures.

The shape of each of the letters "V-A-T" describes the process flow.

- **V-plant** – A V-plant transforms a few inputs into a wide variety of products in a "one to many" product flow. This type of process should be master scheduled at the raw materials level. The primary problem in V-plants is allocating the material properly to competing products.

- **A-plant** – An A-plant transforms (often assembles) a wide variety of inputs into a small variety of final products in a "many to one" product flow. This type of process should be master scheduled at the finished products level. The primary problem in A-plants is synchronizing the incoming materials so that all of the materials are available when needed.

- **T-plant** – A T-plant builds standard parts up to a certain point (the crossbar of the "T") and then assembles these into a wide variety of end products. The components for the lower part of the "T" are built to inventory and then "mixed and matched" in a wide variety of ways for a customer order. Examples include appliances ("white goods") and computers that have many standard inputs but can result in a variety of end items. This type of process should be master scheduled at the finished components level. T-plants suffer from both synchronization problems of A-plants (parts are not all available for an assembly) and the stealing problems of V-plants (one assembly steals parts that could have been used in another).

Wikipedia lists the fourth process type as an I-plant, which is a simple linear process such as an assembly line. The primary work is done in a straight sequence of events. The constraint is the slowest operation.

The terms V-plant, A-plant, and T-plant are probably not the best terms. These terms describe the Bill of Material rather than the plant.

See *Bill of Material (BOM)*, *Theory of Constraints (TOC)*.

vehicle scheduling program (VSP) – See *Traveling Salesperson Problem (TSP)*.

vendor certification – See *supplier qualification and certification*.

Vendor Managed Inventory (VMI) – A supplier-customer relationship where the vendor assumes responsibility for managing the replenishment of stock. ✪

VMI overview

Rather than a customer submitting orders, the vendor will replenish stock as needed. This is sometimes referred to as supplier-managed inventory (SMI) or co-managed inventory. Our suppliers not only supply us goods – but they also manage our inventory so that we can both benefit.

Vendor Managed Inventory (VMI) is a supplier-customer agreement in which the supplier is responsible for maintaining the customer's inventory levels. The supplier has access to the customer's inventory data and is responsible for generating purchase orders. In a typical supplier-customer relationship, customers evaluate their own inventory position and place orders when they believe it is time. With VMI, the supplier generates the order for the customer. VMI is sometimes called "Supplier Managed Inventory" (SMI). To some, the word "vendor" connotes a distant, non-partner, almost adversarial relationship, whereas the word "supplier" connotes a closer relationship. VMI does not change the ownership of inventory. With consignment inventory, the supplier retains ownership of the inventory and payment is not made until the item is sold.

In VMI, the normal trading relationship is reversed. Instead of the customer managing its own stock and deciding when and how much more to buy, the supplier does the supply planning for the customers. For many companies that have tried VMI, it has produced good results in terms of sales, service, and profitability for both trading partners.

With VMI, the supplier provides not only items but also provides inventory management services for the customer. These services might include deciding when and how much to replenish in order to satisfy mutually agreeable service levels (fill rates). This practice is sometimes called continuous replenishment or Quick

Response. However, some would argue that continuous replenishment is broader because it focuses on the use of point-of-sale customer data to trigger warehouse shipping, whereas VMI focuses on the manufacturer or distributor taking responsibility for the inventory in a customer's facility.

VMI is not new

What we call VMI today has been going on for quite a long time. For example:
- Supermarkets and vending machines have used this concept for decades.
- Frito Lay's drivers/salespersons stock the shelves for their small retail customers to keep the shelves full, the product fresh, and the paperwork simple. Much fresh product moves into convenience shops in the same way.
- Hopson Oil, a home heating oil supplier, automatically schedules deliveries for fuel oil based on consumption forecasts for each customer, and has for more than 20 years. In this way, they keep their order-taking costs down and keep it simple for their customers, who need not order competing fuels.

As the examples show, many suppliers have looked after tracking inventory and ordering for customers who are too small to have inventory systems of their own, or have done it as a value-added service for larger customers. The same motivations are at work today.

VMI Implementation

VMI is relatively easy to implement. Technical aspects of VMI are usually fairly easy with ready availability of EDI, bar-coding, cheap computing power, and good software. However, VMI programs still have both strategic and operational challenges. At the strategic level, a high-level decision must be made about how the company wants to position itself. Are there benefits to stronger supply chain co-operation? If so, has a high-level decision been made to share the necessary information? Operationally, job functions, processes, and performance measurements all need to change in order to get the most benefit. Resistance will be felt from employees who fear change.

Advantages and disadvantages of VMI (vis-à-vis a traditional purchasing relationship)

Advantages of VMI	Disadvantages of VMI
• Maximizes "in-stock" position. • Sales higher for both vendor and customer. • Improves data accuracy and speed. • Improves forecast accuracy. • Reduces inventory and inventory carrying cost. • Reduces transportation costs. • Reduces transaction costs. • Reduced coordination cost in the supply chain. • Reduces overall supply chain costs. • Handles promotions better.	• Increases vendor's share of the administrative costs (headcount, etc.). • Complicates volume discounts and special pricing. • Complicates the system in the short run. • Risks loss of control and loss of flexibility. • Penalizes the manufacturer with a short-term immediate volume reduction.

VMI Conclusions

Although VMI is not a new concept; it has grown dramatically in the last few years. Firms, researchers, and consultants are still trying to figure out when and where it is most applicable. However, it is clear that many firms have been able to gain significant benefits when VMI concepts are applied carefully. The article by Johnson (1998) provides a good overview of this subject.

The paper "Vendor Managed Inventory" is on the *OMWW CD* available from www.ClamshellBeachPress.com. ☻

See *consignment inventory, delegation, JIT II, outsourcing, supply chain management.*

vertical integration – The process a firm uses to acquire sources of supply (upstream suppliers) and/or channels of distribution (downstream buyers). ✪

Because it can have a significant impact on a business unit's position in its industry with respect to cost, differentiation, and other strategic issues, the vertical scope of the firm is an important consideration in corporate strategy. Expansion of activities downstream is referred to as "forward integration," and expansion upstream is referred to as "backward integration."

The two primary issues that should be considered when evaluating vertical integration alternatives are cost and control.

The potential advantages of vertical integration include:
- Reduce transportation costs if common ownership results in closer geographic proximity.
- Improve supply chain coordination.
- Provide more opportunities to differentiate by means of increased control over inputs.
- Capture upstream and/or downstream profit margins.
- Increase entry barriers to potential competitors, for example, if the firm can gain sole access to a scarce resource.
- Gain access to downstream distribution channels that otherwise would be inaccessible.
- Facilitate investment in highly specialized assets in which upstream or downstream players may be reluctant to invest.
- Lead to expansion of core competencies.

The potential disadvantages of vertical integration include:
- Cause capacity imbalance. For example, the firm may need to build excess upstream capacity to ensure that its downstream operations have sufficient supply under all demand conditions.
- Potentially cause higher costs due to low efficiencies resulting from lack of supplier competition.
- Decrease flexibility due to previous upstream or downstream investments. (Note however, that flexibility to coordinate vertically-related activities may increase.)
- Decrease ability to support product variety if significant in-house development is required.
- Developing new core competencies may compromise existing competencies.
- Increase bureaucratic costs.

Some situational factors favoring vertical integration include:
- Taxes and regulations on market transactions.
- Obstacles to the formulation and monitoring of contracts.
- Strategic similarity between the vertically-related activities.
- Sufficiently large production quantities so the firm can benefit from economies of scale.
- Reluctance of other firms to make investments specific to the transaction.

The following situational factors tend to make vertical integration less attractive:
- The quantity required from a supplier is much less than the minimum efficient scale for producing the product.
- The product is a widely available commodity and its production cost decreases significantly as cumulative quantity increases.
- The core competencies between the activities are very different.
- The vertically adjacent activities are in very different types of industries. For example, manufacturing is very different from retailing.
- The addition of the new activity places the firm in competition with another player with which it needs to cooperate. The firm may then be viewed as a competitor rather than as a partner.

Alternatives to vertical integration may provide many of the same benefits without the risks. Some of these alternatives include: (1) long-term explicit contracts, (2) franchise agreements, (3) joint ventures, and (4) co-location of facilities (Greaver, 1999).

Some of the ideas for the above were adapted from quickmba.com/strategy/vertical-integration.

See *forecasting*, *make versus buy decision*, *operations strategy*, *outsourcing*, *supply chain management*.

virtual organization – A business model where the selling organization is able to pull together business partners to satisfy a customer order, launch a new product, or supply a product to a market without owning many of the key components of the system.

Virtual organizations have significant flexibility benefits, but given the tenuous nature of their relationships they may not be sustainable. Many high-technology development firms design products and then find contract manufacturers to build them and distributors to find markets for them.

See *operations strategy*.

vision statement – See *mission statement*.

visual control – A lean manufacturing concept of designing systems that have a simple performance indicator and metrics that can be seen and understood almost immediately.

Visual controls are simple, easy-to-see clues that give managers and workers information about the status of a system. For example, a shadow board quickly and clearly shows which tools are missing. In contrast, most computer-based information systems require users to go through several screens to check if a particular value is in range. Computer-based information systems could be designed to follow visual principles, but most of them do not meet lean manufacturing standards.

See *5S, andon light, lean thinking, shadow board*.

VMI – See *Vendor Managed Inventory*.

VOC – See *voice of the customer*.

Voice of the Customer (VOC) – The stated and unstated customer requirements. ✪

It is important for organizations to understand their customers' needs and desires as they change over time. Note that the customer can be either internal or external to the organization. This understanding, called the "voice of the customer," should inform both new product development and process improvement efforts. One of the main keys to success is to intentionally and formally include the VOC in a process improvement program.

The VOC is an important part of most Lean Sigma programs because it defines the key performance measures. The VOC is also critical to successful new product development.

The voice of the customer can be captured in a variety of ways such as:

- Interviews
- Customer satisfaction surveys
- Market research surveys
- E-surveys
- Comment cards
- Focus groups
- Customer specifications

- Contractual requirements
- Observation
- Warranty data
- Field reports
- Complaint logs
- Customer loyalty (i.e., repeat sales)

Many of the entries listed below discuss specific VOC tools.

See *Analytical Hierarchy Process (AHP), critical incidents method, Critical To Quality (CTQ), Customer Relationship Management (CRM), Kano Analysis, lean sigma, New Product Development (NPD), Process Improvement Program, Pugh Matrix, quality, Quality Function Deployment (QFD)*.

voice picking – A speech recognition system that allows warehouse workers to enter data into the computer system with verbal communication.

Voice picking is a feature available in many warehouse management systems. Voice picking allows workers' hands to be free while working. Benefits claimed for voice picking include improved accuracy, productivity, accuracy, and reliability.

Acknowledgments: CSOM MBA 09 students Puneet Gupta, Randolph Cooper, and Ravi Kiran contributed to this entry.

See *Warehouse Management System (WMS)*.

V-plant – See *VAT analysis*.

VSP (Vehicle Scheduling Problem) – See *Traveling Salesperson Problem (TSP)*.

W

Wagner-Whitin lotsizing algorithm − A dynamic programming algorithm for finding the optimal solution for the time-varying demand lotsizing problem.

A good implementation of this algorithm (including the pseudocode) can be found in Evans (1985).

The Excel workbook "lotsizing.xls" implements the Wagner-Whitin algorithm along with several other algorithms for time-varying demand. The paper "Lotsizing" and the Excel workbook "lotsizing.xls" are on the ***OMWW CD*** available from www.ClamshellBeachPress.com. ●

See *lotsizing methods, time-varying demand lotsizing problem.*

wait time − A random variable indicating the time that a customer (or an order) is delayed before starting in a process; also called waiting time or queue time. ✪

The average wait time (queue time) is an important system performance measure. A similar measure is the time in system. The time in system is the wait time (queue time) plus the time in service. The average time in system is the average queue time plus the average service time. In the lean manufacturing philosophy, all wait time is considered to be wasteful.

See *Little's Law, queuing theory, utilization, value added ratio, Work-in-Process (WIP) inventory.*

Warehouse Management System (WMS) − A software application that manages the operations of a warehouse or distribution center.

The purpose of a WMS is to manage the storage and retrieval of materials in a building and handle the transactions associated with those movements. The benefits claimed by WMS software vendors include (1) reduced inventory, (2) reduced labor cost, (3) increased storage capacity, (4) improved customer service, and (5) improved inventory accuracy.

A WMS is a tool for efficiently handling warehousing tasks such as receiving, putaway (stocking), cycle counting, picking, consolidating, packing, and shipping. Newer warehouse management systems include tools that support more complex tasks such as inventory management, product allocations, shipment planning, workforce planning/labor management, and productivity analysis. The WMS guides the operator or machine with information about item locations, quantities, units of measure and other relevant information to determine where to stock, where to pick, and in what sequence to perform each operation. Warehouse Management Systems can be stand alone systems, modules in an ERP system, or modules in a supply chain execution suite.

Traditionally, WMS have used bar codes or smart codes to capture data; however, more recently, radio frequency technology (RFID) capability has been implemented to provide real time information.

Acknowledgments: CSOM MBA students Dwight Porter, James Sonterre, and John Tiedeman contributed to this entry. Some of the above content was adapted from inventoryops.com/warehouse_management_systems. htm, May 3, 2008. This website provides much more detail on this subject.

See *ABC classification, Advanced Shipping Notification (ASN), cross-docking, dock-to-stock, fixed storage location, golden zone, inventory management, logistics, Over/Short/Damaged Report (OSD Report), picking, random storage location, Transportation Management System (TMS), voice picking, zone picking, zone storage location.*

warranty − A guarantee given from the seller to the purchaser stating that a product is reliable and free from known defects and that the seller will repair or replace defective parts within a given time limit and under certain conditions.

From Old North French, from feminine past participle of warantir, to guarantee. (Source: Adapted from dictionary.com, May 14, 2004.)

Blischke and Murty (1992) and Murty and Blischke (1992) provide a good summary of the warranty literature.

See *product design quality, service guarantee, Service Level Agreement (SLA).*

water spider − A lean manufacturing practice of assigning a skilled worker to make rounds on a timed route to re-supply parts to the point-of-use on the production line; a worker who follows a timed material delivery route.

The water spider's job is to follow the schedule and keep the inventory between a minimum and maximum level. They typically use a cart to deliver materials to workstations in predefined quantities at least every one to two hours on a fixed time schedule. This ensures that the manufacturing line has the right amount of inventory at the right time. Compared to traditional methods, material delivery routes stock line bins more frequently and in smaller quantities, resulting in reduced WIP inventory and reduced waiting time for parts.

The water spider has a routine and knows all processes thoroughly enough to step in if needed. Water spiders sometimes also assist with changeovers, provide tools and materials, and provide other help needed to maintain flow. At Toyota, performing the water spider role is a prerequisite for supervision and management positions. The water spider is named after the whirligig beetle that swims about quickly in the water. The Japanese word for water spider is mizusumashi.

See *lean thinking*.

waterfall – See *waterfall scheduling*.

waterfall scheduling – (1) A project management approach that does not allow a step to be started until all previous steps are complete; (2) A lean methodology that schedules customers to arrive every few minutes.

Definition (1) – The project management context: In a waterfall process, steps do not overlap. The Gantt Chart for a waterfall process looks like a waterfall with each phase joined with a finish-to-start relationship. The term is often used in a software development context where the design step is not allowed to begin until the requirements step is complete, the coding step is not allowed to begin until the design step is complete, etc. The waterfall process only works well in a situation where the domain is fully specified, well-structured, and well-understood. In the software development world, the term "waterfall process" is often used to criticize old thinking that does allow for iterative, spiral, and lean development approaches.

Definition (2) – The customer scheduling context: Some lean healthcare consultants use the term "waterfall scheduling" to mean scheduling patients to arrive every few minutes rather than in batches every half-hour. Batch arrivals cause bottlenecks for receptionists and nurses and cause long waits for many patients. Therefore, waterfall scheduling in this context is a good thing because it tends to spread out the arrivals.

See *concurrent engineering, Gantt Chart, New Product Development (NPD), project management, stage-gate process, transactional process improvement*.

wave picking – An order picking method in a warehouse in which all zones are picked at the same time.

With wave picking, all zones are picked at the same time and the items are later sorted and consolidated to fill individual orders. The general principle is to handle each case efficiently two times, rather than inefficiently once. Wave picking is the quickest method for picking multi-item orders; however, the sorting and consolidation process can be difficult. Operations with a high total number of SKUs and moderate to high picks per order may benefit from wave picking.

A wave is an automated grouping of orders by a specific set of criteria. Orders may be grouped by priority level, by freight carrier, by shipment type, or by destination. These bundled orders are then released to the pick area (different zones in the warehouse) as a group. Clearly, the rate for each of the two handling steps, batch picking and container loading (consolidation), must be considerably more than twice as fast as the single step in traditional serial order picking to make wave picking worthwhile.

The two options for wave packing include fixed-wave picking and dynamic-wave picking. With fixed-wave picking, orders are not sent off to be packed until the entire wave's worth of items has been picked. With dynamic-wave picking, each order is sent to the packer as it is completed. Dynamic wave picking presents several challenges. A dedicated resource must watch the sorting line for the completed orders. Once an order is completed, the employee must replace it with an empty carton for a new order. The sorter cannot deliver new orders to that location until the old orders have been cleared away.

Although wave picking is one of the fastest methods for picking multiple line orders, some distribution centers struggle with order consolidation, sorting, and verifying that the contents are correct.

Acknowledgments: CSOM MBA 09 students Puneet Gupta, Randolph Cooper, and Ravi Kiran contributed to this entry.

See *batch picking, picking, zone picking*.

waybill – A shipping document issued by a carrier identifying the shipper, date of shipment, carrier, number of parcels, weight, receiver and date received.

Unlike a bill of lading, which includes much of the same information, a waybill is not a document of title.

See *bill of lading, Cash on Delivery (COD), FOB, terms*.

WBS – See *work breakdown structure*.

weeks supply – See *periods supply.*

Weibull distribution – A continuous probability distribution for modeling lifetimes of objects, time to failure, or time to complete a task that has a long tail; a probability distribution that is commonly used in reliability theory and maintenance for extreme values.

Density and distribution functions: The density and distribution functions for the Weibull distribution for $x > 0$ are $f(x) = \alpha\beta^{-\alpha}x^{\alpha-1}\exp(-(x/\beta)^{\alpha})$ and $F(x) = 1 - \exp(-(x/\beta)^{\alpha})$, where $\alpha > 0$ is the shape parameter and $\beta > 0$ is the scale parameter. Some sources also add a location parameter γ by replacing x with $(x - \gamma)$.

Statistics: Range $[0, \infty)$, mean $\beta\Gamma(1 + 1/\alpha)$, median $\beta\ln(2)^{1/\alpha}$, mode $\beta[(\alpha-1)/\alpha]^{1/\alpha}$ if $\alpha \geq 1$ and 0 otherwise, variance $(\beta^2/\alpha)[2\Gamma(2/\alpha) - (1/\alpha)\Gamma(1/\alpha)^2]$, where $\Gamma()$ is the Gamma function.

Excel: In Excel, the Weibull density and distribution functions are WEIBULL(x, α, β, FALSE) and WEIBULL(x, α, β, TRUE). Excel has no inverse function for the Weibull, but the inverse can easily be calculated with the Excel formula $x = \beta*(-\ln(1-F(x)))^{\wedge}(1/\alpha)$.

Excel simulation: In an Excel simulation, Weibull distributed random variates can be generated with the inverse transform method with $x = \beta*(-\ln(\text{RAND}()))^{\wedge}(1/\alpha)$.

Graph: The graph below shows the density function for the Weibull distribution with $(\alpha, \beta) = (2, 1)$.

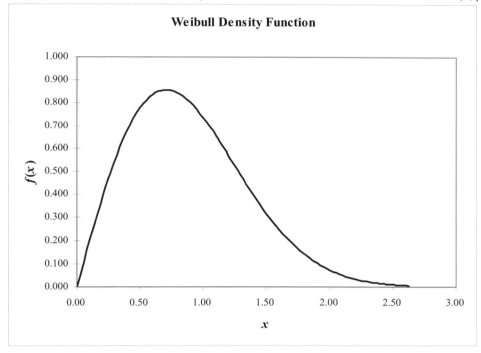

Estimating parameters: It is a non-trivial matter to estimate the Weibull distribution parameters (α, β) from a given set of observations. The reader is referred to Law and Kelton (2000) for the details.

Relationships to other distributions: The exponential distribution is a special case of the Weibull when $\alpha = 1$, and the Rayleigh distribution is a special case of the Weibull when $\alpha = 2$. When alpha = 3, the Weibull appears similar to the normal distribution.

History: The Weibull distribution was named after Swedish engineer and scientist Ernst Hjalmar Waloddi Weibull (1887-1979). (Source: Wikipedia.org, November 20, 2007)

The Excel workbook "Distributions.xls" is on the *OMWW CD* available from www.ClamshellBeachPress.com.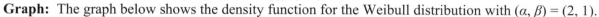

See *bathtub curve, beta distribution, exponential distribution, inverse transform method, Total Productive Maintenance (TPM).*

Weighted MAPE – See *Mean Absolute Percent Error (MAPE).*

Winsorizing – A simple bounding procedure that replaces values greater than the maximum value allowed with the maximum value; similarly, Winsorizing replaces values less than the minimum value with the minimum value.

Winsorizing is also called bounding. Data can be Winsorized by setting a maximum and minimum value or by defining the upper and lower percentiles allowed on the cumulative distribution.

See *forecast error metrics*, *Mean Absolute Percent Error (MAPE)*, *Relative Absolute Error (RAE)*, *trim*.

WIP – See *Work-in-Process (WIP) inventory*.

WMS – See *Warehouse Management System (WMS)*.

work breakdown structure (WBS) – A project management tool that defines the hierarchy of project activities (tasks) needed to complete the project. ✪

The WBS is like a "bill of material" for the project and is often drawn like the roots of a tree. It is important to understand that the WBS is not used to communicate the precedence relationships between tasks, the required resources for each task, or the project schedule. It simply lists all of the tasks required for the project, starting at the highest level of aggregation and goes down to a detailed list of all of the tasks. The work breakdown structure is a tool for defining the tasks in a project schedule, but does not create the project schedule itself.

For example, the top level of the WBS for a wedding might include (a) invitations, (b) dresses/tuxes, (c) church, and (d) reception. The example below shows a small portion of the WBS for this simple example. This WBS could be broken down into much more detail as needed. The lowest level of the WBS should define all of the specific tasks needed to complete the project. It is important to understand that the WBS is not a schedule or sequence of activities; it is simply a hierarchical list of activities that need to be done to complete the project.

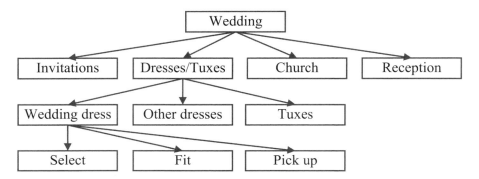

The WBS is a useful way to (a) identify all tasks needed for a project, (b) break down large tasks into more manageable ones, and (c) organize and communicate the list of tasks.

At one point, the U.S. Air Force encouraged suppliers to define its WBS so that all tasks required no more than one week of work.

See *Critical Path Method (CPM)*, *Earned Value Management (EVM)*, *mindmap*, *Project Evaluation and Review Technique (PERT)*, *project management*.

work center – See *workcenter*.

work measurement – The process of estimating the standard time required for a task; also called labor standards, engineered labor standards, labor management systems, and Methods Time Measurement (MTM). ✪

The main reasons for a work measurement system (labor management system) include:

- **Cost accounting** – Standard times are used to assign both labor and overhead cost to products and/or jobs.
- **Evaluation of alternatives** – Standard times are used to help evaluate new equipment investments or changes in the current equipment configuration.
- **Evaluation and reward systems** – Standard times are often used as a basis of comparison for evaluating and rewarding direct labor, where workers rewarded when they "beat" the standard times.
- **Scheduling** – Jobs, workers, and machines are often scheduled based on standard times.

The three common ways to measure the time for a task are time study, standard data, and work sampling. A time study can be used for almost any existing job with a relatively short duration. Standard data only requires that the analyst determine which elemental motions (e.g., pick, drop, etc.) are required for the job. Once these are determined, the analyst simply looks these up in the reference database and adds them up to "assemble" the total time for the task. The data for this type of analysis is often called pre-determined motion and time data. Work sampling takes a large number of random "snapshots" (samples) of the process over several weeks and estimates how much time is spent in each "state" based on the percentage of the random samples found in each state.

See *normal time, performance management system, performance rating, scientific management, socio-technical design, standard time, time study, work sampling.*

work sampling – The application of statistical sampling methods to estimate the percentage of time that a worker is spending on each activity (or in each "state").

This approach to work measurement should only be used for long cycle tasks. Work sampling is also called occurrence sampling.

For example, a hospital administrator wants to know how much time nurses are sitting at the nursing station per day. The person responsible for collecting the data takes a large number of random "snapshots" (samples) of the process over several weeks. Work sampling assumes that the percentage of the samples in each activity (state) is proportional to the percentage of work time in each activity. From these snapshots, the administrator can estimate how much time nurses spent at the nursing station per day on average.

The primary advantage of work sampling is that the data is gathered over a relatively long time period so the sample is likely to be representative of the process. In contrast, a time study makes more sense for a task that requires a relatively short amount of time with the observer recording each repetition of the process.

See *normal time, sampling, standard time, time study, work measurement.*

work simplification – The process of reducing the complexity of a process.

Work simplification involves designing the job to have fewer stages, steps, moves, and interdependences, thus making the job easier to learn, perform, and understand. This is closely related to work standardization. While normally applied only to repetitive factory and service work, it can also be applied to less repetitive knowledge work done by professionals and salaried workers. Simplicity is highly valued in lean thinking.

See *Business Process Re-engineering (BPR), error proofing, Failure Mode and Effects Analysis (FMEA), job enlargement, socio-technical design, standardized work.*

work standardization – See *standardized work.*

work standards – See *standardized work.*

workcenter – A group of similar machines or processes used to make a product; an area where work is performed by people and/or machines.

The routing defines the sequence of processes (workcenters) required to make a product.

See *cellular manufacturing, facility layout, routing.*

workforce agility – The ability of the employees in a firm to adapt to change.

The main motives for pursuing workforce agility can be classified as follows (Hopp and Van Oyen, 2001):

- **Improved efficiency:** Deadlines are met with greater accuracy, cycle times are reduced, and a desired throughput is achieved with less WIP because idle time in the production line is decreased.
- **Enhanced flexibility:** Overtime costs and productivity losses due to absenteeism, and turnover may be significantly reduced because cross-trained workers can absorb some or all of the work of absent workers.
- **Improved quality:** Workers' overall knowledge of the system increases, which enables them to spot and fix quality problems and to pursue both incremental and innovative improvement.
- **Improved culture:** The working environment is improved due to increased job satisfaction, worker motivation, and reduced ergonomic stress.

See *cross-training, job rotation, learning organization.*

Work-in-Process (WIP) inventory – Orders or materials that have been started in a production process, but are not yet complete; sometimes called Work-in-Progress. ✪

WIP includes orders or materials in queue waiting to be started, in the process of being setup, currently being run, waiting to be moved to the next operation, and being moved. WIP inventory is usually valued as the sum of the direct labor, materials, and overhead for all operations that have been completed. Some factories assign manufacturing overhead to a product when it is started; others assign manufacturing overhead when it is completed. Goldratt recommends not assigning overhead at all.

See *blocking, cellular manufacturing, CONWIP, finished goods inventory, Little's Law, throughput accounting, wait time.*

Work-in-Progress inventory (WIP) – See *Work-in-Process (WIP) inventory.*

X

x-bar chart – A quality control chart that monitors the mean performance of a process. ✪

A sample of n parts is collected from a process at regular intervals (either time intervals or production quantity intervals). The mean of the sample is plotted on the control chart and the process is evaluated to see if it is "under control" or not. This chart is called an $\bar{x}$-chart (for the sample mean $\bar{x}$) and is read "x-bar."

See *control chart, Statistical Process Control (SPC)*.

XML (eXtensible Markup Language) – A language used for creating web pages.

XML is an extensible version of HTML (Hypertext Markup Language). Another popular way to create web pages is ASP (Active Server Pages). XML is also a robust and flexible next generation alternative to EDI.

See *Electronic Data Interchange (EDI)*.

Y

yield – (1) Manufacturing: The percent of units started in a process that are completed satisfactorily; (2) Finance: The rate of return paid on an investment. ✪

In the manufacturing context, process yield is used as both (a) as a planning factor (before production) to increase the production start quantity so that the final quantity meets the requirements and (b) as a performance measure (after production). Process yield planning factors are found in the Bill of Material. For example, if the requirement is for 100 units and the process yield is 80%, the start quantity should be 100/0.8 = 125 units.

Six Sigma consultants often promote a demanding yield metric called Rolled Throughput Yield (RTY), sometimes called "first pass yield." This is the percent of units that pass through the process without needing any rework. The table below compares the traditional process yield with Rolled Throughput Yield.

	Process yield	Rolled Throughput Yield
Definition	Percent of units started that are completed without defects, including units that were successfully reworked.	Percent of units that pass through the entire process without needing any rework.
Other names	Yield; final yield	First pass yield; first time yield
Uses	Best metric for production planning	Best metric for performance measurement
Benefits	True measure of yield	Exposes the hidden factory by making rework more visible
Calculation	Product of the process yields for each step in the process. Process yield is also the ratio of the final output to the starting input.	Product of the RTY for each step in the process.
Criticisms	Does not indicate rework, which is clearly a non-value adding activity. May not be a very demanding standard.	Rework and repair is often hidden and not recorded. Multiple defects occurring on a single unit are not captured.

Source: Professor Arthur V. Hill

The table below provides a simple example of these metrics. Overall process yield is 90%, but the extensive rework is not evident in this measure. However, the RTY at 9.3% makes this problem very clear.

Step	In	Fail	Rework	Out	Process yield	Rolled Throughput Yield (RTY)
1	100	30	20	90	90.0%	50.0%
2	90	20	20	90	100.0%	55.6%
3	90	30	30	90	100.0%	33.3%
				Overall	90.0% [a]	9.3% [b]

[a] Calculated as 90.0% x 100.0% x 100.0% = 90.0% or just 90/100 = 90.0%.   Source: Professor Arthur V. Hill

[b] Calculated as 50.0% x 55.6% x 33.3% = 9.3%.

Process yield is one of the three dimensions of Overall Equipment Effectiveness, an important performance measure in many firms. Note that yield has very little relationship to the concept of "yield management."

Acknowledgments: CSOM MBA 10 student Meifeng (Caroline) Liu contributed to this entry.

See *hidden factory, operations performance metrics, Overall Equipment Effectiveness (OEE), scrap.*

yield management – A set of metrics and tools for maximizing revenue for organizations that have relatively fixed costs; sometimes called "revenue management" or "perishable asset resource management." ✪

The goal – For many capital-intensive businesses such as airlines, hotels, theaters, stadiums, and utilities, maximizing revenue is equivalent to maximizing profit because nearly all costs are relatively fixed. The goal is to maximize revenue per unit of resource ($/room night, $/seat mile, etc.). The goal is not to maximize utilization, although that is usually the result.

The control variables – Yield management systems change prices and capacity allocations over time as the date of the event approaches. For example, airlines change their prices thousands of times every day.

The performance metrics – The following yield management terms are used in the airline industry:

Available Seat Miles (ASM) – A measure of capacity defined as the number of seat miles that are available for purchase on an airline.

Revenue Passenger Miles (RPM) – The number of available seat miles (ASM) actually sold. This is a measure of an airline's traffic.

Load Factor – The RPM divided by the ASM. Alternatively, this can be measured by the percentage of seats that were sold compared to the number of seats that could have been sold.

Yield – How much an airline makes per revenue passenger mile (RPM).

Revenue per Available Seat Mile (RASM) – Sometimes called the "unit revenue," this metric has become the industry standard and is tracked each month because it gives a good overall picture of how an airline is performing.

Cost Per Available Seat Mile (CASM) – A widely used metric indicating the cost divided by the available miles that could have been flown (not the miles actually flown) whether those seats were occupied or not.

Stage Length – The length of the average flight for a particular airline. As stage length increases, costs per mile tend to go down. Consequently, increases in the stage length of an airline will tend to bode well for the cost side, all other things being equal.

Some of the above was adapted from "Airlines Speak a Language All Their Own," planebusiness.com/perspectives/planebasics.html.

The booking curve – The booking curve is an important control tool for yield management. See the entry entitled *booking curve.*

Other factors – Hotels and airlines place great importance on no-show factors, cancellations/reservation adjustments, and "wash" for groups, all of which help determine the necessary level of "oversell." Businesses with perishable inventory must remember that when the forecasted demand is below capacity, it is better to sell the room at a lower rate than to not sell it at all. In the hotel business, the term revenue management is often equated with getting "heads in beds." Additional ways to maximize revenues are to implement length of stay or stay restrictions, to overbook effectively, to take advantage of up-sell opportunities, and to allocate correct inventory to the appropriate channels (discounts in particular). An up and coming trend in the hotel business is to move all segments, not just e-channels and rack (standard), to dynamic pricing structures. This will enable the hotels to better control one of the larger segments: the negotiated/volume accounts.

The paper "Yield Management" on the *OMWW CD* available from www.ClamshellBeachPress.com. ◉

See *booking curve, capacity, congestion pricing.*

Y-tree – A tool for creating a strategic linkage between the efforts of individuals and the goals of the organization; also called a "goal tree."

The Y-tree begins at the highest level of organizational goals and breaks these down into intermediate goals and objectives, which are finally translated into specific projects. A Y-tree is essentially a strategy map, but goes one step further by connecting the metrics to action plans and projects. Like a strategy map, a Y-tree represents the firm's hypotheses and beliefs about how the highest level performance variables are connected to intermediate performance measures and how the firm can "move the needle" on these measures with specific projects. All projects should have an explicit connection to a higher level goal.

Bossidy, Charan, and Burck (2002) point out that one of the most significant problems with strategic planning is that the strategies too often are not translated into actions. The y-tree (along with similar concepts of the balanced scorecard and hoshin planning) is a means of accomplishing this difficult task.

At 3M, the highest-level elements of the Y-trees are growth, productivity/cost, and cash. These are often supplemented with two additional high-level strategies, namely emphasis on the customer and emphasis on corporate values and reputation.

The table below is a simplified example created by Professor Hill with many of the boxes not filled in yet. Excel is a good tool to use to create and maintain a Y-tree.

Super Y metrics	Little y metrics	Critical x metrics	Action plans/projects
Growth	Fill rate	Average leadtime	Queue time reduction project
		Leadtime variation	Machine reliability project
	Product quality	DPMO	Filler line project
Cash	Carrying cost	Lotsize inventory	SMED project
		Safety stock inventory	Forecasting project

Acknowledgments: CEMBA 06 students Matthew Tempelis, Sommer Swanke, Kevin Thayer, Claudiomir Berte, Gagan Kumar, and Julie Morman contributed to this entry.

See *balanced scorecard, benchmarking, causal map, DuPont Analysis, financial performance metrics, hoshin, issue tree, MECE, operations performance metrics, strategy map.*

Z

Zero Defects – A concept that stresses elimination of all defects; sometimes abbreviated ZD.

Deming introduced the zero defects concept to Japanese manufacturers after World War II. This approach differs from the traditional American approach promoted by American military standards such as Mil Standard 105D that allowed for a certain percentage of defects, known as an "Acceptable Quality Level" or AQL.

See *Acceptable Quality Level (AQL), Six Sigma, Statistical Process Control (SPC), Total Quality Management (TQM).*

zero inventory – A term used to describe a JIT inventory system.

Professor Bob Hall (Indiana University) popularized this term with a book of the same name. However, this term seems to have fallen into disuse partly because lean thinking is much broader than just reducing inventory.

See *inventory management, lean thinking, one-piece flow.*

zero sum game – A game theory term used to describe a conflict where the sum of payoffs for the players in the game is zero; also known as a "constant sum game."

In a zero sum game, one player's payoff can only improve at the expense of the other players. The standard metaphor here is that the players are dividing up the pie, but the size of the pie does not change with the number of players or with any decision made by any player.

See *game theory, Prisoners' Dilemma.*

zone picking – An order picking method where a warehouse is divided into several pick zones.

Order pickers are assigned to a specific zone and only pick the items in that zone. Orders are moved from one zone to the next (usually on conveyor systems) as they are picked. This is also known as "pick-and-pass." Adapted from http://accuracybook.com/glossary.htm, September 7, 2006.

See *Automated Storage & Retrieval System (AS/RS), batch picking, picking, Warehouse Management System (WMS), wave picking.*

zone storage location – A warehouse management practice that defines storage areas (zones) dedicated to particular types of items.

A zone might be created based on temperature requirements, security, typical container size, frequency of picks, etc. Within a zone, the warehouse could use either a fixed or random storage location system.

See *fixed storage location, random storage location, Warehouse Management System (WMS).*

USEFUL LINKS

Topic	Websites
e-business terms	www.lanxess.com/lcs/en/ebusiness/ebusiness_glossar/
ERP terms	http://www.4eto.co.uk/ERP-Dictionary-Category.asp
Financial terms	www.forbes.com/tools/glossary/index.jhtml
	www.duke.edu/~charvey/Classes/wpg/glossary.htm
Forecasting terms	http://armstrong.wharton.upenn.edu/dictionary/defined%20terms.html
General terms	www.en.wikipedia.org/wiki/Main_Page
Industrial engineering terms	http://www.iienet2.org/Details.aspx?id=645
International trade terms	www.itds.treas.gov/glossaryfrm.html.
Inventory terms	www.inventoryops.com/dictionary.htm
Inventory record accuracy	http://accuracybook.com/glossary.htm
Lean terms	www.fredharriman.com/resources/documents/FHcom_Kaizen_Terminology_03.pdf
	www.leanaffiliates.com/glossary/glossary_d.htm
	www.gemba.com/resources.cfm?id=41
Logistics terms	www.clm1.org/Website/Resources/Terms.asp
	www.tli.gatech.edu/apps/glossary/
Manufacturing terms	www.successfulleanmanufacturing.com/Glossary.htm
	www.glossaryofmanufacturing.com
	www.industryweek.com/manufacturing101/glossary.aspx
Marketing terms	www.marketingpower.com/mg-dictionary.php
Math programming terms	http://glossary.computing.society.informs.org/index.php?page=index_page.html
New product development terms	www.npd-solutions.com/glossary.html
	www.pdma.org/library/glossary.html
Six Sigma terms	www.isixsigma.com/dictionary
Statistics terms	www.cas.lancs.ac.uk/glossary_v1.1/main.html
	http://stat-www.berkeley.edu/~stark/SticiGui/Text/gloss.htm
Supply chain terms	www.cscmp.org/Downloads/Resources/glossary03.pdf
	http://bridgefieldgroup.com/bridgefieldgroup/glos1.htm#A
Theory of Constraints terms	www.pinnacle-strategies.com/glossary.htm
	http://www.goldratt.com/
Transportation terms	http://www.eyefortransport.com/glossary/ab.shtml
Quality terms	www.asq.org/glossary/index.html
	www.1stnclass.com/quality_glossary.htm
	www.isixsigma.com/dictionary/glossary.asp
Warehousing terms	http://fcn.state.fl.us/fcn/centers/purchase/standardmanual/glossary.htm

GENERAL REFERENCES

Blackstone, John H. Jr., and James F. Cox III (2004). *APICS Dictionary - Eleventh Edition*, 126 pages.

Gass, Saul I., and Carl M. Harris, editors (2000). *Encyclopedia of Operations Research and Management Science - Second Edition*, Springer, 960 pages.

Marchwinski, Chet, and John Shook, editors (2006). *Lean Lexicon*, Lean Enterprise Institute, 102 pages.

Salvendy, Gavriel, editor (2001). *Handbook of Industrial Engineering - Third Edition*, Wiley-Interscience, 2796 pages.

Slack, Nigel and Michael Lewis, editors (2006). *Blackwell Encyclopedia of Management – Operations Management*, Second Edition, Blackwell Publishing Limited, 376 pages.

Swamidass, Paul M., editor (2000). *Encyclopedia of Production and Manufacturing Management*, Springer, 1048 pages.

REFERENCES

Allen, D. (2001). *Getting Things Done – The Art of Stress-Free Productivity*, Penguin Books, New York, New York.

Armstrong J., (Ed.) (2000). *Principles of Forecasting: A Handbook for Researchers and Practitioners*, Kluwer Academic Pub.

Armstrong, J.S. (ed.) (2001). "The Forecasting Dictionary," *Principles of Forecasting: A Handbook for Researchers and Practitioners*, Kluwer Publishers, Norwell, MA.

Armstrong, J.S., and F. Collopy (1992). "Error measures for generalizing about forecasting methods: Empirical comparisons," *International Journal of Forecasting*, 8 (1), 69-80.

Assimakopoulos, V., K. Nikolopoulos (2000). "The Theta Model: A Decomposition Approach to Forecasting," *International Journal of Forecasting*, 16 (4), 521-530.

Assimakopoulos, V., K. Nikolopoulos (2005). "Fathoming the Theta model," Working paper, National Technical University of Athens.

Axelrod, R. (1984). *The Evolution of Cooperation*.

Barach, P., and S.D. Small (2000). "Reporting and preventing medical mishaps: lessons from non-medical near miss reporting systems," *British Medical Journal*, 320 (7237), 759–763. Found on the web at www.pubmedcentral.nih.gov/articlerender.fcgi?artid=1117768, January 23, 2008.

Barrentine, L.B. (2003). *Concepts for R&R Studies*, Second Edition, ASQ Quality Press, Milwaukee, Wisconsin.

Bass, F. (1969). "A new product growth for model consumer durables," *Management Science*, 15 (5), 215-227.

Bartels, A. (2000). "The Difference between e-business and e-commerce," *Computerworld*, October 30.

Berry, L.L., L.P. Carbone, and S.H. Haeckel (2002). "Customer Experiences Must Be Managed," *Sloan Management Review*, Spring, 85-89. (This can be found on the web at http://wehner.tamu.edu/ mktg/faculty/berry/articles/Managing_the_Total_Customer_Experience.pdf.)

Blischke, W.R., and D.N.P. Murty (1992). Product warranty management – I: A taxonomy of warranty policies, *European Journal of Operational Research* 62 (2), 127-148.

Bossidy, L., R. Charan, C. Burck (2002). *Execution: The Discipline of Getting Things Done*, Crown Business.

Box, G.E.P., G.M. Jenkins, G.C. Reinsel, and G. Jenkins (1994). *Time Series Analysis: Forecasting & Control*, 3-rd edition, Prentice-Hall.

Brandenburger, A.M. and B.J. Nalebuff (1996). *Co-Opetition: A Revolution Mindset That Combines Competition and Cooperation*, Currency.

Brown, R.G. (1967). *Decision Rules for Inventory Management*, New York: Holt, Rinehart and Winston.

Buffa, E.S., G.C. Armour, and T.E. Vollmann (1964). "Allocating facilities with CRAFT," *Harvard Business Review*, 42, 136-158.

Carbone, L. (2004). *Clued In: How to Create Customer Experiences so They Will Come Back Again and Again*, Pearson Education.

Chase, R.B., F.R. Jacobs, and N.J. Aquilano (2006). *Operations Management for Competitive Advantage*, 11-th edition, McGraw-Hill.

Christensen, C.M. (1997). *The Innovator's Dilemma*. Harvard Business School Press.

Christensen, C.M., and M.E. Raynor (2003). *The Innovator's Solution*. Harvard Business School Press.

Clark, K., and S. Wheelwright (1992). "Organizing and leading heavyweight development teams," *California Management Review*, 34(3), 9-28.

Cohen, W.M., and D.A. Levinthal (1990). "Absorptive capacity: A new perspective on learning and innovation," *Administrative Science Quarterly*, 35 (1), 128-152.

Collins, J. and Porras, J. (1996). "Building Your Company's Vision," *Harvard Business Review*, 74 (5), 65-77.

Collopy, F., and J.S. Armstrong (2000). "Another error measure for selection of the best forecasting method: The Unbiased Absolute Percent Error," www.forecastingprinciples.com /paperpdf/armstrong-unbiasedAPE.pdf, October 7, 2006.

Cooper, R. (1993). *Winning at New Products*, 2nd Edition, Reading, MA: Addison-Wesley Publishing.

Cooper, R. (2001). *Winning at New Products: Accelerating the Process from Idea to Launch*, Perseus Publishing.

Coyle, J.J., E.J. Bardi, and C.J. Langley (2002). *Management of Business Logistics: A Supply Chain Perspective*, South-Western, seventh edition.

Coyne, K.P., S.J.D. Hall, and P.G. Clifford (1997). "Is your core competence A MIRAGE?," *McKinsey Quarterly*, 1, 40-54.

Croston, J.D. (1972). "Forecasting and stock control for intermittent demands," *Operational Research Quarterly*, 23 (3), 289-303.

Dennis, P. (2002). *Lean Production Simplified: A Plain-Language Guide to the World's Most Powerful Production System*, Productivity Press.

DeMast, J., and A. Trip (2005). "Gauge R&R Studies for Destructive Measurement." *Journal of Quality Technology*, 37(1), 40-49.

Drucker, P.F. (1954). *The practice of management*. New York: Harper.

Drucker, P.F. (1959). *Landmarks of Tomorrow*, Heinemann, London.

Dudek, R.A., S.S. Panwalkar, and M.L. Smith (1992). "The lessons of flowshop scheduling research," *Operations Research*, 40 (1), 7–13.

Elkington, J. (1994). "Towards the sustainable corporation: Win-win-win business strategies for sustainable development." *California Management Review*, 36(2), 90-100.

Englund, R.L., Graham, R.J., Dinsmore, P.C. (2003). *Creating the Project Office – A Manager's Guide to Leading Organizational Change*, Josey-Bass (Wiley).

Evans, J.R. (1985). "An Efficient Implementation of the Wagner-Whitin Algorithm for Dynamic Lot-Sizing," *Journal of Operations Management*, 5 (2), 229-235.

Evers, P.T. (1995). "Expanding the Square Root Law: An Analysis of Both Safety and Cycle Stocks," *The Logistics and Transportation Review*, 31 (1), 1-20.

Feigenbaum, A.V. (1983). *Total Quality Control*, Third edition, McGraw-Hill.

Fine, C.H. (1995). *Clockspeed: Winning Industry Control in the Age of Temporary Advantage*, Perseus Books Group.

Fisher, M. (1997). "What is the Right Supply Chain for Your Product," *Harvard Business Review*, March-April 1997, 105-116.

Friedman, T.L. (2005). *The World Is Flat: A Brief History of the Twenty-first Century*, Farrar, Straus and Giroux, New York, NY.

Galley, M. (2008). *Cause Mapping Workbook*, ThinkReliability, info@thinkreliability.com.

Gano, D.L. (2007). *Apollo Root Cause Analysis - Effective Solutions to Everyday Problems Every Time*, Apollonian Publications, Richland, Washington.

Gardner, E.S. (2005). "Exponential smoothing: The state of the art – Part II," unpublished working paper, Bauer College of Business, University of Houston, www.bauer.uh.edu: gardner.

George, M.L., D. Rowlands, and B. Kastle (2003). *What is Lean Six Sigma?*, McGraw-Hill.

Goldman, S.L., R.N. Nagel, and K. Preiss (1995). *Agile Competitors and Virtual Organizations*, New York, Van Nostrand Reinhold.

Goldratt, E.M., and J. Cox (1992). *The Goal: A Process of Ongoing Improvement*, North River Press.

Goldratt, E.M., (1994). *It's Not Luck*, Massachusetts: North River Press.

Goldratt, E.M., E. Schragenheim, and C.A. Ptak (2000). *Necessary But Not Sufficient*, North River Press.

Graham, D., and T. Bachmann (2004). *IDEATION: The Birth and Death of Ideas*, Wiley, May.

Greaver, M.F. (1999). *Strategic Outsourcing: A Structured Approach to Outsourcing Decisions and Initiatives*, AMACOM/American Management Association.

Gunasekaran, A., and E.W.T. Ngai (2005). "Build-to-order supply chain management: a literature review and framework for development, *Journal of Operations Management*, 23 (5), 423-451.

Hammer, M. and J.A. Champy (1993). *Reengineering the Corporation: A Manifesto for Business Revolution*, Harper Business Books, New York, ISBN 0-06-662112-7.

Hansen, M.T., Nohria, N., and Tierney, T. (1999). "What's your strategy for managing knowledge?" *Harvard Business Review*, March-April, 107-116.

Harry, Mikel (1988). *The Nature of Six Sigma Quality*, Rolling Meadows, IL: Motorola University Press. ISBN 9781569460092.

Harry, M. and R. Schroeder (2000). *Six Sigma*, Random House.

Hayes, R.H. and S.C. Wheelwright (1979). "Link Manufacturing Process and Product Life Cycles," *Harvard Business Review*, January-February, 133-140.

Hayes, R.H. and S.C. Wheelwright (1979). "The Dynamics of Process-Product Life Cycles." *Harvard Business Review*, January-February, 127-136.

Hays, J.M., and A.V. Hill (2001). "A Preliminary Investigation of the Relationships between Employee Motivation: Vision, Service Learning, and Perceived Service Quality." *Journal of Operations Management*, 19 (3), 335-349.

Hummel, C.E. (1967). *The Tyranny of the Urgent*, Intervarsity Press, Downer's Grove, Illinois.

Hays, J.M., and A.V. Hill (1999). "The Market Share Impact of Service Failures," *Production and Operations Management*, 8 (3), 208-220.

Hays, J.M., T. Bouzdine-Chameeva, S.M. Goldstein, A.V. Hill, and A.J. Scavarda (2007). "Applying the Collective Causal Mapping Methodology to Operations Management Curriculum Development," *Decision Science Journal of Innovative Education*, 5 (2), 267-287.

Heskett, J.L., W.E. Sasser, and L.A. Schlesinger (1997). **The Service Profit Chain,** Free Press.

Heskett, J.L., T.O. Jones, G. Loveman, W.E. Sasser Jr., and L.A. Schlesinger (1994). "Putting the Service-Profit Chain to Work," *Harvard Business Review*, March-April, 164-170.

Hill, A.V. (1992). *Field Service Management: An Integrated Approach to Increasing Customer Satisfaction*, Business One Irwin, Homewood, Illinois. ISBN: 155623547X.

Hill, A.V. (2010). *Personal Operations Management – Lean Principles for Getting Good Things Done*, Clamshell Beach Press.

Hill, A.V., V. Giard, and V.A. Mabert (1989). "A Decision Support System for Determining Optimal Retention Stocks for Service Parts Inventories," *IIE Transactions*, 21 (3), 221-229.

Hill, A.V., J.M. Hays, and E. Naveh (2000). "A Model for Optimal Delivery Time Guarantees," *Journal of Service Research*, 2 (3), 254-264.

Hill, A.V., and I.S. Khosla (1992). "Models for Optimal Lead Time Reduction," *Production and Operations Management*, 1 (2), 185-197.

Hill, A.V., and W.J. Sawaya III (2004). "Production Planning for Medical Devices with an Uncertain Approval Date," *IIE Transactions*, 36 (4), 307-317.

Hill, A.V., and T.E. Vollmann (1986). "Reducing Vendor Delivery Uncertainties in a JIT Environment," *Journal of Operations Management*, 6 (4), 381-392.

Hopp, W.J. (2006). *Supply Chain Science*, New York: McGraw-Hill.

Hopp, W.J. and M.P. Van Oyen (2001). "Agile workforce evaluation: A framework for cross-training and coordination." *Proceedings 2001 NSF Design and Manufacturing Grantees Conference*. Tampa Florida.

Hopp, W.J. and M.L. Spearman (2004). "To Pull or Not to Pull: What Is the Question?," *MSOM*, 6 (2), 133–148.

Humphries, W.S. (1989). *Managing the Software Process (The SEI Series in Software Engineering)*, Addison-Wesley Professional.

Hyer, N. and U. Wemmerlov (2002). *Reorganizing the Factory: Competing through Cellular Manufacturing*, Productivity Press.

Hyer, N.L., and U. Wemmerlov (2002). "The Office that Lean Built," *IIE Solutions*, 34 (1010), 36-43.

Hyndman, R.J., and A.B. Koehler (2006). "Another look at measures of forecast accuracy," *International Journal of Forecasting*, 22 (4), 679-688.

Hyndman, R.J., and B. Billah (2003). "Unmasking the Theta Method," *International Journal of Forecasting*, 19 (2), 287-290.

Johnson, G. (1998). "Vendor-Managed Inventory," *APICS Performance Advantage*, June, 30-32.

Juran, J.M. (1986). "The Quality Trilogy - A Universal Approach to Managing for Quality," paper presented at the ASQC 40th Annual Quality Congress in Anaheim, California.

Kaplan, R.S., and D.P. Norton (1992). "The Balanced Scorecard – Measures That Drive Performance," *Harvard Business Review*, January-February, 71-79.

Kaplan, R.S., and D.P. Norton (2000). "Having Trouble with Your Strategy? Then Map It," *Harvard Business Review*, September-October, 167-176.

Kaplan, R.S., and D.P. Norton (2004). *Strategy Maps: Converting Intangible Assets into Tangible Outcomes*, Harvard Business School Press, Boston, MA.

Kaplan, R.S., and D.P. Norton (2004). "Measuring the Strategic Readiness of Intangible Assets," *Harvard Business Review*, 82 (2), 52-63.

Kaplan, R.S., and D.P. Norton (2006). *Alignment: Using the Balanced Scorecard to Create Corporate Synergies*, Harvard Business School Press, Boston, MA.

Kim, W.C. and Renée Mauborgne (2005). *Blue Ocean Strategy: How to Create Uncontested Market Space and Make Competition Irrelevant*, Harvard Business School Press.

Kotha, S. (1995). "Mass Customization: Implementing the Emerging Paradigm for Competitive Advantage," *Strategic Management Journal*, 16 (Special Issue), 21-42.

Kutner, M.H., J. Neter, C.J. Nachtsheim, and W. Wasserman (2004). *Applied Linear Statistical Models*, McGraw Hill: Irwin, 5th edition.

Law, A.M. and W.D. Kelton (2000). *Simulation Modeling and Analysis*, McGraw-Hill.

Lee, H.L., V. Padmanabhan, and S. Whang (1997). "The Bullwhip Effect in Supply Chains," *Sloan Management Review*, Spring, 93-102.

Likert, R. (1932), "A Technique for the Measurement of Attitudes," *Archives of Psychology*, 140, 1–55.

Ling, R.C., and W.E. Goddard (1995). *Orchestrating Success: Improve Control of the Business with Sales & Operations Planning*, John Wiley & Sons.

Littlefield, T.K., Jr. and P.H. Randolph (1987). "Reply: An Answer to Sasieni's Question on Pert Times," *Management Science*, 33 (10), 1357-1359.

Love, R.F., J.G. Morris, and G.O. Wesolowsky (1988). *Facilities Location Models & Methods*, North Holland, New York.

Macomber, H. and G. Howell (2004). "Two great wastes in organizations -- A Typology for Addressing the Concern for the Underutilization of Human Potential," paper presented at the 12th Annual Meeting of the International Group for Lean Construction in Copenhagen, Denmark.

Mahajan, V., E. Muller, and F. Bass (1995). "Diffusion of new products: Empirical generalizations and managerial uses," *Management Science*, 14 (3): G79-G88.

Maister, D.H. (1976). "Centralization of Inventories and the 'Square Root Law," *International Journal of Physical Distribution*, 6 (3), 124-134.

Marchwinski, C. and J. Shook (2006). *Lean Lexicon – A Graphical glossary for lean Thinkers*, Third Edition, Lean Enterprise Institute, Cambridge, MA.

McKone, K. and E. Weiss (2002). "Guidelines for Implementing Predictive Maintenance," *Production Operations Management*, 11(2), 109-124.

Metes, G., J. Gundry, and P. Bradish (1997). *Agile Networking: Competing Through the Internet and Intranets*, Upper Saddle River New Jersey, Prentice-Hall PTR.

Miller, J.G., and T.E. Vollmann (1985). "The Hidden Factory," *Harvard Business Review*, 63(5), 142-150.

Minto, B. (1996). *The Pyramid Principle: Logic in Writing, Thinking, and Problem Solving*, Minto International.

Morgan, J.M., and J.K. Liker (2006). *The Toyota Product Development System: Integrating People, Process and Technology*, Productivity Press.

Murty, D.N.P., and W.R. Blischke (1992). Product warranty management – II: An integrated framework for study, *European Journal of Operational Research* 62 (3), 261-281.

Nahmias, S. (2004). *Production and Operations Analysis*, McGraw-Hill: Irwin, 5-th Edition.

Noreen, E., D. Smith, and J.T. Mackey (1995). *TOC and Its Implications for Management Accounting*, North River Press.

Oberholzer-Gee, F., and V. Calanog (2007). "The Speed of New Ideas: Trust, Institutions and the Diffusion of New Products," working paper, Wharton School, University of Pennsylvania.

Ohno, T. (1978). *Toyota Production System: Beyond Large Scale Production*, Productivity Press, New York, New York. (English translation copyrighted 1988 by Productivity Press, ISBN 0-915299-14-3.)

Ord, K., M. Hibon, and S. Makridakis (2000). "The M3-Competition," *International Journal of Forecasting*, 16 (4), 433-436.

Parkinson, C.N. (1958). *Parkinson's Law: The Pursuit of Progress*, John Murray, London.

Dennis, Pascal (2002). *Lean Production Simplified: A plain-language guide to the world's most powerful production system*, Productivity Press.

Pine, B.J. (1993). *Mass Customization: The New Frontier in Business Competition*, Harvard Business School Press.

Pine, B.J., and J.H. Gilmore (1998). "Welcome to the Experience Economy," *Harvard Business Review*, July-August, 97-105.

Pine, B.J., and J.H. Gilmore (1999). *The Experience Economy: Work Is Theater and Every Business a Stage*, Harvard Business School Press.

Pine, B.J., and J.H. Gilmore (2007). *Authenticity: What Consumers Really Want*, Harvard Business School Press.

Porter, A.M. (2000). "The virtual corporation: Where is it?," *Purchasing* (www.purchasing.com), March 23.

Porter, M.E. (1985). *Competitive Advantage*, London, Free Press.

Press, W.H., B.P. Flannery, S.A. Teukolsky, and W.T. Vetterling (2002). *Numerical Recipes in FORTRAN: The Art of Scientific Computing*, Cambridge University Press, Second Edition.

Rasiel, E.M. (1998). *The McKinsey Way - Using the Techniques of the World's Top Strategic Consultants to Help You and Your Business*, McGraw-Hill.

Rasiel, E.M. and P.N. Friga (2001). *The McKinsey Mind: Understanding and Implementing the Problem-Solving Tools and Management Techniques of the World's Top Strategic Consulting Firm*, McGraw-Hill.

Raturi, A.S., and A.V. Hill (1988). "An Experimental Analysis of Capacity-Sensitive Setup Parameters for MRP Lotsizing," *Decision Sciences*, 19 (4), 782-800.

Reichheld, F.F. (2003). "The One Number You Need to Grow," *Harvard Business Review*, Reprint R0312C, OnPoint 5534, 1-10.

ReVelle, J.B. (2004). *Quality Essentials: A Reference Guide from A to Z*, ASQ Quality Press.

Roberts, D.M. (1978). *Statistical Auditing*, American Institute of Certified Public Accountants, New York, New York.

Roth, A.E. and A. Ockenfels (2002). "Last-Minute Bidding and the Rules for Ending Second-Price Auctions: Evidence from eBay and Amazon Auctions on the Internet," *Am. Economic Review*, 92 (4), 1093-1103.

Rother, M., J. Shook, J. Womack, and D. Jones (2003). *Learning to See Version*, Lean Enterprise Institute.

Sasieni, M.W. (1986). "A Note on Pert Times," *Management Science*, 32 (12), 1652-1653.

Scavarda, A.J., T. Bouzdine-Chameeva, S.M. Goldstein, J.M. Hays, and A.V. Hill (2006). "A Methodology for Constructing Collective Causal Maps," *Decision Sciences*, 37 (2), 263-283.

Schilling, M.A. (2000). "Toward a general modular systems theory and its application to interfirm product modularity," *Academy of Management Review*, 25 (2), 312-334.

Schlangenstein, M. (2005). "Southwest Airlines Profit Jumps," *Bloomberg News*, April 15, Page E05.

Schneiderman, A.M. (1999). "Why Balanced Scorecards Fail!," *Journal of Strategic Performance Measurement*, Special Edition, p. 6 (Also found at http//www.schneiderman.com).

Schonberger, R.J. (1982). *Japanese Manufacturing Techniques: Nine Hidden Lessons in Simplicity*, Free Press, New York, NY. ISBN: 0029291003.

Schonberger, R.J. (1986). *World Class Manufacturing - The Lessons of Simplicity Applied*. The Free Press, New York.

Schroeder, R.G. (2008). *Operations Management: Contemporary Concepts and Cases*, Fourth Edition, McGraw-Hill Irwin, Boston.

Schroeder, R.G., M.J. Pesch (1994). "Focusing the factory: eight lessons," *Business Horizons*, Sept.-Oct., 76-81.

Schultz, T.R. (1989). *Business Requirements Planning -- The Journey of Excellence*, The Forum Ltd.

Sethi, A.K. and S.P. Sethi (1990). "Flexibility in Manufacturing: A Survey," *International Journal of Flexible Manufacturing Systems*, 2 (4), 289–328.

Shewhart, W.A. (1939). *Statistical Method from the Viewpoint of Quality Control*, Dover, New York.

Silver, E.A., D.F. Pyke, and R. Peterson (1998). *Inventory management and production planning and scheduling*, Third edition, John Wiley & Sons, New York.

Simon, H.A. (1957). *Models of Man: Social and Rational*, Wiley & Sons, New York, New York.

Skinner, W. (1974). "The Focused Factory," *Harvard Business Review*, May-June, 113-121.

Spear, S. and H.K. Bowen (1999). "Decoding the DNA of the Toyota Production System," *Harvard Business Review*, September-October, 96-106.

Spear, S. (2008). *Chasing the Rabbit--How Market Leaders Outdistance the Competition and How Great Companies Can Catch Up and Win*, McGraw-Hill.

Spearman, M.L., W.J. Hopp, and D.L. Woodruff (1989). "A Hierarchical Control Architecture for CONWIP Production Systems," *Journal of Manufacturing and Operations Management*, 16 (2), 147-171.

Stalk, G. (1988). "Time: The Next Source of Competitive Advantage," *Harvard Business Review*, 66 (4), 41-52.

Stalk, G. and T.M. Hout (1990). *Competing Against Time*, The Free Press, New York, New York.

Starr, M., and D. Miller, D. (1962). *Inventory control: Theory and practice*, Englewood Cliffs (NJ): Prentice Hall.

Stata, R. (1989). "Organizational Learning - The Key to Management Innovation," *Sloan Management Review*, 30 (3), 63-74.

Sterman, J. (1992). "Teaching Takes Off, Flight Simulators for Management Education," *OR/MS Today*, October, 40-44. Also see Professor Sterman's webpage web.mit.edu/jsterman/www.

Stork, K. (1998). "Why Supplier Scorecards are Critical," *Purchasing*, 125 (5), 31.

Stuart, F.I. (2006). "Designing and executing memorable service experiences: Lights, camera, experiment, integrate, action!," *Business Horizons*, 49 (2), 149-159.

Taylor, F.W. (1911). *The Principles of Scientific Management,* Harper Brothers, New York.

Thiel, H. (1966). *Applied Economic Forecasting*. Chicago: Rand McNally

Turing, A.M. (1950), "Computing machinery and intelligence," *Mind*, 59, 443-460.

Tversky, A., and D. Kahneman (1974). "Judgment under uncertainty: Heuristics and biases." *Science*, 185 (4157), 1124-1130.

Von Neumann, J. and O. Morgenstern (1944). *Theory of Games and Economic Behavior*, John Wiley & Sons, Inc.

Vergin, R.C., and K. Barr (1999). "Building Competitiveness in Grocery Supply through Continuous Replenishment Planning," *Industrial Marketing Management*, 28 (2), 145-53.

Vollmann, T.E., W.L. Berry, D.C. Whybark, F.R. Jacobs (2004). *Manufacturing Planning and Control Systems for Supply Chain Management*, Fifth Edition, McGraw-Hill.

Walden, D., C. Berger, R. Blauth, D. Boger, C. Bolster, G. Burchill, W. DuMouchel, F. Pouliot, R. Richter, A. Rubinoff, D. Shen, and M. Timko (1993). "Kano's Methods of Understanding Customer-defined Quality," *The Center for Quality Management Journal* (special issue), 2 (4).

Wallace, T.F. (2004). *Sales & Operations Planning: The How-to Handbook*, 2nd Edition, T.F. Wallace & Company.

Womack, J.P. and D.T. Jones (2003). *Lean Thinking*, Simon and Schuster.

Winters, P.R. (1960). "Forecasting sales by exponentially smoothed weighted moving averages," *Management Science*, 6 (3), 324-342.

Zhang, W., A.V. Hill, R.G. Schroeder, and K. Linderman (2006). "Process Improvement Program Management and Organizational Performance," University of Minnesota working paper.

Zhang, W., A.V. Hill, R.G. Schroeder, and K. Linderman (2008). "Process Improvement Program Management and Organizational Performance," accepted for publication by *Operations Management Research*.

Zinn, W., M. Levy, and D.J. Bowersox, (1989). "Measuring the effect of inventory centralization/ decentralization on aggregate safety stock: The 'square root law' revisited," *Journal of Business Logistics*, 10 (1), 1-14.

Zook, C. (2004). *Beyond the Core: Expand Your Market without Abandoning Your Roots*, Harvard Business School Press.

The operations management whitepapers and Excel workbooks referenced in this encyclopedia with the symbol ⊙ can be found on the *Operations Management Whitepapers & Workbooks (OMWW) CD 2009 Edition* available from www.ClamshellBeachPress.com. These and other files are also available as downloads from the Clamshell Beach Press website. The "WP" product codes are whitepapers and the "EW" product codes are Excel workbooks. The file names for the whitepapers are the same as the name of the whitepaper with a .pdf file name extension.

OMWW CD 2009 Edition – Table of Contents (alphabetical by topic and within topic)

Location models

CBP EW 57-03 AL - The Adaptive Location/ Allocation Optimization Tool (AL.xls)
CBP WP 57-20 Location Theory
CBP EW 57-15 The Gravity Model (Gravity.xls)

Lotsizing

CBP WP 57-08 Economic Lot Scheduling Problem
CBP EW 57-12 Economic Lot Scheduling Problem (ELSP.xls)
CBP WP 57-21 Lotsizing
CBP EW 57-18 Lotsizing (Lotsizing.xls)
CBP EW 58-04 Multi-item Newsvendor Problem
CBP EW 57-13 The Economic Order Quantity (EOQ.xls)
CBP EW 57-20 The Newsvendor Model (Newsvendor.xls)
CBP WP 57-23 The Newsvendor Problem

New product development

CBP EW 57-06 Check Digit (Check digit.xls)
CBP WP 57-04 Commonality
CBP EW 57-07 Commonality (Commonality.xls)

Operations research

CBP EW 57-19 Netsolver (Netsolver.xls)
CBP WP 58-05 Newton's Method

Operations strategy

CBP WP 57-15 How to Create a Mission Statement
CBP WP 57-39 Process is Everything
CBP WP 57-30 Strategy Maps and Causal Maps

Personal operations management

CBP EW 57-35 Personal Operations Management (POM.xls)
CBP WP 57-42 The Pay it Forward Series
(The whitepaper on Personal Operations Management is now a book by the same name.)

Price optimization

CBP WP 57-12 Forecasting Demand Based on Price and Leadtime
CBP EW 57-23 Price Optimization (Price optimization.xls)
CBP EW 57-22 Price-Leadtime Elasticity of Demand (Price-leadtime elasticity of demand.xls)

Process improvement

CBP WP 58-04 Benchmarking, Best Practices, and Leading Practices
CBP WP 57-03 Brainstorming with the Nominal Group Technique
CBP WP 57-41 Error Proofing
CBP EW 57-34 Failure Modes and Effects Analysis (FMEA.xls)
CBP WP 57-19 Learning Models
CBP EW 57-16 Learning Models (Learning models.xls)
CBP WP 58-10 Overall Equipment Effectiveness
CBP WP 57-24 Process Improvement Checklist
CBP WP 58-11 Process Improvement Tools Self-Assessment Survey
CBP EW 58-05 Project Management Hopper (Project Management Hopper.xls)

Project management

CBP WP 58-09 An Overview of the Minto Pyramid Principle
CBP WP 57-25 Project Charters
CBP EW 57-32 Project Schedule Template (Project schedule template.xls)
CBP WP 57-37 Stakeholder Analysis

Quality and statistics

CBP WP 57-02 Audit Sampling
CBP EW 57-04 Audit Sampling (Audit sampling.xls)
CBP EW 57-08 Confidence Intervals (Confidence intervals.xls)
CBP EW 57-09 Distributions (Distributions.xls)
CBP WP 57-06 Dollar Unit Sampling
CBP EW 57-11 Dollar Unit Sampling (DUS.xls)
CBP WP 58-15 Empirical Probability Distributions with Theoretical Tails
CBP WP 57-05 Estimating Confidence Intervals and Required Sample Sizes
CBP EW 57-26 Sigma Level (Sigma level.xls)
CBP WP 58-17 The Hypergeometric Distribution
CBP EW 58-03 Empirical Probability Distributions with Theoretical Tails.xls

Service operations

CBP EW 57-24 Queuing Models (Queuing Models.xls)
CBP WP 57-38 Queuing Theory
CBP EW 57-25 Service Guarantee (Service guarantee.xls)
CBP EW 57-29 Student Project Assignment Technique (SPAT.xls)
CBP EW 57-31 Staffit (Staffit.xls)
CBP WP 57-31 Traveling Salesperson Problem
CBP WP 58-03 Yield Management

Supply chain games

CBP EW 58-01 The Donut Shop (donut shop.xls)
CBP EW 58-02 The GatorDrink Game (GatorDrink.xls)

Theory of constraints

CBP WP 57-07 Drum-Buffer-Rope
CBP WP 57-32 Theory of Constraints
CBP WP 57-33 Throughput Accounting

The *Whitepapers and Workbooks for Operations Management CD* can be ordered from Clamshell Beach Press.
Additional copies of the *Encyclopedia of Operations Management* can also be ordered from Clamshell Beach Press.
Most whitepapers and Excel workbooks are also available to download from Clamshell Beach Press.
Clamshell Beach Press can be found on the web at **www.ClamshellBeachPress.com**.